Applied Mathematics 9

**Addison-Wesley
Secondary
Mathematics
Authors**

Elizabeth Ainslie
Paul Atkinson
Maurice Barry
Cam Bennet
Barbara J. Canton
Ron Coleborn
Fred Crouse
Garry Davis
Mary Doucette
Bonnie Edwards
Jane Forbes
George Gadanidis
Liliane Gauthier
Florence Glanfield
Katie Pallos-Haden
Carol Besteck Hope
Terry Kaminski
Brendan Kelly
Stephen Khan
Ron Lancaster
Duncan LeBlanc
Kevin Maguire
Jim Nakamoto
Paul Pogue
Linda Rajotte
Brent Richards
Kevin Spry
David Sufrin
Peter Taylor
Paul Williams
Elizabeth Wood
Rick Wunderlich
Paul Zolis
Leanne Zorn

Robert Alexander

Lynda Cowan   **Antonietta Lenjosek**
Peter J. Harrison   **Nick Nielsen**
Rob McLeish   **Margaret Sinclair**

Addison
Wesley

Toronto

Developmental Editor
Ingrid D'Silva

Senior Consulting Mathematics Editor
Lesley Haynes

Coordinating Editor
Mei Lin Cheung

Production Coordinator
Stephanie Cox

Editorial Contributors
Kelly Davis
Gay McKeller
Alison Rieger
Judy Wilson
Christina Yu

Product Manager
Anne-Marie Scullion

Managing Editor
Enid Haley

Publisher
Claire Burnett

Design/Production
Pronk&Associates

Art Direction
Pronk&Associates

Electronic Assembly/Technical Art
Pronk&Associates

The publisher has taken every care to meet or exceed industry specifications for the manufacturing of textbooks. The spine and the endpapers of this sewn book have been reinforced with special fabric for extra binding strength. The cover is a premium, polymer-reinforced material designed to provide long life and withstand rugged use. Mylar gloss lamination has been applied for further durability.

ISBN: 0-201-77119-5

This book contains recycled product and is acid free.

Printed and bound in Canada

1 2 3 4 5 FP 06 05 04 03 02

Reviewers

Joe DiGiorgio
Cardinal Carter Catholic High School
York Catholic District School Board
Aurora

Rod Forcier
Head of Mathematics and Computers
Christ the King Secondary School
Georgetown

Duncan LeBlanc
Head of Mathematics
Sir Robert L Borden Business and
Technical Institute
Toronto

Gizele Price
Holy Name of Mary Secondary School
Dufferin-Peel Catholic District School Board
Mississauga

Bill Sherman
Head of Mathematics
Lasalle Secondary School
Sudbury

Wendy Solheim
Head of Mathematics
Thornhill Secondary School
Thornhill

Contents

Contents

9 Geometry

Contents

Welcome to Applied Mathematics 9 ONTARIO

We hope this book helps you see that mathematics is useful, interesting, and enjoyable.

This book is about ...

... Relationships

Real-life situations often involve two quantities that relate to each other in a systematic way. In this book, you will investigate relationships many times, to develop an understanding of special relationships, and how to analyse them.

... Technology

Calculators and computers are common tools in the world, and they will be important tools in your study of mathematics. Graphing software and graphing calculators enable you to examine relationships in different ways: by listing values in a table, by making a graph, by using an equation. This book also provides opportunities for using spreadsheet software, as well as dynamic geometry software.

... Problem Solving

One of the most important reasons for studying mathematics is to develop new ways to solve problems. In this book, you will find a wide variety of problems, and develop different strategies for solving them. Some of these problems have many parts, or different approaches. These rich problems are emphasized in the Mathematical Modelling sections.

Chapter Introduction

Each chapter starts with a short **Mathematical Modelling** section that presents a rich problem. At the start of each chapter, you may not have the mathematical skills you need to solve the problem. You will return to the problem at the end of the chapter, after developing those skills.

Curriculum Correlation relates the Ontario curriculum guidelines to what you will learn in the chapter.

Necessary Skills

The first section in each chapter gives you a chance to review topics and skills you will need for the chapter.

Numbered Sections

These develop the new content of the course through **Investigations, Examples**, and **Exercises**.

Watch for **Take Note** boxes: they highlight important results or definitions.

Exercises are organized into A, B, and C categories according to their level of difficulty.

✓ You'll see that some exercises have a check mark beside them; try these exercises to be sure you have covered all core curriculum requirements.

Each exercise set identifies one exercise for each of the four categories of the provincial **Achievement Chart**.

- Knowledge/Understanding
- Thinking/Inquiry/Problem Solving
- Communication
- Application

These labelled exercises show you what to expect when you are being assessed on any of the four categories. Our selection provides examples only. Each exercise set has many exercises that relate to each of the categories of achievement.

Ongoing Review

In each chapter:

- A **Self-Check** provides mid-chapter review, including a multiple-choice **Preparation for Ontario Testing** example.

- A **Mathematical Toolkit** summarizes important chapter results.

- **Review Exercises** provide extra practice for the contents of a chapter.

- The **Self-Test** models the type of chapter test your teacher might give. The **Preparation for Ontario Testing** example can help you prepare for the provincial math test.

At the end of chapters 3, 6, and 9, look for **Cumulative Reviews** that cover material from chapter 1 forward.

Numeracy Skills Appendix

This appendix provides the opportunity to review basic numeracy skills. Each numbered item presents a single skill with examples and a short exercise set for practice. You can use these any time you need a quick refresher.

Technology provides tools for learning and doing mathematics in ways that were not possible a few years ago.

Graphing Technology

The graphing calculator helps you explore relationships graphically, numerically, and symbolically. It does not replace the need to develop good graphing skills, but it can enhance your mathematical understanding.

In some *Investigations*, you will learn specific steps for the TI-83 graphing calculator. Any comparable calculator would also be appropriate for completing the work. In *Examples* and *Exercises*, you will see more opportunities for using the graphing calculator.

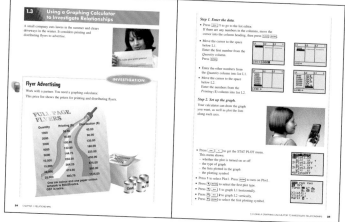

Dynamic Geometry Software

The Geometer's Sketchpad is a powerful technology tool designed for mathematics classrooms. Chapter 9 includes *Investigations* that feature *The Geometer's Sketchpad*.

With this software, you can create geometric figures. When you stretch, skew, or move the figures, you can observe the effects and make general conclusions.

This book provides explicit instruction in the use of *The Geometer's Sketchpad*.

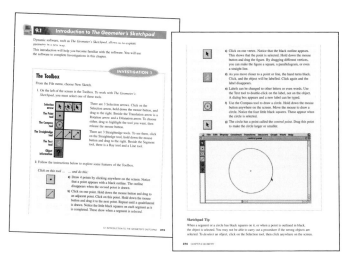

Communication is a key part of all learning. It is also a critical part of how you demonstrate your mathematical ability. This book provides many ways for you to improve your mathematical communication.

Presentations of **Example Solutions** model clear and concise mathematical communication. Following a **Solution** to an **Example** will help you develop clear communication skills.

Discuss questions ask you to think about solutions or the implications of new concepts, and to share your thinking. The more you "talk through" the math, the more likely you will understand the concepts.

Selected exercises ask you to explain your reasoning, or describe your findings. Each numbered section also contains an exercise highlighted with a "Communication" emphasis.

Assessment •

Several features in this book relate to a balanced assessment approach.

- **Achievement Chart Categories** are highlighted in each exercise set.
- **Communication** opportunities appear in **Examples**, *Discuss* suggestions, and exercises.
- **Self-Checks** support your knowledge and understanding.
- **Mathematical Modelling** presents applied problems for you to solve.
- **Self-Tests** provide a sample of the type of chapter test your teacher might use.
- **Preparation for Ontario Testing** exercises appear in every Self-Test and in every Self-Check, providing opportunities for you to practise answering provincial test-type exercises.

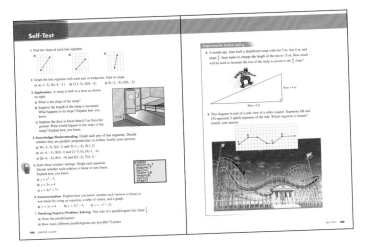

CHAPTER 1

Relationships

By the end of this chapter, you will:

- Describe possible situations for graphs.
- Represent data with tables of values and graphs. Describe and analyse relationships.
- Collect, organize, and analyse data, with and without technology. Decide whether results are reasonable for the situation.
- Communicate findings of an experiment and solutions to problems. Justify your conclusions.
- Pose and solve problems about investigations and experiments.
- Decide whether relations are linear or non-linear.
- Decide whether situations are proportional.

Relating Animal and Human Lifetimes

People who own pets can become very attached to them. They sometimes think of this question:

How can the lifetime of an animal be related to a human lifetime?

In Section 1.6, you will develop some models that relate the lifetime of a cat or dog to a human lifetime.

12   14   16   18   20   21

64   72   80   88   96   100

Graphing Data

Example

Describe the relationship in the table. Graph the data.

Centimetres	0	20	40	60	80	100	120	140	160	180	200
Metres	0	0.2	0.4	0.6	0.8	1.0	1.2	1.4	1.6	1.8	2.0

Solution

In the table, the number of centimetres is 100 times the number of metres since 1 m = 100 cm.
Plot *Centimetres* along the horizontal axis and *Metres* along the vertical axis.
Choose a horizontal scale of 1 square represents 20 cm, and a vertical scale of 1 square represents 0.2 m. Mark the points to represent the data. Join the points.

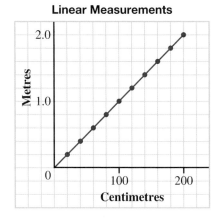

Exercises

1. Calculate each length in centimetres. Use or extend the above table or graph to check whether your answers are reasonable.

   a) 0.4 m   b) 1.5 m   c) 1.93 m   d) 0.7 m   e) 2.14 m

2. Use the graph above to estimate each length in metres. Use the table above to check.

   a) 120 cm   b) 86 cm   c) 54 cm   d) 2 cm   e) 197 cm

3. a) Copy and complete this table.

Distances Travelled at 40 km/h

Time (h)	0	2	4	6	8	10	12	14	16	18	20	22	24
Distance (km)	0	80	160	240									960

b) Graph the data. Plot *Time* along the horizontal axis and *Distance* along the vertical axis.

4. Calculate the distance travelled at 40 km/h for each time. Use or extend the table or graph in exercise 3 to check.

a) 6 h

b) 11 h

c) 20.5 h

d) 17 h

e) 26 h

f) 27.5 h

Distance = speed × time

Reading a Graph

Example

This graph shows the fuel needed by a car owner.

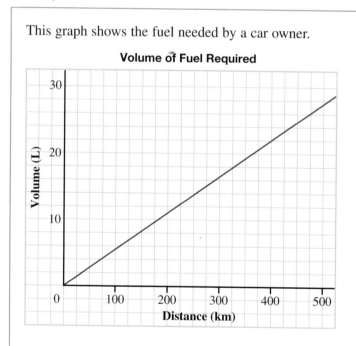

Volume of Fuel Required

How much gas is required to drive 400 km?

Necessary Skills

Solution

Place a ruler vertically from 400 km to the graph. Then place a ruler horizontally from the graph to the vertical axis. The ruler meets the axis at 22 L.

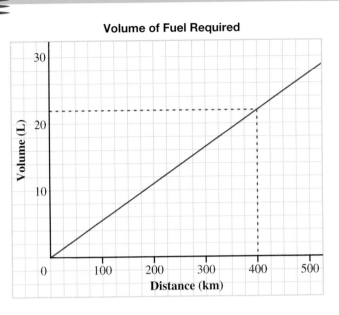

Volume of Fuel Required

Exercises

1. Use the graph in the *Example*. Estimate the amount of gas for each distance.

   a) 50 km   **b)** 200 km   **c)** 475 km   **d)** 500 km

2. How far do you think the car owner can drive on 10 L of gas?

3. Use the graph *Population of Canada*.

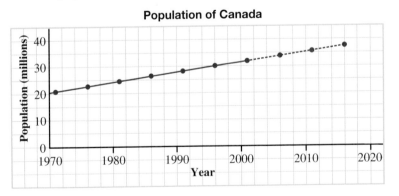

Population of Canada

a) Estimate the year that Canada's population was about 30 000 000.

b) Estimate Canada's population in 1980 and in 2040.

c) What assumptions are you making about the population in 2040? Explain.

A graph is a picture of a relationship between two quantities.
A graph shows how one quantity is related to another.

Relating Height and Time at Canada's Wonderland

Vikings Rage™, a ride at Canada's Wonderland, is a large ship that swings higher and higher.

1. Imagine you are on *Vikings Rage*. Visualize how your height above the ground changes from the beginning to the end of the ride.

   Which graph best represents the relationship between your height above ground and the length of time you are on the ride? Explain your choice.

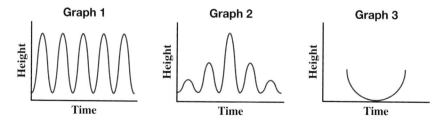

Drop Zone Stunt Tower™ is a 23-storey free-fall ride. People in open seats are lifted to the top of the ride, where there is brief stop. Then they are dropped straight down, reaching speeds of 100 km/h before coming to a complete stop.

2. Imagine you are on *Drop Zone Stunt Tower*. Visualize how your height above the ground changes from the beginning to the end of the ride.

   Which graph best represents the relationship between your height above ground and the length of time you are on the ride? Explain your choice.

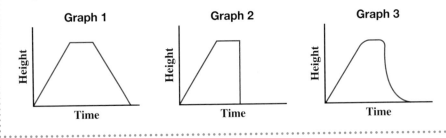

In the *Investigation*, each graph is a *distance-time graph* because distance (or height) is plotted against time. A distance-time graph is *not* a picture of the motion taking place; it shows how the distance changes with time.

In part 1 of the *Investigation*, Graph 2 best represents the ride. Over time, the height for each swing increases to a maximum, then decreases.

In part 2 of the *Investigation*, Graph 3 best represents the ride. The time to go up is greater than the time to come down. On the way down, your height above the ground changes quickly as you come to an abrupt stop.

Example 1

a) Describe the relationship represented by each graph.

i)
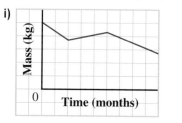

ii)
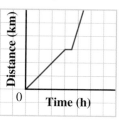

b) Describe a possible situation for each graph.

Solution

a) **i)** As time passes, the mass in kilograms decreases, then increases a little, then decreases.

ii) As time passes, the distance in kilometres increases, then stays the same, then increases at a faster rate than before.

b) **i)** A possible situation is a person on a diet. During the first months, the person loses mass quickly. Then the person gains some mass over a longer period of time, and then loses even more mass.

ii) A possible situation is a person driving a car. The graph shows she drives at a constant speed, stops for a short time, then continues at a faster speed.

Example 2

Draw a graph for each situation. Describe how each graph fits the situation.

a) the motion of a person on a trampoline

b) the heights and ages of a family

c) the money in the wallet of a person on a shopping trip

Solution

a) The person gets on a trampoline, bounces to a height of 0.75 m, falls, bounces higher to 1.0 m, falls, bounces higher to 1.25 m, falls, bounces higher to 1.5 m, then falls and stops.

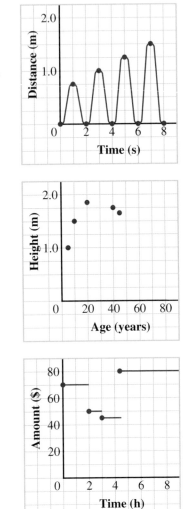

b) There are 5 people in the family. A 6-year-old child is 1.0 m tall. A 12-year-old child is 1.5 m. Another person is 20 years old and 1.85 m. A parent is 40 years old and 1.75 m. The other parent is 45 years old and 1.65 m.

c) The person starts with $70. After 2 h, he spends $20. After another hour, he spends $5. About an hour and a half later, he goes to a bank machine and withdraws $35. He then has $80 in total.

Discuss

How are these graphs similar? How are they different?

1.1 Exercises

A ✓

1. Which graphs show both quantities increasing?

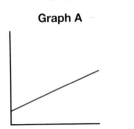

Graph A   Graph B   Graph C   Graph D

2. Which graphs show one quantity decreasing then increasing?

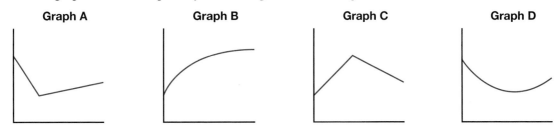

| Graph A | Graph B | Graph C | Graph D |

3. Which graph best represents each situation?

a) the height of a tree over time

b) the height of a Ferris wheel seat as the wheel rotates

c) the number of hours you sleep each day over your lifetime

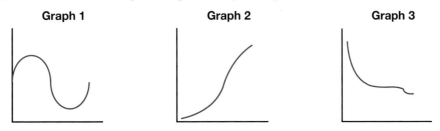

| Graph 1 | Graph 2 | Graph 3 |

4. This graph shows the height of water in a bathtub over a period of time. Think about the label on each axis and the changes in the graph. Describe what happened to the water in the bathtub.

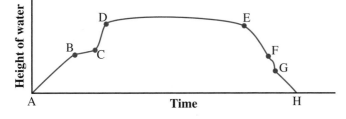

5. Describe the relationship indicated by each graph.

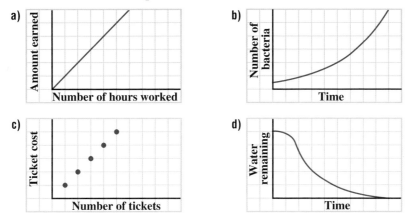

a) Amount earned vs. Number of hours worked

b) Number of bacteria vs. Time

c) Ticket cost vs. Number of tickets

d) Water remaining vs. Time

6. Knowledge/Understanding This graph shows Shakira's distance from home during a walk. Describe the walk.

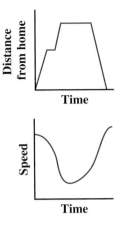

7. This graph shows the speed of Raoul's bike as he rides to school. Describe Raoul's ride.

8. Application In a science experiment, students suspended an object on a spring. They pulled the object down and released it to measure its motion. The graph shows the height of the object above the floor during the first few seconds of the experiment.

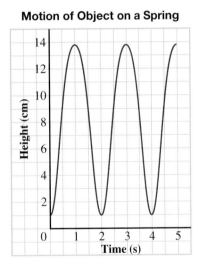

Motion of Object on a Spring

a) Find the height of the object at 1 s, 2 s, and 3 s.

b) Find when the object was:
   i) 6 cm above the floor
   ii) 10 cm above the floor

c) How long does it take the object to move up and down once?

9. Communication Suggest a possible situation for each graph. Describe the significance of any key points or changes in the graph.

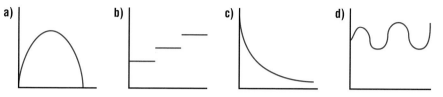

a) b) c) d)

10. For each activity, draw a graph with the axes shown. Label the units.

a) Graph the height above sea level for a person walking along a level road, climbing a hill, stopping to rest at the top, then walking down the hill.

b) Graph the height, above the water surface, for a person diving off a board.

c) Graph the height, above the bottom of a hill, for a ski-jumper.

d) Graph the height, above the bottom of a hill, for a skier in a slalom race.

Height

Time

11. Thinking/Inquiry/Problem Solving Draw a graph to represent each statement. Suggest two quantities that could be described by the graph. Record them on the axes.

a) When one quantity increases, the other increases.

b) When one quantity decreases, the other decreases.

c) When one quantity decreases, the other increases.

d) When one quantity increases, the other decreases.

12. Select one graph you drew in exercise 11. Describe how your graph fits the situation.

By conducting experiments and measuring, we can discover relationships between data.

A Pendulum Experiment

Work with a partner.

You need:
- about 1 m of string
- a small object such as a key or washer
- tape
- a metre stick or measuring tape
- a watch that measures tenths of a second

1. Copy this table.

A Pendulum Experiment

Length of pendulum (cm)	Time for 5 swings (s)

2. Make a pendulum by tying an object to a string. Tape the string to the edge of a desk so the object hangs freely close to the floor.

3. **a)** Measure the length of the pendulum. Record it in the table.

   b) Pull the object to an angle of about 30° from the rest position. Release it. One partner counts 5 swings back and forth, while the other measures the time and records it in the table.

4. Repeat exercise 3 for shorter and shorter pendulum lengths. To shorten the length, lift the tape and pull up the string. Use 6 different lengths, including very short lengths.

5. Graph the data, using appropriate scales. Decide whether to join the points.

6. **a)** How does the amount of time change as the length of the string decreases? Explain whether this makes sense.

   b) Describe the relationship between the amount of time for the pendulum to swing 5 times and the length of the string.

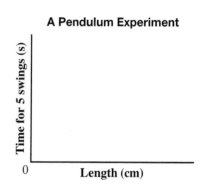

A Pendulum Experiment

7. Use the graph to estimate how long it takes a 45-cm pendulum to swing back and forth 5 times.

8. Write a report to describe your experiment and what you found out. Include the graph in your report and justify your findings.

Graphs and tables of data show relationships between quantities.
A relationship between two quantities is a *relation*.

Example 1

Students measured the space occupied by identical books on a shelf.
Describe patterns in their table of values and graph.

Number of books, x	Shelf space (cm), y
1	3
2	6
3	9
4	12
5	15

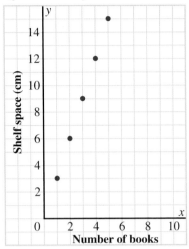

Space Used by Books on a Shelf

Solution

The table shows that as the number of books
increases by 1, the shelf space increases by 3 cm.

Start at any point on the graph. Move horizontally
and vertically to the next point. Each move is
1 unit right and 3 units up. The points lie on a
straight line. This is a result of constant changes
in the table of values.

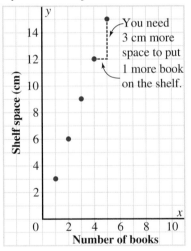

Space Used by Books on a Shelf

Discuss

Why are the points not joined?

Example 2

This table of values and graph show the heights and bases of triangles whose area is 30 square units. Describe patterns in the table of values. Relate the patterns to the graph.

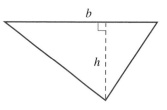

For a triangle, $A = \dfrac{bh}{2}$
A represents the area, b represents the base, and h represents the height.

Height, x	Base, y
1	60
2	30
3	20
4	15
5	12

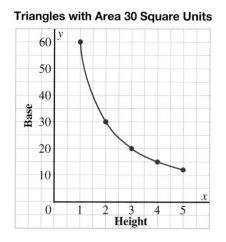

Solution

In the table, the height increases by a *constant* amount; the base decreases by a different amount.
As the height increases, the base decreases.
This pattern results in a curved graph that goes down to the right.

A small increase in the height results in a large decrease in the base.
A large increase in the height results in a small decrease in the base.

Each product of the height and base is 60.

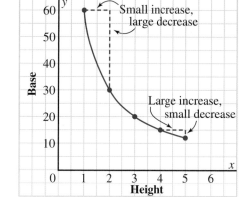

Discuss

Why are the points joined?

Example 1 illustrates a linear relation.
Example 2 illustrates a non-linear relation.

Differences in *y*-coordinates

We can also identify a linear relation by *differences*. We include a third column in each table of values in *Examples 1* and *2*. To complete the *Difference* column, take each *y*-coordinate and subtract the previous *y*-coordinate.

Number of books, *x*	Shelf space (cm), *y*	Difference
1	3	
		$6 - 3 = 3$
2	6	
		$9 - 6 = 3$
3	9	
		$12 - 9 = 3$
4	12	
		$15 - 12 = 3$
5	15	

Height, *x*	Base, *y*	Difference
1	60	
		$30 - 60 = -30$
2	30	
		$20 - 30 = -10$
3	20	
		$15 - 20 = -5$
4	15	
		$12 - 15 = -3$
5	12	

In *Example 1*, the *x*-coordinates increase by the same amount, and the differences in *y*-coordinates are equal.

In *Example 2*, the *x*-coordinates increase by the same amount, but the differences in *y*-coordinates are not equal.

TAKE NOTE

Linear and Non-Linear Relations

- The points on the graph of a *linear relation* in *x* and *y* lie on a straight line. If the numbers in the *x*-column of the table of values change by a constant amount, the differences in the *y*-coordinates are equal.

- The points on the graph of a *non-linear relation* in *x* and *y* do not lie on a straight line. If the numbers in the *x*-column of the table of values change by a constant amount, the differences in the *y*-coordinates are not equal.

A **1.** Does each graph represent a linear relation or a non-linear relation? How do you know?

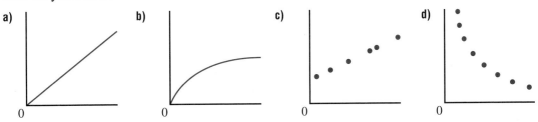

a)   b)   c)   d)

2. Does each table of values represent a linear relation or a non-linear relation? How do you know?

a)

x	y	Difference
2	3	
		3
4	6	
		3
6	9	
		3
8	12	
		3
10	15	

b)

x	y	Difference
1	12	
		–6
2	6	
		–2
3	4	
		–1
4	3	
		–1
6	2	
		–1
12	1	

c)

x	y	Difference
6	12	
		–3
5	9	
		–3
4	6	
		–1
3	5	
		–2
2	3	
		–2
1	1	

d)

x	y	Difference
2	12	
		–3
4	9	
		–3
6	6	
		–3
8	3	
		–3
10	0	

B **3. Knowledge/Understanding** For each table of values, calculate the differences. Describe the relationship between each pair of quantities.

a)

Mass suspended from a spring, x (g)	Extension of the spring, y (mm)	Difference
1	24	
2	48	
3	72	
4	96	
5	120	

b)

Distance from the basket, x (m)	Percent of baskets sunk, y	Difference
2	82	
3	68	
4	50	
5	30	
6	25	

c)

Time of day, x	Temperature, y (°C)	Difference
10:00	22	
11:00	25	
12:00	28	
13:00	27	
14:00	25	

4. a) Graph the data. Plot *Number of coins* horizontally.

Number of coins	4	8	12	16	20
Mass (g)	100	200	300	400	500

b) Describe patterns in the data. Relate the patterns to the graph.

c) What is the mass of one coin? 18 coins?

5. a) Graph the data. Plot *Length of side* horizontally.

Length of side (cm)	1	2	3	4	5
Area of square (cm²)	1	4	9	16	25

b) Describe patterns in the data. Relate the patterns to the graph.

c) What is the area of a square with side length 3.5 cm?

d) What is the side length of a square with area 20 cm²?

e) Look at the table. When the length of one side is doubled does the area double? Why or why not?

For a square, $A = s^2$
A represents the area and s represents the side length.

6. a) Graph the data. Plot *Number of stairs climbed* horizontally.

Number of stairs climbed	5	10	15	20	25
Heart rate (beats/min)	70	80	98	119	147

b) Describe patterns in the data. Relate the patterns to the graph.

c) What is the heart rate after climbing 18 stairs? 13 stairs?

d) About how many stairs were climbed when the heart rate was 85 beats/min? 130 beats/min?

e) Suppose you climbed a very long flight of stairs. Would your heart rate change more rapidly near the beginning or the end of your climb? Explain.

7. a) Graph each relation in exercise 3.

b) For each graph, describe how one quantity changes as the other changes.

8. Investigation: Mass of Textbooks You need a scale that measures up to 20 kg.

a) Copy the table. Measure and record the masses of increasing numbers of your mathematics book.

Number of books	1	2	3	4	5	6	7	8	9	10
Mass (kg)										

b) Graph the data in the table. Plot *Number of books* horizontally.

c) Describe any patterns in the table. Relate the patterns to the graph.

d) Is the relation between the number of books and the mass linear or non-linear? How do the table and the graph show this?

e) Summarize your experiment and what you found out. Include the graph and table of values.

f) Pose a problem regarding the mass of books in the Investigation. Exchange problems with a classmate. Solve the problem posed by your classmate.

9. Communication Suppose the mass in exercise 8 was measured in grams. Would this affect whether the relation is linear or non-linear? Use the table and graph to support your answer.

10. Investigation: Comparing Ounces with Millilitres
Find cans with capacities labelled in both millilitres (mL) and fluid ounces (fl. oz.).

mL is a metric unit. fl.oz. is an imperial unit.

a) Record the capacities in a table.

Description	Capacity (mL)	Capacity (fl. oz.)

b) Predict the shape of the graph that represents the relation between these capacities.

c) Graph the capacities. Plot *Capacity (mL)* horizontally.

d) Is the relation between millilitres and fluid ounces linear or non-linear? How do the table and graph support your answer?

e) How does the graph compare with your prediction? Explain any differences between your prediction and the results.

f) Use the graph to convert each capacity to millilitres.

   i) 15 fl. oz.   **ii)** 22 fl. oz.   **iii)** 20 fl. oz.   **iv)** 30 fl. oz.   **v)** 32 fl. oz.

11. **Application** The chart shows stopping distances on a dry, clean, level pavement. This information is used in drivers' education courses. Stopping distance is the sum of the driver reaction distance and the braking distance.

a) What is meant by "driver reaction distance"?

b) What is meant by "braking distance"?

c) Graph the data. How did you join the points? Explain.

d) What is the average stopping distance for a speed of 65 km/h? 95 km/h?

e) How does a wet road affect stopping distance?

f) How would the graph change in each situation?

  i) The road is wet.

  ii) The road is not level.

  iii) The road is gravel.

g) What other factors affect stopping distance?

Speed (km/h)	Average stopping distance (nearest metre)
20	8
30	12
40	17
50	23
60	31
70	41
80	52
90	66
100	81
110	99
120	120
130	143

12. **Thinking/Inquiry/Problem Solving** Psychologists have conducted experiments to measure how much people remembered what they learned. The results of the experiment are shown in the table and in the graph. Sketch what the graph *Percent Forgotten vs. Time in Days* would look like. Explain how you came up with your graph.

Time (days)	Percent remembered
1	84
5	71
15	61
30	56
60	54

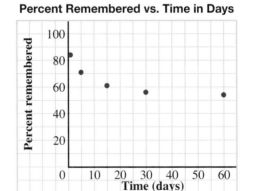

Percent Remembered vs. Time in Days

1. This graph represents the distance from shore during a boat ride. Describe the boat ride.

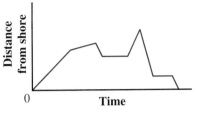

2. Describe the relation between the two quantities. Explain how one quantity changes as the other increases or decreases.

Temperature (°C)	0	20	40	60	80	100
Temperature (°F)	32	68	104	140	176	212

For an equilateral triangle, $P = 3s$
P represents the perimeter and s represents the side length.

3. a) Copy and complete this table for the perimeters of equilateral triangles.

Side length (cm)	1	2	3	4	5	6
Perimeter (cm)						

   b) Graph the data. Plot *Side length (cm)* horizontally.

   c) As the side length increases, what happens to the perimeter?

   d) Is the relation linear or non-linear? Explain how the table of values and graph show this.

   e) Use the graph to estimate the perimeter of a triangle with each side length.

   i) 3.5 cm   ii) 4.25 cm   iii) 0.5 cm   iv) 0.75 cm

   f) Write a problem regarding side length. Solve your problem.

Preparation for Ontario Testing

4. Frieda walks to the corner store to buy milk, then returns home. Which graph best represents her walk?

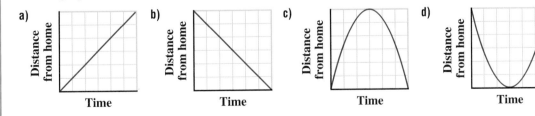

A small company cuts lawns in the summer and clears driveways in the winter. It considers printing and distributing flyers to advertise.

Flyer Advertising

Work with a partner. You need a graphing calculator.

This price list shows the prices for printing and distributing flyers.

FULL PAGE FLYERS

Quantity	Printing ($)	Distribution ($)
1000	56.95	45.00
2000	78.90	90.00
3000	100.85	135.00
4000	122.80	180.00
5000	144.75	225.00
10,000	254.50	450.00
15,000	364.25	675.00
20,000	474.00	900.00
25,000	583.75	1125.00

One ink colour and one paper colour.
Artwork is $50.00 extra.
GST is extra.

Step 1. Enter the data.

- Press [STAT] **1** to go to the list editor.
  If there are any numbers in the columns, move the
  cursor into the column heading, then press [CLEAR] [ENTER].

- Move the cursor to the space
  below L1.
  Enter the first number from the
  Quantity column.
  Press [ENTER].

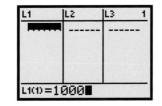
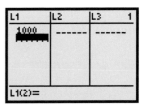

- Enter the other numbers from
  the *Quantity* column into list L1.
- Move the cursor to the space
  below L2.
  Enter the numbers from the
  Printing ($) column into list L2.

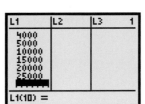
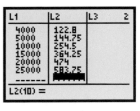

Step 2. Set up the graph.

Your calculator can draw the graph
you want, as well as plot the lists
along each axis.

- Press [2nd] [Y=] to get the STAT PLOT menu.
  This menu shows:
  – whether the plot is turned on or off
  – the type of graph
  – the lists plotted in the graph
  – the plotting symbol
- Press **1** to select Plot1. Press [ENTER] to turn on Plot1.
- Press [▼] [ENTER] to select the first plot type.
- Press [▼] [2nd] **1** to graph L1 horizontally.
- Press [▼] [2nd] **2** to graph L2 vertically.
- Press [▼] [ENTER] to select the first plotting symbol.

Step 3. Set up the window.

- Press [WINDOW].
- Enter Xmin = 0, Xmax = 25 000, and Xscl = 5000 to show quantities up to 25 000 on the horizontal axis.
- Enter Ymin = 0, Ymax = 600, and Yscl = 100 to show costs up to $600 on the vertical axis.

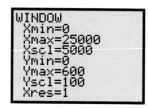

Step 4. Graph the data.

- Press [GRAPH] to graph L2, the cost of printing, against L1, the quantity.

  1. a) Does the relation appear linear or non-linear? Explain how you know.

  b) Explain whether the relation is reasonable for the data.

  2. Sketch the graph. Label the axes including units.

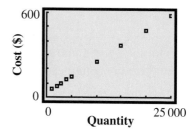

Operating with lists

The price list on page 24 states that artwork is $50.00 extra. You can use the calculator to add the cost of artwork to the printing cost.

- Press [STAT] **1** to go to the list editor. Move the cursor to the heading L3.
- Press [2nd] **2** [+] 50 [ENTER] to add 50 to each number in L2, and show the results in L3.

  3. Predict how the graph of L3, the cost of printing with art, against L1, the quantity, will compare with the first graph for the cost of printing without art.

To check your prediction:

- Press [2nd] [Y=] to get the STAT PLOT menu.
- Press **2** to select Plot2. Press [ENTER] to turn on Plot2.
- Press [▼] [ENTER] to select the first plot type.
- Press [▼] [2nd] **1** to graph L1 horizontally.
- Press [▼] [2nd] **3** to graph L3 vertically.
- Press [▼] [▶] [ENTER] to select the second plotting symbol.

- Press GRAPH to graph the cost of printing without art on the same screen as the cost of printing with art.

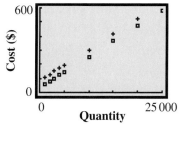

4. a) Sketch the graph. Label the axes, including units.

  b) How are the lists L2 and L3 related? Explain whether this is reasonable for adding the cost of $50 to the cost of printing each quantity.

  c) How does the graph show this relation?

Viewing coordinates of points

- Press TRACE. The flashing cursor is on a plotted point, with its coordinates at the bottom of the screen.

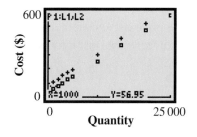

- Use the arrow keys to move the cursor.

5. a) What happens when you press ◄ and ►?

  b) What happens when you press ▲ and ▼?

6. a) Trace to find the cost of printing 15 000 flyers without art.

  b) Trace to find the cost of printing 15 000 flyers with art.

Managing lists

The price list on page 24 shows the cost of distributing the flyers. You can use the calculator to add the printing and distribution costs.

- Press STAT **1** to go to the list editor.
  Move the cursor to the heading L3.
  Press CLEAR ENTER to clear L3.

- Enter the distribution cost in L3.

- Move the cursor to the heading L4.
  Press 2nd **2** + 2nd **3** ENTER to add the printing cost in L2 and the distribution cost in L3, and show the results in L4.

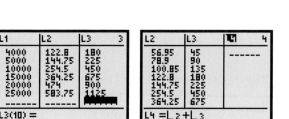

7. Predict how the graph of the cost of printing plus distribution will compare with the graph of the cost of printing.

To check your prediction:

- Press [2nd] [Y=] to get the STAT PLOT menu.
  Press **2** to select Plot2.
- Press [▼] [▼] [▼] [2nd] **4** to graph L4 against L1.
- Press [WINDOW]. Change window settings so that the whole
  graph will show. Enter Ymax = 2000 and Yscl = 200.
- Press [GRAPH].

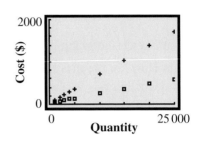

8. Trace to find the cost of printing and distributing
15 000 flyers without art.

The price list shows that GST is extra. You can use the calculator
to multiply the cost by 1.07 to find the cost with GST.

- Press [STAT] **1** to go to the list editor.
- Move the cursor to the heading L5.
  Press [2nd] **4** [×] 1.07 [ENTER] to calculate the
  cost including GST, and show the results in L5.
- Press [2nd] [Y=] to get the STAT PLOT menu.
  Press **2** to select Plot2.
- Press [▼] [▼] [▼] [2nd] **5** to graph L5 against L1.
- Press [GRAPH] to display L5, the total cost, including
  GST, of printing and distributing flyers without art,
  against L1, the quantity.

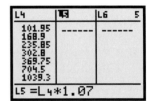

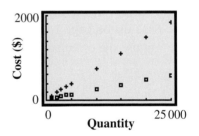

9. Trace to find the total cost, including GST, of
printing and distributing 15 000 flyers.

10. Sketch the graph, and label the axes.

11. Communication Explain whether you would advise the company
to advertise with flyers. Support your advice with data from the
Investigation.

1.4 Using a Motion Detector to Investigate Relationships

You can use technology to gather data and display graphs. In this *Investigation*, you will use a TI-83 graphing calculator connected to a Calculator-Based Ranger™ (CBR™) unit. A CBR is a sonic motion detector that collects data and displays them on the calculator screen.

The instructions for the *Investigation* assume the RANGER program has been transferred to your calculator.

Checking for the Ranger program

To check whether the RANGER program has been transferred to your calculator:

- Connect the CBR to the calculator with the connecting cable.
- Turn on the calculator, then press [PRGM]. A list of programs stored in memory appears. If RANGER appears in the list, the program has been transferred. If RANGER does not appear, continue with the following steps.

Transferring the RANGER program to the calculator

- On the calculator, press [2nd] [X,T,θ,n] [▶] [ENTER].
  The calculator will show it is waiting to receive the program.
- On the CBR, open the pivoting head and press [82/83]. The CBR will send this program to the calculator.

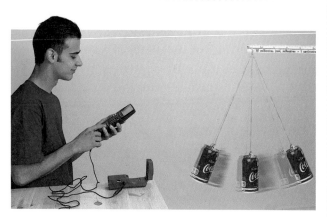

Pendulum Experiment

You will use the CBR to measure its distance from a swinging pendulum. The calculator displays a graph to show how this distance changes as the pendulum swings back and forth.

Work with a partner. You need:

- about 1 m of string
- an empty pop can
- a TI-83 graphing calculator
- a CBR and connecting cable
- a metre stick

Step 1. Set up the experiment.

- Set up the pendulum and CBR as shown. Use an object as large as a pop can for the weight. This is needed so that the CBR measures the distance to the object, not an object beyond it. Make the string as long as possible.
- Place the CBR at least 50 cm from the closest position of the object.
- Connect the CBR to the calculator with the connecting cable.
- Turn on the calculator. Press ⃞PRGM.
- Choose RANGER. Press ⃞ENTER.
- Press ⃞ENTER ⃞ENTER to display the main menu.
- Press **2** to choose SET DEFAULTS.
- Make sure the cursor is beside START NOW. If not, use the arrow keys to move it.
- Start the pendulum swinging.

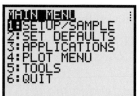

Step 2. Collect and graph the data.

- Press ⃞ENTER when you are ready to begin. The calculator displays a distance-time graph that follows the motion of the pendulum.
- To make the calculator redraw the graph in a better position on the screen, press ⃞ENTER **1**.
- To repeat, press ⃞ENTER **3**. Repeat until you are satisfied with the result.
- Leave the graph on the screen while you complete the following exercises. Since the data for this graph are in your calculator, you can disconnect the cable so that someone else can use the CBR.

1. Look at the graph. What quantity is represented along

   a) the horizontal axis?   b) the vertical axis?

2. Sketch the distance-time graph, or use a computer linkup to print it. Label the axes with the units.

3. Is the graph linear or non-linear? How do you know?

4. Describe what happens to the plotted points in each case.

   a) The object is moving toward the CBR.

   b) The object is moving away from the CBR.

   c) The pendulum slows down.

Viewing coordinates of points

You can view the coordinates of some points on the graph. These correspond to the data the CBR gathered.

5. Press ⌈TRACE⌋ and the arrow keys to move the flashing cursor along the graph. Its coordinates appear on the screen.

   a) What was the maximum distance from the object to the CBR?

   b) What was the minimum distance from the object to the CBR?

   c) How many complete swings are represented on the graph?

6. The period of the pendulum is the time for one complete swing. Find the period of the pendulum as accurately as you can.

7. a) Suppose you pulled the object farther from the rest position before starting the pendulum. Predict how the distance-time graph would change.

   b) Use the CBR and calculator to check your prediction.

8. a) Suppose you repeated the experiment with a longer pendulum. Predict how the distance-time graph would change.

   b) Use the CBR and calculator to check your prediction.

9. a) Suppose you repeated the experiment with a shorter pendulum. Predict how the distance-time graph would change.

   b) Use the CBR and calculator to check your prediction.

10. **Communication** The graphs in the *Investigation* show the relation between two quantities. Describe these two quantities, and explain how they are related. Include sketches of graphs to illustrate your description.

The graph from page 16 is repeated here. It shows a relationship between two quantities.

- These quantities are related by multiplication and division.
- The points on the graph lie on a straight line through the origin.
- The line goes up to the right.

Any situation that has these properties is a *proportional situation*. To solve problems in proportional situations, use multiplication or division.

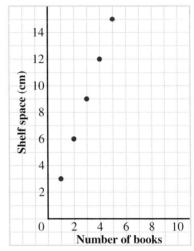

Space Used by Books on a Shelf

Example 1

Marcia works in a card store after school. In 4 h, Marcia earns $20.

a) What is Marcia's hourly rate of pay?

b) How much does Marcia earn in 8 h?

c) How long does Marcia work to earn $100?

d) Use the data from parts a to c. Make a table of values. Draw a graph to show how Marcia's earnings are related to the number of hours she works.

e) Do Marcia's earnings show a proportional situation? Explain how you know.

Solution

a) Marcia earns $20 in 4 h.

So, in 1 h, Marcia earns $\frac{20}{4} = 5$.

Marcia's rate of pay is $5/h.

b) Marcia earns $5 per hour.

So, in 8 h, Marcia earns $8 \times 5 = 40$.

Marcia earns $40 in 8 h.

c) Marcia earns $5 per hour.

So, to earn $100, Marcia works $\frac{100}{5} = 20$.

Marcia works 20 h to earn $100.

d)

Time (h)	Earnings ($)
4	20
1	5
8	40
20	100

Marcia's Earnings

e) Marcia's earnings show a proportional situation. The quantities are the time Marcia works and the amount she earns. These quantities are related by multiplication and division. The points on the graph lie on a straight line through the origin. These points go up to the right.

Discuss

Suppose Marcia's hourly rate increased. How would the graph change?

Example 2

At the bulk-food store, Jerry bought 200 g of mixed nuts that cost $2.50.

a) What is the cost of 1 g of nuts?

b) What is the price for 450 g of nuts?

c) What mass of nuts would cost $6.25?

d) Show the results of parts a to c in a table. Draw a graph.

Solution

a) 200 g of nuts cost $2.50.

For 1 g: $\frac{2.50}{200} = 0.0125$

One gram of nuts costs $0.01.

b) 1 g of nuts costs $0.0125.

For 450 g: $450 \times 0.0125 \doteq 5.63$

The price for 450 g of nuts is $5.63.

c) $0.0125 buys 1 g.

For $6.25: $\frac{6.25}{0.0125} = 500$

500 g of nuts would cost $6.25.

> The cost of 1 g of nuts is the unit price.

d)

Mass (g)	Price ($)
200	2.50
450	5.63
500	6.25

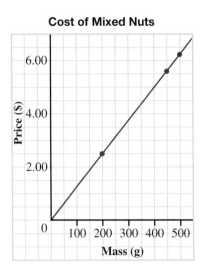

Cost of Mixed Nuts

Discuss

Suppose the price per gram decreased. How would the graph change?

Is this a proportional situation? How do you know?

In part b, why is the cost for 1 g of nuts written with more than 2 decimal places?

1.5　Exercises

Use mental math where possible.

A

1. One cheeseburger costs $1.29. What is the cost for each number of cheeseburgers?

　a) 3　　　　　**b)** 5　　　　　**c)** 20　　　　　**d)** 12

2. One tennis ball costs $0.72. What is the cost for each number of tennis balls?

　a) 2　　　　　**b)** 4　　　　　**c)** 6　　　　　**d)** 13

3. Find each unit price. Round to the nearest cent.

　a) A box of 15 sports drinks costs $23.99.

　b) A box of 12 markers costs $34.59.

　c) A package of 500 sheets of paper costs $5.99.

4. Find each unit price to the nearest cent.

　a) Message pads cost $4.40 for 10.

　b) Business envelopes cost $8.99 for 100.

　c) Blank CDs cost $11.99 for 10.

B **5.** A customer buys 400 g of candy for $2.40. Find the cost of each mass. Check with a calculator.

    a) 800 g   **b)** 100 g   **c)** 200 g   **d)** 1600 g

6. A case of 24 cans of pop costs $6.96.

    a) What is the unit price per can?

    b) What is the cost of a dozen cans of pop?

7. Six bottles of motor oil cost $11.34.

    a) What is the unit price?

    b) What is the price for 10 bottles? 40 bottles? 100 bottles?

    c) Show the results in a table.

    d) Draw a graph. Plot *Number of bottles* horizontally and *Cost* vertically. Include the units.

    e) Does the graph represent a proportional situation? How do you know?

8. The gas tank in May's car holds 45 L of gas. The cost for a fill-up is $27.86.

    a) What is the price per litre? Round to the nearest cent.

    b) For this unit price, what is the cost of 35 L of gas?

    c) How many litres could May buy with $10.00?

9. The Red Shield Telethon raised $42 500 in the first 20 min.

    a) At this rate, how much would be raised in 1 h? 3 h? 8 h?

    b) Show the results in a table.

    c) Draw a graph to show the relationship between the time and the amount raised.

    d) At this rate, about how long would it take to raise $1 000 000?

    e) Suppose the amount raised per hour increased. How would the graph change? Explain.

    f) Is this a proportional situation? Explain how the table and graph show this.

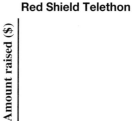

10. Knowledge/Understanding Tina works part-time for a landscaping company. She is paid hourly and earns $28.70 in 3.5 h.

    a) How much does she earn in 1 h? 9 h? 12 h? 20 h?

    b) How many hours would she work to earn $287?

    c) Show the results of parts a and b in a table.

    d) Draw a graph to show how the amount earned is related to the time worked. Plot *Time worked* horizontally.

e) Suppose Tina's hourly rate increased. How would the graph change? Explain.

f) Is this a proportional situation? Explain how you know.

11. a) Taborah had 12 hits in 30 attempts at bat. About how many attempts at bat would she need for 100 hits?

b) What assumption is made in part a? Do you think this assumption is realistic? Explain your reason.

12. Application Which cola special is the better value?

1.5-L bottle	$1.29
Case of 24 x 355-mL cans	$5.99

13. A 5-kg bag of grass seed covers an area of 300 m^2.

a) What mass of grass seed is needed to cover a football field 150 m by 60 m?

b) Explain how you could estimate to check your answer.

14. Communication Explain what is meant by a *proportional situation*. Use an example to illustrate your explanation.

15. Thinking/Inquiry/Problem Solving
The giant sequoia trees on the west coast of North America are among the world's tallest and oldest living things. Some of them are 3200 years old. An average sequoia pumps about 1000 L of water from its roots to its leaves every 24 h.

How long would it take to pump the amount of water that would fill a pop can? Explain how you got your answer.

1.6 Relating Animal and Human Lifetimes

On page 3, you considered the problem of comparing the lifetime of an animal with a human lifetime.

There is no exact formula. Several models have been proposed by veterinarians and scientists. Your task is to make a graph to show how the models relate the lifetime of a cat or dog to a human lifetime. You will compare the models, then determine which model you think is best.

You will need grid paper, some coloured pencils or markers, and a ruler.

1. Prepare a grid with axes as shown. Make the grid as large as possible. You may need to experiment to find the best way to set up the axes and the scales.

   a) Plot the animal's age along the horizontal axis. Since the expected lifetime for a cat or dog is no more than 20 years, label the horizontal scale from 0 to 20.

   b) Plot a person's age along the vertical axis. Label the vertical scale from 0 to 100.

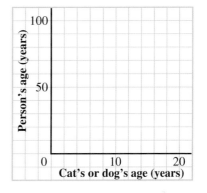

Model 1

One year of a cat's life is equivalent to 7 years of a person's life.

2. **a)** Copy and complete this table.

Cat's age (years)	1	2	3	4	5	6	7	8	9	10
Person's age (years)	7	14								

   b) Graph the data from your table. Decide whether it makes sense to join the points on the graph. Label your graph.

   c) Do you think this model is reasonable? Why?

Model 2

This model for cats appeared in an article in *Reader's Digest*.

The first year of a cat's life equals about 21 human years. For each additional year, count 4 human years for each year of the cat's life.

3. a) Copy and complete this table.

Cat's age (years)	1	2	3	4	5	6	7	8	9	10
Person's age (years)	21	25								

b) Graph the data on the same grid as Model 1. Label the graph.

4. Compare the graph of this model with the graph of Model 1.

  a) State two ways in which Model 2 differs from Model 1.

  b) Explain what these differences mean in terms of relating the lifetime of a cat to a human lifetime.

Model 3

This model for dogs appeared in an article in *The Toronto Star*.

The first year of a dog's life equals about 15 human years. The second year adds another 10 years. For each additional year, count 5 human years for each year of the dog's life.

5. a) Copy and complete this table.

Dog's age (years)	1	2	3	4	5	6	7	8	9	10
Person's age (years)	15	25	30							

  b) Graph the data on a grid similar to the one in exercise 1.

  c) How is Model 3 similar to Model 2?

  d) Do you think it would be reasonable to use either Model 2 or Model 3 for both cats and dogs? Why?

6. Which graph shows a proportional situation? How do you know?

7. Choose the model that you think is the best one for relating the lifetime of an animal to a human lifetime. Explain your choice.

MATHEMATICS TOOLKIT

Relation

- A relationship between two quantities can be shown on a graph.

Linear Relation	Non-Linear Relation
• If the numbers in the *x*-column of the table of values change by a constant amount, the differences in the *y*-coordinates are equal.	• If the numbers in the *x*-column of the table of values change by a constant amount, the differences in the *y*-coordinates are not equal.
• The points on the graph lie on a straight line.	• The points on the graph do not lie on a straight line.

Proportional Situation

- Quantities are related by multiplication and division.
- Points on the graph lie on a straight line through 0.
- The graph goes up to the right.

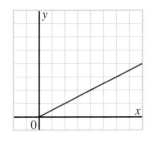

1.1   **1.** For each graph, explain how the quantities change.

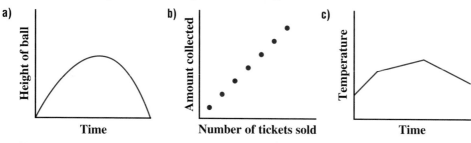

a) Height of ball / Time

b) Amount collected / Number of tickets sold

c) Temperature / Time

2. a) Sketch a graph to show the water level in a sink.
- Start with an empty sink with the plug in.
- Turn on the tap.
- Turn off the tap.
- Turn on the tap again.
- Turn off the tap.
- Take out the plug.

b) Describe how your graph shows the water level.

1.2   **3.** Describe the relationship between the two quantities.

Time a tap is on (min)	2	4	6	8	10	12	14	16	18
Depth of water in fish pond (cm)	1	2	3	4	5	6	7	8	9

4. a) Investigation: Metric and Imperial Units Measure the lengths of 6 objects in centimetres and in inches. Record the lengths in a table.

> Centimetre is a metric unit. Inch is an imperial unit.

Object	Length (cm)	Length (in.)

b) Does the table of values show a linear or non-linear relation? How do you know?

c) Graph the lengths.

d) Does the graph show a linear or non-linear relation? How do you know?

e) Use the data to write a problem about an object and its length.

f) Solve the problem you wrote in part e.

Metric and Imperial Units

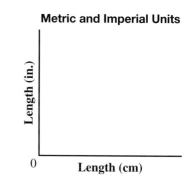

Length (in.) / Length (cm) / 0

5. a) Suppose distances are measured in both metres and feet. Predict if there is a relationship between the two measures. Explain.

b) Choose 6 distances to measure in feet and in metres. Record the data in a table.

c) Graph the data.

d) Compare the table and the graph with your prediction. Explain any differences between your prediction and results.

Metric and Imperial Units

Distance (ft.) vs Distance (m)

Metre is a metric unit. Foot is an imperial unit.

1.4 **6.** Suppose you use a graphing calculator and CBR to graph the distance between the CBR and a swinging pendulum.

a) Sketch a graph that could appear on the calculator screen.

b) How does your graph represents this situation?

1.5 **7.** What is the price per package for each kind of paper?

a) 10 packages of computer paper cost $119.90.

b) 10 packages of copy paper cost $109.70.

c) 10 packages of 3-hole punched paper cost $229.80.

d) 10 packages of green paper cost $149.90.

8. Raj earned $40.50 for working 6 h in a grocery store.

a) What is Raj's hourly rate of pay?

b) How much does Raj earn in 12 h? 24 h?

c) How long does Raj work to earn $216?

d) Show the results of parts a to c in a table.

e) Graph the data. Plot *Time worked* horizontally.

f) Do Raj's earnings show a proportional situation? How do the table and graph show this?

g) Suppose Raj took another job with a lower hourly rate. How would the graph change?

9. Marta's hockey team can buy a dozen black pucks for $16.95 or 3 dozen orange pucks for $45.95.

a) What is the unit price for each puck?

b) Which is the better price per puck?

1. This graph represents the speed of a ride at an amusement park. Describe how the speed changes.

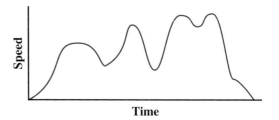

2. **Knowledge/Understanding**

   a) Copy and complete the table. It shows the dimensions of rectangles with area 24 cm².

Width (cm)	1	2	3	4	6	8	12	24
Length (cm)	24	12						

   b) Graph the data. Plot *Width* horizontally.

   c) Use the graph to estimate the length of a rectangle with width 5 cm.

   d) What happens to the length as the width increases? Why?

   e) Is the relation linear or non-linear? How do the table of values and graph show this?

   f) Do the graph and table show a proportional situation? How do you know?

3. **Thinking/Inquiry/Problem Solving** In exercise 2b, how would the graph change if the area of the rectangle was 36 cm²? Explain your ideas.

4. **Communication** This graph represents the cost for printing flyers. Pose a problem about this relation. Solve your problem.

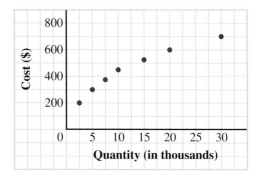

5. A package of 12 pens costs $15.48.

   a) At this rate, what is the cost of 1 pen? 36 pens? 50 pens? 100 pens?

   b) Show the data in a table.

   c) Graph the data. Plot *Number of pens* horizontally.

   d) Does the graph represent a proportional situation? Explain how you know.

   e) **Application** Describe how the graph in part c would change for each situation.
      i) The pens were on sale at a cheaper price.
      ii) The pens were purchased individually for $1.39 each.

6. Three sisters, Sam, Dina, and Nat, decided to race.

  • The youngest, Sam, was allowed to start ahead of the others.

  • The oldest, Nat, had to wait for 1 s after their father said "Go."

Match each sister with the line A, B, or C, which represents her race. **Explain your choices**.

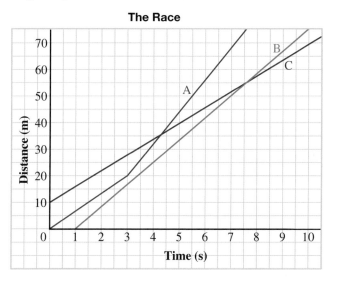

The Race

7. Avinash tried his new snowboard at "Snowboarders Only Resort." The following graph shows his first run.

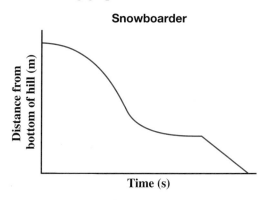

Snowboarder

  • The vertical axis shows his distance from the bottom of the hill.

  • The horizontal axis shows time in seconds.

Write a description Avinash's first run.

2 Powers and Roots

By the end of this chapter, you will:

- Evaluate powers. Calculate with powers. Calculate square roots.

- Understand zero and negative exponents.

- Use patterns to find the rules for multiplying and dividing monomials.

- Evaluate powers with natural number exponents and rational number bases.

- Represent very large and very small numbers in scientific notation.

- Use the Pythagorean Theorem to calculate side lengths of right triangles.

- Use a scientific calculator for calculations with exponents.

- Decide whether answers are reasonable by considering likely results for the situations and by estimating.

- Communicate solutions to problems, and justify your reasoning in solving problems.

How Thick Is the Pile of Paper?

Imagine folding a piece of paper in half, forming 2 layers. Then, fold the paper in half again to form 4 layers. Suppose you were to continue folding in half as long as possible.

How many times could you fold the paper before it is impossible to make another fold?

Suppose it were possible to fold the paper 50 times. About how high do you think the pile of paper would be?

You will investigate this problem in Section 2.8.

Powers

For the *power* 2^5:

- the *base* is 2. The base is the number that is repeatedly multiplied.
- the *exponent* is 5. The exponent is the number of times that the base is multiplied.

power 2^5 $\leftarrow$ exponent
$\leftarrow$ base

We say "2 to the fifth" or "2 to the power 5."

We write: $2^5 = 2 \times 2 \times 2 \times 2 \times 2$
$= 32$

Example

Evaluate each power.

a) 4^2 **b)** 3^3 **c)** 1^4

Solution

a) $4^2 = 4 \times 4$ **b)** $3^3 = 3 \times 3 \times 3$ **c)** $1^4 = 1 \times 1 \times 1 \times 1$
$= 16$ $= 27$ $= 1$

Exercises

1. Evaluate each power.

a) 10^2 **b)** 10^3 **c)** 10^4 **d)** 10^5

2. Look at exercise 1. How can you mentally evaluate a power with base 10?

3. Explain what each power means. Evaluate each power.

a) 5^4 **b)** 7^3 **c)** 3^2 **d)** 10^5

4. Evaluate each power. Calculate mentally if possible.

a) 6^2 **b)** 5^3 **c)** 4^2 **d)** 1^8

5. Write a rule about evaluating a power with base 1. Use a calculator to check your rule.

6. Use a calculator to evaluate each power.

a) 21^3 **b)** 9^7 **c)** 130^4 **d)** 19^5

Recall the rules for multiplying integers.

When two integers have the same sign, their product is positive.

$$(+) \times (+) = + \quad (-) \times (-) = +$$

When two integers have different signs, their product is negative.

$$(+) \times (-) = - \quad (-) \times (+) = -$$

Recall that a power is a repeated multiplication. For example, $2^3 = 2 \times 2 \times 2$

Example 1

Write each power as a product. Then evaluate.

a) 4^5 **b)** $(-6)^8$ **c)** $(-5)^4$

Solution

Since these require several multiplications, use a calculator.

a) $4^5 = (4)(4)(4)(4)(4)$

    Press: 4 [^] 5 [ENTER =]

    $4^5 = 1024$

```
4^5
          1024
```

b) $(-6)^8 = (-6)(-6)(-6)(-6)(-6)(-6)(-6)(-6)$

    Press: [( ] [(-)] 6 [ )] [^] 8 [ENTER =]

    $(-6)^8 = 1\ 679\ 616$

```
(−6)^8
        1679616
```

c) $(-5)^4 = (-5)(-5)(-5)(-5)$

    Press: [( ] [(-)] 5 [ )] [^] 4 [ENTER =]

    $(-5)^4 = 625$

```
(−5)^4
          625
```

In part c, the brackets are significant.

$$(-5)^4 = (-5)(-5)(-5)(-5)$$
$$= 625$$

$$-5^4 = -(5)^4$$
$$= -(5)(5)(5)(5)$$
$$= -625$$

A rational number is a number that can be written as a fraction, a terminating decimal, or a repeating decimal. A rational number can be positive or negative.

Products of Integers and Rational Numbers

- The product of positive rational numbers is positive. $(+) \times (+) \times (+) = +$
- The product of an even number of negative rational numbers is positive.
  $(-) \times (-) \times (-) \times (-) = +$
- The product of an odd number of negative rational numbers is negative.
  $(-) \times (-) \times (-) = -$

A power with a rational-number base is evaluated in the same way as a power with an integer base.

We can use the rules for multiplying integers and rational numbers to predict whether a product is positive or negative.

Example 2

Write each power as a product. Then evaluate.

a) $\left(\dfrac{2}{3}\right)^3$ **b)** $\left(-\dfrac{5}{4}\right)^2$ **c)** $\left(-\dfrac{3}{10}\right)^5$

Solution

a) $\left(\dfrac{2}{3}\right)^3 = \dfrac{2}{3} \times \dfrac{2}{3} \times \dfrac{2}{3}$

$= \dfrac{2 \times 2 \times 2}{3 \times 3 \times 3}$

$= \dfrac{8}{27}$

b) $\left(-\dfrac{5}{4}\right)^2 = \left(-\dfrac{5}{4}\right)\left(-\dfrac{5}{4}\right)$

$= \dfrac{(-5) \times (-5)}{4 \times 4}$

$= \dfrac{25}{16}$

There is an even number of negative rational numbers. So, the product is positive.

c) $\left(-\dfrac{3}{10}\right)^5 = \left(-\dfrac{3}{10}\right)\left(-\dfrac{3}{10}\right)\left(-\dfrac{3}{10}\right)\left(-\dfrac{3}{10}\right)\left(-\dfrac{3}{10}\right)$

There is an odd number of negative rational numbers. So, the product is negative. Use a calculator.

Press: $($ $(-)$ 3 $A\%$ 10 $)$ $\wedge$ 5 $\boxed{\text{ENTER}}$

$\left(-\dfrac{3}{10}\right)^5 = -0.002\ 43$

$$(-3 \lrcorner 10)\wedge 5$$
$$-0.00243$$

Example 3

Evaluate each power to 2 decimal places.
Estimate to check whether the answers are reasonable.

a) $(-1.25)^4$ **b)** 10.2^5 **c)** $(-2.9)^3$

Solution

a) $(-1.25)^4$

Use a calculator.

Press: ((-) 1.25) ^ 4 [ENTER =]

$(-1.25)^4 \doteq 2.44$

> $(-1.25)^4$
> 2.44140625

Check.

1.25 is greater than 1 and $1^4 = 1$; 2.44 is slightly greater than 1.

$(-1.25)^4$ has an even number of negative rational numbers, so the answer is positive.

So, $(-1.25)^4 \doteq 2.44$ is reasonable.

b) 10.2^5

Press: 10.2 ^ 5 [ENTER =]

$10.2^5 \doteq 110\ 408.08$

> 10.2^5
> 110408.0803

Check.

$10.2 \doteq 10$ and $10^5 = 100\ 000$; 100 000 is close to 110 408.08.

So, $10.2^5 \doteq 110\ 408.08$ is reasonable.

c) $(-2.9)^3$

Press: ((-) 2.9) ^ 3 [ENTER =]

$(-2.9)^3 \doteq -24.39$

> $(-2.9)^3$
> -24.389

Check.

2.9 is almost 3 and $3^3 = 27$; 24.39 is close to 27.

$(-2.9)^3$ has an odd number of negative rational numbers, so the answer is negative.

So, $(-2.9)^3 \doteq -24.39$ is reasonable.

A **1.** Evaluate. Round to 3 decimal places where necessary.

✓ a) $(-5)(-5)(-5)(-5)(-5)$

b) $(6)(6)(6)(6)(6)(6)(6)$

c) $(-9.1)(-9.1)(-9.1)(-9.1)$

d) $(2.85)(2.85)(2.85)(2.85)(2.85)$

e) $\left(\dfrac{1}{4}\right)\left(\dfrac{1}{4}\right)\left(\dfrac{1}{4}\right)$

f) $\left(-\dfrac{7}{3}\right)\left(-\dfrac{7}{3}\right)\left(-\dfrac{7}{3}\right)\left(-\dfrac{7}{3}\right)\left(-\dfrac{7}{3}\right)\left(-\dfrac{7}{3}\right)$

✓ **2.** Write each power as a product. Then evaluate.

a) $(-2)^1$ b) $(-2)^2$ c) $(-2)^3$

d) $(-2)^4$ e) $(-2)^5$ f) $(-2)^6$

✓ **3.** Write each power as a product. Then evaluate.

a) $\left(-\dfrac{1}{2}\right)^1$ b) $\left(-\dfrac{1}{2}\right)^2$ c) $\left(-\dfrac{1}{2}\right)^3$

d) $\left(-\dfrac{1}{2}\right)^4$ e) $\left(-\dfrac{1}{2}\right)^5$ f) $\left(-\dfrac{1}{2}\right)^6$

✓ **4.** Evaluate each power mentally.

a) 4^1 b) 7^1 c) 1^1 d) 10^1

e) $(-4)^1$ f) $(-7)^1$ g) $(-1)^1$ h) $(-10)^1$

B **5. a)** Evaluate.

i) 10^2 ii) $(-10)^3$ iii) $(-10)^4$ iv) 10^5 v) $(-10)^6$

b) How would you evaluate a power of 10 mentally?

✓ **6. a)** Evaluate.

i) $(-3)^1$ ii) $(-3)^2$ iii) $(-3)^3$ iv) $(-3)^4$ v) $(-3)^5$

b) Communication Explain how you know whether a power with a negative base is positive or negative.

7. Evaluate. Record only answers less than 1. Round to 3 decimal places where necessary.

a) $\left(\dfrac{2}{3}\right)^4$ b) $(1.02)^3$ c) $(-0.6)^8$ d) $\left(\dfrac{6}{5}\right)^2$ e) $(-3.2)^5$

8. Write each power as a product. Then evaluate.

a) $\left(\dfrac{1}{3}\right)^4$ b) $\left(-\dfrac{3}{5}\right)^3$ c) $\left(-\dfrac{10}{3}\right)^4$ d) $\left(\dfrac{5}{8}\right)^2$

9. Evaluate each power. Round to 2 decimal places where necessary. Estimate to check whether the answers are reasonable.

a) 3.8^4 b) $(-1.9)^5$ c) 2.25^6 d) $(-0.1)^2$

✓ 10. **Knowledge/Understanding** Evaluate each power. Round to 3 decimal places where necessary.

a) 3^6

b) $(-5)^9$

c) 2.1^5

d) $\left(\dfrac{2}{5}\right)^4$

e) $(-1.7)^4$

f) $\left(-\dfrac{3}{11}\right)^3$

✓ 11. a) Evaluate.

i) $(-4)^2$ ii) -4^2 iii) $-(-4)^2$ iv) 4^2

b) Describe the differences among the four powers in part a.

12. a) Evaluate each power without rounding.

i) $(0.25)^3$

ii) $\left(\dfrac{1}{4}\right)^3$

iii) $(-0.8)^4$

iv) $\left(-\dfrac{4}{5}\right)^4$

v) $(-0.5)^2$

vi) $\left(-\dfrac{1}{2}\right)^2$

b) Which results from part a are equal? Why are they equal? How might you use this when entering powers on a calculator?

13. a) **Application** Evaluate each power. Make decisions about rounding you think are appropriate.

i) Dinosaurs became extinct about 90^4 years ago.
ii) In 2001, the population of Canada was about 6.8^9.
iii) The area of Ontario is about 102.5^3 km^2.

b) Explain your decisions about rounding in part a.

14. **Thinking/Inquiry/Problem Solving**

a) List the powers of $(-2)^n$ from $n = 1$ to $n = 8$. Evaluate each power.

b) When is $(-2)^n$ positive? Explain.

c) When is $(-2)^n$ negative? Explain.

d) When is $-(-2)^n$ positive? Explain.

e) When is $-(-2)^n$ negative? Explain.

2.2 Multiplying and Dividing Powers

Recall that a power represents repeated multiplication. In each *Investigation*,
you will examine patterns you can use to multiply and divide powers efficiently.

Multiplying Powers

1. Copy and complete this table.

Product of powers	Product form	Power form
$10^2 \times 10^3$	$(10 \times 10) \times (10 \times 10 \times 10)$	10^5
$10^3 \times 10^4$		
$10^3 \times 10^6$		
$5^4 \times 5^5$		
$5^3 \times 5^1$		
$2^2 \times 2^9$		

2. Extend the table. Make up 5 more examples. Add them to the table.

3. Look at the table.

   a) State a rule for multiplying powers of 10. Explain why your rule works.

   b) State a rule for multiplying powers of 5.

   c) State a rule for multiplying powers with the same base.

Investigation 1 shows this pattern:

Multiplying Powers

Since a^3 means $a \times a \times a$ and a^4 means $a \times a \times a \times a$,

$$a^3 \times a^4 = (a \times a \times a) \times (a \times a \times a \times a)$$
$$= a^7$$

The powers a^3 and a^4 have the same base. The base is a.

We find the product $a^3 \times a^4$ by writing the base a and adding the exponents: $a^3 \times a^4 = a^{3+4}$
$$= a^7$$

Dividing Powers

1. Copy and complete this table.

Quotient of powers	Quotient form	Power form
$10^5 \div 10^3$	$\dfrac{10 \times 10 \times 10 \times 10 \times 10}{10 \times 10 \times 10}$	10^2
$10^8 \div 10^5$		
$10^7 \div 10^3$		
$5^{10} \div 5^4$		
$5^5 \div 5^4$		
$9^8 \div 9^3$		

2. Extend the table. Make up 5 more examples. Add them to the table.

3. Look at the table.

a) State a rule for dividing powers of 10. Explain why your rule works.

b) State a rule for dividing powers of 5.

c) State a rule for dividing powers with the same base.

Investigation 2 shows this pattern:

Dividing Powers

Since a^5 means $a \times a \times a \times a \times a$ and a^3 means $a \times a \times a$,

$$a^5 \div a^3 = \frac{a \times a \times a \times a \times a}{a \times a \times a}$$
$$= a^2$$

The powers a^5 and a^3 have the same base. The base is a.

We find the quotient $a^5 \div a^3$ by writing the base a and subtracting the exponents: $a^5 \div a^3 = a^{5-3}$
$$= a^2$$

Exponent Law for Multiplying Powers

To multiply powers with the same base, write the base and add the exponents.
$a^n \times a^m = a^{n+m}$, where n and m are natural numbers.

Exponent Law for Dividing Powers

To divide powers with the same base, write the base and subtract the exponents.
$a^n \div a^m = a^{n-m}$, where n and m are natural numbers, and $n > m$, and $a \neq 0$.

Discuss

Why do we include "$a \neq 0$" in the exponent law for dividing powers?

Example 1

Write each product as a single power. Then evaluate.

a) $2^3 \times 2^2$ b) $(-3)^4 \times (-3)$

A single power is one base with one exponent.

Solution

a) $2^3 \times 2^2 = 2^{3+2}$
$= 2^5$
$= 32$

b) $(-3)^4 \times (-3) = (-3)^4 \times (-3)^1$
$= (-3)^{4+1}$
$= (-3)^5$
$= -243$

When no exponent is written, it is understood the exponent is 1.

Example 2

Write each quotient as a single power. Then evaluate.

a) $2^3 \div 2^2$ b) $(-3)^4 \div (-3)$

Solution

a) $2^3 \div 2^2 = \dfrac{2^3}{2^2}$
$= 2^{3-2}$
$= 2^1$
$= 2$

b) $(-3)^4 \div (-3)^1 = \dfrac{(-3)^4}{(-3)^1}$
$= (-3)^{4-1}$
$= (-3)^3$
$= -27$

Example 3

Write each expression as a single power. Evaluate to 3 decimal places, where necessary.

a) $(3.2)^5 \times (3.2)^4$ **b)** $\dfrac{(-4.8)^5}{(-4.8)^2}$ **c)** $\dfrac{8^{200}}{8^{199}}$

Solution

a) $(3.2)^5(3.2)^4 = 3.2^{5+4}$ Use a calculator.
$$= 3.2^9$$
$$\doteq 35\,184.372$$

```
(3.2)^9
         35184.37209
```

b) $\dfrac{(-4.8)^5}{(-4.8)^2} = (-4.8)^{5-2}$ Use a calculator.
$$= (-4.8)^3$$
$$= -110.592$$

```
(-4.8)^3
         -110.592
```

c) $\dfrac{8^{200}}{8^{199}} = 8^{200-199}$
$$= 8^1$$
$$= 8$$

In *Example 3* part c, we used exponent laws (instead of a calculator) to calculate large numbers mentally.

2.2   Exercises

A

1. Write each product as a single power.

a) $2^5 \times 2^4$ **b)** $3^2 \times 3^5$ **c)** $10^2 \times 10^9$

d) $12^8 \times 12^3$ **e)** $7^2 \times 7^4$ **f)** $8^3 \times 8^5$

2. Write each quotient as a single power.

a) $2^5 \div 2^4$ **b)** $3^5 \div 3^2$ **c)** $10^9 \div 10^2$

d) $12^8 \div 12^3$ **e)** $7^4 \div 7^3$ **f)** $8^5 \div 8^3$

3. Write each expression as a single power. Do not evaluate.

a) $3^4 \times 3^6$ **b)** $7^4 \times 7^7$ **c)** $(-5)^{16} \times (-5)^9$

d) $\dfrac{1.5^{18}}{1.5^6}$ **e)** $\dfrac{(-6)^8}{(-6)^2}$ **f)** $\dfrac{(-2.3)^7}{(-2.3)^3}$

4. Write each expression as a single power. Do not evaluate.

a) $3^8 \div 3^3$ **b)** $2^{16} \div 2^7$ **c)** $(-8)^{20} \div (-8)^5$

d) $2.1^5 \times 2.1^5$ **e)** $(-8)^5 \times (-8)$ **f)** $(-1.7)^4 \times (-1.7)^3$

B **5.** Write each product as a single power. Evaluate. Round to 3 decimal places where necessary.

a) $3^3 \times 3^5$ **b)** $(-2.1)^2 \times (-2.1)^5$ **c)** $(-5)^3 \times (-5)^2$

d) $(-8.6) \times (-8.6)$ **e)** 4.6×4.6^6 **f)** $(-1.25)^4 \times (-1.25)^4$

6. Write each quotient as a single power. Evaluate. Round to 3 decimal places where necessary.

a) $9^4 \div 9^2$ **b)** $(-1)^8 \div (-1)^5$ **c)** $(-8.7)^7 \div (-8.7)^4$

d) $(-0.2)^{10} \div (-0.2)^8$ **e)** $6.84^6 \div 6.84^2$ **f)** $(-9)^8 \div (-9)^4$

7. Knowledge/Understanding Write each expression as a single power. Then evaluate.

a) $3^3 \times 3^2$ **b)** $9^4 \div 9^2$ **c)** $(-8)^7 \div (-8)^4$

d) $(-2.3) \times (-2.3)^3$ **e)** $2^2 \times 2^2 \times 2^2$ **f)** $(7.1)^5 \div (7.1)^3$

8. Evaluate to 3 decimal places.

a) $(4.6)^2 \times (4.6)^4$ **b)** $(-1.7)^5 \div (-1.7)^2$ **c)** $(8.3)^7 \div (8.3)^4$

d) $(-3.7)^4 \times (-3.7)^3$ **e)** $0.2^4 \div 0.2$ **f)** 0.1×0.1^2

9. Communication

a) A rectangular wheat field is 10^5 m long and 10^3 m wide. Explain how to find its area.

b) Another rectangular field is $10\,000$ m wide. Its area is 10^9 m². Explain how to find its length.

10. Application The tallest tree in the world is about 10^2 m tall. The highest mountain is about 10^4 m. About how many times as high as the tree is the mountain? Does this make sense? Explain.

11. a) Write each expression as a single power.

    i) $6^5 \times 6^2$ **ii)** $6^2 \times 6^5$ **iii)** $6^7 \div 6^2$ **iv)** $6^7 \div 6^5$

    v) $(-7)^8 \div (-7)^5$ **vi)** $(-7)^8 \div (-7)^3$ **vii)** $(-7)^3 \times (-7)^5$ **viii)** $(-7)^5 \times (-7)^3$

b) Explain what your results from part a show about the relationship between multiplying and dividing powers.

12. a) List the powers of 2 to 2^8. Evaluate each power.

 b) Use your answers from part a. Evaluate each expression by multiplying or dividing powers.
   i) 16×16 **ii)** 32×4 **iii)** $256 \div 8$ **iv)** $128 \div 32$

13. a) Earth's diameter is about 10^7 m. The diameter of the largest known star is 10^{12} m. About how many times as great as the diameter of Earth is the diameter of the largest star?

 b) Astronomers estimate that there are about 10^{11} galaxies in the universe. Each galaxy contains about 10^{11} stars. About how many stars are in the universe?

14. Thinking/Inquiry/Problem Solving A telephone tree is used to send messages. The person at the top of the tree calls 2 people. Each person calls 2 more people. Suppose it takes 1 min to call someone. The photographs show the process. The message is relayed until the bottom row has 256 people. How long does this take?

15. Write each expression as a single power. Then evaluate.

 a) $\dfrac{10^5 \times 10^2}{10^3}$ **b)** $\dfrac{2^7 \times 2^3}{2^4}$ **c)** $\dfrac{3^{12}}{3 \times 3^6}$

 d) $\dfrac{(-5)^9 \times (-5)}{(-5)^4}$ **e)** $\dfrac{6^7 \times 6^{11}}{6^8 \times 6^2}$ **f)** $\dfrac{(-1)^{10}}{(-1)^5 \times (-1)}$

2.3   Power of a Power

An expression such as $(2^4)^3$ is a power of a power.

$(2^4)^3$ means $2^4 \times 2^4 \times 2^4$.

So, $(2^4)^3 = 2^4 \times 2^4 \times 2^4$

$ = 2^{4+4+4}$

$ = 2^{12}$

The exponent of 2^{12} is the product of the exponents in the expression $(2^4)^3$.

That is, $(2^4)^3 = 2^{4 \times 3}$

$ = 2^{12}$

We use this result to write an exponent law for a power of a power.

TAKE NOTE

Exponent Law for a Power of a Power

$(a^m)^n = a^{mn}$, where m and n are integers

We can use this exponent law to simplify expressions with powers.

Example 1

Write as a power with a single exponent.

a) $(4^2)^5$ **b)** $(2^3)^2$ **c)** $(m^3)^3$

Solution

a) $(4^2)^5 = 4^{2 \times 5}$ **b)** $(2^3)^2 = 2^{3 \times 2}$ **c)** $(m^3)^3 = m^{3 \times 3}$

$ = 4^{10}$ $ = 2^6$ $ = m^9$

Example 2

Write as a single power, then evaluate.

a) $(2^2)^4$ **b)** $(3^2)^2$

Solution

a) $(2^2)^4 = 2^{2 \times 4}$ **b)** $(3^2)^2 = 3^{2 \times 2}$

$ = 2^8$ Use a calculator. $ = 3^4$ Use a calculator.

$ = 256$ $ = 81$

A **1.** Write as a power with a single exponent.

a) $(2)^2$ b) $(2^2)^2$ c) $(2^3)^2$ d) $(2^4)^2$

e) $(2^5)^2$ f) $(2^6)^2$ g) $(2^7)^2$ h) $(2^8)^2$

✓ **2.** Write as a power with a single exponent.

a) (2^2) b) $(2^2)^2$ c) $(2^2)^3$ d) $(2^2)^4$

e) $(2^2)^5$ f) $(2^2)^6$ g) $(2^2)^7$ h) $(2^2)^8$

3. What do you notice about the results of exercises 1 and 2? Explain the results.

✓ **4.** Write as a power with a single exponent.

a) $(a^2)^4$ b) $(b^3)^5$ c) $(c^7)^2$ d) $(d^4)^3$

B **5. Knowledge/Understanding** Write as a single power, then evaluate.

a) $(10^2)^3$ b) $(3^2)^2$ c) $(4^3)^2$ d) $(10^4)^2$

6. Write as a single power, then evaluate.

a) $(5^2)^2$ b) $(4^2)^4$ c) $(2^{-3})^2$ d) $(6^{-1})^2$

7. Use a calculator. Evaluate each expression in two different ways:

i) Complete the operations in brackets first. Then evaluate.

ii) Use the exponent laws first. Then evaluate.

Compare the results. Confirm they are equal.

a) $(3^2)^4$ b) $[(-2)^6]^2$

✓ **8.** Express as a single power. Use the power of a power law. Then use the law for multiplying powers. Do not evaluate.

a) $(3^2)^3 \times (3^4)^2$ b) $(7^3)^2 \times (7^8)^2$

c) $(8^{-5}) \times (8^3)^{-4}$ d) $(29^{-6})^2 \times (29^3)^4$

✓ **9.** Express as a single power. Use the power of a power law. Then use the law for dividing powers. Do not evaluate.

a) $\dfrac{(6^5)^2}{(6^2)^3}$ b) $\dfrac{(15^3)^4}{(15^5)^2}$

c) $\dfrac{(4^{-2})^{-3}}{(4^{-6})^{-2}}$ d) $\dfrac{(101^{-8})^{-4}}{(101^{-7})^{-5}}$

Use this table of powers of 2 to complete exercises 10 and 11.

$2^{25} = 33\,554\,432$	$2^8 = 256$
$2^{24} = 16\,777\,216$	$2^7 = 128$
$2^{23} = 8\,388\,608$	$2^6 = 64$
$2^{22} = 4\,194\,304$	$2^5 = 32$
$2^{21} = 2\,097\,152$	$2^4 = 16$
$2^{20} = 1\,048\,576$	$2^3 = 8$
$2^{19} = 524\,288$	$2^2 = 4$
$2^{18} = 262\,144$	$2^1 = 2$
$2^{17} = 131\,072$	$2^0 = 1$
$2^{16} = 65\,536$	$2^{-1} = 0.5$
$2^{15} = 32\,768$	$2^{-2} = 0.25$
$2^{14} = 16\,384$	$2^{-3} = 0.125$
$2^{13} = 8192$	$2^{-4} = 0.0625$
$2^{12} = 4096$	$2^{-5} = 0.031\,25$
$2^{11} = 2048$	$2^{-6} = 0.015\,625$
$2^{10} = 1024$	$2^{-7} = 0.007\,812\,5$
$2^9 = 512$	$2^{-8} = 0.003\,906\,25$

✓ **10. Application** Use the powers in the table. Find each answer without using a calculator.

a) 128×256 b) 4096×512 c) $\dfrac{65\,536}{2048}$

d) $\dfrac{8192}{1024}$ e) 64^3 f) 4^7

11. Use the powers in the table. Find each answer without using a calculator.

a) 0.125×0.0625 b) $131\,072 \times 0.007\,812\,5$ c) $\dfrac{16\,384}{0.031\,25}$

d) $\dfrac{0.015\,625}{0.031\,25}$ e) 0.25^3 f) 0.125^{-2}

✓ **12. Communication** Explain why you add the exponents when you write $2^4 \times 2^3$ as a power, and why you multiply the exponents when you write $(2^4)^3$ as a power.

Suppose we apply the exponent law to $2^3 \div 2^3$: $2^{3-3} = 2^0$

Suppose we apply the exponent law to $2^2 \div 2^5$: $2^{2-5} = 2^{-3}$

The power 2^3 means $2 \times 2 \times 2$, but we cannot explain powers such as 2^0 and 2^{-3} in this way. We cannot multiply 0 twos together. We cannot multiply -3 twos together.

To understand powers such as 2^0 and 2^{-3}, we look at number patterns.

INVESTIGATION

Descending Powers

1. Copy this table. Evaluate each power down to 2^1.
   Write your answers in the *Number* column.
   What pattern do you see?

2. Continue the pattern from exercise 1 to complete the
   Number column. Write these numbers as fractions.

3. Write the denominator of each fraction as a power of 2.
   What do you notice?

4. Use the pattern in your results from exercise 3.

   a) Write 2^{-5} as a fraction.

   b) Write 2^{-6} as a fraction.

   c) Express each fraction in parts a and b as a power of 2.

Power	Number
2^4	
2^3	
2^2	
2^1	
2^0	
2^{-1}	
2^{-2}	
2^{-3}	
2^{-4}	

5. Copy each table. Use the method of exercises 1 to 3 to complete each table.

a)

Power	Number
3^4	
3^3	
3^2	
3^1	
3^0	
3^{-1}	
3^{-2}	
3^{-3}	
3^{-4}	

b)

Power	Number
10^4	
10^3	
10^2	
10^1	
10^0	
10^{-1}	
10^{-2}	
10^{-3}	
10^{-4}	

We can generalize the *Investigation* results as follows:

TAKE NOTE

Zero Exponent

x^0 is equal to 1: that is, $x^0 = 1$ $(x \neq 0)$

Negative Integer Exponent

x^{-n} is the reciprocal of x^n: that is, $x^{-n} = \dfrac{1}{x^n}$ $(x \neq 0$ and n is an integer)

Similarly, $\dfrac{1}{x^n} = x^{-n}$ $(x \neq 0$ and n is an integer)

We can use these definitions to evaluate a power with any integer exponent.

Example

Evaluate each power.

a) 5^{-2} **b)** $(-3)^{-1}$ **c)** $\dfrac{1}{5^{-2}}$

Solution

a) $5^{-2} = \dfrac{1}{5^2}$

$= \dfrac{1}{25}$

b) $(-3)^{-1} = \dfrac{1}{(-3)^1}$

$= \dfrac{1}{-3}$

$= -\dfrac{1}{3}$

c) $\dfrac{1}{5^{-2}} = \dfrac{5^2}{1}$

$= 25$

Discuss

How are the powers in parts a and c related?

(A) **1.** Write each power with a positive exponent.

a) 2^{-7} b) 3^{-2} c) 4^{-1} d) 5^{-8} e) 2^{-9} f) 10^{-3}

2. Write each power with a positive exponent.

a) $\dfrac{1}{3^{-3}}$ b) $\dfrac{1}{4^{-1}}$ c) $\dfrac{1}{2^{-7}}$ d) $\dfrac{1}{10^{-6}}$ e) $\dfrac{1}{9^{-8}}$ f) $\dfrac{1}{5^{-5}}$

(B) **3.** Write each power with a positive exponent. Then evaluate.

a) 3^{-1} b) 2^{-2} c) 7^{-1} d) 10^{-5} e) 3^{-3} f) 6^{-2}

4. Write each power with a positive exponent. Then evaluate.

a) $\dfrac{1}{2^{-1}}$ b) $\dfrac{1}{3^{-2}}$ c) $\dfrac{1}{5^{-2}}$ d) $\dfrac{1}{2^{-3}}$ e) $\dfrac{-1}{4^{-2}}$ f) $\dfrac{-1}{10^{-4}}$

5. Use a calculator to evaluate each power.

a) 0.2^{-1} b) 0.25^{-2} c) 0.5^{-3} d) $(-2)^0$ e) 1.5^{-1} f) $(-1.2)^{-2}$

6. a) Evaluate each power.

   i) 6^0 **ii)** $(-3)^0$ **iii)** 1.8^0 **iv)** 5.6^0 **v)** $(-0.8)^0$ **vi)** $(-10)^0$

b) Look at the results of part a. Write a rule for evaluating a power when the exponent is 0.

7. Use a calculator to evaluate each power. Round to 6 decimal places where necessary.

a) 4^{-5} b) 5^{-4} c) $(-5)^{-6}$ d) $(-6)^{-3}$ e) 1.2^{-10}

8. Knowledge/Understanding Evaluate each power. Round to 4 decimal places where necessary.

a) 3^{-5} b) $\dfrac{1}{4^{-2}}$ c) $(0.35)^{-3}$ d) 9^0 e) 7^{-2} f) $(-1.5)^0$

9. Evaluate.

a) 10^3 b) 10^2 c) 10^1 d) 10^0

e) 10^{-1} f) 10^{-2} g) 10^{-3} h) 10^{-4}

10. Communication Evaluate. How are the powers in each pair similar? How are they different?

a) 4^3 and 4^{-3} b) 4^3 and -4^{-3} c) $(-4)^3$ and -4^{-3}

11. Thinking/Inquiry/Problem Solving Is a power with a negative exponent always negative? Is it always positive? Or, is it sometimes negative and sometimes positive? Explain. Look at the exercises you have completed to help you.

12. Application There is only one integer n so that $n^n = \dfrac{1}{4}$. This integer is negative. What is the integer? Justify your answer.

13. Scientists grow bacteria in a culture for medical research. This table shows how the number of a typical bacterium doubles every hour.

Time	Elapsed time after noon, (h)	Number of bacteria
noon	0	1000×2^0
1:00 P.M.	1	1000×2^1
2:00 P.M.	2	1000×2^2
3:00 P.M.	3	1000×2^3

a) Evaluate the powers in the table to find the number of bacteria at each time.

   i) noon   ii) 1:00 P.M.

   iii) 2:00 P.M.   iv) 3:00 P.M.

b) The number of bacteria after n hours is 1000×2^n, where n is the elapsed time in hours. Find the number of bacteria for each elapsed time.

   i) 3 h   ii) 6 h   iii) 9 h   iv) 12 h

c) An hour before noon, the value of n is -1. Evaluate each expression to find the number of bacteria each number of hours before noon.

   i) For 1 h before noon, the number of bacteria is 1000×2^{-1}.
   ii) For 2 h before noon, the number of bacteria is 1000×2^{-2}.
   iii) For 3 h before noon, the number of bacteria is 1000×2^{-3}.

d) How many bacteria are in the culture for each number of hours before noon? Round to the nearest whole number, if necessary.

   i) 3 h   ii) 4 h   iii) 6 h   iv) 8 h

14. Consider a square with side length 2 units. Its area is 2^2 units^2. Imagine cutting the square in half, then repeatedly cutting the remaining region in half. The area of each region, in square units, is shown.

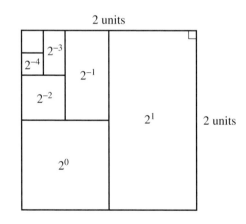

a) Explain why the areas are $2^2, 2^1, 2^0, 2^{-1}, 2^{-2}, 2^{-3}, 2^{-4}$, and so on.

b) Suppose we label the regions in part a from 1 to 7. We can write the areas of the regions in a table.

Region	1	2	3	4	5	6	7
Area (square units)	2^2	2^1	2^0	2^{-1}	2^{-2}	2^{-3}	2^{-4}

Use a whole sheet of grid paper. Graph the data in the table. Describe the graph.

2.5 Scientific Notation

We can use scientific notation to express very large numbers and very small numbers.

TAKE NOTE

Scientific Notation

To write a number in scientific notation, write it as the product of:
a number between 1 and 10, and a power of 10.

There are about 120 000 000 000 stars in our galaxy, the Milky Way.

The zeros in this very large number are placeholders. They show the position of the decimal point. The decimal point at the end of the number is not shown. To express the number of stars in our galaxy using scientific notation, we write:

$$120\,000\,000\,000 = 1.2 \times 100\,000\,000\,000$$
$$= 1.2 \times 10^{11}$$

The number of stars in our galaxy is about 1.2×10^{11}.

Hydrogen is the most abundant element in the universe. The mass of a hydrogen atom is about 0.000 000 000 000 000 000 000 001 67 g.

The zeros in this very small number are placeholders. They show the position of the decimal point. To express the mass of a hydrogen atom using scientific notation, we write:

$$0.000\,000\,000\,000\,000\,000\,000\,001\,67$$
$$= 1.67 \times 0.000\,000\,000\,000\,000\,000\,000\,001$$
$$= 1.67 \times 10^{-24}$$

The mass of a hydrogen atom is about 1.67×10^{-24} g.

> 120 000 000 000
> The true place of the decimal is 11 right, so 10^{11}.
> 1.2 is between 1 and 10.
> 10^{11} is a power of 10.

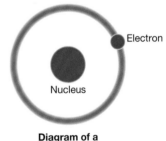

Electron

Nucleus

Diagram of a hydrogen atom

> 0.000 000 000 000 000 000 000 001 67
> The true place of the decimal is 24 left, so 10^{-24}.
> 1.67 is between 1 and 10.
> 10^{-24} is a power of 10.

Example 1

Write in scientific notation.

a) 1 350 000   b) 0.002 796

Solution

a) 1 350 000

Place the decimal point to the right of the first non-zero digit.
1.350 000

The true position of the decimal point is 6 places to the right,
so multiply 1.35 by 10^6.
$1\,350\,000 = 1.35 \times 10^6$

b) 0.002 796

Place the decimal point to the right of the first non-zero digit.
0 002.796

The true position of the decimal point is 3 places to the left,
so multiply 2.796 by 10^{-3}.
$0.002\,796 = 2.796 \times 10^{-3}$

Discuss

In parts a and b, how did we know which power of 10 to use?
How did we know whether the exponent was positive or negative?

We can reverse the process of *Example 1* to write a number in scientific notation in standard form.

Example 2

Write in standard form.

a) 2.376×10^9 b) 1.48×10^{-7}

Solution

a) 2.376×10^9

To multiply 2.376 by 10^9, move the decimal point 9 places to the right.
Write zeros as place holders.
$2.376 \times 10^9 = 2\,376\,000\,000.$
$2.376 \times 10^9 = 2\,376\,000\,000$

b) 1.48×10^{-7}

To multiply 1.48 by 10^{-7}, move the decimal point 7 places to the left.
Write zeros as place holders.

$$1.48 \times 10^{-7} = 0.\underset{\smile\,\smile\,\smile}{000\,000\,}148$$

$$1.48 \times 10^{-7} = 0.000\,000\,148$$

Discuss

When writing a number in scientific notation in standard form, how do you know which way to move the decimal point?

To calculate with numbers in scientific notation, we can use the exponent key on a calculator to input a power of 10.

For the TI-30X IIS calculator, press (2nd) (x^{-1}) for EE. For a different calculator, check its manual.

Example 3

Simplify. Check whether the answers are reasonable.

a) $(3.3 \times 10^5) \times (6.0 \times 10^{24})$ **b)** $\dfrac{2.1 \times 10^7}{1.9 \times 10^{-30}}$

Solution

a) $(3.3 \times 10^5) \times (6.0 \times 10^{24})$

Press: 3.3 (2nd) (x^{-1}) 5 (×) 6 (2nd) (x^{-1}) 24 (ENTER =)

$(3.3 \times 10^5) \times (6.0 \times 10^{24}) = 1.98 \times 10^{30}$

$\boxed{\begin{array}{l} 3.3E5*6E24 \\[4pt] \hfill 1.98_{\times10}30 \end{array}}$

Check.

$$3.3 \times 10^5 \times 6.0 \times 10^{24} \doteq 3 \times 6 \times 10^{5+24}$$
$$= 18 \times 10^{29}$$
$$= 1.8 \times 10^1 \times 10^{29}$$
$$= 1.8 \times 10^{30}$$

The answer is reasonable.

b) $\dfrac{2.1 \times 10^7}{1.9 \times 10^{-30}}$

Press: 2.1 (2nd) (x^{-1}) 7 (÷) 1.9 (2nd) (x^{-1}) ((-)) 30 (ENTER =)

$\dfrac{2.1 \times 10^7}{1.9 \times 10^{-30}} \doteq 1.1053 \times 10^{37}$

$\boxed{\begin{array}{l} 2.1E7/1.9E-30 \\[4pt] 1.105263158_{\times10}37 \end{array}}$

Check.

$$\frac{2.1 \times 10^7}{1.9 \times 10^{-30}} \doteq \frac{2 \times 10^7}{2 \times 10^{-30}}$$
$$= \frac{2}{2} \times \frac{10^7}{10^{-30}}$$
$$= 1 \times 10^{7-(-30)}$$
$$= 1 \times 10^{37}$$

The answer is reasonable.

A 1. Write each exponent.

a) $6\,300\,000 = 6.3 \times 10^{\square}$

b) $0.000\,481 = 4.81 \times 10^{\square}$

c) $70\,000 = 7.0 \times 10^{\square}$

d) $0.000\,000\,029 = 2.9 \times 10^{\square}$

e) $941\,000\,000 = 9.41 \times 10^{\square}$

f) $0.000\,09 = 9.0 \times 10^{\square}$

2. Write in scientific notation.

a) $300\,000\,000$ b) $30\,000\,000$ c) $3\,000\,000$ d) $300\,000$

e) $30\,000$ f) 3000 g) 300 h) 30

3. Write in scientific notation.

a) 0.4 b) 0.04 c) 0.004 d) 0.0004

e) $0.000\,04$ f) $0.000\,004$ g) $0.000\,000\,4$ h) $0.000\,000\,04$

4. Write in standard form.

a) 5.0×10^8 b) 5.0×10^7 c) 5.0×10^6 d) 5.0×10^5

e) 5.0×10^4 f) 5.0×10^3 g) 5.0×10^2 h) 5.0×10^1

5. Write in standard form.

a) 6.3×10^{-1} b) 6.3×10^{-2} c) 6.3×10^{-3} d) 6.3×10^{-4}

e) 6.3×10^{-5} f) 6.3×10^{-6} g) 6.3×10^{-7} h) 6.3×10^{-8}

B 6. Write in scientific notation.

a) $450\,000$ b) 201 c) 9300 d) 37

e) $58\,000$ f) $579\,000$ g) $60\,000$ h) $1\,010\,000$

7. Write in scientific notation.

a) 0.0029 b) $0.000\,002\,5$ c) $0.000\,018$ d) 0.54

e) $0.000\,004\,8$ f) 0.007 g) $0.000\,51$ h) $0.000\,000\,99$

8. **Communication** Can every number can be written in scientific notation? Explain.

9. Complete this table.

		Standard Form	Scientific Notation
a)	Temperature of the sun's interior	$1\,300\,000°C$	
b)	Thickness of a piece of paper	$0.000\,01$ m	
c)	Mass of an electron		9.2×10^{-28} g
d)	Estimated age of Earth	$4\,500\,000\,000$ years	
e)	Diameter of a hydrogen atom	$0.000\,000\,005$ cm	
f)	Land area of Earth		1.5×10^8 km^2

10. Scientific calculators display results differently. What do you think each display means?

a) Calculator 1

   i) | 2.5^{12} |

   ii) | 6.25^{-10} |

b) Calculator 2

   i) | $3.125E{-}16$ |

   ii) | $4E24$ |

c) Calculator 3

   i) | $4.33333E22$ |

   ii) | $5.E{-}40$ |

11. When asked to express 1500 in scientific notation, Kimi replied 15×10^2. Why is this not correct?

12. Knowledge/Understanding Write in scientific notation.

   a) 1200   **b)** 270 000   **c)** 400   **d)** 0.24

   e) 0.0007   **f)** 0.000 014 8   **g)** 13 600   **h)** 0.000 018 8

   i) 18×10^2 **j)** 142×10^5 **k)** 16×10^{-2} **l)** 236×10^{-6}

13. Write in standard form.

   a) 1.8×10^5 **b)** 2.9×10^4 **c)** 3.3×10^7 **d)** 4.4×10^9

   e) 1.6×10^{-1} **f)** 8.4×10^{-2} **g)** 2.24×10^{-4} **h)** 1.88×10^{-5}

   i) 2.41×10^{-10} **j)** 1.87×10^6 **k)** 3.02×10^{-3} **l)** 2.16×10^{-1}

14. Simplify.

   a) $(1.4 \times 10^{10}) \times (3.71 \times 10^{14})$ **b)** $(3.62 \times 10^{-23}) \times (5.9 \times 10^6)$

   c) $(1.2 \times 10^{-13}) \times (4.0 \times 10^9)$ **d)** $(7.12 \times 10^{-21}) \times (5.6 \times 10^8)$

15. Simplify.

   a) $(3.0 \times 10^7) \times (4.0 \times 10^8)$ **b)** $(9.8 \times 10^{11}) \times (1.3 \times 10^4)$

   c) $(2.4 \times 10^{-9}) \times (5.6 \times 10^8)$ **d)** $(4.15 \times 10^{-26}) \times (3.2 \times 10^{-9})$

✓ **16.** Write each number in scientific notation.

   a) 5 thousand   **b)** 5 hundred thousand

   c) 5 million   **d)** 5 billion

✓ **17.** Simplify. Check whether the answers are reasonable.

   a) $(5.9 \times 10^5) \times (4.7 \times 10^{-8})$ **b)** $(3.53 \times 10^9) \div (8.0 \times 10^{-5})$

   c) $(2.4 \text{ million}) \times (6.5 \text{ million})$ **d)** $1 \div (5 \text{ billion})$

18. Simplify. Check whether the answers are reasonable.

a) $\dfrac{3.72 \times 10^{10}}{1.47 \times 10^{8}}$ b) $\dfrac{9.0 \times 10^{-2}}{3.3 \times 10^{7}}$ c) $\dfrac{2.43 \times 10^{-7}}{2.3 \times 10^{-4}}$ d) $\dfrac{2.55 \times 10^{-9}}{3.0 \times 10^{15}}$

19. Application A TV program about sea otters made these statements:

- 1 cm^2 of a sea otter's fur contains about 20 000 hairs.
- A sea otter has about 8 billion hairs.

a) Write the two numbers in scientific notation.

b) Calculate the area of a sea otter's body, in square centimetres.

c) Express your answer to part b in square metres. Does the result seem reasonable? Explain.

20. a) All matter is made of atoms. Atoms are so small that 6.022×10^{23} gold atoms have a mass of about 200 g. Write 6.022×10^{23} in standard form.

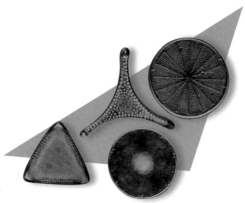

b) Diatoms are a primary source of food in the sea. A diatom measures about 0.0005 mm across. Write this measurement in scientific notation.

c) The mass of Earth is about 6.0×10^{24} kg. The mass of the sun is about 3.3×10^{5} times the mass of Earth. Calculate the mass of the sun.

d) Write a question that involves scientific notation. Answer your question. Trade questions with a classmate. Then compare answers.

21. Thinking/Inquiry/Problem Solving One *light-year* is the distance light travels in 1 year. The speed of light is 3×10^{8} m/s. How far is 1 light-year in kilometres?

distance = speed × time

m/s is metres per second.

22. Express each number in this news item in scientific notation.

A new fingerprinting method uses gold particles to bind to the proteins every finger leaves behind. The amount of protein is tiny—only one billionth of a gram per print. The gold particles are about two thousandths of a millimetre in diameter.

1. Write each power as a product. Then evaluate.

a) $\left(\frac{7}{10}\right)^2$ **b)** $\left(-\frac{3}{8}\right)^4$ **c)** $\left(\frac{5}{6}\right)^5$ **d)** $\left(-\frac{2}{11}\right)^3$

2. Evaluate each power. Round to 3 decimal places where necessary.

a) $(-10)^5$ **b)** 2.5^7 **c)** 9^6 **d)** $\left(-\frac{2}{3}\right)^7$ **e)** $\left(\frac{6}{7}\right)^2$

3. Write as a single power, then evaluate. Round to 3 decimal places where necessary.

a) $4^3 \times 4$ **b)** $(-7)^6 \div (-7)^5$ **c)** $(5.1)^2 \times (5.1)^6$ **d)** $(-5.4)^9 \div (-5.4)^7$

4. Write as a single power, then evaluate. Round to 3 decimal places where necessary.

a) $(2^3)^2$ **b)** $(7^2)^2$ **c)** $(1.6^{-4})^{-2}$ **d)** $[(-2.1)^7]^0$

5. Write each power with a positive exponent.

a) 7^{-5} **b)** $\frac{1}{6^{-3}}$ **c)** $\frac{1}{2^{-9}}$ **d)** 8^{-6} **e)** $\frac{1}{7^{-4}}$

6. Evaluate each power. Round to 6 decimal places where necessary.

a) $(-5)^{-6}$ **b)** 1.7^{-5} **c)** $(-2.5)^{-2}$ **d)** $(-7.2)^0$ **e)** 6^{-3}

7. Write in scientific notation.

a) $130\,000$ **b)** $0.000\,29$ **c)** 45×10^5 **d)** 992×10^{-4}

8. Write in standard form.

a) 7.5×10^5 **b)** 8.0×10^{-3} **c)** 1.02×10^6 **d)** 9.23×10^{-7}

9. Simplify.

a) $(4.7 \times 10^6) \times (3.12 \times 10^5)$ **b)** $(6.0 \times 10^{-4}) \times (8.3 \times 10^{-7})$

c) $\dfrac{2.5 \times 10^7}{3.0 \times 10^4}$ **d)** $\dfrac{8.21 \times 10^{-5}}{1.7 \times 10^6}$

Preparation for Ontario Testing

10. A mass of about 200 g of gold contains 6.022×10^{23} atoms.

What is the number of atoms in 1 g of gold?

a) 3.011×10^{-21}

b) 3.011×10^{21}

c) 1.2044×10^{-26}

d) 1.2044×10^{26}

Graphing Squares

Consider squares with side lengths that increase by 1 cm.

1. Copy and continue the table for squares with side lengths up to 15 cm.

Side length x, (cm)	Area y, (cm²)
0	0
1	1
2	4
3	9

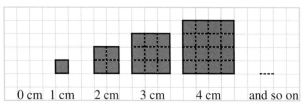

0 cm 1 cm   2 cm   3 cm   4 cm   and so on

2. Use the table. Find the area of a square with each side length.

   a) 5 cm   **b)** 11 cm   **c)** 14 cm

3. Use the table. Find the side length of a square with each area.

   a) 36 cm^2 **b)** 81 cm^2 **c)** 25 cm^2

4. Can you use the table to find the area of a square with side length 4.5 cm? Explain.

5. Can you use the table to find the side length of a square with area 120 cm^2. Explain.

6. Graph the data in exercise 1. Draw the graph as large as possible. Plot *Area (cm²)* vertically and *Side length (cm)* horizontally.

7. Should you connect the points with a smooth curve? Explain.

8. Use the graph. Estimate the side length of a square with each area.

   a) 30 cm^2 **b)** 57 cm^2 **c)** 183 cm^2

9. Use the graph. Estimate the area of a square with each side length.

   a) 7.5 cm   **b)** 9.5 cm   **c)** 12.25 cm

10. The equation for the graph is $y = x^2$. Look at each pair of numbers in the table.

   a) How is the second number related to the first number?

   b) How is the first number related to the second number?

When we square a number, we multiply it by itself:

$$5^2 = 5 \times 5 \qquad\qquad (-5)^2 = (-5) \times (-5)$$
$$= 25 \qquad\qquad\qquad = 25$$

Since $5 \times 5 = 25$, we say that 5 is a square root of 25. We write $\sqrt{25} = 5$.

Since $(-5) \times (-5) = 25$, another square root of 25 is -5.

A square root is a number that produces a given number when mulitplied by itself.

All positive numbers have square roots.

A *perfect square* is a number whose square roots are integers. For example, 64 is a perfect square because its square roots are 8 and -8.

Using the radical sign, $\sqrt{}$, means only the positive square root.

So, the square roots of 64 are 8 and -8. But $\sqrt{64}$ is 8.

Example 1

Find the square roots of each perfect square.

a) 49 **b)** 100 **c)** 1

Solution

a) Since $7 \times 7 = 49$ and $(-7) \times (-7) = 49$, the square roots of 49 are 7 and -7.

b) Since $10 \times 10 = 100$ and $(-10) \times (-10) = 100$, the square roots of 100 are 10 and -10.

c) Since $1 \times 1 = 1$ and $(-1) \times (-1) = 1$, the square roots of 1 are 1 and -1.

We can use a calculator to determine the square root of a number that is not a perfect square. For the TI-30X IIS calculator, press [2nd] [x^2] for $\sqrt{}$.

Example 2

Calculate each square root to 3 decimal places.

a) $\sqrt{40}$ **b)** $\sqrt{0.6}$

Solution

a) $\sqrt{40}$ Press: [2nd] [x^2] 40 [)] [ENTER =]

$\sqrt{40} \doteq 6.325$

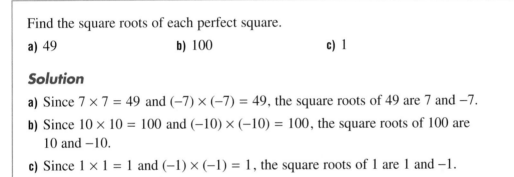

$\sqrt{(40)}$

6.32455532

b) $\sqrt{0.6}$ Press: [2nd] [x^2] 0.6 [)] [ENTER =]

$\sqrt{0.6} \doteq 0.775$

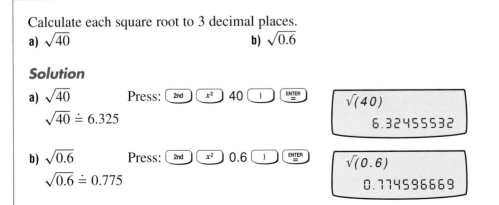

$\sqrt{(0.6)}$

0.774596669

A   **1.** What is the square of each number?

    a) 4   **b)** 8   **c)** 1   **d)** 9   **e)** 14

2. Use the completed table from the *Investigation*. What is the area of a square with each side length?

    a) 6 cm   **b)** 0 cm   **c)** 10 cm   **d)** 7 cm

3. Use the completed table from the *Investigation*. What is the side length of a square with each area?

    a) 4 cm^2 **b)** 1 cm^2 **c)** 25 cm^2 **d)** 9 cm^2

B   **4.** What are the two square roots of each number?

    a) 4   **b)** 9   **c)** 49   **d)** 81   **e)** 1

5. What are the two square roots of each number?

    a) 64   **b)** 25   **c)** 100   **d)** 16   **e)** 36

6. Find the square roots of each number to 1 decimal place. To check your answers, compare the results with those you obtained in exercise 4.

    a) 5   **b)** 10   **c)** 50   **d)** 75   **e)** 2

7. Find the square roots of each number to 1 decimal place. To check your answers, compare the results with those you obtained in exercise 5.

    a) 60   **b)** 30   **c)** 95   **d)** 15   **e)** 40

8. Evaluate.

    a) $\sqrt{16}$ **b)** $\sqrt{4}$ **c)** $\sqrt{64}$ **d)** $\sqrt{36}$ **e)** $\sqrt{100}$

9. Evaluate.

    a) $\sqrt{9}$ **b)** $\sqrt{49}$ **c)** $\sqrt{81}$ **d)** $\sqrt{1}$ **e)** $\sqrt{25}$

10. Why are there 2 square roots for each answer in exercises 4 and 5? Why is there one square root for each answer in exercises 8 and 9?

11. Knowledge/Understanding Use a calculator. Evaluate to 1 decimal place.

    a) $\sqrt{76}$ **b)** $\sqrt{86}$ **c)** $\sqrt{117}$ **d)** $\sqrt{140}$ **e)** $\sqrt{45}$ **f)** $\sqrt{105}$

12. Evaluate.

    a) $\sqrt{144}$ **b)** $\sqrt{14\,400}$ **c)** $\sqrt{1\,440\,000}$

    d) $\sqrt{1.44}$ **e)** $\sqrt{0.0144}$ **f)** $\sqrt{0.000\,144}$

13. Find the area of the square with each side length.

    a) 3.2 cm   **b)** 10.8 m   **c)** 0.1 cm   **d)** 300 m

14. Find the side length of the square with each area. Round to 1 decimal place where necessary.

a) 400 cm^2 b) 0.25 m^2 c) 90 cm^2

d) 150 cm^2 e) 300 cm^2 f) $25\,000 \text{ m}^2$

15. Application A square garden has area 230 m^2.

a) How long is each side of the garden, to the nearest centimetre?

b) How much fencing is needed to enclose the garden?

16. a) Find the side length of each square to the nearest unit.

i) The Great Pyramid in Egypt has a square base that covers $52\,441 \text{ m}^2$.

ii) The outer walls of the Hanging Gardens of Babylon enclosed a square with an area of 8121 km^2.

iii) The area of the base of the Eiffel Tower is $10\,282 \text{ m}^2$.

b) Measure the side lengths of a square object. Calculate the area. Trade areas with a classmate, and calculate the side lengths.

17. Communication Explain the difference between the square root of a number and the square of a number. Use a diagram, examples, and words in your explanation.

18. a) Use a calculator to find each square root.

i) $\sqrt{3\,000\,000}$ ii) $\sqrt{30\,000}$ iii) $\sqrt{300}$

iv) $\sqrt{3}$ v) $\sqrt{0.03}$ vi) $\sqrt{0.0003}$

b) Look at the results in part a. Explain the pattern.

19. Thinking/Inquiry/Problem Solving A square has one vertex at $(0, 0)$ and an area of 49 square units. Draw the 4 possible squares on a grid. Name the coordinates of the other 3 vertices of each square.

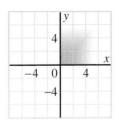

20. What happens when you try to use a calculator to find the square root of a negative integer such as -3? Why do you think this happens?

The Pythagorean Theorem relates the areas of the squares on the sides of a right triangle. Centuries ago, different civilizations knew this property of right triangles.

Egypt, 2000 B.C.E.

The Egyptians may have used a knotted rope with triangle side lengths of 3, 4, and 5 units to design the pyramids.

Babylonia, 1700 B.C.E.

Clay tablets show that the Babylonians knew how to calculate the length of the diagonal of a square.

Greece, 540 B.C.E.

The Pythagorean Theorem is named after the Greek philosopher, Pythagoras. He was the first to prove that this theorem applies to all right triangles.

China, 200 B.C.E.

About the time of the Han period, the Chinese text Chòu-peï contained a discussion of the Pythagorean Theorem based on this diagram.

In a right triangle, the side opposite the right angle is the *hypotenuse*. The two shorter sides are the *legs*.

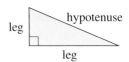

The Pythagorean Theorem

In a right triangle, the area of the square on the hypotenuse is equal to the sum of the areas of the squares on the other two sides.

The side opposite the right angle is the hypotenuse. The two shorter sides are the legs.

The hypotenuse is the longest side.

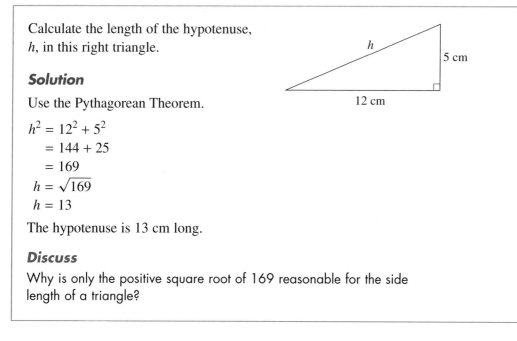

The area of this square ....

... is equal to the sum of the areas of these two squares.

For the right triangle shown:

- Area of square on AB = Area of square on BC + Area of square on AC
- That is, $AB^2 = BC^2 + AC^2$

We can use the Pythagorean Theorem to calculate the length of a side of a right triangle if we know the lengths of the other 2 sides.

Example 1

Calculate the length of the hypotenuse, h, in this right triangle.

h

5 cm

12 cm

Solution

Use the Pythagorean Theorem.

$h^2 = 12^2 + 5^2$

$\quad = 144 + 25$

$\quad = 169$

$h = \sqrt{169}$

$h = 13$

The hypotenuse is 13 cm long.

Discuss

Why is only the positive square root of 169 reasonable for the side length of a triangle?

Example 2

An extension ladder is 7.0 m long. The bottom of the ladder is 2.0 m from the base of a wall. How high up the wall does the ladder reach?

Solution

Draw a diagram. Let w metres represent the height that the ladder reaches up the wall.
Use the Pythagorean Theorem.

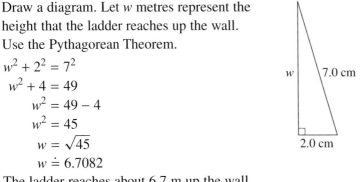

$w^2 + 2^2 = 7^2$
$w^2 + 4 = 49$
$w^2 = 49 - 4$
$w^2 = 45$
$w = \sqrt{45}$
$w \doteq 6.7082$

The ladder reaches about 6.7 m up the wall.

Discuss

Why is only the positive square root used here?

The Pythagorean Theorem can be used on a coordinate grid because the grid defines right angles.

Example 3

A line segment joins the points P(-1, 3) and Q(4, 6). Calculate the length of PQ to 1 decimal place.

Solution

Plot P and Q on a grid.
Draw a right triangle with PQ as the hypotenuse.
Count squares to find the lengths of the legs.
They are 5 units and 3 units.

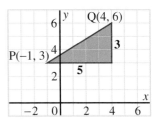

Use the Pythagorean Theorem.

$PQ^2 = 5^2 + 3^2$
$\quad\;\; = 25 + 9$
$\quad\;\; = 34$
$PQ = \sqrt{34}$
$PQ \doteq 5.8310$

Line segment PQ is about 5.8 units long.

A 1. Identify the hypotenuse in each triangle.

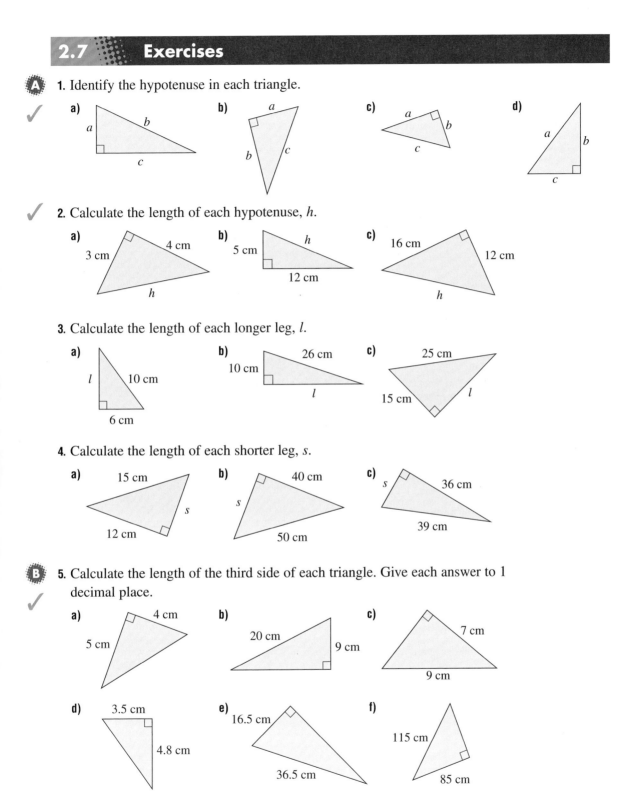

2. Calculate the length of each hypotenuse, h.

3. Calculate the length of each longer leg, l.

4. Calculate the length of each shorter leg, s.

B 5. Calculate the length of the third side of each triangle. Give each answer to 1 decimal place.

6. Calculate the length of each line segment. The grid has 1-cm squares.

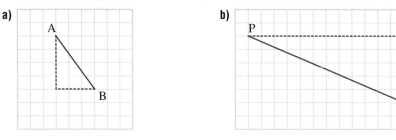

a)

b)

7. Knowledge/Understanding Calculate the length of the third side of each triangle. Round to 1 decimal place.

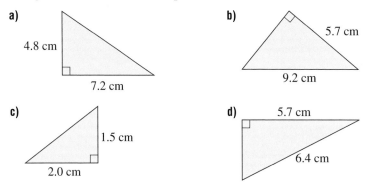

a)

4.8 cm

7.2 cm

b)

5.7 cm

9.2 cm

c)

1.5 cm

2.0 cm

d)

5.7 cm

6.4 cm

8. Calculate the length of a diagonal of each rectangle. Give each length to 1 decimal place where necessary.

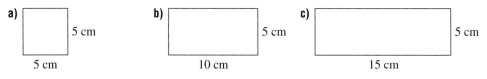

a)

5 cm

5 cm

b)

5 cm

10 cm

c)

5 cm

15 cm

9. For each diagram, calculate the distance between S and T.

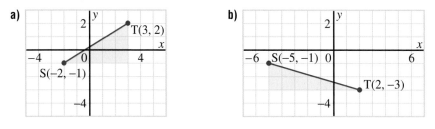

a)

T(3, 2)

S(−2, −1)

b)

S(−5, −1)

T(2, −3)

10. Calculate the length of each line segment.

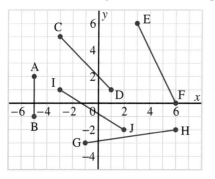

11. Plot each pair of points. Calculate the distance between them. Estimate to check.

   a) A(1, 3), B(5, 5)   **b)** C(6, 0), D(8, 2)   **c)** E(–3, 2), F(1, –3)

   d) G(–4, 2), H(–1, 3)   **e)** J(–1, –4), K(2, –1)   **f)** L(–3, 1), M(0, –1)

12. Communication A triangle has vertices J(–3, 2), K(2, 3), and L(4, –1).

   a) Explain how to calculate the side lengths of the triangle in units.

   b) Follow your explanation. Make any changes to your explanation that you think would help someone use it.

   c) Follow explanations by a few classmates to calculate the side lengths. Describe what you learned by using their explanations.

   d) Describe the role of the Pythagorean Theorem in your explanation for calculating the side lengths.

13. A rectangle has vertices P(–3, –2), Q(1, 2), R(3, 0), and S(–1, –4).

   a) Draw the rectangle on grid paper. Calculate its length and width.

   b) Calculate its area.

   c) Calculate the lengths of its diagonals.

14. Application The dimensions of a computer screen are 28 cm by 21 cm. The size of the screen is the length of its diagonal.

   a) What is size of this screen?

   b) What are advantages of using the Pythagorean Theorem instead of measuring to determine the size?

15. a) Calculate the length of a diagonal of each rectangle to the nearest unit. You might draw diagrams to help you visualize the figures.

   i) A volleyball court is 18 m long and 9 m wide.

   ii) Each side length of a baseball diamond is 2743 cm.

   iii) A basketball court is 28 m long and 15 m wide.

   iv) A hockey rink is about 30 m wide and 60 m long.

   b) Choose a sport from part a. Explain whether the length of the diagonal seems reasonable.

16. a) Measure the length, width, and height of a cardboard box.

b) Calculate the length of the diagonal of each face of the box.

c) Calculate the length of the body diagonal.

d) Check part c by measuring the body diagonal as shown in the photograph. Compare the value for the body diagonal you got from using the Pythagorean Theorem to the value you got from measuring.

e) Suppose you wanted to put a metal rod in the box. What is the length of the longest rod that would fit? Explain how you know.

17. Thinking/Inquiry/Problem Solving A 5-m ladder is placed against a wall. The base of the ladder is 3 m from the wall. The top of the ladder is then lowered 2 m. How far is the base of the ladder from the wall?

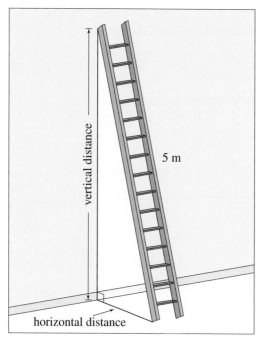

vertical distance

5 m

horizontal distance

On page 45, you considered this situation: a piece of paper is folded in half as many times as possible.

You will need a sheet of blank paper and a ruler.

1. Fold the paper in half, forming 2 layers of paper.
Fold it in half again, forming 4 layers.
Continue to fold in half as long as you can.

2. Copy this table. Record your results.
Extend the table at least as far as the maximum number of folds you were able to make.

Number of folds	Number of layers
0	1
1	
2	
3	

3. As you fold, the pile of paper becomes thicker. At some point, it will be about 1 mm thick.

a) How many layers of paper are there when the pile is about 1 mm thick?

b) Use the result of part a. Estimate the thickness of the sheet of paper you started with.

4. Suppose you could fold the paper 10 times.

a) How many layers of paper would there be?

b) About how thick would the pile of paper be?

5. Suppose you could fold the paper 50 times.

a) How many layers of paper would there be?

b) About how thick would the pile of paper be? Express your answer in the most appropriate unit of measurement.

c) Compare your answer in part b with the measures in the chart that follows. Which measure is closest to the thickness of the pile of paper that is folded 50 times?

Height of an adult	2 m
Height of a 2-storey house	10 m
Height of a 10-storey apartment building	50 m
Height of the CN Tower	550 m
Height of jet aircraft in flight	12 000 m
Height of the space shuttle in orbit	200 km
Distance to the moon	380 000 km
Distance to the sun	150 000 000 km

6. As you fold, the area of paper on the top layer becomes smaller.

a) Measure the length and the width of the unfolded piece of paper in millimetres.

b) Calculate the area of the paper in square millimetres.

c) Add another column to your table for the area of the top layer. Write your answer from part a in the first row. Calculate the area of the top layer for each number of folds. Enter the results in the new column.

Number of folds, f	Number of layers, l	Area of top layer, a (mm^2)
0	1	
1		
2		
3		

7. Suppose you could fold the paper 10 times. What would the area of the top layer be?

8. Suppose you could fold the paper 50 times.

   a) What would the area of the top layer be?

   b) Compare your answer in part b with the areas in the chart below. Which area is closest to the area of the top layer of the pile of paper that is folded 50 times?

Area of one face of a sugar cube	100 mm^2
Area of this circle: •	1 mm^2
Area of the dot in this letter: i	0.01 mm^2
Area of a pollen grain	0.001 mm^2
Area of a pit in a CD track	10^{-5} mm^2

9. Your table in exercise 6 is a mathematical model. It represents the number of layers and the area of the top layer when the piece of paper is folded over and over again. List any assumptions for this model.

10. Use the data in the first 2 columns of your table in exercise 6.

    a) Draw a graph of the number of layers, l, against the number of folds, f. Plot f horizontally and l vertically.

    b) Should the points be joined? Explain.

    c) Is the relation linear or non-linear? Explain.

    d) Describe how the number of layers changes as the number of folds increases.

11. Use the data in the 1st and 3rd columns of your table in exercise 6.

    a) Draw a graph of the area of the top layer, a, against the number of folds, f.

    b) Should the points be joined? Explain.

    c) Is the relation linear or non-linear? Explain.

    d) Describe how the area of the top layer changes as the number of folds increases.

12. **Communication** Write about this experiment. Explain what you did and what you found out. Include the tables of values and graphs in your explanation.

MATHEMATICS TOOLKIT

Products of Rational Numbers

- Rational numbers can be written as fractions or decimals; for example, $\frac{1}{2}$, $-\frac{5}{3}$, $0.\overline{3}$, -8, ...
- The product of positive rational numbers is positive. $(+) \times (+) \times (+) = +$
- The product of an even number of negative rational numbers is positive.
  $(-) \times (-) \times (-) \times (-) = +$
- The product of an odd number of negative rational numbers is negative.
  $(-) \times (-) \times (-) = -$

Exponent Laws

- Multiplying powers: $a^n \times a^m = a^{n+m}$, n and m are integers.
- Dividing powers: $a^n \div a^m = a^{n-m}$, n and m are integers.

$$5^6 \times 5^2 = 5^{6+2}$$
$$= 5^8$$

$$5^6 \div 5^2 = 5^{6-2}$$
$$= 5^4$$

Power of a Power

- $(a^m)^n = a^{mn}$, m and n are integers.

$$(5^2)^3 = 5^{2 \times 3}$$
$$= 5^6$$

Zero Exponent

- $a^0 = 1$ $(a \neq 0)$

Negative Integer Exponent

- $a^{-n} = \frac{1}{a^n}$ $(a \neq 0$ and n is an integer.$)$
- $\frac{1}{a^n} = a^{-n}$ $(a \neq 0$ and n is an integer.$)$

$$5^{-1} = \frac{1}{5}$$

$$\frac{1}{5} = 5^{-1}$$

Scientific Notation

- To write a number in scientific notation,
  write it as the product of: a number between
  1 and 10 and a power of 10.

$$53\,000 = 5.3 \times 10^4$$
$$0.0041 = 4.1 \times 10^{-3}$$

Squares and Square Roots

- All positive numbers have square roots.
- When taking the square root, consider positive and negative values.
- The radical sign, $\sqrt{\ }$, means evaluate only the positive square root.

The Pythagorean Theorem

- $h^2 = l^2 + s^2$

2.1   **1.** Write each power as a product. Then evaluate.

  a) $(1.4)^3$ **b)** $(-8)^5$ **c)** $\left(-\dfrac{5}{8}\right)^2$ **d)** $(-2.6)^4$

2. Evaluate. Round to 3 decimal places where necessary.

  a) $(-1.8)^3$ **b)** 4^2 **c)** $(2.4)^4$

  d) $(-0.9)^3$ **e)** $\left(\dfrac{7}{2}\right)^2$ **f)** $\left(-\dfrac{4}{5}\right)^1$

3. Evaluate mentally.

  a) 10^4 **b)** 10^6 **c)** 10^2 **d)** 10^9

4. Evaluate.

  a) The Solar System has 3^2 planets.   **b)** Each year has 2^2 seasons.

5. Make up a statement similar to exercise 4. Trade statements with classmates and evaluate the powers.

6. Evaluate.

  a) $\left(-\dfrac{1}{2}\right)^3$ **b)** $\left(-\dfrac{2}{4}\right)^3$ **c)** $\left(-\dfrac{6}{12}\right)^3$ **d)** $\left(-\dfrac{5}{10}\right)^3$

7. Evaluate.

  a) $\left(-\dfrac{15}{20}\right)^4$ **b)** $\left(-\dfrac{3}{4}\right)^4$ **c)** $\left(-\dfrac{75}{100}\right)^4$ **d)** $\left(-\dfrac{6}{8}\right)^4$

2.2   **8.** Write each product as a single power.

  a) $3^5 \times 3^2$ **b)** $(-2)^4 \times (-2)^3$ **c)** $2^3 \times 2^5$ **d)** $(-15)^3 \times (-15)^2$

9. Write each quotient as a single power.

  a) $4^5 \div 4^3$ **b)** $3^8 \div 3^6$ **c)** $\dfrac{12^9}{12^8}$ **d)** $\dfrac{16^3}{16^2}$

10. Write each product as a single power. Evaluate. Round to 3 decimal places where necessary.

  a) $(-1)^2 \times (-1)^2$ **b)** $3.2^3 \times 3.2^5$ **c)** $(-0.8)^1 \times (-0.8)^1$
  d) $6.25^2 \times 6.25^3$ **e)** $10^3 \times 10^4$ **f)** $(-1.5)^2 \times (-1.5)$

11. Write each quotient as a single power. Evaluate. Round to 3 decimal places where necessary.

  a) $8^7 \div 8^3$ **b)** $(-7)^6 \div (-7)^5$ **c)** $(-1.6)^5 \div (-1.6)^2$
  d) $(-5.4)^9 \div (-5.4)^7$ **e)** $(-0.9)^8 \div (-0.9)^4$ **f)** $1.25^5 \div 1.25^4$

2.3   **12.** Write as a single power. Do not evaluate.

  a) $(3^2)^5$ **b)** $(3^5)^4$ **c)** $(3^{-2})^3$ **d)** $(3^2)^0$

13. Write as a single power.

a) $(m^3)^5$ b) $(m^2)^6$ c) $(m^{-5})^{-1}$ d) $(m^{-2})^3$

14. Write as a single power, then evaluate.

a) $(2^2)^3$ b) $(-4^2)^2$ c) $(-5^7)^0$ d) $(3^{-2})^{-3}$

2.4   **15.** Write each power with a positive exponent.

a) 5^{-3} b) $\dfrac{1}{4^{-2}}$ c) 6^{-4} d) $\dfrac{1}{10^{-3}}$ e) 2^{-5} f) $\dfrac{1}{3^{-6}}$

16. Use a calculator to evaluate each power. Round to 4 decimal places where necessary.

a) 4^{-5} b) $(-6)^{-3}$ c) 1.8^{-1} d) $(-3.4)^{-2}$ e) 5^{-4} f) $(-2.4)^{-3}$

17. Evaluate each power.

a) $(-5)^0$ b) 2^0 c) 4.7^0 d) $(-9.5)^0$ e) $(-1.1)^0$ f) 5.6^0

2.5   **18.** Write in scientific notation.

a) 64 000   b) 0.0045   c) 0.000 006

d) 7 250 000 000   e) 4×10^5 f) 800×10^{-4}

19. Write in standard form.

a) 4.8×10^8 b) 7.31×10^{-4} c) 3.0×10^{-6}

d) 1.07×10^2 e) 6.1×10^{-9} f) 8.02×10^{-5}

20. When you write a number in scientific notation, explain how you know whether the exponent is positive or negative.

21. Simplify. Check whether the answers are reasonable.

a) $(3.2 \times 10^4) \times (1.0 \times 10^{-6})$ b) $(8.14 \times 10^2) \times (9.5 \times 10^8)$

c) $(6.03 \times 10^{-5}) \times (4.6 \times 10^{-1})$ d) $(3.8 \times 10^{-7}) \times (7.1 \times 10^3)$

22. Simplify.

a) $\dfrac{7.1 \times 10^{-4}}{8.0 \times 10^6}$ b) $\dfrac{1.0 \times 10^{-1}}{3.48 \times 10^{-5}}$

23. One grain of grass pollen has an estimated mass of 0.000 000 005 g. Write this mass in scientific notation.

24. Every atom contains electrons and protons. Write each mass in standard form.

a) An electron has a mass of 9.11×10^{-28} g.

b) A proton has a mass of 1.67×10^{-24} g.

2.6   **25.** What are the square roots of each number?

a) 64   b) 4   c) 36   d) 144   e) 1

26. Evaluate.

a) $\sqrt{9}$ b) $\sqrt{16}$ c) $\sqrt{100}$

d) $\sqrt{25}$ e) $\sqrt{121}$ f) $\sqrt{10\,000}$

27. Find the square roots of each number. Round to 1 decimal place.

a) 80   b) 25   c) 98

d) 150   e) 83   f) 210

28. Evaluate. Round to 1 decimal place.

a) $\sqrt{20}$ b) $\sqrt{65}$ c) $\sqrt{180}$ d) $\sqrt{1256}$ e) $\sqrt{948}$

29. a) Find the perimeter of a square with area 49 cm².

     b) Find the approximate perimeter of a square with area 150 cm².

2.7   **30.** Calculate the length of the third side of each triangle to 1 decimal place.

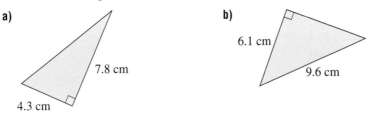

a)

7.8 cm

4.3 cm

b)

6.1 cm

9.6 cm

31. Calculate the length of a diagonal of each rectangle to 1 decimal place.

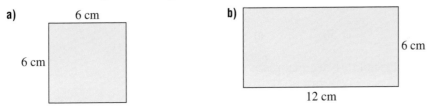

a)

6 cm

6 cm

b)

6 cm

12 cm

32. Plot each pair of points. Calculate the distance between them.

a) L(2, 4), M(−3, 1)   b) J(0, −5), K(−6, −8)   c) E(−2, 6), F(6, 3)

33. a) Is the hypotenuse always the longest side of a right triangle? How do you know?

     b) Explain how you can use your answer for part a to check calculations with the Pythagorean Theorem.

1. Evaluate each power. Round to 4 decimal places where necessary.

   a) 7^4 b) $(-1.2)^{-5}$ c) $(-8.6)^0$ d) 12^{-2} e) $\left(\dfrac{3}{5}\right)^6$ f) 10^0

2. **Knowledge/Understanding** Write each expression as a power. Evaluate each power. Round to 3 decimal places where necessary.

   a) $8^3 \times 8^2$ b) $(-1.4)^8 \div (-1.4)^3$ c) $5^6 \div 5^2$ d) $(-10)^6 \times (-10)^5$

3. Write in scientific notation.

   a) 201 000 b) 0.0009 c) 735 200 d) 0.000 007 8

4. Write in standard form.

   a) 9.0×10^{-6} b) 3.4×10^8 c) 1.65×10^9 d) 8.22×10^{-4}

5. **Communication** Explain what you know about a number in scientific notation from the sign of its exponent.

6. Simplify. State in scientific notation.

   a) $(3.8 \times 10^{-4}) \times (2.0 \times 10^3)$ b) $\dfrac{1.0 \times 10^2}{4.53 \times 10^{-3}}$

7. Find the square roots of each number. Round to 1 decimal place where necessary.

   a) 15 b) 100 c) 50 d) 1 e) 82

8. Find each square root. Round to 1 decimal place where necessary.

   a) $\sqrt{64}$ b) $\sqrt{42}$ c) $\sqrt{120}$ d) $\sqrt{81}$ e) $\sqrt{6}$

9. Calculate the length of the third side of each triangle. Round to 1 decimal place.

   a) 6.4 cm, 3.2 cm b) 8.5 cm, 2.7 cm

10. **Application** A triangle has side lengths 3.6 m, 4.8 m, and 6.0 m.

    a) If the triangle were a right triangle, which side would be the hypotenuse? Why?

    b) Is the triangle a right triangle? Why?

11. **Thinking/Inquiry/Problem Solving** Suppose the length and width of a rectangle are doubled. Predict what would happen to the lengths of its diagonals. Explain why your prediction is reasonable. Use the Pythagorean Theorem to show whether your prediction is true for two examples.

12. The area of a rectangle is given by the formula, $A = lw$.
    A scientist looking at bacteria under a microscope noticed
    a rectangular cluster of bacteria.

    2.8×10^{-5} cm

    1.6×10^{-5} cm

    Find the approximate area of the
    rectangle. Show your work.

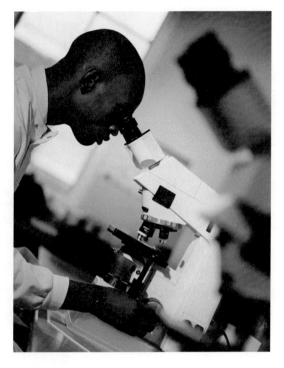

13. Javier simplified $2^3 \times 2^4$ as: $2^3 \times 2^4 = 2^{12}$
    His friend, Miriam, correctly told Javier to add the exponents as shown:
    $2^3 \times 2^4 = 2^7$
    "But why add?" Javier asked. "It says to multiply."

    Explain why adding the exponents is correct.

3

Algebra

By the end of this chapter, you will:

- Expand and simplify expressions.

- Use algebra to solve equations.

- Use equations to solve problems. Compare using equations with other methods to solve the same problem.

- Manipulate first-degree polynomials to solve equations.

- Communicate solutions to problems, and justify your reasoning in solving problems.

Estimating Heights

Scientists and doctors can estimate the height of a human based on his or her remains. Scientists use formulas that relate the sizes of some parts of the human body.

Andrew is an anthropologist. A radius bone from the arm of a human was discovered at an excavation site. It measured 24.5 cm. Andrew will use this measurement to determine the approximate height of the person.

In Section 3.6, you will develop mathematical models to solve this problem.

Necessary Skills

Solving Equations by Inspection

Recall that an equation is a way to write a word sentence about a mathematical situation.

For example, $x + 3 = 5$ is read "A number plus 3 equals 5."

To solve an equation means to find the value of the variable that makes the equation true.

The solution of the equation $x + 3 = 5$ is $x = 2$, because $2 + 3 = 5$.

Example

Solve.

a) $10 + a = 14$ **b)** $c - 3 = 8$ **c)** $3m = 18$ **d)** $\frac{n}{2} = 5$

Solution

a) $10 + a = 14$

What number, added to 10, makes 14?
Since $10 + 4 = 14$, the solution is $a = 4$.

b) $c - 3 = 8$

From what number do we subtract 3
to get 8? Since $11 - 3 = 8$, the solution
is $c = 11$.

c) $3m = 18$

What do we multiply 3 by, to get 18?
Since $3 \times 6 = 18$, the solution is $m = 6$.

d) $\frac{n}{2} = 5$

What number do we divide by 2 to get 5?
Since $\frac{10}{2} = 5$, the solution is $n = 10$.

Exercises

1. Solve.

    a) $x + 5 = 12$ **b)** $3 + m = 8$ **c)** $15 = a + 9$ **d)** $21 = 14 + n$

    e) $x - 5 = 12$ **f)** $10 - m = 8$ **g)** $15 = a - 9$ **h)** $12 = 14 - n$

2. Solve.

    a) $2a = 16$ **b)** $3n = 24$ **c)** $30 = 6x$ **d)** $42 = 7m$

    e) $\frac{n}{2} = 3$ **f)** $\frac{x}{3} = 5$ **g)** $8 = \frac{m}{4}$ **h)** $1 = \frac{a}{9}$

Writing Simple Equations

We can use algebra to write a word sentence as an equation.

Example

Write an equation to represent each sentence.

a) Three more than a number is 12.

b) A number decreased by two is six.

c) Six times a number is 24.

d) A number divided by four is five.

Solution

a) Three more than a number is 12.
Let the number be n.
Then, three more than the number is $n + 3$; this equals 12.
So, the equation is $n + 3 = 12$.

b) A number decreased by two is six.
Let the number be x.
Then, the number decreased by two is $x - 2$; this equals 6.
So, the equation is $x - 2 = 6$.

c) Six times a number is 24.
Let the number be y.
Then, six times the number is $6y$; this equals 24.
So, the equation is $6y = 24$.

d) A number divided by four is five.
Let the number be m.
Then, the number divided by four is $\frac{m}{4}$; this equals 5.
So, the equation is $\frac{m}{4} = 5$.

Exercises

1. Write an equation to represent each sentence.

a) Two more than a number is nine.

b) Five less than a number is 11.

c) A number subtracted from 12 is six.

d) Eight more than a number is 20.

2. Solve each equation from exercise 1.

3. Write an equation to represent each sentence.

a) Five times a number is 20.

b) A number divided by three is 12.

c) A number times four is 28.

d) Two divided into a number is seven.

4. Solve each equation from exercise 3.

The area of this rectangular garden can be calculated in two ways.

Method 1:

Total area = width × length

$$= 5(4 + 6)$$
$$= 5(10)$$
$$= 50$$

Method 2:

Total area = area with flowers + area with vegetables

$$= 5 \times 4 + 5 \times 6$$
$$= 20 + 30$$
$$= 50$$

For both methods, the area is 50 m².

$$5(4 + 6) = 5 \times 4 + 5 \times 6$$

In arithmetic, we write equations such as: $5(4 + 6) = 5 \times 4 + 5 \times 6$

In algebra, we use variables to write the equation: $a(b + c) = ab + ac$.
This equation is called the *distributive law*.

TAKE NOTE

Distributive Law

$a(b + c) = ab + ac$

$a(b - c) = ab - ac$ where a, b, and c are any real numbers

We can use algebra tiles to represent algebraic expressions.

This tile is a 1-tile.
It represents one unit, or 1.

To represent the opposite,
which is −1, flip the tile.

This tile below is a variable tile. It represents
a variable. For example, if you are using s,
you can call this tile an s-tile.

To represent the opposite of s, which
is −s, flip the tile.

To represent the expression $s + 4$ with algebra tiles, use one s-tile and four 1-tiles.

To represent $2w + 10$, use two w-tiles and ten 1-tiles.

To represent $2(w + 5)$, form two equal groups of tiles. Each group contains one w-tile and five 1-tiles.

The algebra tiles demonstrate an example of the distributive law: $2(w + 5) = 2w + 10$
When we write an expression without brackets, we *expand* it.

Algebra Tiles and the Distributive Law

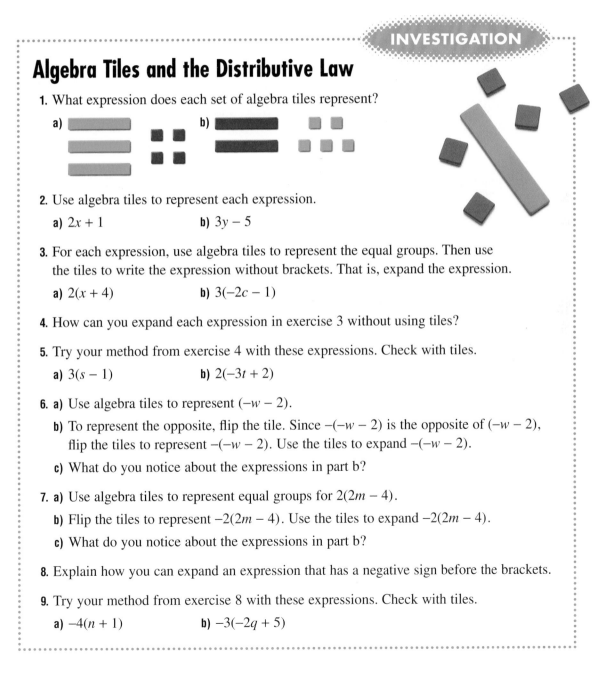

1. What expression does each set of algebra tiles represent?

a)

b)

2. Use algebra tiles to represent each expression.

a) $2x + 1$
b) $3y - 5$

3. For each expression, use algebra tiles to represent the equal groups. Then use the tiles to write the expression without brackets. That is, expand the expression.

a) $2(x + 4)$
b) $3(-2c - 1)$

4. How can you expand each expression in exercise 3 without using tiles?

5. Try your method from exercise 4 with these expressions. Check with tiles.

a) $3(s - 1)$
b) $2(-3t + 2)$

6. a) Use algebra tiles to represent $(-w - 2)$.

b) To represent the opposite, flip the tile. Since $-(-w - 2)$ is the opposite of $(-w - 2)$, flip the tiles to represent $-(-w - 2)$. Use the tiles to expand $-(-w - 2)$.

c) What do you notice about the expressions in part b?

7. a) Use algebra tiles to represent equal groups for $2(2m - 4)$.

b) Flip the tiles to represent $-2(2m - 4)$. Use the tiles to expand $-2(2m - 4)$.

c) What do you notice about the expressions in part b?

8. Explain how you can expand an expression that has a negative sign before the brackets.

9. Try your method from exercise 8 with these expressions. Check with tiles.

a) $-4(n + 1)$
b) $-3(-2q + 5)$

Example 1

a) Use algebra tiles to represent the expression $5 - 2x$.

b) Use algebra tiles to represent the expression $-(5 - 2x)$.

Solution

a) $5 - 2x$

Use five 1-tiles and two flipped x-tiles.

b) $-(5 - 2x)$

Just as $-x$ represents the opposite of x, so $-(5 - 2x)$ represents the opposite of $5 - 2x$. Use tiles to represent $5 - 2x$. Then flip the tiles.
$-(5 - 2x) = -5 + 2x$, or $2x - 5$

Discuss

How is expanding $-(5 - 2x)$ the same as multiplying 5 by -1 and multiplying $-2x$ by -1?

Example 2

Use algebra tiles to represent each expression. Use the result to expand the expression.

a) $2(3x - 4)$ **b)** $-3(p - 3)$

Solution

a)

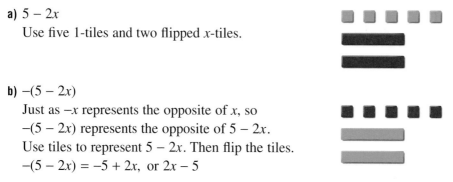

Think …

2 equal groups of tiles

$2(3x - 4)$

Each group has three x-tiles and four flipped 1-tiles.

In all, there are six x-tiles and eight flipped 1-tiles.
So, $2(3x - 4) = 6x - 8$

b)

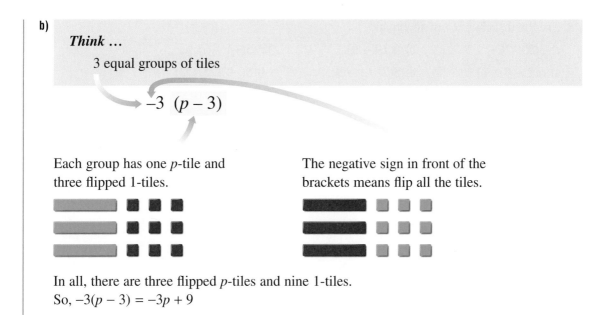

Think …

3 equal groups of tiles

$$-3 \; (p - 3)$$

Each group has one p-tile and three flipped 1-tiles.

The negative sign in front of the brackets means flip all the tiles.

In all, there are three flipped p-tiles and nine 1-tiles.
So, $-3(p - 3) = -3p + 9$

Instead of using algebra tiles, we can use the distributive law to expand an expression.

Example 3

Expand using the distributive law.

a) $6(3n + 4)$

b) $-3(4b - 7)$

Solution

a) $6(3n + 4) = 6(3n) + 6(4)$
$= 18n + 24$

b) $-3(4b - 7) = -3(4b) - 3(-7)$
$= -12b + 21$

3.1   Exercises

1. Write two different expressions for the total area of the gardens.

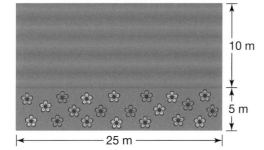

10 m

5 m

25 m

2. Use the distributive law to expand.

a) $3(5 + 7)$ b) $6(19 - 9)$ c) $5(-4 + 6)$

d) $6(2 + 7 + 1)$ e) $3(2 - 1 + 9)$ f) $5(-4 - 5 + 2)$

3. Use the distributive law to expand.

a) $-(2x + 1)$ b) $-(2x - 1)$ c) $-(-2x + 1)$

d) $-(-2x - 1)$ e) $-(1 + 2x)$ f) $-(1 - 2x)$

4. Expand.

a) $4(8 + 3m)$ b) $-4(8 + 3m)$ c) $4(-8 + 3m)$

d) $4(8 - 3m)$ e) $4(3m + 8)$ f) $-4(3m + 8)$

5. What expression does each group of algebra tiles represent?

6. Suppose you flipped all the tiles in exercise 5. What expression would each group of algebra tiles represent?

B **7.** Expand using the distributive law.

a) $3(5 + 8)$ b) $5(6 - 4)$ c) $11(5 - 7)$ d) $-6(8 - 4)$

e) $12(5 - 6)$ f) $-4(7 - 9)$ g) $13(1 + h)$ h) $8(11 - d)$

8. Expand using the distributive law.

a) $5(4 + 10 + 2)$ b) $4(11 - 5 - 2)$ c) $9(4 + 5 - 8)$ d) $-8(9 - 2 + 8)$

9. Use algebra tiles to represent each expression.

a) $3a + 5$ b) $-4c - 6$ c) $-2e + 4$ d) $-1 - 6g$

e) $4q + 7$ f) $-6 - 3k$ g) $7 - 2t$ h) $-3 + 5s$

10. Use algebra tiles to represent each expression.

a) $4z - 6$ b) $-3 + 2a$ c) $-3x + 5$ d) $-7 - k$

e) $8 + 6c$ f) $-p - 4$ g) $6x + 1$ h) $-7 - 4t$

11. Communication Which expression is equivalent to $3(2y - 5)$? Explain your choice.

a) $2y - 15$ b) $6y - 15$ c) $2y + 15$ d) $6y - 5$

12. **a) Knowledge/Understanding** Use algebra tiles to represent each expression. Use the tiles to write the expression without brackets.

  i) $5(k + 1)$ **ii)** $2(3 - 2w)$ **iii)** $4(2m + 1)$ **iv)** $-1(4 + 5y)$

  v) $-3(2 - p)$ **vi)** $3(1 - 3b)$ **vii)** $-2(4t - 5)$ **viii)** $-4(2s + 2)$

  b) Write a rule for determining whether a term is positive or negative after expanding. Check whether your rule works for 3 expressions in part a.

13. Only two expressions in each set are equal. Which are they? Use algebra tiles to justify your answer.

  a) $3x + 2$ $3x - 2$ $2 + 3x$ $2 - 3x$

  b) $-4g + 5$ $-5g + 4$ $-5g - 4$ $4 - 5g$

  c) $2j - 7$ $7 - 2j$ $-7 - 2j$ $-2j + 7$

  d) $-5b + 3$ $-3 - 5b$ $-5 + 3b$ $-5b - 3$

14. Which of the following expressions is equal to $5(m + 3) - 16$? Explain.

  a) $5(m + 3 - 16)$ **b)** $5m + 15 - 16$ **c)** $5m + 15 - 80$

15. **Application** Expand using the distributive law.

  a) $3(x + 2y - 7)$ **b)** $-2(a - 5b + 2)$ **c)** $-(6m - 7n)$

  d) $4(9p + q - 9r)$ **e)** $5(x + 6y - 4)$ **f)** $3(7c - 9 + d)$

16. **Thinking/Inquiry/Problem Solving**
  A rectangular garden is made up of smaller gardens as shown.

  a) Write as many different expressions as you can think of to represent the total area of the garden.

  b) How can you use the distributive law to compare the expressions in part a?

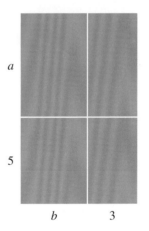

17. **Thinking/Inquiry/Problem Solving** Decide whether each statement is always true, sometimes true, or never true. Justify your answers.

  a) A 1-tile is positive and a flipped 1-tile is negative.

  b) A variable tile is positive and a flipped variable tile is negative.

  c) The variable x is positive and $-x$ is negative.

In arithmetic, we add, subtract, multiply, and divide numbers.

In algebra, we add, subtract, multiply, and divide algebraic expressions.

The terms represented by variable tiles are *variable* terms.
The terms represented by 1-tiles are *constant* terms.

When we add or subtract expressions using algebra tiles, we use the *Zero Principle*.

The Zero Principle

A 1-tile plus a flipped 1-tile have the sum 0.
Any two opposite tiles have the sum 0.

So, we can add or remove pairs of opposite tiles without changing the value of an expression.

We see: or 

We think:
The sum of each pair is 0.

We use the Zero Principle when we combine groups of tiles. For example, these groups of tiles represent $4x$, $-2x$, and 5, respectively.

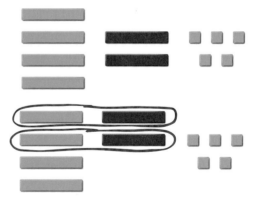

We use the Zero Principle to remove two pairs of opposite tiles. Two variable tiles and five 1-tiles remain. We cannot combine the variable tiles and 1-tiles since they are not the same type.

Like terms contain the same variable. For example, $4x$ and $-2x$ are like terms.
7 and -3 are like terms. Since they contain no variables they are *constant* terms.
Like terms can be combined to *simplify* an expression.

We write: $4x - 2x + 5 = 2x + 5$

TAKE NOTE

The terms $4x$ and $-2x$ are *like* terms because they contain the same variable.
Similarly, 7 and -3 are *like* terms. They contain no variables. The terms $2x$
and 5 are not like terms, so they cannot be combined.

When we combine like terms, we simplify the expression.

Example 1

a) Use algebra tiles to simplify the expression $4a + 3 + 2a - 4$.

b) What is the value of this expression for each value of a?

   i) $a = 8$ **ii)** $a = -2$

Solution

a)

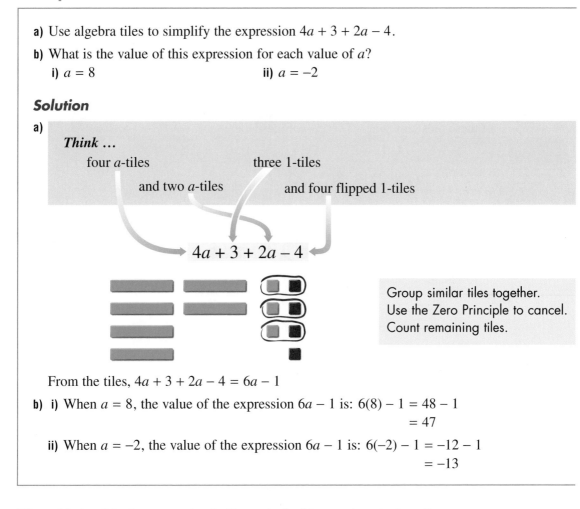

Think ...

    four a-tiles   three 1-tiles

      and two a-tiles   and four flipped 1-tiles

$$4a + 3 + 2a - 4$$

Group similar tiles together.
Use the Zero Principle to cancel.
Count remaining tiles.

From the tiles, $4a + 3 + 2a - 4 = 6a - 1$

b) **i)** When $a = 8$, the value of the expression $6a - 1$ is: $6(8) - 1 = 48 - 1$
                                                          $= 47$

   ii) When $a = -2$, the value of the expression $6a - 1$ is: $6(-2) - 1 = -12 - 1$
                                                            $= -13$

We could simplify the expression in *Example 1* without using algebra tiles.
We do this in *Example 2*.

Example 2

Simplify the expression $4a + 3 + 2a - 4$ by combining like terms.

Solution

$$4a + 3 + 2a - 4 = 4a + 2a + 3 - 4 \qquad \text{Rearrange to group like terms.}$$
$$= 6a - 1 \qquad\qquad\quad \text{Note: the sign of the term moves with the term.}$$

In *Example 2*, we combined the variable terms $4a$ and $2a$. In the term $4a$, 4 is the *coefficient*. In the term $2a$, 2 is the coefficient. In both terms, a is the variable.

Example 3

Use algebra tiles to combine like terms: $2(x + 2) - 3(2 - x)$

Solution

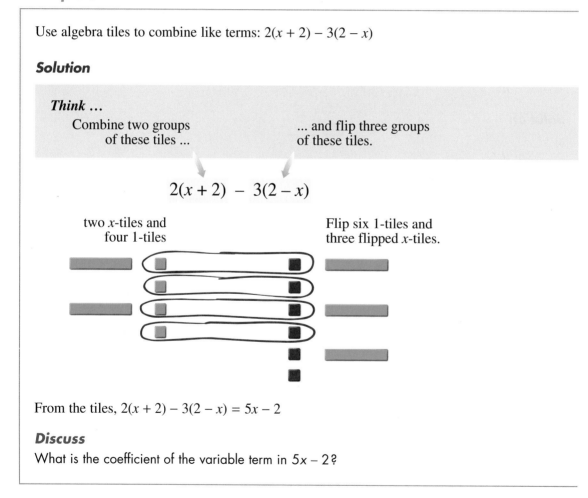

Think ...

Combine two groups of these tiles ...

... and flip three groups of these tiles.

$$2(x + 2) \; - \; 3(2 - x)$$

two *x*-tiles and four 1-tiles

Flip six 1-tiles and three flipped *x*-tiles.

From the tiles, $2(x + 2) - 3(2 - x) = 5x - 2$

Discuss

What is the coefficient of the variable term in $5x - 2$?

When we do not use algebra tiles, we use the distributive law.

Example 4

Simplify the expression $2(x + 2) - 3(2 - x)$.

Solution

$$2(x + 2) - 3(2 - x) = 2(x) + 2(2) - 3(2) - 3(-x)$$
$$= 2x + 4 - 6 + 3x$$
$$= 2x + 3x + 4 - 6$$
$$= 5x - 2$$

Discuss

Why does it make sense to have the same results in *Examples 3* and *4*?

3.2 Exercises

A

1. Which are like terms?

a) $5x$, $-2x$ b) $3a$, 7 c) $2x$, -1 d) 4, 8

e) $2x$, $3y$ f) $-5c$, c g) $-x$, $4x$ h) 3, $3s$

i) $8k$, $-4k$, 3 j) $9p$, -4, $7p$ k) $2s$, $2t$, $2u$ l) -82, $6w$, $-8v$

2. There are 5 pairs of like terms. Find all 5 pairs.

$2x$ $-3y$ $5w$ $-y$ 3 $-x$ $5z$ $4w$ -1 $-2z$

3. Find the like terms for $4a$.

7 $2a$ $-x$ -4 a $-4b$ $-2a$ 0 $3z$

4. Find the like terms for 9.

$9x$ 5 -9 0 $9a$ $-3y$ -1 $2a$ 4

5. Identify the constant terms.

3 $2b$ -8 0 x $-8y$ 10 -1 $5k$

6. Identify the variable terms.

4 $-s$ $2y$ $7m$ $-3a$ -6 $4x$ 2 n

B

7. Combine like terms. Write an expression for each using x.

a)

b)

c)

✓ **8.** Combine like terms.

    a) $5a - 5a$ **b)** $8 + 8$ **c)** $-2x + 2x$

    d) $7 - 7$ **e)** $-1 + 1$ **f)** $-3b - 3b$

✓ **9.** Find the value of each expression.

    a) $4(-2) + 1$ **b)** $3(4) - 3$ **c)** $7(-1) - 2$

10. Use algebra tiles to combine like terms.

    a) $6s + 3s$ **b)** $4v - 2v$ **c)** $-5b + 2b + 4b$

    d) $7p - p + 3p$ **e)** $-6c - 2c - c$ **f)** $6t + 5 + 2t$

✓ **11.** Simplify. Use algebra tiles if you like.

    a) $5 - 2a - 3a$ **b)** $11n - 12n + 6$ **c)** $9 - 4d + 3d$

    d) $4u - 6 + u + 3$ **e)** $-k + 2k - 3k + 4k$ **f)** $-6q - 2q + q - 7$

12. Simplify. Use algebra tiles if you like.

    a) $3x + 4x - 3x$ **b)** $-3a + 2a - a$ **c)** $-8 + 5c - 3c$

    d) $3k - 2 - k + 1$ **e)** $5(2b + 1) + 3b$ **f)** $-4u + 1 - 2(2 + 3u)$

13. Use the Zero Principle to simplify mentally. Write only the result.

    a) $6x - 6x + 2$ **b)** $-7 + s + 7$ **c)** $2d - d - d$

    d) $3a - 2 + 1 + 1$ **e)** $4y - 3 - 4y + y$ **f)** $8f + 2 - 8f$

14. Explain your method from exercise 13. Write an expression you can simplify mentally using the Zero Principle.

15. Expand. Then combine like terms. Find the value when $x = 0$.

    a) $3(x - 2) + 4$ **b)** $-x - 5 + 2(1 + 3x)$ **c)** $-3 + 4(1 - x) + 5x$

    d) $-8(-x - 1) - 3x - 5$ **e)** $2(x + 3) - (5 - x)$ **f)** $-3(2 + 3x) + 8x - 3$

16. **Knowledge/Understanding** Simplify each expression. Find its value when $x = 1$.

    a) $-7x + 12 - 2x$ **b)** $8x + 3 - 11x - 7$ **c)** $10(x - 5) + 7x - 2$

    d) $9 + 3x - (8x - 12)$ **e)** $5x + 3(4x - 2) - 12$ **f)** $2(3x + 2) + 4(2 + x)$

✓ **17.** Simplify each expression. Find its value when $x = -3$.

    a) $4x + 2x - 2$ **b)** $5x - 6x - 2$ **c)** $11x - 5 - 7x - 4$

    d) $9 + 3x - (8x - 12)$ **e)** $2x + 3(4x - 2)$ **f)** $-8(3 - 2x) - 7 - 6x$

18. Simplify each expression. Find its value when the variable has the given value.

    a) $4a + 7a - 3$ for $a = 3$ **b)** $-3m + 21 + 7m$ for $m = -7$

    c) $15(s + 2) - s$ for $s = 0$ **d)** $20x - 3 - 6x$ for $x = 2$

19. Simplify each expression. Find its value when: **i)** $x = 7$ **ii)** $x = -2$

   a) $9x - 5 - 6x + 4$

   b) $8x - 2 - 6x - 6$

   c) $-3(x - 1) - (2x - 3)$

   d) $5x - 3(x - 4)$

   e) $-(x - 2) + 4(3 - x)$

   f) $7(1 - x) - 2(3x - 2)$

20. Communication In exercise 19, we could find the value of each expression when $x = 7$ and when $x = -2$ without simplifying. Why do we simplify first?

21. Simplify.

   a) $7a + 3a + 2(a - 5)$

   b) $-(3m + 2) - 3(1 + 4m)$

   c) $20s - 7 + 5(3 - s)$

   d) $4x - 3 - (x - 1)$

   e) $4(5p - 4) - 1 - 3(6p - 2)$

   f) $-32g + 5(2 - 3g) + (-3)$

22. Simplify.

   a) $m - 2 + 5(m - 2)$

   b) $2(a + 3) - 1 - 3a - (2a - 5)$

   c) $3x - 2 + 7(1 - x) - 7$

   d) $2s - 1 - 4(s - 2) + 3(s + 1)$

   e) $7(-2d - 4) - 6d - 8$

   f) $5(q - 7) - (q + 4)$

23. Thinking/Inquiry/Problem Solving

   a) If possible, simplify each expression. If it is not possible, explain why.

   i) $2 + 3x + 0$ **ii)** $-7v + v + 2 + 1$ **iii)** $64v$

   b) In your opinion, which expression is simpler? Give a reason for your opinion.

   i) $7(x - 4)$ **ii)** $7x - 28$

   c) Without using the words "simple," "simpler," or "simplest," explain what the word "simplify" means.

24. Application Write an expression for the perimeter of each rectangle. Simplify the expression.

   a) x , 3

   b) $2x$, x

3.3 Solving Equations Algebraically

On page 94, you solved equations by inspection. To solve by inspection, you look at an equation and calculate the solution. Some equations cannot be easily solved this way. They must be solved algebraically.

To solve an equation algebraically:

- Collect like terms: variable terms on one side of the equation and constant terms on the other side.
- Simplify each side of the equation.
- Isolate the variable. Divide each side of the equation by the coefficient of the variable term.

Example 1

Solve algebraically.

$12 + k = 4 - 3k$

Solution

$12 + k = 4 - 3k$	Collect the k-terms on the left side.
$12 + k + 3k = 4 - 3k + 3k$	To use the Zero Principle, add $3k$ to each side.
$12 + 4k = 4$	Collect the constant terms on the right side.
$12 + 4k - 12 = 4 - 12$	Subtract 12 from each side.
$4k = -8$	Isolate the variable.
$\frac{4k}{4} = \frac{8}{4}$	Divide each side by the coefficient, 4.
$k = -2$	

To check the solution of an equation you have solved:

- Substitute the solution for the variable in each side of the **original** equation.
- Simplify each side of the equation. If the results are the same, the solution is correct.

Example 2

Solve algebraically. Check the solution.

$3x - 17 = 28$

Solution

$$3x - 17 = 28$$
$$3x - 17 + 17 = 28 + 17 \qquad \text{Add 17 to each side.}$$
$$3x = 45$$

$$\frac{3x}{3} = \frac{45}{3} \qquad \text{Divide each side by 3.}$$

$$x = 15$$

Check.

Substitute $x = 15$ in each side of the original equation: $3x - 17 = 28$

Left side $= 3x - 17$ Right side $= 28$
$$= 3(15) - 17$$
$$= 45 - 17$$
$$= 28$$

Since both sides are equal, $x = 15$ is correct.

Discuss

Describe the steps for substituting a solution in an equation to check.

We can use an equation to model a situation and solve a related problem.

Example 3

Nasmin has \$15 and saves \$4 per week. Her savings, N dollars, after w weeks can be modelled by the equation $N = 15 + 4w$.

Mayumi has \$24 and saves \$3 per week. Her savings, M dollars, after w weeks can be modelled by the equation $M = 24 + 3w$.

a) How much will each girl have after 5 weeks?

b) Who will be the first to have \$55 for a computer game?

Solution

a) To find how much each girl will have after 5 weeks, substitute $w = 5$, then solve.

For Nasmin:
$$
\begin{aligned}
N &= 15 + 4w \\
&= 15 + 4(5) \\
&= 15 + 20 \\
&= 35
\end{aligned}
$$

Nasmin will have $35 after 5 weeks.

For Mayumi:
$$
\begin{aligned}
M &= 24 + 3w \\
&= 24 + 3(5) \\
&= 24 + 15 \\
&= 39
\end{aligned}
$$

Mayumi will have $39 after 5 weeks.

b) To find how long before each girl has $55, substitute $N = 55$ and $M = 55$, then solve for w.

For Nasmin:
$$
\begin{aligned}
N &= 15 + 4w \\
55 &= 15 + 4w
\end{aligned}
$$

$55 - 15 = 15 + 4w - 15$ Subtract 15 from each side.

$40 = 4w$

$\dfrac{40}{4} = \dfrac{4w}{4}$ Divide each side by 4.

$10 = w$

Nasmin will have $55 after 10 weeks.

For Mayumi:
$$
\begin{aligned}
M &= 24 + 3w \\
55 &= 24 + 3w
\end{aligned}
$$

$55 - 24 = 24 + 3w - 24$ Subtract 24 from each side.

$31 = 3w$

$\dfrac{31}{3} = \dfrac{3w}{3}$ Divide each side by 3.

$10.3 \doteq w$ Use a calculator.

Mayumi will have $55 after 11 weeks.
Nasmin will have $55 first.

Discuss

Why is Mayumi's time not rounded down to 10 weeks?

A   **1.** Solve each equation.

    a) $a + 2 = 5$ **b)** $v - 1 = 4$ **c)** $7 - c = -1$ **d)** $6 + b = 0$

    e) $5 = n - 3$ **f)** $8 = 15 - s$ **g)** $j + 2 = -3$ **h)** $x + 5 = 9$

2. Solve each equation.

    a) $3t = 27$ **b)** $4k = -20$ **c)** $-6 = 3b$ **d)** $-5s = 35$

3. Solve each equation.

    a) $5j = 15$ **b)** $4p = -20$ **c)** $-3s = 9$ **d)** $c - 5 = -2$

    e) $15 - p = 12$ **f)** $a + 6 = 8$ **g)** $-2v = -10$ **h)** $t - 4 = 1$

4. Check whether the solution $x = -3$ is correct for each equation.

    a) $9x = 27$ **b)** $4 + x = 1$ **c)** $3x + 5 = -4$ **d)** $7x = -21$

    e) $2x - 3 = 3$ **f)** $-9 = 3 + 4x$ **g)** $-x = -3$ **h)** $6 - x = 3$

5. Solve. Check by substituting.

    a) $4v = 12$ **b)** $j + 27 = 30$ **c)** $24 - p = 20$ **d)** $-4c = -28$

    e) $q + 7 = 11$ **f)** $36 = -4h$ **g)** $-5g = 3$ **h)** $c - 5 = 6$

B   **6. Knowledge/Understanding** Solve each equation.

    a) $4x = -28$ **b)** $3a - 1 = 20$ **c)** $12 + 5y = -13$

    d) $7p + 14 = 0$ **e)** $8z - 42 = 2z$ **f)** $3f = 12f + 21$

7. Solve each equation.

    a) $-3 + x = -4x - 43$ **b)** $12m - 25 = 4m + 7$ **c)** $2e - 6 = -5 - 4e$

    d) $24 - 4c = 15 - c$ **e)** $6b - 8 = 4 - 3b$ **f)** $-5b + 9 = 3b - 15$

8. Solve each equation. Check the solution.

    a) $7 = 23 - 4x$ **b)** $3a - 10 = 10$ **c)** $8 - 2z = 5 + 3z$

    d) $4m + 9 = 2m$ **e)** $12x + 17 = 10 - 2x$ **f)** $5 - 3k = -4$

9. Solve each equation. Check each solution.

    a) $5x + 4 = 40$ **b)** $9 - 2a = a + 5$ **c)** $2 - 4x = 1 - x$

    d) $3 + 7c = 2c - 3$ **e)** $2 = 9a - 3$ **f)** $5 - 6n = 2n + 5$

10. Lester has $53 in savings. Each week he saves $16. His total savings are modelled by the equation $S = 53 + 16n$, where S is his savings in dollars, and n is the number of weeks.

    a) To determine how much money Lester will have after 3 weeks, substitute $n = 3$. Calculate S.

    b) Lester wants to buy a pair of in-line skates for $165, including taxes. To find how many weeks it will take him to save $165, substitute $S = \$165$. Solve for n.

11. Callum drove at an average speed of 90 km/h. The distance Callum drove can be modelled by the equation $d = 90t$, where d kilometres is the distance driven and t hours is the length of time.

    a) How far had Callum travelled after each length of time?
       i) 1 h   **ii)** 3 h   **iii)** 5 h   **iv)** 6 h

    b) How many hours had Callum driven to travel each distance?
       i) 180 km   **ii)** 225 km   **iii)** 360 km   **iv)** 315 km

    c) What assumptions did you make in parts a and b? How reasonable do you think these assumptions are?

12. The cost, C dollars, to produce a school yearbook is modelled by the equation $C = 8000 + 9n$, where n is the number of yearbooks printed.

a) What does each term on the right side of the equation represent?

b) The yearbook committee has a budget of $10 000. Calculate the number of yearbooks produced for $10 000. Substitute $C = 10\,000$, then solve for n.

c) How many yearbooks are produced for $20 000?

13. Application Volcanoes and geysers illustrate that Earth's interior is very hot. The equation $T = 10d + 20$ is used to estimate the temperature, T degrees Celsius, at a depth of d kilometres.

a) What does each term on the right side of the equation represent?

b) To estimate the depth where the temperature is 50°C, substitute $T = 50$, then solve for d.

c) Estimate the depth for each temperature.
  i) 60°C   ii) 90°C   iii) 80°C   iv) 70°C

d) At what depth is the temperature 100°C?

e) Order the depths in parts b to d from least to greatest. Explain whether this order is reasonable for the given temperatures.

14. Thinking/Inquiry/Problem Solving

a) A rectangular field is 135 m long and requires 450 m of fencing to enclose it. Calculate the width of the field.

b) Another field is 45 m wide and requires 380 m of fencing. How long is the field?

c) Explain how you calculated each length in parts a and b.

15. Communication Suppose a classmate phones you for help to solve this equation: $3x + 7 = x - 5$. Explain how you would solve the equation over the phone.

16. One side of a rectangle is 6 cm. The perimeter of the rectangle is numerically equal to its area.

a) What do you think "numerically equal" means?

b) Find the lengths of the other sides of the rectangle.

c) Verify your answer by calculating the perimeter and area of the rectangle.

3.4   Simplifying Equations before Solving

In Section 3.3, we solved equations by collecting like terms. In this section, we will use the distributive law to simplify equations, before solving.

Example 1

Solve.

a) $2(3m - 4) = 10$ **b)** $9 = -4(2t - 7)$

Solution

a) $2(3m - 4) = 10$ Use the distributive law.
$2(3m) - 2(4) = 10$
$6m - 8 = 10$

$6m - 8 + 8 = 10 + 8$ Add 8 to each side.
$6m = 18$

$\dfrac{6m}{6} = \dfrac{18}{6}$ Divide each side by 6.
$m = 3$

b) $9 = -4(2t - 7)$ Use the distributive law.
$9 = -4(2t) - 4(-7)$
$9 = -8t + 28$

$9 - 28 = -8t + 28 - 28$ Subtract 28 from each side.
$-19 = -8t$

$\dfrac{-19}{-8} = \dfrac{-8t}{-8}$ Divide each side by -8.
$\dfrac{-19}{-8} = t$

$t = \dfrac{19}{8}$, or 2.375

Discuss
How could you check each solution?

Example 2

Solve $3(a - 3) + 4a + 7 = 5a - 3$.
Check the solution.

Solution

$$3(a - 3) + 4a + 7 = 5a - 3 \qquad \text{Use the distributive law.}$$
$$3a - 9 + 4a + 7 = 5a - 3$$
$$7a - 2 = 5a - 3$$
$$7a - 2 + 2 = 5a - 3 + 2 \qquad \text{Add 2 to each side.}$$
$$7a = 5a - 1$$
$$7a - 5a = 5a - 1 - 5a \qquad \text{Subtract } 5a \text{ from each side.}$$
$$2a = -1$$
$$\frac{2a}{2} = \frac{-1}{2} \qquad \text{Divide each side by 2.}$$
$$a = -\frac{1}{2}$$

Check.
Substitute $a = -\frac{1}{2}$ in each side of the equation.

Left side $= 3(a - 3) + 4a + 7$ $\qquad$ Right side $= 5a - 3$

$$= 3\left(-\frac{1}{2} - 3\right) + 4\left(-\frac{1}{2}\right) + 7 \qquad\qquad = 5\left(-\frac{1}{2}\right) - 3$$
$$= 3\left(-\frac{1}{2} - \frac{6}{2}\right) - 2 + 7 \qquad\qquad\quad = -\frac{5}{2} - 3$$
$$= 3\left(-\frac{7}{2}\right) + 5 \qquad\qquad\qquad\quad = -\frac{5}{2} - \frac{6}{2}$$
$$= -\frac{21}{2} + \frac{10}{2} \qquad\qquad\qquad\qquad = -\frac{11}{2}$$
$$= -\frac{11}{2}$$

Or use a calculator.

Left side

Press: 3 `(` `(-)` 1 `A%` 2 `-` 3
`)` `+` 4 `(` `(-)` 1 `A%`
2 `)` `+` 7 `ENTER =`

```
3(-1⌍2-3)+4(-1⌍2)+7
              -5⌍1/2
```

Right side

Press: 5 `(` `(-)` 1 `A%` 2 `)`
`-` 3 `ENTER =`

```
5(-1⌍2)-3
              -5⌍1/2
```

Since both sides are equal, $a = -\frac{1}{2}$ is correct.

Discuss

What happens if you substitute $a = -0.5$ in each side of the equation? Why?

A 1. Solve each equation.

a) $4b - 8b = 24$ b) $-27 = -9t + 6t + 3$ c) $13 + 4q = -2q + 12 + q$

d) $24 - 6j = 36$ e) $7 + 7k = 2k - 8$ f) $6s - 30 = 24$

✓ 2. Solve.

a) $4x + 6x = -20$ b) $50 = 8x - x + 1$

c) $3x - 2 + x = 5 + 7x - 3$ d) $3x + x = 6 - x$

3. Solve. Check each solution.

a) $5c + 2c + 6 = 34$ b) $4y - 7y = 18$

c) $12 = 2x - 7x - 8$ d) $-10 = -n + 2 - 2n$

✓ 4. Solve.

a) $2(x + 1) = 4$ b) $3(x + 1) = 6$ c) $4(x + 1) = 8$

d) $5(x + 1) = 10$ e) $6(x + 1) = 12$ f) $7(x + 1) = 14$

5. Solve.

a) $-2(x + 1) = 4$ b) $-3(x + 1) = 6$ c) $-4(x + 1) = 8$

d) $-5(x + 1) = 10$ e) $-6(x + 1) = 12$ f) $-7(x + 1) = 14$

✓ 6. Solve.

a) $4 = 2(x - 1)$ b) $6 = 3(x - 1)$ c) $8 = 4(x - 1)$

d) $10 = 5(x - 1)$ e) $12 = 6(x - 1)$ f) $14 = 7(x - 1)$

B 7. Solve.

a) $2(x - 4) = 10$ b) $5(x - 6) = -15$ c) $2(4 - 3m) = 13$

d) $-3(n + 2) = 12$ e) $7 = -2(-3 - y)$ f) $3(2t + 6) = 0$

8. **Knowledge/Understanding** Solve. Check each solution.

a) $7x - 3x + 5 = 7$ b) $6 = 4x - x + 9$

c) $3(n + 2) = 21$ d) $-(3d + 4) = 5(2 - d)$

9. Solve each equation.

a) $9x - 1 - 7x - 4 = 5x$ b) $3(1 - 2y) + y = 2$ c) $4 = 6 - 2(x + 1)$

d) $-3(2 - a) - a = 1$ e) $-2(3n - 1) + 2n = 4$ f) $2(p + 1) = 3(p - 1)$

✓ 10. **Communication** When checking a solution, is it better to substitute the solution in the original equation? Why should each side be simplified separately when checking? Use an example in your explanation.

11. **Application** Keyboarding speed, S, is measured in words per minute. It is calculated using the equation $5S = w - 10e$, where w is the number of words typed in 5 min and e is the number of errors.

   a) Marti typed 275 words in 5 min and made 8 errors. Substitute $w = 275$ and $e = 8$. What was her speed?

   b) In keyboarding, a word is 5 characters. So, the number of words typed is $\dfrac{\text{the number of characters}}{5}$. Boris typed 1250 characters in 5 min. He had a speed of 40 words/min. Substitute for w and S. How many errors did he make?

   c) Jake made 3 errors in 5 min and had a speed of 30 words/min. How many words did he type?

✓ 12. **Thinking/Inquiry/Problem Solving** A store hires students to replace employees who are on vacation. A student worked for 7 h, 3 h, 6 h, and 5 h at an hourly rate and received a $20 bonus. The amount earned was $188.

   a) Write an equation that can be used to solve for the hourly rate.

   b) Find the hourly rate.

   c) Use your general knowledge to explain whether your solution is reasonable.

C 13. In the 1970s, Canada started using the Celsius scale for temperature instead of the Fahrenheit scale. An approximate rule for converting Celsius to Fahrenheit is "Double the temperature in degrees Celsius then add 30." This rule is modelled by the equation $F = 2C + 30$, where F is a temperature in degrees Fahrenheit and C is a temperature in degrees Celsius.

   a) Use the equation to estimate each temperature in degrees Fahrenheit.

   i) $6°C$ ii) $28°C$ iii) $0°C$ iv) $-20°C$

   b) Use the equation to estimate each temperature in degrees Celsius.

   i) $-5°F$ ii) $80°F$ iii) $-30°F$ iv) $54°F$

   c) Use the thermometer at the right to estimate each temperature from parts a and b.

   d) Compare the advantages of using an equation to model the relationship between Fahrenheit and Celsius temperatures with the advantages of reading a thermometer. Explain why both methods result in estimated temperatures.

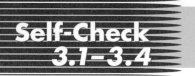

1. Use the distributive law to expand.

   a) $4(3 + 2)$ b) $-5(-2 + 1)$ c) $-(-6 - 4)$

   d) $5(2 - 3y)$ e) $-(6j + 2)$ f) $-7(-3 - 4p)$

2. Combine like terms.

   a) $5a - a + 4$ b) $6k - 3 + 1 - 2k$ c) $7 + 2 - 4b + 1 - b$

3. Simplify each expression. Find its value when $x = -2$.

   a) $2x - 7 + 1 - 3x$ b) $4x - x + 2 + 5$ c) $-8 - 5x + 3 - 2x + x$

   d) $1 - 4x + 2(3x - 1)$ e) $4(6 - x) + 4$ f) $3x - 4(2x - 4) - 2$

4. Solve.

   a) $8x = -24$ b) $7 + a = -2$ c) $b - 3 = 0$

   d) $n - 1 = 5$ e) $42 = -6z$ f) $2c = -1$

5. Solve. Check each solution.

   a) $2m + 1 = -3$ b) $k + 9 = 2k$ c) $1 - 4y = 13$

   d) $7 = 4 - 3b$ e) $8 - j = j + 4$ f) $-3p + 2 = -p + 6$

6. Solve.

   a) $8 = 2(x + 4)$ b) $-(x + 1) = 15$ c) $4(x - 3) = -1$

   d) $3(2 + x) = -3$ e) $16 = -2(x - 4)$ f) $-5(x - 2) = 0$

7. Solve. Check each solution.

   a) $2(g - 6) = -4$ b) $5(x - 3) = 1 + x$

   c) $-2(3 - c) = -3(2c + 1)$ d) $a + 3 = 2(a - 1)$

Preparation for Ontario Testing

8. The total earnings, E dollars, a bike courier earns is made up of a daily flat rate of $25, plus $8 per delivery, where d represents the number of deliveries. Which equation represents this relationship?

   a) $E = 25d + 8$

   b) $E = 25 + 8d$

   c) $E = d(25 + 8)$

   d) $E = 25 + 8$

3.5 Solving Problems Using Algebraic Modelling

Suppose this pattern of figures continues. One figure will have 20 blue squares. How many green squares will it have?

To solve this problem, we could continue to draw all the figures until we reach the figure with 20 blue squares. This could be tedious.
Another way is to write an equation that relates the number of blue and green squares in each figure.

In each figure, there are 4 more blue squares than green squares.
Let g represent the number of green squares.
Let b represent the number of blue squares.
The number of blue squares is 4 more than the number of green squares: $b = 4 + g$

For 20 blue squares, $b = 20$; so, substitute $b = 20$.
The equation becomes $20 = 4 + g$.
Solve this equation: $20 - 4 = g$
$$g = 16$$
There will be 16 green squares in the figure with 20 blue squares.

We can solve a problem in many ways. One method is to model the situation with an equation. To use an equation:

• Use a variable to represent the unknown quantity.

• Express any other unknown quantities in terms of this variable, if possible.

• Write an equation, then solve it.

• State the answer to the problem.

• Check the answer by substituting it in the problem. Also check that the solution is reasonable.

Example

Every October, Canine Vision Canada sponsors a national Walk-a-dog-a-thon. Ashok and Lisa took part in the walk-a-thon. They walked a total distance of 14 km. Lisa dropped out after twisting her ankle during the walk. Ashok finished the walk. He walked 6 km farther than Lisa. How far did Lisa walk?

Solution

Let x kilometres represent the distance Lisa walked.
Since Ashok walked 6 km farther than Lisa, the distance Ashok walked is $(x + 6)$ kilometres.
The total distance they walked is 14 km. So,
Distance Lisa walked + Distance Ashok walked = 14

$$x + (x + 6) = 14$$
$$2x + 6 = 14 \qquad \text{Solve this equation.}$$
$$2x + 6 - 6 = 14 - 6$$
$$2x = 8$$
$$\frac{2x}{2} = \frac{8}{2}$$
$$x = 4$$

Lisa walked 4 km.

Check.
Ashok walked 4 km + 6 km = 10 km.
The total distance was 4 km + 10 km = 14 km.
The solution is correct.

Discuss

What other way could you check the solution?

3.5   Exercises

B

✓

1. **Knowledge/Understanding** Suppose a person earns e dollars per hour. Write an expression for each amount.

   a) the amount earned for 1 hour plus a bonus of $5

   b) the amount earned for 3 h

   c) the amount earned for 1 hour less a deduction of $3

   d) the amount earned for 2 h plus $10 commission

   e) the amount earned for 5 h less $5 spent on transportation

2. Ravi is 8 years older than Natasha. Let Natasha's age be a years.

   a) The expression for Ravi's age is ☐ years.

   b) The expression for the sum of Ravi's and Natasha's ages is ☐ years.

   c) The sum of their ages is 42. Find their ages.

3. The ages of Kirsten and Victor total 27 years. Let y years represent Kirsten's age.

   a) The expression for Victor's age is ☐ years.

   b) The expression for twice Kirsten's age is ☐ years.

   c) Victor's age plus twice Kirsten's age is 43. Find Kirsten's and Victor's ages.

4. The combined mass of a dog and a cat is 28 kg. Let the cat's mass be m kilograms.

   a) The expression for the dog's mass is ☐ kilograms.

   b) The expression for three times the cat's mass is ☐ kilograms.

   c) The dog is three times as heavy as the cat. Find the mass of the dog and of the cat.

5. Lesley's mass is 7.5 kg less than her twin brother Shelby's. Let s kilograms represent Shelby's mass.

   a) Lesley's mass is ☐ kilograms.

   b) The sum of their masses is ☐ kilograms.

   c) The sum of their masses is 116.5 kg. Find the mass of Lesley and of Shelby.

6. Let n represent the number of fish in Linda's aquarium.

   a) **i)** John's aquarium has 3 more fish than Linda's. Write an expression for the number of fish in John's aquarium.

   ii) Suppose John's aquarium has 11 fish. Write an equation. Use it to find the number of fish in Linda's aquarium.

   b) **i)** Adriana's aquarium has twice as many fish as Linda's. Write an expression for the number of fish in Adriana's aquarium.

   ii) Suppose Adriana's aquarium has 24 fish. Write an equation. Use it to find the number of fish in Linda's aquarium.

   c) **i)** Brett's aquarium has one-third as many fish as Linda's. Write an expression for the number of fish in Brett's aquarium.

   ii) Suppose Brett's aquarium has 9 fish. Write an equation. Use it to find the number of fish in Linda's aquarium.

7. Members of the school band sold chocolate bars to raise money. Livio sold twice as many bars as Shaun. They sold a total of 48 bars. How many did each boy sell?

8. **Thinking/Inquiry/Problem Solving** Find two consecutive numbers with the sum 273.

9. Marisa and Sandy ran as far as they could in 30 min. Sandy ran 2 km farther than Marisa. They ran a total distance of 9 km. How far did each run?

10. **Communication** Jaquie and her brother Michel entered a weekend fishing derby. The mass of fish Jaquie caught was four times the mass of Michel's catch. Their total catch was 25 kg. Explain how to use an equation to find the mass of fish each person caught.

11. A package deal for skis and boots costs $225. The skis cost $60 more than the boots. How much do the skis cost?

12. **Application** A movie and popcorn cost $14. The movie costs $5 more than the popcorn.

   a) Model this relationship with an equation to find the cost of the movie.

   b) Explain how you could reason out the solution from part a to find the cost of the movie. Why does your reasoning make sense?

   c) Suppose the movie cost $7 more than the popcorn. Use your method from part a or b to find the cost of the movie.

   d) Suppose the movie cost $3 more than the popcorn. Use the costs from parts b and c to explain what the cost of the movie would be.

   e) Choose a solution strategy you used for this exercise and explain an advantage of it.

13. Zelma used 500 cm of trim to frame a banner. The banner is 22 cm wide. How long can it be?

   22 cm

14. A cord with a length of 118 cm is cut into two pieces. One piece is 18 cm longer than the other. How long are the pieces?

15. An airplane travels eight times as fast as a car. The difference in their speeds is 420 km/h. How fast does each vehicle travel?

3.6   Estimating Heights

On page 93, you considered the following problem.

A radius bone from the lower arm of a human was discovered at an excavation site. It measured 24.5 cm. Andrew's task is to use this measurement to determine the approximate height of the person. How can he solve this problem?

In this section, you will consider some models for solving this problem.

Using a Measuring Model

Work with a partner. You will need a tape measure or metre stick.

1. It is impossible to measure your radius bone because you are not a skeleton. So, we measure the lower arm instead. To measure the lower arm, place your hand flat against a wall. Your partner will measure from your wrist to the tip of your elbow. Record the length in the table.

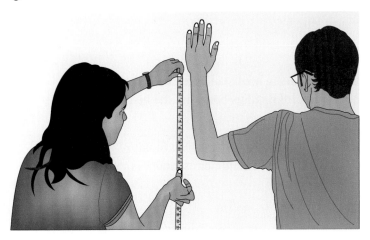

2. Measure and record your heights, in centimetres.

3. Combine your data with those of other students in your group or class. Record the data in a table.

Females		Males	
Length of Lower Arm (cm)	Height (cm)	Length of Lower Arm (cm)	Height (cm)

4. Does your data include a lower arm length of 24.5 cm? If so, what might be the answer to the problem? If not, explain how you might use your data to approximate the answer.

Using a Graphical Model

You will need two sheets of grid paper; one for the female data, and the other for the male data. Construct each graph using the following steps.

5. a) Draw axes on a grid. Label *Height* (*cm*) vertically.
   Label *Length of lower arm* (*cm*) horizontally.

   b) Determine a scale for the graph. Label the origin 0.
   Use the same scale for both axes. Write a title for your graph.

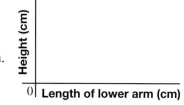

   c) Plot the data.
   i) What do you notice about the points on your graph?
   ii) Draw the best straight line through the points.

   d) Look at the line. What happens to the height as the length of the lower arm increases?

   e) What is the relationship between a person's height and the length of their lower arm? Explain.

   f) How can you use your graph to solve Andrew's problem?

   g) Suppose you know a person's height. How could you use the graph to determine her or his lower arm length?

Using an Algebraic Model

Scientists have taken measurements from many adults and then used the data to find a relationship between the length of the radius bone and the height for females and males.

The formulas for females and males are given below. In each formula, r represents the length of a person's radius bone, in centimetres, and h is the person's approximate height, in centimetres.

Female: $h = 3.34r + 81.2$ Male: $h = 3.27r + 85.9$

6. a) A female has a radius bone that measures 21.6 cm. Determine her height. Will a male have the same height? Justify your answer.

   b) Use the algebraic model to solve Andrew's problem. Estimate the height of the person if the radius bone is from a female and if the radius bone is from a male.

   c) i) Choose a lower arm length from the female data you collected. Substitute this value into the formula for females. What value do you get for the height?
   ii) Compare this number with the height measurement recorded in your table. Are they the same?

   d) Repeat part c for a lower arm length from the male data.

7. Communication You have considered 3 models: measuring, graphical, and algebraic. Which model would you choose to solve a problem similar to Andrew's? Justify your choice.

Distributive Law

- $a(b + c) = ab + ac$
- $a(b - c) = ab - ac$ where a, b, and c are any real numbers

Terms

- A variable term contains a variable, for example, $2x$ and $-x$.
- A constant term does not contain a variable, for example, 7 and -3.
- Like terms contain the same variable and can be combined.

The Zero Principle

- Any two opposite terms have the sum 0.

Solving Equations

- Collect like terms with variable terms on one side of the equation and constant terms on the other side.
- Simplify each side.
- Divide each side by the coefficient of the variable term.

Algebraic Modelling

- Use a variable to represent the unknown quantity.
- Express other unknown quantities in terms of the variable.
- Write, then solve, an equation.
- State the answer.

3.1

1. Which two expressions in each set are equal? Use the distributive law to justify your answers.

   a) $7x - 5$ $-(7x + 5)$ $5 - 7x$ $-7x - 5$

   b) $-(4y - 1)$ $-4y - 1$ $-4y + 1$ $-(-4y + 1)$

   c) $-3(b - 6)$ $-3b - 18$ $3b - 18$ $3(b - 6)$

   d) $-7(2s + 7)$ $-7(2s - 7)$ $-14s + 49$ $14s - 49$

2. Use the distributive law to expand.

   a) $5(1 + 6)$ b) $-9(4 - 7)$ c) $-4(-2 - 10)$

   d) $3(-5 + 9)$ e) $-(3 + 5 - 6)$ f) $8(-1 + 8 - 4)$

3. Expand.

a) $4(q + 4)$ **b)** $-3(-d + 5)$ **c)** $2(2x + 9)$

d) $-5(6 - 5a)$ **e)** $-8(-3s - 6)$ **f)** $-7(1 - 7r)$

3.2 **4. Combine like terms.**

a) $8y + 2y$ **b)** $2 + 4a - 3$ **c)** $s - 1 - 2s + 3$

d) $2x + 7 + 3x - 5$ **e)** $3m - 12 - 7m + 2$ **f)** $-3(2q - 5) + 8q - 9$

5. Simplify.

a) $4y - 11 - 9y + 16$ **b)** $5t - 2(3 + 9t)$ **c)** $-2(4m - 7) - 13$

d) $5(2x - 3) + 10 - 3x$ **e)** $-3 - x + 2(5x - 4)$ **f)** $7(2x - 3) - 5 - 2x$

6. Simplify. Find each value when $x = 4$.

a) $5x + 2x + 1$ **b)** $8x - 3 + 4x + 9$ **c)** $2x - 7 - 6x + 3$

d) $x - 4x + 3x - x$ **e)** $-3(x + 2) - 4x$ **f)** $2x + 11 - 4(3x + 7)$

7. Simplify. Find each value when $x = -3$.

a) $8 + 3x - 2x$ **b)** $5x + x - 1 + 3$ **c)** $-2 + x - 4 + 2x$

d) $3x - 2 + 4(x - 5)$ **e)** $4 - 5x - (x + 2)$ **f)** $-3(4x + 1) - (-7x - 5)$

3.3 **8. Solve.**

a) $6c = -6$ **b)** $m + 2 = 0$ **c)** $y - 1 = 4$

d) $2 = 5 + t$ **e)** $p - 3 = 10$ **f)** $9g = 81$

g) $5 - u = 4$ **h)** $-32 = 4w$ **i)** $5h = -1$

9. Solve.

a) $3x + 2 = 8$ **b)** $2x - 3 = 1$ **c)** $7 - 4x = -5$

d) $3x + 4 = 2x - 3$ **e)** $2x - 5 = 6x + 7$ **f)** $3x - 1 = 5x - 9$

g) $12 + 4x = 5x + 8$ **h)** $-3x + 4 = -5x + 10$ **i)** $-7 - 3x = 8 + 2x$

10. Solve each equation. Check each solution.

a) $2x + 7 = 17$ **b)** $3 - 2x = 15$ **c)** $-40 = -4 + 4x$

d) $3x - 2 = 5x + 8$ **e)** $7 - 5x = 6 + x$ **f)** $-11 + 6x = -6x + 13$

3.4 **11. Solve.**

a) $2(x + 1) = 4$ **b)** $-(x - 2) = -3$ **c)** $-2(x + 3) = -8$

d) $6 = 3(x - 1)$ **e)** $4(x + 4) = 8$ **f)** $9 = -3(x - 5)$

g) $-(x - 1) = -1$ **h)** $3 = 2(x + 2)$ **i)** $3(x - 2) = -4$

12. Solve each equation.

a) $3(a + 2) = 2$ b) $-(g - 1) = 7$ c) $2(n - 4) = 0$

d) $-2(k + 3) = -3$ e) $4(2b + 1) = 9b$ f) $5(j - 2) = -3$

g) $3 = 4(y + 2)$ h) $-2 = -(3x - 1)$ i) $0 = 3(-r + 1)$

13. Solve each equation. Check each solution.

a) $2(x + 1) = 3(x - 2)$ b) $5(2x - 3) = 10$

c) $4(-2 - x) = -5(2x + 4)$ d) $-2(1 - x) = 3(2 - x)$

3.5 **14.** The difference between two masses is 5 kg. Let m kilograms represent the lighter mass.

a) An expression for the heavier mass is ☐ kilograms.

b) An expression for twice the lighter mass is ☐ kilograms.

c) The heavier mass plus twice the lighter mass is 20 kg. Find the masses.

15. For two consecutive numbers, the sum of the smaller number plus twice the larger number is 38. What are the numbers?

16. a) The length of a rectangle is 3 cm greater than the width. Let w centimetres represent the width. Write an expression for the length.

b) Write an expression for the length plus the width.

c) Write an expression for the perimeter.

d) The perimeter is 18 cm. Use this measure and the expression in part c to write an equation.

e) Solve the equation to find the width.

f) What is the length of the rectangle?

g) Sketch the rectangle and check your solution.

17. The length of a rectangle is 5 cm longer than the width. The perimeter is 54 cm. What are the dimensions of the rectangle?

18. An apple orchard sells baskets of Macintosh and Delicious apples. The orchard has 8 times as many baskets of Macintosh apples as Delicious apples. The orchard has a total of 153 baskets of apples. How many baskets of each type are there?

1. Expand.

   a) $2(j - 5)$ **b)** $-(4m + 1)$ **c)** $-3(6 - 2g)$

   d) $5(3a - 3)$ **e)** $-4(-2 + 7s)$ **f)** $6(5r - 4)$

2. **Knowledge/Understanding** Simplify.

   a) $4b + b - 2$ **b)** $6 - 3d + 2 + d$ **c)** $-n + 5 - 2n + 3n$

   d) $6(f - 3) + 1$ **e)** $-(4 - 3e) - 5 + e$ **f)** $1 + 2(t + 3) - 3(t - 4)$

3. Solve. Check each solution.

   a) $x + 4 = -2$ **b)** $8 - k = 9$ **c)** $-3h = 30$

   d) $2f - 7 = 5$ **e)** $6 + 3y = -8 + 2y$ **f)** $1 + 4j = 2j - 9$

4. Solve.

   a) $2(x - 3) = 6$ **b)** $7 = -(x + 1)$

   c) $5x = 2x + 3(2x + 1)$ **d)** $-2(x - 5) = x - 2$

5. Solve.

   a) $-x + 4(x - 1) = 4x$ **b)** $1 + x = 5(x - 3)$

   c) $4 - (x + 4) = -1$ **d)** $4(x + 2) = 6 - 2(2x + 1)$

6. **Communication** Explain why substituting a solution in the original equation provides a method of checking whether the solution for an equation is correct. Use an equation from one of these exercises to illustrate your answer.

7. **Thinking/Inquiry/Problem Solving** Write two different equations that have the solution $x = -1$. Solve each equation to check.

8. Gerri earned $20 more cutting lawns on Tuesday than on Monday. She earned a total of $140 on these two days. Write then solve an equation to find how much Gerri earned each day.

9. **Application** The perimeter of a rectangle is 40 cm. The difference between the lengths of the longer and shorter sides is 6 cm. Write then solve an equation to find the lengths of the sides. Illustrate your solution with a diagram and explain why it is reasonable.

10.

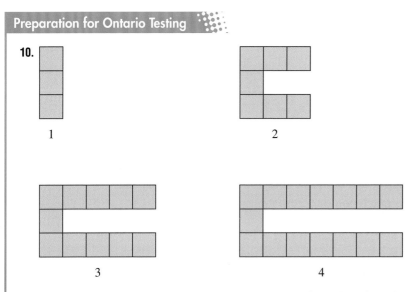

1   2

3   4

After looking at the diagrams above, Anya realized that there is a pattern that can be modelled by the equation, $s = 4d - 1$ where s is the number of small squares, and d is the diagram number.

If the pattern is continued, which diagram number would have 91 squares? Show your work.

11. In this triangle, the largest angle is three times greater than the smallest. The other angle is two times greater than the smallest.

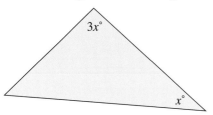

Doug wanted to know the measure of each angle. He started his solution as shown in the above diagram. His friend, Mark, reminded him that the angles in a triangle have to add to 180°.

Complete Doug's solution to find the measure of each angle in the triangle. Show your work.

1. a) A car is travelling at a constant speed on a highway. The driver increases the speed to pass another car, then returns to the original speed. Which graph best describes this motion? Explain.

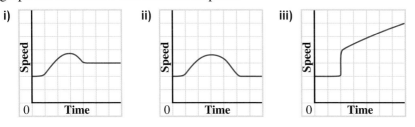

b) Choose a graph from part a that does not describe the motion of the car. Describe a situation the graph could represent.

2. Describe a situation each graph below could represent. State the labels of each axis.

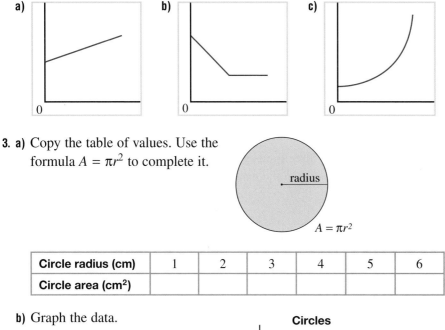

3. a) Copy the table of values. Use the formula $A = \pi r^2$ to complete it.

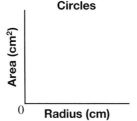

Circle radius (cm)	1	2	3	4	5	6
Circle area (cm²)						

b) Graph the data.

Circles

c) Describe patterns in the table of values. Relate the patterns to the graph.

d) Is the relation linear or non-linear? Explain how you know.

4. A laser printer can print 4 pages of text per minute.

    a) At this rate, how many pages could it print in 5 min?

    b) How long would it take to print a 50-page report?

5. Express as a single power.

    a) $4^1 \times 4^5$ **b)** $(-5)^3 \times (-5)^2$ **c)** $(-3)^4 \times (-3)^5$ **d)** $2^6 \times 2^3$

    e) $(-1)^6 \div (-1)^3$ **f)** $6^7 \div 6^4$ **g)** $\dfrac{4^8}{4^3}$ **h)** $\dfrac{7^5}{7^2}$

6. Evaluate each power.

    a) 5^0 **b)** 3^{-5} **c)** $(-5)^{-1}$ **d)** $(-3)^{-5}$ **e)** 3^0

7. Write in scientific notation.

    a) 2 000 000   **b)** 0.005   **c)** 527 000   **d)** 0.000 431

    e) 0.000 002 5   **f)** 700 120 000   **g)** 19 000   **h)** 0.000 000 16

8. Evaluate.

    a) $\sqrt{16}$ **b)** $\sqrt{4}$ **c)** $\sqrt{49}$ **d)** $\sqrt{64}$ **e)** $\sqrt{144}$

9. Find the square roots of each number. Round to 1 decimal place where necessary.

    a) 25   **b)** 256   **c)** 169   **d)** 90   **e)** 5

10. The bottom of an 8.0-m ladder is 2.0 m from the base of a building. How high up the building does the ladder reach? Round to the nearest tenth of a metre.

11. Each day Naj walks home from school around a field (shown in blue). One day he decides to walk through the field instead of around it (shown in red). Which route is longer? How much longer?

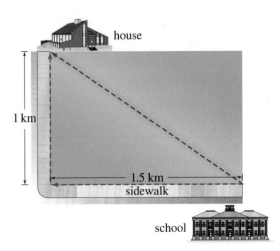

12. Expand using the distributive law.

    a) $3(2x + 7)$ **b)** $-5(4 + 3n)$ **c)** $12(4s - 5)$

    d) $-2(4b - 3)$ **e)** $-(6p + 10)$ **f)** $-6(-3c - 5)$

13. Simplify each expression. Evaluate each expression for the given value.

    a) $5t + 2t - 1 - t$ for $t = 1$

    b) $3(4a - 2) - (a + 3)$ for $a = 5$

    c) $4 + 2(x - 1) - 6x$ for $x = -3$

14. Solve each equation.

    a) $8x = -2$ **b)** $4(a - 10) = 15$ **c)** $2 - y = 16$

    d) $8m + 27 = 3$ **e)** $3(b - 1) = 4$ **f)** $-(3m + 2) = 1$

By the end of this chapter, you will:

- Construct tables of values, graphs, and formulas to represent linear relations.

- Relate straight lines to linear relations and curves to non-linear relations.

- Use a table of values to determine whether a relation is linear or non-linear.

- Compare equations of straight lines and non-linear relations.

- Identify practical situations involving slopes, then calculate the slopes.

- Find the slope of a line segment using the formula: slope $= \dfrac{\text{rise}}{\text{run}}$

- Plot points on a coordinate grid.

- Graph lines by hand and with graphing calculators.

- Communicate solutions with clear reasons.

Designing a Staircase

Have you ever tripped while walking up a flight of stairs?
Careful planning and precise measurement are extremely important when building a staircase.

As you progress through this chapter, you will:

- Relate slopes to staircases.

- Measure staircases, then calculate their slopes.

- Create and interpret diagrams and tables of values for staircases.

- Use slopes to investigate parallel and perpendicular parts of staircases.

- Explain whether your measurements and calculations are reasonable for staircases.

In Section 4.8, you will examine the parts and measurements of a staircase.

Necessary Skills

Simplifying Fractions and Reciprocals

To simplify a fraction, divide the numerator and denominator by the greatest common factor.

Example 1

Simplify.

a) $\dfrac{8}{-4}$ b) $\dfrac{-24}{18}$

Solution

a) $\dfrac{8}{-4} = \dfrac{2}{-1}$ Divide numerator and denominator by 4.

   $= -2$ $2 \div (-1) = -2$

b) $\dfrac{-24}{18} = \dfrac{-4}{3}$ Divide numerator and. denominator by 6.

   $= -\dfrac{4}{3}$

To write the reciprocal of a fraction, turn it upside down.

Example 2

a) Write the reciprocal of $\dfrac{2}{3}$.   b) Write the reciprocal of –4.

Solution

a) The reciprocal of $\dfrac{2}{3}$ is $\dfrac{3}{2}$.

b) Write –4 as $-\dfrac{4}{1}$.

  The reciprocal is $-\dfrac{1}{4}$.

Exercises

1. Simplify.

a) $\dfrac{-4}{2}$ b) $\dfrac{3}{-1}$ c) $\dfrac{12}{6}$ d) $\dfrac{10}{-5}$ e) $\dfrac{8}{4}$ f) $\dfrac{-9}{3}$

2. Write each reciprocal.

a) $\dfrac{4}{7}$ b) $-\dfrac{1}{6}$ c) $\dfrac{4}{3}$ d) –4   e) 1   f) $\dfrac{-5}{8}$

3. Write each reciprocal. If possible, simplify first.

a) –2   b) $\dfrac{1}{5}$ c) $\dfrac{-5}{10}$ d) $\dfrac{8}{12}$

e) 5   f) $\dfrac{-1}{4}$ g) $\dfrac{3}{9}$ h) $\dfrac{8}{-10}$

Order of Operations

The order of operations for whole numbers also applies to integers.

Do the operations within brackets.	**B**rackets
Simplify numbers with exponents.	**E**xponents
Multiply and divide from left to right.	**D**ivision
	Multiplication
Add and subtract from left to right.	**A**ddition
	Subtraction

Division / **M**ultiplication — In the order that they occur, from left to right

Addition / **S**ubtraction — In the order that they occur, from left to right

Example

Simplify.

a) $10 + 3(-4)$ **b)** $3(5) - 4$ **c)** $5(-1) + (-2)^2$

Solution

a) $10 + 3(-4) = 10 - 12$ First multiply: $3(-4)$
$\qquad\qquad\quad = -2$

b) $3(5) - 4 = 15 - 4$ First multiply: $3(5)$
$\qquad\qquad = 11$

c) $5(-1) + (-2)^2 = 5(-1) + (4)$ Calculate: $(-2)^2 = (-2)(-2)$ Next multiply: $5(-1)$
$\qquad\qquad\qquad = -5 + 4$ $\qquad\qquad\qquad\qquad = 4$
$\qquad\qquad\qquad = -1$

Exercises

1. Simplify.

a) $3 + (-2)(4)$ **b)** $3 - (-2)(4)$ **c)** $-3 + (-2)(4)$

d) $3 - (-2)(-4)$ **e)** $-3 - (-2)(-4)$ **f)** $-3 - (2)(4)$

2. Simplify.

a) $5(-1) + 7$ **b)** $(-3)(2) - 10$ **c)** $(-1)(-4) + 2$

d) $(4)(-3) + 22$ **e)** $(-2)^2 + 3(-3)$ **f)** $8(-2) - (-3)^2$

The slant or incline of a roof is its *slope*.

For any incline, we can measure two distances — the rise and the run.

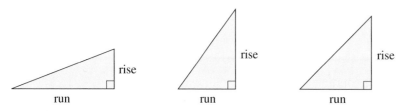

The rise and the run determine the slope of the incline.

INVESTIGATION

The Slope of a Roof

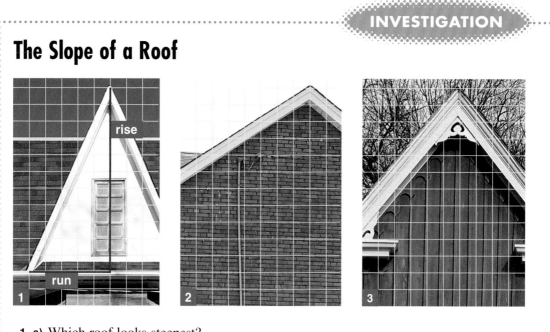

1. **a)** Which roof looks steepest?

   b) Which roof looks the least steep?

   c) List the roofs from steepest to least steep.

2. Picture 1, above, shows the rise and run of the first roof.

   a) Copy this table. Count the squares on the grids to complete the 2nd and 3rd columns.

   b) Record $\frac{rise}{run}$ for each roof to complete the 4th column.

Roof	rise	run	$\dfrac{rise}{run}$	$\dfrac{rise}{run}$ as a decimal
1				
2				
3				

From the *Investigation*, you should have found that the greater the slope, the
steeper the line. The same is true for a line or line segment.

The slope of a line indicates how steep it is.

TAKE NOTE

Slope

$$\text{Slope} = \frac{\text{rise}}{\text{run}}$$

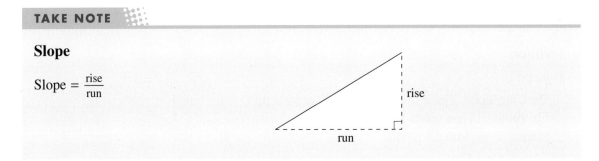

Example 1

Find the slope of each line segment.

a)

b)

Solution

a)

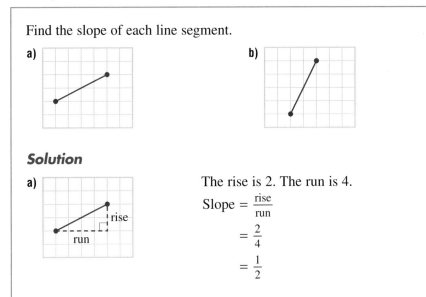

The rise is 2. The run is 4.

$$\text{Slope} = \frac{\text{rise}}{\text{run}}$$

$$= \frac{2}{4}$$

$$= \frac{1}{2}$$

b)

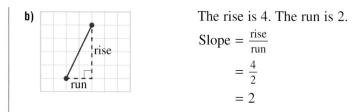

The rise is 4. The run is 2.

$$\text{Slope} = \frac{\text{rise}}{\text{run}}$$

$$= \frac{4}{2}$$

$$= 2$$

Discuss

Which line segment is steeper? How do you know?

Example 2

On grid paper, draw a line segment with each slope.

a) $\frac{3}{5}$ **b)** 4

Solution

a) Slope $= \frac{3}{5}$

Mark any point. The rise is 3, so count 3 squares up.
The run is 5. Then count 5 squares right.
Mark a point. Join the points.

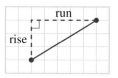

b) Slope $= 4$ or $\frac{4}{1}$

Mark any point. The rise is 4 so count 4 squares up.
The run is 1. Then count 1 square right.
Mark a point. Join the points.

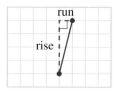

Example 3

Each diagram shows the rise and run
of a wave. Scientists have found that
a wave breaks when its slope is
greater than $\frac{2}{7}$. Find out whether
each wave would break.

a)

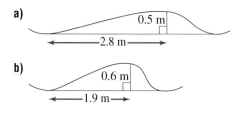

b)

0.6 m

1.9 m

Solution

Find the slope of each wave.

a) Slope $= \dfrac{\text{rise}}{\text{run}}$

$\quad = \dfrac{0.5}{2.8}$

$\quad \doteq 0.179$

b) Slope $= \dfrac{\text{rise}}{\text{run}}$

$\quad = \dfrac{0.6}{1.9}$

$\quad \doteq 0.316$

Compare each slope to $\dfrac{2}{7}$.

$\dfrac{2}{7} \doteq 0.286$

In part a, the slope is less than $\dfrac{2}{7}$ ($0.179 < 0.286$), so the wave does not break.

In part b, the slope is greater than $\dfrac{2}{7}$ ($0.316 > 0.286$), so the wave does break.

4.1   Exercises

A **1.** Identify the rise and run for each slope.

a) $\dfrac{5}{9}$ b) $\dfrac{1}{8}$ c) 4

d) $\dfrac{7}{3}$ e) 1   f) $\dfrac{2}{3}$

2. Sketch a roof with each slope. Label the rise and run in each sketch.

a) $\dfrac{2}{7}$ b) $\dfrac{8}{3}$ c) $\dfrac{1}{5}$

3. Write each slope as a fraction in simplest form or as an integer.

a) $\dfrac{3}{9}$ b) $\dfrac{9}{3}$ c) $\dfrac{8}{12}$ d) $\dfrac{4}{6}$

> To simplify a slope, divide the rise and run by the same factor.

B **4. Knowledge/Understanding** Calculate each slope.

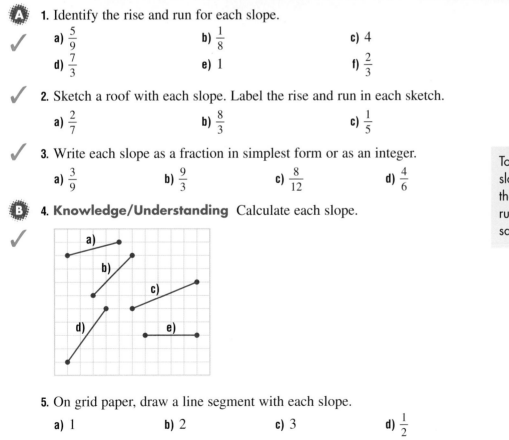

5. On grid paper, draw a line segment with each slope.

a) 1   b) 2   c) 3   d) $\dfrac{1}{2}$

e) $\dfrac{1}{3}$ f) $\dfrac{1}{4}$ g) $\dfrac{2}{3}$ h) $\dfrac{5}{2}$

6. Simplify to find out which slopes are equal.

a) $\frac{6}{18}$ b) $\frac{15}{5}$ c) $\frac{12}{8}$ d) $\frac{1}{3}$ e) $\frac{8}{12}$ f) $\frac{10}{5}$

7. Find the slope of AB in each diagram.

a)   b)

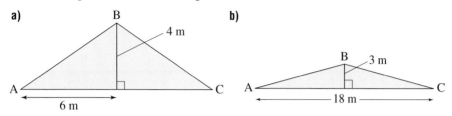

8. Each staircase has a board placed along it. Find the rise, run, and slope for each staircase.

a)   b)

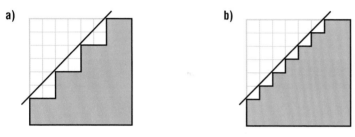

9. Copy each staircase on grid paper. Draw the board that would lie on the staircase. What is the slope of each staircase?

a)   b)

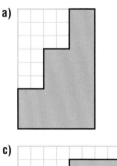

c)

10. a) Pick a staircase in your home or school. Measure its rise and run.

b) Calculate the slope of the staircase.

c) Compare your results with those of your classmates. Discuss similarities and differences.

11. Application This drawing represents the side view of part of a roller coaster. The side of each grid square represents 1 m.

a) Find the height of each hill.

b) Which hill has a steeper climb? How do you know?

c) Explain how two roller-coaster hills can have the same height but not the same steepness.

d) How would the steepness affect the roller coaster's speed?

12. A section of a roller-coaster track rises 25 m over a horizontal distance of 15 m. What is the slope of this section of the track?

13. Communication Explain how the slope of a segment is defined by its rise and run. Include sketches of:

• a slope greater than 1

• a slope equal to 1

• a slope between 0 and 1

14. Thinking/Inquiry/Problem Solving
Draw line segments to show your answers.

a) Suppose the rise of a line segment remains the same, but the run increases. What happens to the slope?

b) Suppose the rise of a line segment decreases, but the run remains the same. Does the slope increase or decrease?

c) Suppose both the rise and run of a line segment are doubled. What happens to the slope? How do you know?

You have worked with both horizontal and vertical number lines.

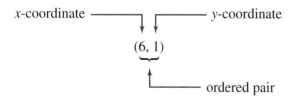

When a vertical number line and a horizontal number line intersect at right angles and at the point zero on each line, they form axes on a *coordinate plane*.

The number lines intersect at the *origin*, which we label zero. The horizontal axis is labelled *x*. The vertical axis is labelled *y*.

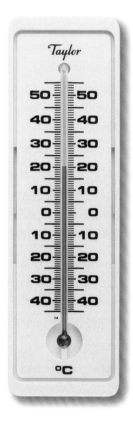

The axes divide the coordinate plane into four sections. These sections are known as *quadrants*. Any point in the plane can be described by its coordinates.

The coordinates of point A are (6, 1). The *x*-coordinate is 6. It represents the distance and direction from zero along the horizontal number line.

The *y*-coordinate is 1. It represents the distance and direction from zero along the vertical number line.

The two coordinates together, (6, 1), are an *ordered pair*.

x-coordinate ⎯⎯⎯⎯⎯⎯⎯⎯⎯⎯⎯ *y*-coordinate

(6, 1)

ordered pair

To plot the point B(−5, −3), begin at the origin. Move 5 units left, then 3 units down. Mark the point B.

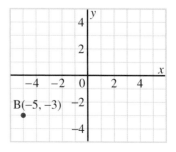

Example

Plot and label each point.

a) A(−3, 2)   b) B(0, 4)   c) C(−1, 0)   d) D(4, −2)

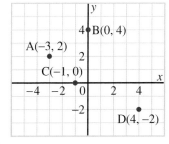

Solution

To plot each point, we can begin at its *x*-coordinate on the *x*-axis.

a) To plot A(−3, 2), begin at −3 on the *x*-axis, then move up
2 units. Label point A.

b) To plot B(0, 4), begin at 0, then move up 4 units. Label point B.

c) To plot C(−1, 0), begin at −1 on the *x*-axis. Since the *y*-coordinate is 0,
we do not move up or down. Label point C at −1 on the *x*-axis.

d) To plot D(4, −2), begin at 4 on the *x*-axis, then move down 2 units.
Label point D.

4.2 Exercises

A

1. Name the coordinates of each point.

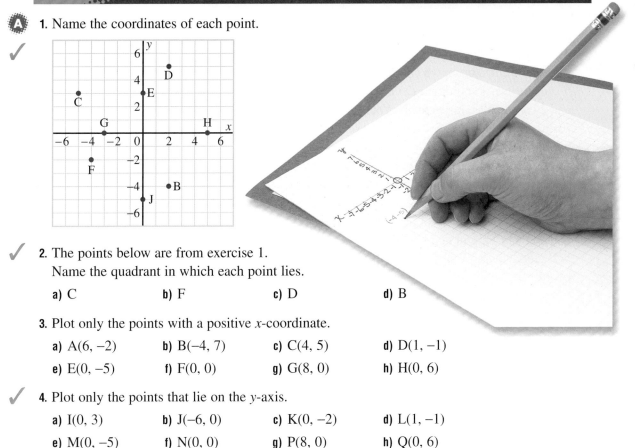

2. The points below are from exercise 1.
Name the quadrant in which each point lies.

a) C   b) F   c) D   d) B

3. Plot only the points with a positive *x*-coordinate.

a) A(6, −2)   b) B(−4, 7)   c) C(4, 5)   d) D(1, −1)

e) E(0, −5)   f) F(0, 0)   g) G(8, 0)   h) H(0, 6)

4. Plot only the points that lie on the *y*-axis.

a) I(0, 3)   b) J(−6, 0)   c) K(0, −2)   d) L(1, −1)

e) M(0, −5)   f) N(0, 0)   g) P(8, 0)   h) Q(0, 6)

5. Plot only the points that lie on the *x*-axis.

a) R(–7, 0)   **b)** S(2, 0)   **c)** T(0, 0)   **d)** U(0, 4)

e) V(–2, 2)   **f)** W(0, –4)   **g)** X(–2, 0)   **h)** Y(0, –7)

6. Plot only the points in quadrant 2.

a) A(4, –2)   **b)** B(–4, –2)   **c)** C(–4, 2)   **d)** D(4, 2)

e) E(–5, –1)   **f)** F(–5, 1)   **g)** G(5, 1)   **h)** H(5, –1)

7. a) Which of these points lie in quadrant 3?
F(8, –3), G(–6, –7), H(7, 1), I(0, –9), J(–8, 6),
K(–7, –9), L(–4, 6), M(8, –9), N(–10, 10)

b) How are all the points in quadrant 3 similar?

8. Plot each set of points to form a figure.

a) Square ABCD: A(1, 1), B(1, 5), C(–3, 5), D(–3, 1)

b) Parallelogram JKLM: J(1, –3), K(5, 1), L(8, 1), M(4, –3)

c) Quadrilateral PQRS: P(–3, 0), Q(–6, –2), R(4, –4), S(10, 0)

9. Activity: Battleship Play with a partner.
Draw axes for 2 coordinate planes. Ensure
each plane has values up to 10 and –10
along the *x*- and *y*-axes, respectively. Draw
five ships anywhere on one coordinate
plane. The ships occupy 6 coordinates,
5 coordinates, 4 coordinates, 3 coordinates,
and 2 coordinates, respectively. Your
partner will also draw five ships on one
coordinate plane. You will try to locate the
positions of your partner's ships. Start by
naming coordinates, for example (2, –4).
If that coordinate locates one of your
partner's ships, she/he will reply "hit."
If there is no ship in that location, she/he
will reply "miss." Your partner will state
coordinates to locate your ships. Take
turns until all of one person's ships have been hit.

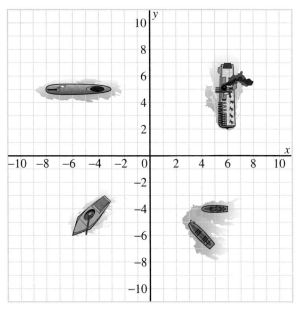

Use the second coordinate plane to mark coordinates you have asked
your partner about. Mark each hit with a checkmark, each miss with an X.
This is your tracking sheet.

10. **Knowledge/Understanding** Plot these points. Join them in order. What figure do you see?

(2, 1), (5, 5), (1, 2), (0, 5), (−1, 2), (−5, 5), (−2, 1), (−5, 0), (−2, −1), (−5, −5), (−1, −2), (0, −5), (1, −2), (5, −5), (2, −1), (5, 0)

11. a) Plot these points. Join them in order. What figure do you see?

(0, 0), (0, 1), (−2, 1), (−2, 2), (−4, 2), (−4, 3), (−6, 3), (−6, 4), (−8, 4), (−8, 5)

b) Continue the pattern in part a for 5 more points. Record the coordinates for these points.

12. What are the coordinates of the point that is on both the *x*-axis and the *y*-axis? What is this point called?

13. **Communication** For each line or quadrant, explain what all the points have in common.

a) on the *x*-axis   b) on the *y*-axis   c) in quadrant 1   d) in quadrant 4

14. **Application** Draw a design on the coordinate plane. Make sure each vertex is at an intersection of grid lines. List the coordinates of the vertices. Exchange coordinates with a partner. Draw the design from your partner's coordinates. Compare designs with those of your partner.

15. For each list:

a)	b)	c)
(−3, 5)	(−3, −5)	(−3, 9)
(−2, 4)	(−2, −3)	(−2, 4)
(−1, 3)	(−1, −1)	(−1, 1)
(0, 2)	(0, 1)	(0, 0)
(1, 1)	(1, 3)	(1, 1)
(2, 0)	(2, 5)	(2, 4)
(3, −1)	(3, 7)	(3, 9)

i) Plot the points on a grid.

ii) Describe the geometric pattern.

iii) Write the coordinates of two other points that fit the pattern.

16. **Thinking/Inquiry/Problem Solving** The points S(2, 2) and T(−2, 2) are two vertices of a square. What are the possible coordinates of the other two vertices? Find as many answers to this question as you can.

In Section 4.1, all the line segments had positive slopes. That is, all the segments rose to the right.

When a line segment falls to the right, it has a negative slope.

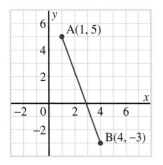

The rise is –5.
The run is 4.
The slope is $\frac{-5}{4}$ or $-\frac{5}{4}$.

We can now find the slope of a line segment on the coordinate plane.

Example 1

Find the slope of line segment AB.

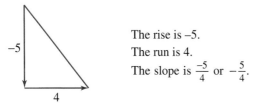

Solution

Count squares vertically from A to B.
The rise is 8 down, or –8.
Count squares horizontally from A to B.
The run is 3 right, or 3.

Slope of AB $= \frac{\text{rise}}{\text{run}}$

$= \frac{-8}{3}$

$= -\frac{8}{3}$

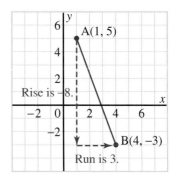

Discuss

What other way could you draw the rise and the run in this diagram?
Find the slope using this new rise and run.

Example 2

Find the slope of each line segment.

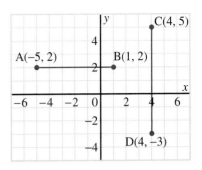

Solution

Since there is no change vertically from A to B, the rise is 0.
Count squares horizontally from A to B.
The run is 6 right, or 6.

Slope of AB $= \dfrac{\text{rise}}{\text{run}}$

$= \dfrac{0}{6}$

$= 0$

Count vertically from C to D. The rise is 8 down, or -8.
Since there is no change horizontally from C to D, the run is 0.

Slope of CD $= \dfrac{\text{rise}}{\text{run}}$

$= \dfrac{-8}{0}$

The denominator is 0, and division by 0 is not defined.
The slope of CD is *undefined*.

Example 2 shows that a horizontal line segment has slope 0, and a vertical line segment has a slope that is undefined.

TAKE NOTE

Slopes of Line Segments

A line segment that *rises* to the right has a *positive* slope.	A line segment that *falls* to the right has a *negative* slope.	The slope of a horizontal line segment is zero.	The slope of a vertical line segment is undefined.
		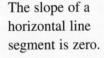	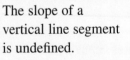

Example 3

This diagram represents a side view of a water coaster.

Find the slope of each segment.

a) AB **b)** BC

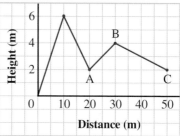

Solution

a) Line segment AB has endpoints A(20, 2) and B(30, 4).

$$\text{Slope of AB} = \frac{\text{rise}}{\text{run}}$$

$$= \frac{2}{10}$$

$$= \frac{1}{5}$$

The slope of AB is $\frac{1}{5}$.

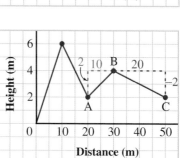

b) Line segment BC has endpoints B(30, 4) and C(50, 2).

$$\text{Slope of BC} = \frac{\text{rise}}{\text{run}}$$

$$= \frac{-2}{20}$$

$$= -\frac{1}{10}$$

The slope of BC is $-\frac{1}{10}$.

1. Find the slope of each line segment.

a)

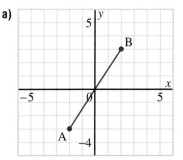

b)

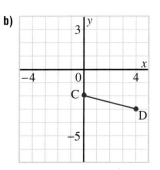

c)

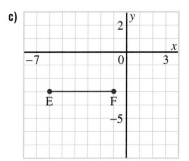

d)

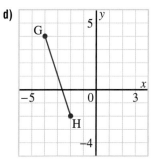

2. Simplify each slope.

a) $\frac{8}{-2}$

b) $\frac{6}{10}$

c) $\frac{-4}{6}$

d) $\frac{3}{-12}$

e) $\frac{-8}{6}$

f) $\frac{5}{10}$

3. a) Which line segments have negative slopes?

b) How are all the line segments with negative slopes similar?

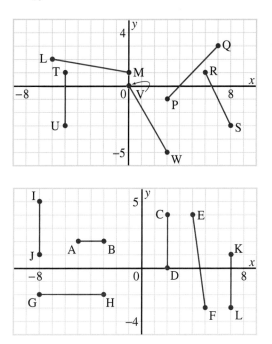

4. a) Which line segments have undefined slopes?

b) How are all the line segments with undefined slopes similar?

5. Find the slope of each line segment.

a)

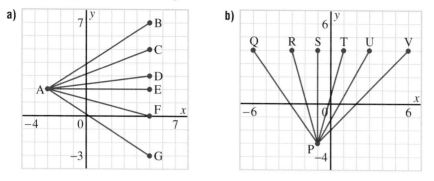

b)

6. Graph each pair of points on a separate grid. Find the slope of AB.

a) A(−7, 4), B(−3, 3)   **b)** A(3, 6), B(3, 1)   **c)** A(1, −5), B(4, −1)

d) A(−3, −4), B(1, −7)   **e)** A(0, 0), B(4, −6)   **f)** A(−8, −4), B(−8, 2)

7. Knowledge/Understanding For each pair of endpoints:

a) A(−2, 7), B(6, −4)   **b)** C(3, −5), D(8, 10)

c) G(−3, 7), H(−3, −7)   **d)** L(2, −7), M(7, −7)

  i) Graph the line segment.
  ii) State whether the line segment rises to the right, falls to the right, is horizontal, or is vertical.
  iii) Find the slope. State whether it is positive, negative, or neither.
  iv) What do you know about the direction of a line segment and its slope?

8. Each set of points represents a triangle. Graph each triangle. Find the slope of each side.

a) A(5, −1), B(0, 4), C(−2, −5)   **b)** R(−3, 4), S(6, 7), T(2, −3)

9. Communication How are line segments with positive slopes different from line segments with negative slopes? Explain using a diagram.

10. This diagram represents a side view of a railway track on a mountain.

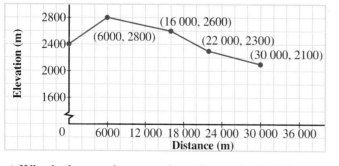

a) Why is there a zigzag mark on the vertical axis?

b) What is the slope of each section of the track?

11. **Application** This diagram represents a side view of a water coaster. The slope of each segment is given. Find the coordinates of each point A to F.

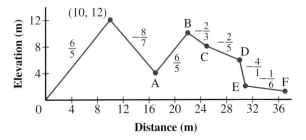

12. **a)** Draw a line segment with each slope. Find the coordinates of the endpoints of each segment.

   i) 3   **ii)** −5   **iii)** $\frac{3}{5}$ **iv)** $-\frac{5}{3}$ **v)** −3   **vi)** 5

   b) Which is the steepest line segment in part a?

   c) Compare your line segments with those of your classmates. Explain any differences.

13. A staircase has three main parts.

   The run or *tread* is the horizontal part of a step.

   The rise or *riser* is the vertical part of a step.

   The *stringers* are the sloping boards running diagonally between floors. The stringers support the staircase.

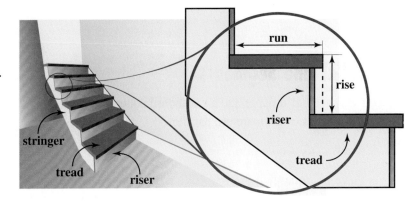

   a) Sketch a staircase on a coordinate plane.

   b) What is the slope of the staircase you sketched in part a?

   c) Compare the slope of the staircase you sketched with those of a few classmates. Explain which staircases might be easier to use.

14. **Thinking/Inquiry/Problem Solving** Use a coordinate plane.

   a) If possible, draw a triangle so that all 3 sides have positive slopes.

   b) If possible, draw a quadrilateral so that 3 sides have positive slopes.

   c) If possible, draw a quadrilateral so that all 4 sides have positive slopes.

   d) For any of parts a to c that you could not draw, explain why. If you drew examples for all 3 parts, explain how you did it.

Lines in the same plane that do not intersect are *parallel lines*.

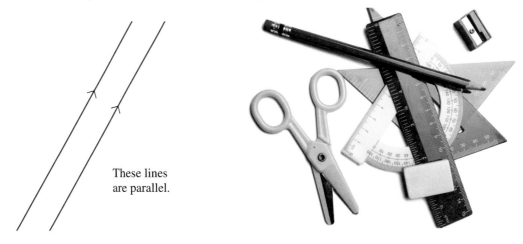

These lines
are parallel.

What parallel line segments can you see in the picture above right?

Parallel Line Segments

You will need grid paper and a cardboard square.
Opposite sides of a square are parallel.

1. Draw *xy* axes on a grid.

2. Place the square on the grid so that one side goes through 2 points
where grid lines meet. Draw line segments along two parallel sides of
the square.

3. Label the line segments AB and DE.

4. Find the slopes of AB and DE.

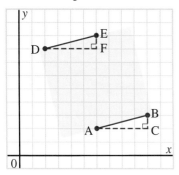

5. Move the square. Repeat exercises 2 to 4 to draw a different pair of parallel line segments.

6. Repeat exercise 5 two more times. Include vertical and horizontal line segments.

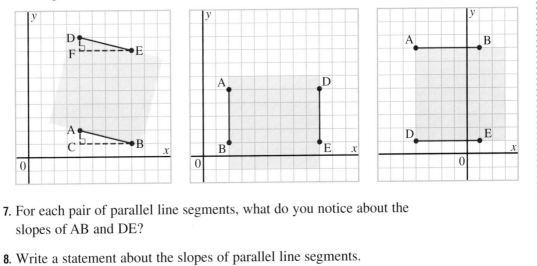

7. For each pair of parallel line segments, what do you notice about the slopes of AB and DE?

8. Write a statement about the slopes of parallel line segments.

The *Investigation* shows that the slopes of parallel line segments are equal.

In this diagram, line segments AB and CD are parallel.

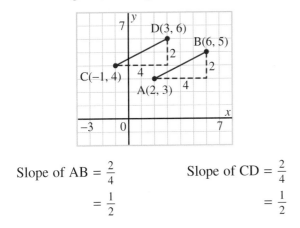

Slope of AB = $\dfrac{2}{4}$ Slope of CD = $\dfrac{2}{4}$

$= \dfrac{1}{2}$ $= \dfrac{1}{2}$

This example illustrates a fundamental property of slope: equal slopes indicate parallel lines.

Parallel Line Segments

If the slopes of two line segments are equal, the segments are parallel.

If two line segments are parallel but not vertical, their slopes are equal.

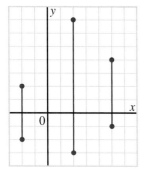

Vertical line segments are parallel.
However, the slope of a vertical line segment
is undefined.
So, we cannot say the slopes of these segments
are equal.

Example 1

Here are the endpoints of pairs of line segments.
Which line segments are parallel? How do you know?

a) W(−3, 3), S(2, 0) and T(−1, −1), Z(7, −7)

b) L(−4, 3), M(−1, 3) and P(0, −2), Q(4, −2)

Solution

a) Graph WS and TZ.

$$\text{Slope of WS} = \frac{\text{rise}}{\text{run}} \qquad \text{Slope of TZ} = \frac{\text{rise}}{\text{run}}$$

$$= \frac{-3}{5} \qquad\qquad\qquad = \frac{-6}{8}$$

$$= -\frac{3}{5} \qquad\qquad\qquad = -\frac{3}{4}$$

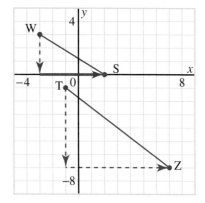

The slopes are not equal, so WS and TZ are not parallel.

b) Graph LM and PQ.

Slope of LM = $\dfrac{\text{rise}}{\text{run}}$ Slope of PQ = $\dfrac{\text{rise}}{\text{run}}$

$= \dfrac{0}{3}$ $= \dfrac{0}{4}$

$= 0$ $= 0$

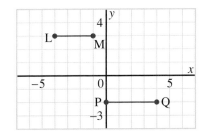

The slopes are equal, so LM and PQ are parallel.

Discuss

Explain how you know the lines are parallel as soon as you graph them.

Example 2

A quadrilateral has vertices A(0, –6), B(2, –1), C(–1, 5), and D(–3, 0). Is the quadrilateral a parallelogram? Explain.

> A parallelogram is a quadrilateral with opposite sides parallel.

Solution

Graph the quadrilateral.

Slope of AB = $\dfrac{\text{rise}}{\text{run}}$ Slope of DC = $\dfrac{\text{rise}}{\text{run}}$

$= \dfrac{5}{2}$ $= \dfrac{5}{2}$

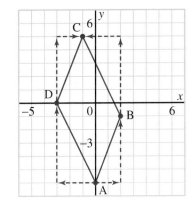

The slopes of AB and DC are equal, so line segments AB and DC are parallel.

Slope of AD = $\dfrac{\text{rise}}{\text{run}}$ Slope of BC = $\dfrac{\text{rise}}{\text{run}}$

$= \dfrac{6}{-3}$ $= \dfrac{6}{-3}$

$= -2$ $= -2$

The slopes of AD and BC are equal, so line segments AD and BC are parallel.

Since both pairs of opposite sides are parallel, ABCD is a parallelogram.

Discuss

Would it be enough to show that two sides are parallel? Explain.

A **1.** For each slope below, choose a slope of a parallel line segment from the box at the right.

a) $\dfrac{6}{4}$ b) $\dfrac{2}{-1}$ c) $\dfrac{0}{5}$

d) $\dfrac{1}{4}$ e) $\dfrac{-2}{8}$ f) $\dfrac{3}{-4}$

$\dfrac{3}{12}$	-2	$-\dfrac{1}{2}$
$-\dfrac{3}{4}$	$-\dfrac{3}{2}$	0
$\dfrac{3}{2}$	$-\dfrac{1}{4}$	$\dfrac{6}{8}$

2. Which pairs of numbers are not slopes of parallel line segments? How do you know?

a) $\dfrac{2}{3}$, $\dfrac{4}{6}$ b) $\dfrac{3}{4}$, $-\dfrac{6}{8}$ c) $\dfrac{5}{10}$, $\dfrac{2}{1}$ d) $\dfrac{5}{6}$, $\dfrac{10}{12}$

e) $\dfrac{-1}{5}$, $\dfrac{-3}{15}$ f) $-\dfrac{8}{4}$, 2 g) $\dfrac{-2}{3}$, $\dfrac{4}{6}$ h) -3, $-\dfrac{9}{3}$

3. Which pairs of line segments are parallel? Explain how you know.

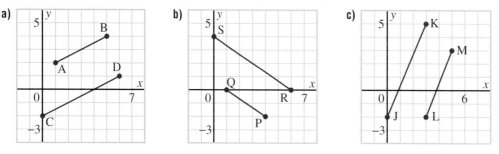

B **4. Knowledge/Understanding** For each pair of points:

a) A(−2, −1), B(1, 5) and C(2, −1), D(4, 3)

b) E(−3, 2), F(5, 5) and O(0, 0), H(5, 2)

c) R(−1, 4), S(7, −2) and T(3, 4), U(9, 0)

   i) Graph the line segment with each set of endpoints.
   ii) Find its slope.
   iii) Are the line segments parallel? Explain how you know.

5. Graph each quadrilateral. Is it a parallelogram? Explain.

a) A(5, 3), B(−3, −3), C(−2, −8), D(6, −2)

b) P(−6, 1), Q(−2, −6), R(10, 2), S(7, 9)

c) J(−4, 5), K(−2, −1), L(6, −4), M(4, 2)

6. Application

a) Graph the points A(1, −2), B(3, 1), C(4, −1), and D(6, 2). Join the points to form a quadrilateral.

b) Find the slope of each side.

c) Identify the type of quadrilateral. Explain how you know.

7. **a)** What is the slope of the *x*-axis?

   b) Draw a line segment parallel to the *x*-axis. Find its slope. What do you notice?

8. **a)** What is the slope of the *y*-axis?

   b) Draw a line segment parallel to the *y*-axis. Find its slope. What do you notice?

9. **a)** The coordinates of the endpoints of a line segment are given. For each line segment, write the coordinates of the endpoints of a parallel line segment.

   i) A(7, 6), B(−6, 3) **ii)** C(−3, 7), D(1, −5)

   iii) E(2, 3), F(−2, −7) **iv)** G(−4, 2), H(6, −4)

   b) Compare your answers for part a with those of a classmate. Explain any differences.

10. **Thinking/Inquiry/Problem Solving**

    a) Plot points A(−2, 0), B(6, 4), and C(−3, 4).

    b) Find the coordinates of a point D on the *y*-axis so that line segment CD is parallel to AB.

11. **a)** On a staircase, how are the slopes of the treads related? How are the slopes of the risers related?

    b) Why is this important for walking on stairs?

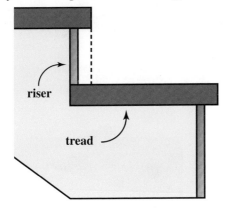

12. **Communication** How can you tell whether two line segments on a grid are parallel? Use examples to illustrate your explanation.

13. **a)** Graph four points that form a parallelogram.

    b) Find the slope of each side.

    c) Explain how you know the figure is a parallelogram.

Lines that meet at right angles (90°) are *perpendicular lines*.

What perpendicular line segments can you see in this picture?

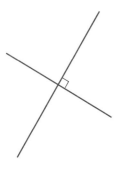

These lines are
perpendicular.

Perpendicular Line Segments

You will need grid paper and the cardboard
square used on page 152.

Adjacent sides of a square are perpendicular.

1. Draw *xy* axes on a grid.

2. Place the square on the grid so that one side
   goes through 2 points where grid lines meet.
   Draw line segments along two perpendicular
   sides of the square.

3. Label the line segments AB and GH.

4. Find the slopes of AB and GH.

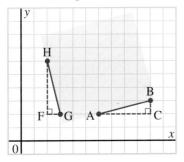

5. Move the square. Repeat exercises 2 to 4 to draw a different pair of perpendicular line segments.

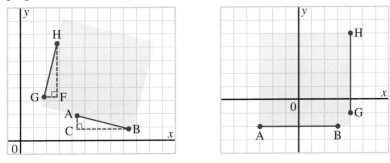

6. Repeat exercise 5 two more times. Include vertical and horizontal line segments.

7. For each pair of perpendicular line segments, what do you notice about the slopes of AB and GH?

8. Write a statement about the slopes of perpendicular line segments.

The *Investigation* shows that the slopes of perpendicular line segments are *negative reciprocals*.

The product of negative reciprocals is −1.

Line segments AB and GH are perpendicular.

$$\text{Slope of AB} = \frac{\text{rise}}{\text{run}} \qquad \text{Slope of GH} = \frac{\text{rise}}{\text{run}}$$

$$= \frac{-3}{2} \qquad\qquad\qquad = \frac{2}{3}$$

$$= -\frac{3}{2}$$

The slopes $-\frac{3}{2}$ and $\frac{2}{3}$ are negative reciprocals.

$$\left(-\frac{3}{2}\right)\left(\frac{2}{3}\right) = -1$$

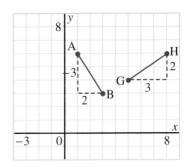

Perpendicular Line Segments

If the slopes of two line segments are negative reciprocals, the segments are perpendicular.

If two segments are perpendicular and neither is vertical, their slopes are negative reciprocals.

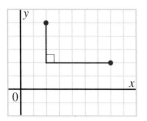

A vertical and a horizontal line segment are perpendicular. However, the slope of the vertical segment is undefined.
So, we cannot say that the slopes of these segments are negative reciprocals.

Example 1

Here are the endpoints of a line segment.
Which pair of line segments are perpendicular? How do you know?

a) R(−2, 5), S(2, 3) and S(2, 3), T(0, 0)

b) D(−2, −3), E(2, −3) and G(4, −3), F(4, 1)

Solution

a) Graph RS and ST.

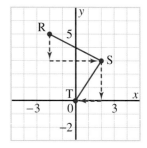

$$\text{Slope of RS} = \frac{\text{rise}}{\text{run}} \qquad \text{Slope of ST} = \frac{\text{rise}}{\text{run}}$$

$$= \frac{-2}{4} \qquad\qquad = \frac{-3}{-2}$$

$$= -\frac{1}{2} \qquad\qquad = \frac{3}{2}$$

The slopes of RS and ST are not negative reciprocals.
So, line segments RS and ST are not perpendicular.

b) Graph DE and GF.

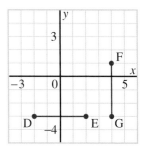

DE is horizontal and GF is vertical. So, segments DE and GF are perpendicular.

Discuss

Do segments need a common endpoint to be perpendicular?
Do they need to intersect to be perpendicular? Explain.

Example 2

A triangle has vertices A(–2, 3), B(8, –2), and C(4, 6).

Is it a right triangle? Explain.

Solution

Graph the triangle.

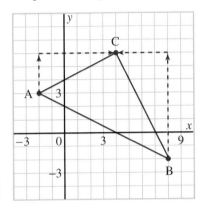

From the graph, ∠C appears to be a right angle. Calculate the slopes of AC and BC.

$$\text{Slope of AC} = \frac{\text{rise}}{\text{run}} \qquad \text{Slope of BC} = \frac{\text{rise}}{\text{run}}$$

$$= \frac{3}{6} \qquad\qquad\qquad = \frac{8}{-4}$$

$$= \frac{1}{2} \qquad\qquad\qquad = -2$$

Since $\frac{1}{2}$ and –2 are negative reciprocals, AC is perpendicular to BC.

So, △ABC is a right triangle.

Discuss

How does drawing the triangle help you determine if it is a right triangle?

4.5   Exercises

A 1. Which pairs of numbers are slopes of perpendicular line segments? How did you decide?

a) $\frac{3}{4}$, $-\frac{4}{3}$ b) $\frac{2}{3}$, $\frac{3}{2}$ c) $\frac{4}{5}$, $-\frac{4}{5}$ d) –4, $\frac{1}{4}$ e) 3, $\frac{1}{3}$

2. Which pairs of line segments are perpendicular? Explain how you know.

a)
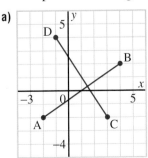

b)
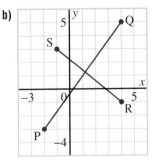

c)
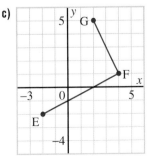

3. For each line segment with the given slope, write the slope of a perpendicular line segment.

a) $\dfrac{2}{3}$ b) $\dfrac{5}{8}$ c) $-\dfrac{3}{4}$ d) $-\dfrac{1}{2}$ e) $-\dfrac{1}{3}$

4. Knowledge/Understanding For each pair of points:

a) O(0, 0), B(6, 4) and C(5, −1), D(1, 5)

b) H(−3, 1), I(6, 4) and J(2, 0), K(0, 6)

c) L(5, −3), M(1, 4) and N(1, −1), P(6, 2)

    i) Graph the line segment with each set of endpoints.

    ii) Find its slope.

    iii) Are the line segments perpendicular? Explain how you know.

5. Graph each triangle. Is it a right triangle? Explain.

a) D(−2, 2), E(−6, 2), F(−6, −1) b) A(3, 0), B(−4, 4), C(−1, −2)

c) P(−3, 1), Q(3, −3), R(7, 3) d) K(3, 2), L(−5, −1), M(−2, −8)

6. Application

a) Graph A(1, −2), B(3, 1), and C(6, −1). Join the points to form a triangle.

b) Find the slope of each side.

c) Identify the type of triangle. Explain your answer.

7. Graph each quadrilateral. Is it a rectangle? Explain.

a) A(5, 4), B(−4, −2), C(−2, −5), D(7, 1)

b) J(−3, 2), K(−2, −3), L(6, −2), M(5, 3)

c) P(5, 1), Q(−4, 4), R(−6, −2), S(3, −5)

> A rectangle has 4 right angles, so the adjacent sides of a rectangle are perpendicular.

8. Graph each line segment with the given endpoints. Find the coordinates of a point C so that AC is perpendicular to AB.

a) A(3, 2), B(6, 8) b) A(0, 5), B(5, 3) c) A(1, 3), B(1, −2)

9. Explain how to decide whether two line segments on a grid are perpendicular. Use examples to illustrate your explanation.

10. Communication Write or draw a plan to help you remember how to use slopes to decide whether line segments are parallel or perpendicular.

11. Thinking/Inquiry/Problem Solving The line segment that joins R(8, 6) and S(4, 8) is the shortest side of right △RST. Point T is on the *x*-axis. Find the possible coordinates of T. Explain your method.

1. Plot only the points with a negative *y*-coordinate.

   a) J(−1, −4)   b) K(4, 1)   c) L(5, −1)   d) M(−3, 0)

2. Find the slope of each line segment.

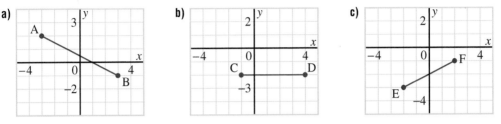

a)   b)   c)

3. a) Sketch a line segment that has a positive slope.

   b) Sketch a line segment that has a negative slope.

   c) How are the line segments in parts a and b different?

4. Graph each pair of line segments. Use slopes to determine whether the segments are parallel, perpendicular, or neither.

   a) R(−3, 3), S(1, 1) and T(0, 0), U(6, −3)

   b) H(−4, −3), I(1, −1) and J(−3, 1), K(3, 4)

   c) E(−6, −2), F(1, −2) and G(−5, −4), H(−5, 4)

5. Graph quadrilateral KLMN with vertices K(1, 2), L(5, 1), M(3, −2), and N(−1, −1). Is quadrilateral KLMN a parallelogram? Use slopes to justify your answer.

Preparation for Ontario Testing

6. Examine the graph of the cost of a banquet at Vittoria's Banquet Hall.

   Which statement is true?

   a) As the number of people attending increases, the cost decreases.

   b) As the number of people attending increases, the cost stays constant.

   c) The graph "Cost at Vittoria's Banquet Hall" is linear.

   d) The graph "Cost at Vittoria's Banquet Hall" is non-linear.

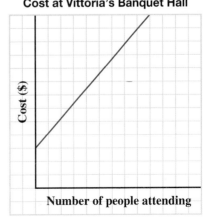

Cost at Vittoria's Banquet Hall

Recall, from Chapter 1, that the points on the graph of a linear relation lie on a straight line. A linear relation can be described by an *equation*. Consider this linear relation:

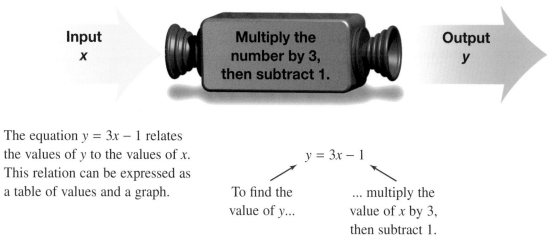

Input
x

Multiply the number by 3, then subtract 1.

Output
y

The equation $y = 3x - 1$ relates the values of y to the values of x. This relation can be expressed as a table of values and a graph.

$$y = 3x - 1$$

To find the value of y...

... multiply the value of x by 3, then subtract 1.

If you have a graphing calculator, complete *Investigation 1*. If you do not have a graphing calculator, complete *Investigation 2*.

INVESTIGATION 1

The Relation $y = 3x - 1$

Setting up an equation

- Press ⌊ Y= ⌋. Use the scroll buttons and ⌊CLEAR⌋ to clear all equations.

- If Plot1, Plot2, and Plot3 at the top of the screen are highlighted, use the scroll buttons and ⌊ENTER⌋ to remove all highlighting.

- Make sure the cursor is beside Y_1. To enter the equation $y = 3x - 1$, press: 3 ⌊X,T,θ,n⌋ ⌊ – ⌋ 1

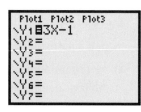

Setting up a table of values

- Press ⌊ 2nd ⌋ ⌊WINDOW⌋ for TBLSET.
  Make sure TblStart = 0 so that the values of x begin at 0.
  Make sure $\triangle$Tbl = 1 so that the values of x increase by 1.
  Make sure Auto is highlighted in the last two lines.

1. a) Press [2nd] [GRAPH] for TABLE.

b) Copy the table from the calculator to your notebook.

x	y
0	−1
1	2
2	5
3	8
4	11
5	14
6	17

X	Y₁
0	-1
1	2
2	5
3	8
4	11
5	14
6	17

X=0

Setting up a graph

- Press [WINDOW]. Enter these values.

```
WINDOW
 Xmin=-23.5
 Xmax=23.5
 Xscl=10
 Ymin=-15.5
 Ymax=15.5
 Yscl=10
 Xres=1
```

2. a) Press [GRAPH].

b) Press [TRACE]. Press [▶] or [◀] to move the cursor along the line until $x = 3$. Compare the value of y on the calculator to the value in the table.

c) Repeat part b for different values of x.

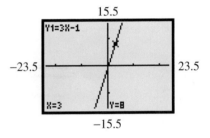

3. a) Add a third column to your table in exercise 1b. Label it *Difference*.
To complete the Difference column, take each y-coordinate and subtract the previous y-coordinate.

x	y	Difference
0	−1	
1	2	2 − (−1) = 3

b) What do you notice about the numbers in the Difference column?

4. a) Use the x- and y-columns of the table of values to graph the relation on grid paper.

b) Explain why it makes sense to connect the points with a straight line.

5. a) Label points A(0, −1) and B(1, 2). Find the slope of AB.

b) Label point C(2, 5). Find the slope of BC.

c) Continue labelling the points from the table of values (D, E, F, G). Find the slope of each line segment (CD, DE, EF, FG).

d) Compare the slopes in parts a to c with the numbers in the Difference column. What do you notice?

INVESTIGATION 2

Using Grid Paper to Investigate $y = 3x - 1$

1. Copy this table. Use the rule below to complete the table.

Input

x

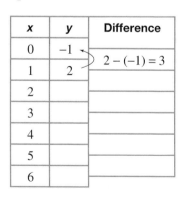

Multiply the number by 3, then subtract 1.

Output

y

Input x	Output y
0	
1	
2	
3	
4	
5	
6	

You have made a table of values for the relation defined by $y = 3x - 1$. The x- and y-values in each row form an ordered pair.

2. a) Add a third column to your table in exercise 1. Label it *Difference*.

To complete the Difference column, take each y-coordinate and subtract the previous y-coordinate.

b) What do you notice about the numbers in the Difference column?

3. a) Use the x- and y-columns of the table of values to graph the relation on grid paper.

b) Explain why it makes sense to connect the points with a straight line.

x	y	Difference
0	−1	
1	2	$2 - (-1) = 3$
2		
3		
4		
5		
6		

4. a) Label points A(0, −1) and B(1, 2).
Find the slope of AB.

b) Label point C(2, 5). Find the slope of BC.

c) Continue labelling the points from the table of values (D, E, F, G). Find the slope of each line segment (CD, DE, EF, FG).

d) Compare the slopes in parts a to c with the numbers in the Difference column. What do you notice?

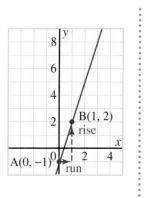

Each *Investigation* shows that:

- A linear relation can be represented by an equation, a table of values, or a graph.
- The graph of a linear relation is a straight line. On a coordinate grid:
  - When the *x*-coordinates increase by the same amount, the differences in *y*-coordinates are equal.
  - When the *x*-coordinates increase by 1, the differences in the *y*-coordinates are equal to the slope of any segment of the line.

Example 1

Graph the relation $y = 8 - 2x$.

Solution

$y = 8 - 2x$

Choose several values of *x*, for example, $x = -2, 0, 2, 4, 6$, and substitute each value in the equation.

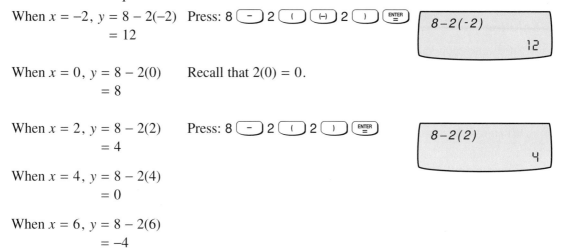

When $x = -2$, $y = 8 - 2(-2)$ Press: 8 − 2 ((−) 2) ENTER
$\qquad = 12$

When $x = 0$, $y = 8 - 2(0)$ Recall that $2(0) = 0$.
$\qquad = 8$

When $x = 2$, $y = 8 - 2(2)$ Press: 8 − 2 (2) ENTER
$\qquad = 4$

When $x = 4$, $y = 8 - 2(4)$
$\qquad = 0$

When $x = 6$, $y = 8 - 2(6)$
$\qquad = -4$

Make a table of values. Plot the points on a grid. Join the points with a straight line. Label the line with its equation.

x	y
−2	12
0	8
2	4
4	0
6	−4

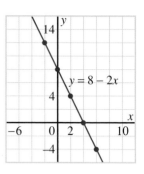

Discuss

Does the table of values show all possible values of x? Explain.

Example 2

Monique has a job at a garden centre. She is paid $10 per hour. Monique's pay, p dollars, and the time she works, h hours, are related by the equation $p = 10h$.

a) Copy and complete the table of values.

b) Graph the relation with h horizontally and p vertically.

c) Is the relation linear? How do you know?

d) What is the slope of any segment of the graph? How is this shown in the table?

e) How much does Monique earn for working 3.5 h?

f) Monique earned $45. How many hours did she work?

h (h)	p ($)	Difference
0	0	
1		
2		
3		
4		
5		
6		

Solution

a) Substitute each value of h in $p = 10h$ to find the corresponding value for p.

When $h = 0$, $p = 10(0)$
$\qquad = 0$

When $h = 1$, $p = 10(1)$
$\qquad = 10$

Continue in this way to complete the table.

Subtract consecutive values of p to complete the Difference column.

h (h)	p ($)	Difference
0	0	
1	10	$10 - 0 = 10$
2	20	$20 - 10 = 10$
3	30	$30 - 20 = 10$
4	40	$40 - 30 = 10$
5	50	$50 - 40 = 10$
6	60	$60 - 50 = 10$

b)

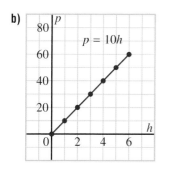

c) The relation is linear because all points on the graph lie on a straight line. The values of h increase by the same amount and the differences are equal. In this example, the differences are 10.

d) Choose points A(1, 10) and B(5, 50).

$$\text{Slope} = \frac{\text{rise}}{\text{run}}$$

$$= \frac{40}{4}$$

$$= 10$$

The slope of AB is 10. This is also the slope of any line segment on the graph. This can also be read from the table. Since the values of h increase by 1, the slope, 10, is the difference in the h-coordinates.

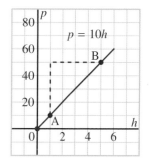

e) Draw a vertical line segment from 3.5 on the horizontal axis. It meets the graph at point (3.5, 35). Monique earns $35 in 3.5 h.

f) Draw a horizontal line segment from 45 on the vertical axis. It meets the graph at (4.5, 45). Monique worked for 4.5 h to earn $45.

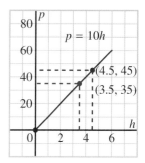

Discuss

Why do the points lie along a straight line?

Why does it make sense to join the points?

A 1. Does each graph represent a linear relation? Explain how you know.

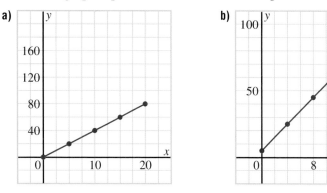

a)

b)

2. a) Does each table of values represent a linear relation? Explain how you know.

i)

x	y	Difference
0	0	
		8
1	8	
		8
2	16	
		8
3	24	
		8
4	32	

ii)

x	y	Difference
0	−3	
		−2
1	−5	
		−2
2	−7	
		−2
3	−9	
		−2
4	−11	

iii)

x	y	Difference
−2	6	
		0
−1	6	
		0
0	6	
		0
1	6	
		0
2	6	

b) For each table of values in part a that represents a linear relation, state the slope of the graph.

B 3. a) Copy and complete each table of values.

i) $y = 2x + 3$

x	y
0	
1	
2	
3	

ii) $y = 5 - 3x$

x	y
0	
2	
4	
6	

iii) $y = -12 + 4x$

x	y
0	
1	
2	
3	

b) Graph each equation.

c) Find the slope for any segment on each graph.

4. a) Copy and complete each table of values.

i) $y = 4x - 1$

x	y
−2	
−1	
0	
1	
2	

ii) $y = -3x + 2$

x	y
−4	
−2	
0	
2	
4	

b) Graph each equation.

c) Find the slope of any segment on each graph.

5. Knowledge/Understanding For each equation below:

a) $y = 2x - 4$ **b)** $y = -5x + 10$

i) Copy and complete the table of values.

x	y	Difference
−2		
−1		
0		
1		
2		
3		
4		

ii) Graph the equation.

iii) Calculate the slope of any segment on the graph.

iv) Compare the slope in part iii and the numbers in the Difference column.
  Is the relation linear? Explain.

6. Enter these window settings. Graph each equation.
  Decide whether each relation is linear. Explain how you know.

a) $y = 5x + 3$ **b)** $y = x + 2$

c) $y = 4x$ **d)** $y = -2x - 4$

e) $y = -x + 6$ **f)** $y = 7x - 3$

To enter $y = -2x - 4$, press:

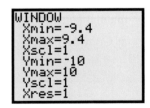

```
WINDOW
Xmin=-9.4
Xmax=9.4
Xscl=1
Ymin=-10
Ymax=10
Yscl=1
Xres=1
```

7. The equation $C = 40t + 20$ represents the cost to repair an appliance. C is the cost in dollars, and t is the time in hours for the repair.

a) Copy and complete this table.

b) Graph the relation on a grid like this:

t (h)	C ($)
0	
2	
3	
5	

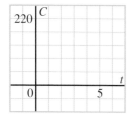

c) Is the relation linear? How do you know?

d) Suppose it takes 4 h to repair an appliance. What would the repair cost?

e) Suppose a repair costs $100. How long would the repair take?

8. This diagram illustrates the relation $y = 2x + 3$.

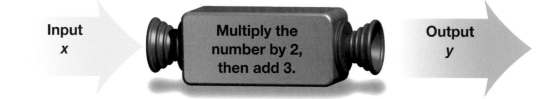

a) Copy and complete this table for 5 values of x from 0 to 10.

b) Graph the relation.

c) Is the relation linear? How does the table show this? How does the graph show this?

x	y	Difference

9. **Application** The cost, C cents, to print and bind n copies of a manual is modelled by the equation $C = 70 + 20n$.

a) Copy and complete this table.

n (copies)	0	20	40	60	80	100
C (¢)						

b) Use the table to draw a graph. Plot n horizontally and C vertically.

c) Use the graph to estimate the cost of 75 copies.

d) Use the graph to estimate how many copies can be printed for $10.

e) Is the relation linear? How do you know?

10. The cost, C dollars, for a school basketball team to play in a tournament is modelled by the equation $C = 300 + 20n$, where n is the number of players.

a) Copy and complete this table.

n (players)	0	2	4	6	8	10	12
C ($)							

b) Graph the relation. Plot n horizontally and C vertically.

c) What is the cost for 11 players to attend the tournament?

d) How many players can attend the tournament for $525?

11. Thinking/Inquiry/Problem Solving Suppose the extra cost for each basketball player in exercise 10 increased from $20 to $32. The equation becomes $C = 300 + 32n$.

a) Predict how the graph would change.

b) Predict how the cost for 11 players would change.

c) Explain how you made your predictions for parts a and b.

✓ **12. Communication** List three methods you can use to present a relation. Choose a relation from this section. Express the relation using each method.

13. The temperature of an old oven is measured in degrees Fahrenheit. This formula converts Fahrenheit temperatures to Celsius temperatures.

$$C = \frac{5}{9}(F - 32)$$

a) Copy and complete this table. Graph the relation.

F (°F)	100	150	200	250	300	350	400
C (°C)							

b) Use the graph to estimate the temperature in degrees Celsius for each Fahrenheit temperature.

    i) 375°F   **ii)** 325°F   **iii)** 275°F

c) Use the graph to estimate the Fahrenheit temperature for each Celsius temperature.

    i) 90°C   **ii)** 120°C   **iii)** 200°C

d) Extend the graph to estimate the temperature in degrees Celsius for each Fahrenheit temperature.

    i) 20°F   **ii)** 0°F   **iii)** 425°F   **iv)** −20°F

e) What is the only temperature that is the same on both scales? How do you know?

Recall, from Chapter 1, that the points on the graph of a non-linear relation do not lie on a straight line.

If you have a graphing calculator, complete *Investigation 1*.
If you do not have a graphing calculator, complete *Investigation 2*.

The Relation $y = x^2 - 3x$

Setup

- Press $\boxed{\text{Y=}}$. Use the scroll buttons and $\boxed{\text{CLEAR}}$ to clear all equations.

- If any of Plot1, Plot2, and Plot3 at the top of the screen are highlighted, use the scroll buttons and $\boxed{\text{ENTER}}$ to remove the highlighting.

- Make sure the cursor is beside $Y_1 =$. To enter the equation $y = x^2 - 3x$, press: $\boxed{\text{X,T,θ,n}}$ $\boxed{x^2}$ $\boxed{-}$ 3 $\boxed{\text{X,T,θ,n}}$

- Press $\boxed{\text{2nd}}$ $\boxed{\text{WINDOW}}$ for TBLSET. Set the table to start at –2 with $\Delta\text{Tbl} = 1$.

- Press $\boxed{\text{WINDOW}}$. Enter these settings.

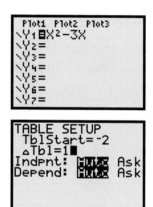

1. Press $\boxed{\text{2nd}}$ $\boxed{\text{GRAPH}}$ for TABLE.

2. Copy this table. Record the values of *y* from the graphing calculator.

x	y	Difference
–2	10	
–1		
0		
1		
2		
3		
4		
5		

3. a) Complete the Difference column by taking each
   y-coordinate and subtracting the previous y-coordinate.

b) What do you notice about the numbers in the
   Difference column?

x	y	Difference
−2	10	
−1	4	$4 - 10 = -6$

4. a) Press GRAPH.

b) Press TRACE. Use the scroll buttons to move the
   cursor until $x = 0$. Compare the value of y on
   the calculator to that in the table.

c) Repeat part b for other values of x from the table.

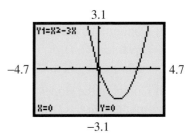

5. a) On grid paper, plot the points from your table of
   values. Draw a smooth curve through the points.
   Your graph should look like the graph at the right.

b) Label points A(−2, 10) and B(−1, 4). Find the
   slope of AB.

c) Label point O(0, 0). Find the slope of BO.

d) Continue labelling the points from your table
   of values (C, D, E, F, G). Find the slope of
   each line segment (OC, CD, DE, EF, FG).

e) Compare the slopes in parts b to d with the numbers
   in the Difference column. What do you notice?

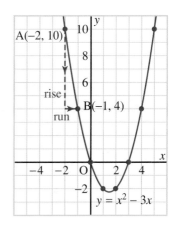

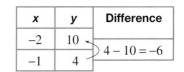

INVESTIGATION 2

Using Grid Paper to Investigate $y = x^2 - 3x$

1. Copy this table. Use the relation $y = x^2 - 3x$
   to complete the y-column.

2. a) Complete the Difference column by taking
   each y-coordinate and subtracting the previous
   y-coordinate.

b) What do you notice about the numbers in the
   Difference column?

x	y	Difference
−2	10	
−1	4	$4 - 10 = -6$
0		
1		
2		
3		
4		
5		

3. a) On grid paper, plot the points from the first two columns of the table of values. Draw a smooth curve through the points.

b) Label points A(−2, 10) and B(−1, 4). Find the slope of AB.

c) Label point O(0, 0). Find the slope of BO.

d) Continue labelling the points from the table of values (C, D, E, F, G). Find the slope of each line segment (OC, CD, DE, EF, FG).

e) Compare the slopes in parts b to d with the numbers in the Difference column. What do you notice?

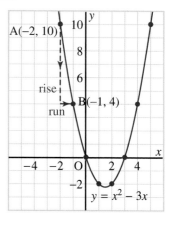

Each *Investigation* shows that:

- A non-linear relation can be represented by an equation, a table of values, or a graph.
- The graph of a non-linear relation is not a straight line.
- When the x-coordinates of a non-linear relation increase by the same amount, the differences in the y-coordinates are not equal.

Example

Use a table of values with a Difference column to determine whether each relation is linear or non-linear.

a) $y = 3x + 4$ **b)** $y = x^2 - 1$

Solution

a) $y = 3x + 4$

Draw a table. Choose values of x from −2 to 2.
Complete the y-column by substituting each value of x in $y = 3x + 4$.
For $x = -2$, $y = 3(-2) + 4$
$\qquad\qquad = -6 + 4$
$\qquad\qquad = -2$
Each x-value is substituted in a similar way.

x	y	Difference
−2	−2	
		$1 - (-2) = 3$
−1	1	
		$4 - 1 = 3$
0	4	
		$7 - 4 = 3$
1	7	
		$10 - 7 = 3$
2	10	

Subtract the y-coordinates to complete the Difference column.
Since the differences are equal, the relation is linear.

b) $y = x^2 - 1$

Draw a table. Choose values of x from -2 to 2.
Complete the y-column by substituting each value
of x in $y = x^2 - 1$.

For $x = -2$, $y = (-2)^2 - 1$
$ = 4 - 1$
$ = 3$

Subtract the y-coordinates to complete the
Difference column.

x	y	Difference
−2	3	
		0 − 3 = −3
−1	0	
		−1 − 0 = −1
0	−1	
		0 − (−1) = 1
1	0	
		3 − 0 = 3
2	3	

Since the differences are not equal, the relation is non-linear.

Discuss

How are the tables of values for linear and non-linear relations different?
How are the graphs different? How are the equations different?

4.7　Exercises

1. Which graphs show non-linear relations? How do you know?

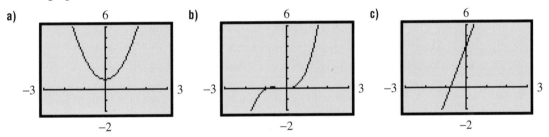

a)　　　　　　b)　　　　　　c)

2. Which graphs show non-linear relations? How do you know?

a)
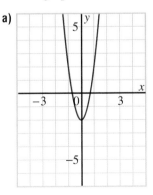

b)
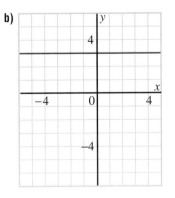

c)
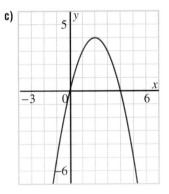

3. Determine whether each table of values represents a linear relation. Explain.

a)

x	y	Difference
−3	9	
		−5
−2	4	
		−3
−1	1	
		−1
0	0	
		1
1	1	
		3
2	4	
		5
3	9	
		7
4	16	

b)

x	y	Difference
−3	−5	
		2
−2	−3	
		2
−1	−1	
		2
0	1	
		2
1	3	
		2
2	5	
		2
3	7	
		2
4	9	

c)

x	y	Difference
−3	15	
		−7
−2	8	
		−5
−1	3	
		−3
0	0	
		−1
1	−1	
		1
2	0	
		3
3	3	
		5
4	8	

4. Knowledge/Understanding

a) Copy and complete each table. Decide whether the relation is linear or non-linear.

i)

x	y	Difference
−2	5	
−1	2	
0	−1	
1	−4	
2	−7	
3	−10	
4	−13	

ii)

x	y	Difference
−2	5	
−1	9	
0	12	
1	14	
2	15	
3	15	
4	14	

iii)

x	y	Difference
−2	5	
−1	5	
0	5	
1	5	
2	5	
3	5	
4	5	

b) For each table in part a, decide whether the graph of the relation is a straight line. Explain how you know.

5. Copy and complete each table. Is each relation linear or non-linear? Explain.

a) $y = x^2 + 1$

x	y	Difference
−2		
−1		
0		
1		
2		

b) $y = 2 − x$

x	y	Difference
0		
2		
4		
6		
8		

c) $y = \dfrac{12}{x}$

x	y	Difference
1		
2		
3		
4		

d) $y = 3 + 4x$

x	y	Difference
−1		
0		
1		
2		
3		

6. Use a table of values with a Difference column to determine whether each relation is linear or non-linear.

a) $y = 1 - x$
b) $y = 2 + x^2$
c) $y = 2 + x$
d) $y = 2 - x^2$

7. Use the results of exercises 5 and 6.

a) List the equations of linear relations.

b) List the equations of non-linear relations.

c) How can you tell by looking at the equation of a relation whether it is linear or non-linear?

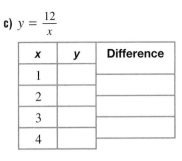

8. Enter these window settings. Graph each equation. Decide whether each relation is linear or non-linear. Explain how you know.

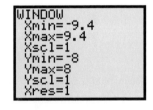

```
WINDOW
Xmin=-9.4
Xmax=9.4
Xscl=1
Ymin=-8
Ymax=8
Yscl=1
Xres=1
```

a) $y = 5 - 2x^2$
b) $y = x + 6$
c) $y = -4x^2$
d) $y = \dfrac{2x}{5}$
e) $y = \dfrac{3}{x}$
f) $y = 5x - 4$
g) $y = x^2 + 5x$
h) $y = -3x^2 - 2$
i) $y = x + x^2$
j) $y = -\dfrac{1}{x}$

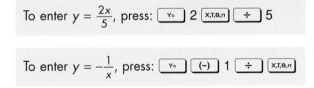

To enter $y = \dfrac{2x}{5}$, press: [Y=] 2 [X,T,θ,n] [÷] 5

To enter $y = -\dfrac{1}{x}$, press: [Y=] [(−)] 1 [÷] [X,T,θ,n]

9. a) For each relation, make a table of values for x-values from −2 to 3. Graph each relation.

i) $y = -3x$ **ii)** $y = -1$ **iii)** $y = x^2 - x$

b) Is each relation linear or non-linear? How does the table of values show this? How does the graph show this?

10. Communication Suppose you are given an equation for a relation. How can you decide whether the relation is linear without graphing it?

11. **a)** Identify the equations of straight lines.

    i) $y = \dfrac{2}{x}$ **ii)** $y = 3x + 1$ **iii)** $y = -4x$ **iv)** $y = 2x^2 + 1$

    v) $y = 2 - 3x$ **vi)** $y = -\dfrac{6}{x}$ **vii)** $y = \dfrac{1}{2}x + 4$ **viii)** $y = -x^2$

    b) Explain how you identified the equations of straight lines.

12. Match each equation with a graph from the screens below.

    i) $y = 5 - x$ **ii)** $y = \dfrac{x^2}{5}$ **iii)** $y = 5$

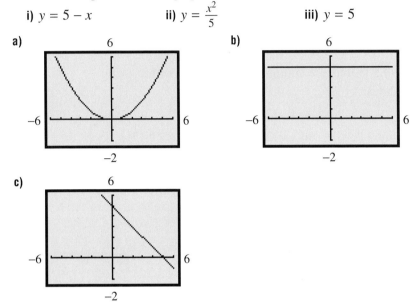

13. A baseball falls from rest.
The approximate distance it falls,
d metres, and the time, t seconds,
are related by the equation $d = 5t^2$.

t (s)	d (m)	Difference
0		
1		
2		
3		
4		

    a) Copy and complete this table.

    b) Is the relation linear or non-linear?
How do you know?

    c) Graph the relation. Plot t horizontally and d vertically.

    d) How does the graph show whether the relation is linear or non-linear?

14. Application Sunscreen protects the skin by reducing the amount of ultraviolet light that hits the skin. Sunscreen is labelled SPF 2, SPF 4, SPF 8, …, SPF 35. SPF is the sunscreen protection factor, s. The percent of ultraviolet light that hits the skin is p. The relation between s and p is $p = \dfrac{100}{s}$.

a) Copy and complete this table.

s (SPF)	p (%)	Difference
2		
8		
15		
25		
35		

b) Is the relation linear or non-linear? Explain how you know.

c) Graph the relation. Plot s horizontally and p vertically.

d) How does the graph show whether the relation is linear or non-linear?

15. Thinking/Inquiry/Problem Solving
Usually, light does not penetrate deeper than 100 m below the surface of the ocean. This table shows the percent of surface light present at various depths.

Depth (m)	Percent of light present
0	100
20	63
40	40
60	25
80	16
100	10

a) Is the relation between light penetration and depth linear or non-linear? Explain how you know.

b) Estimate the depth at which 30% of the light is present.

4.8 :::: Designing a Staircase

Staircases come in many shapes and sizes. There are circular staircases, wide and narrow staircases, long and short staircases.

Recall from page 151 that all staircases have three main parts.

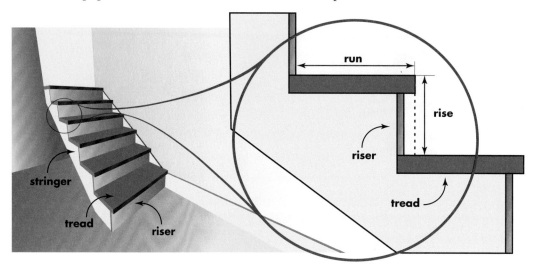

The run or *tread* is the horizontal part of a stair.

The rise or *riser* is the vertical part of a stair.

The *stringers* are the sloping boards running diagonally between floors, on both ends of the treads.

The stringers support and stabilize the staircase. The slope of each stringer determines the steepness of the staircase.

1. Look at these 3 staircases.

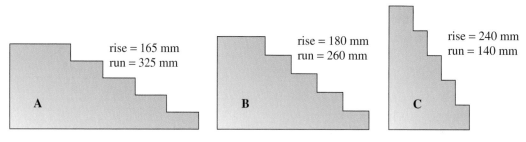

rise = 165 mm
run = 325 mm

A

rise = 180 mm
run = 260 mm

B

rise = 240 mm
run = 140 mm

C

a) How is the number of risers related to the number of treads?

b) Which staircase would most likely be used as the main staircase in a home? Explain your choice.

c) Which staircase is best suited for going up to an attic? Explain.

d) Most staircase accidents occur when the person is going down. Which staircase do you think would be safest? Explain.

2. In the 17th century, architect Francois Blondel used a person's normal walking stride to suggest measurements for the "ideal" staircase. He said the measurement of the run plus twice the rise should equal 620 mm. Carpenters still use the rule today.

The equation that represents the rule is $x + 2y = 620$.

a) Assume that the rule was based on safety. Do you think the rule is equally safe for all people? Explain.

b) Use the equation. Calculate the rise for a staircase with a run of 520 mm. Where might you find a staircase with these measurements?

3. The Canadian Mortgage and Housing Corporation (CMHC) recommends staircase measurements. The maximum rise should be 200 mm and the minimum run should be 250 mm.

a) Use Blondel's rule. Calculate the run that corresponds to the maximum rise recommended by the CMHC. What is the slope of the stringer?

b) Calculate the rise that corresponds to the minimum run. What is the slope of the stringer?

c) The vertical distance between two floors is 2.95 m. Use the CMHC guidelines and Blondel's rule. Calculate the minimum number of treads for a staircase between these floors.

4. A staircase may be constructed off site, then delivered and installed. Suppose a carpenter miscalculated and made a staircase with stringers 55 mm too long. The staircase was installed. Explain the problems that might arise with this staircase.

MATHEMATICS TOOLKIT

Slope

• Slope $= \dfrac{\text{rise}}{\text{run}}$

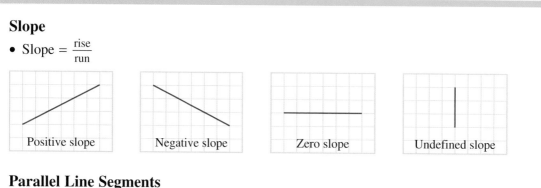

| Positive slope | Negative slope | Zero slope | Undefined slope |

Parallel Line Segments

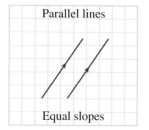 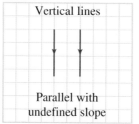 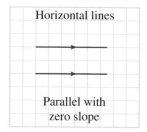

Parallel lines — Equal slopes

Vertical lines — Parallel with undefined slope

Horizontal lines — Parallel with zero slope

Perpendicular Line Segments

Perpendicular lines

$-\dfrac{1}{2}$ $\dfrac{2}{1}$

Slopes are negative reciprocals.

Horizontal and vertical lines are perpendicular.

Slopes are not negative reciprocals.

Linear Relations

• A linear relation can be represented by an equation, a table of values, or a straight-line graph.

$$y = 2x + 1$$

x	y	Difference
−2	−3	
		+2
−1	−1	
		+2
0	1	
		+2
1	3	
		+2
2	5	

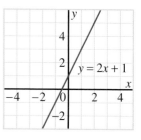

$y = 2x + 1$

- When the x-coordinates increase by the same amount, the differences in the y-coordinates are equal.

- When the x-coordinates increase by 1, the differences in the y-coordinates are equal to the slope of any segment of the line.

Non-Linear Relations

- A non-linear relation can be represented by an equation, a table of values, or a graph that is not a straight line.

$$y = x^2 - 1$$

x	y	Difference
−2	3	
		3
−1	0	
		1
0	−1	
		−1
1	0	
		−3
2	3	

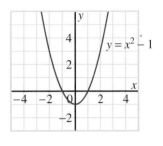

$y = x^2 - 1$

- When the x-coordinates increase by the same amount, the differences in the y-coordinates are not equal.

4.1 1. This diagram is a side view of a roller coaster. Find the slope of each section.

a) AB   b) BC

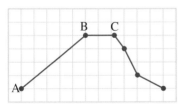

2. Find the slope of each line segment.

a)   b)   c)   d)

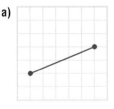 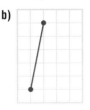 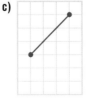 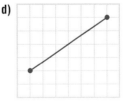

4.2 **3.** Name the coordinates of each point on the coordinate plane at the right.

4. Plot and label these points on a coordinate plane.

   a) A(−2, 5)   **b)** B(0, 0)   **c)** C(6, −1)

   d) D(0, −4)   **e)** E(−1, −3)   **f)** F(−3, −5)

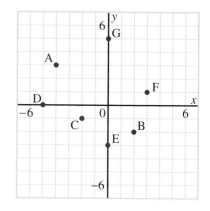

4.3 **5.** Plot points A(3, −2), B(0, 5), C(3, 5), and D(−1, −1). Find the slope of each segment.

   a) AB   **b)** AC   **c)** BC   **d)** CD

4.4 **6.** Start at (1, 1). Draw a line segment with each given slope. Describe each segment, including its direction.

   a) −2   **b)** 0   **c)** $\frac{1}{4}$ **d)** $-\frac{2}{3}$ **e)** −4

7. Graph each pair of line segments with the given endpoints. Are the line segments parallel?

   a) R(−2, 3), S(3, −2) and T(−4, 0), U(−1, −3)

   b) L(−5, 7), M(4, 7) and N(0, −2), P(1, −2)

   c) H(5, 4), I(0, 0) and J(2, −3), K(−4, −7)

   d) W(−4, −3), S(−2, 0) and T(−3, −7), Z(2, −1)

8. A quadrilateral has vertices A(−1, 4), B(−3, −2), C(3, −1), and D(4, 5). Is it a parallelogram? How do you know?

4.5 **9.** Graph each pair of line segments with the given endpoints. Are the line segments perpendicular?

   a) A(−5, 6), B(1, 3,) and C(−4, 3), D(−3, 5)

   b) E(0, −7), F(4, −1) and G(2, −4), H(7, −6)

   c) P(−6, 4), Q(−3, 0) and R(−2, 0), S(1, −4)

   d) K(2, −1), L(4, 3) and M(−1, 3), N(3, 1)

10. A triangle has vertices P(−4, −2), Q(6, 4), and R(−7, 3). Show that △QPR is a right triangle.

11. A quadrilateral has vertices A(−2, 2), B(−1, 3), C(5, −2), and D(4, 3).

   a) Is ABCD a parallelogram? Explain.   **b)** Is ABCD a rectangle? Explain.

4.6 **12. a)** Copy and complete the table of values for $y = -3x + 2$.

   b) Graph the equation.

   c) Calculate the slope of any segment on the graph.

   d) What do you notice about the slope in part c and the numbers in the Difference column?

   e) Is the relation linear? Explain how you know.

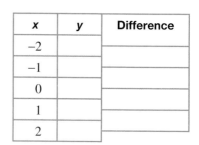

x	y	Difference
−2		
−1		
0		
1		
2		

13. a) Copy each table. Complete the Difference column. Decide whether the relation is linear. Explain how you know.

i)

x	y	Difference
−2	−2	
−1	1	
0	4	
1	7	
2	10	
3	13	
4	16	

ii)

x	y	Difference
−2	9	
−1	7	
0	5	
1	3	
2	1	
3	−1	
4	−3	

b) For each table of values in part a that represents a linear relation, state the slope of the graph.

14. The equation $C = 10h + 5$ represents the cost to rent a video game. C is the cost in dollars, and h is the time in hours playing the video game.

a) Copy and complete this table.

b) Graph the relation.

c) Is the relation linear? How do you know?

d) How much does it cost to play the video game for 3 h?

e) How many hours can you play the video game for $45?

h (h)	C ($)
0	
1	
2	
4	

4.7 **15. a)** For each relation, make a table of values for x-values from −2 to 2. Graph each relation on a separate coordinate plane.

i) $y = 2x - 5$ **ii)** $y = x^2 + 4$ **iii)** $y = -2x^2 - 2x$

b) Is each relation linear or non-linear? How does the table of values show this? How does the graph show this?

16. Enter these window settings. Graph each equation. Decide whether each relation is linear or non-linear. Explain how you know.

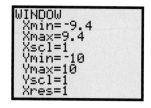

```
WINDOW
 Xmin=-9.4
 Xmax=9.4
 Xscl=1
 Ymin=-10
 Ymax=10
 Yscl=1
 Xres=1
```

a) $y = x^2 + 3$ **b)** $y = -x + 2$ **c)** $y = 6 - 2x$ **d)** $y = 2x^2 - x$

e) $y = x + 5$ **f)** $y = -3x^2$ **g)** $y = 5 - x^2$ **h)** $y = \dfrac{12}{x}$

17. Decide whether each relation is linear or non-linear. Justify each decision.

a) $y = 5x - 1$ **b)** $y = -2x^2 - 6x$ **c)** $y = -2x^2$ **d)** $y = \dfrac{4}{x}$

4.8 **18.** What is the slope of this staircase?

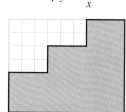

Self-Test

1. Find the slope of each line segment.

a)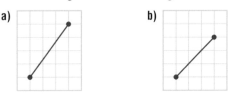

b)

c)

2. Graph the line segment with each pair of endpoints. Find its slope.

   a) A(−1, 5), B(−4, −1)   b) C(3, 2), D(8, −2)   c) E(−2, −5), F(0, −5)

3. **Application** A ramp is built to a door as shown on right.

   a) What is the slope of the ramp?

   b) Suppose the length of the ramp is increased. What happens to its slope? Explain how you know.

   c) Suppose the door is lower than 0.3 m from the ground. What would happen to the slope of the ramp? Explain how you know.

   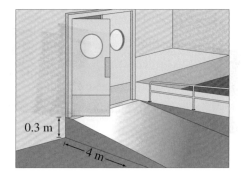

   0.3 m

   4 m

4. **Knowledge/Understanding** Graph each pair of line segments. Decide whether they are parallel, perpendicular, or neither. Justify your answers.

   a) W(−3, 3), S(5, 1) and T(−1, −2), Z(1, 2)

   b) A(−4, −3), B(0, 1) and C(−5, 0), D(−1, −4)

   c) Q(−4, −2), R(2, −4) and S(1, 2), T(4, 1)

5. Enter these window settings. Graph each equation. Decide whether each relation is linear or non-linear. Explain how you know.

   a) $y = x^2 - 5$

   b) $y = 5x + 4$

   c) $y = 4x^2 + 7x$

   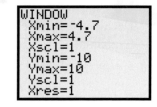

   ```
   WINDOW
   Xmin=-4.7
   Xmax=4.7
   Xscl=1
   Ymin=-10
   Ymax=10
   Yscl=1
   Xres=1
   ```

6. **Communication** Explain how you know whether each relation is linear or non-linear by using an equation, a table of values, and a graph.

   a) $y = 3x + 4$ b) $y = 2x^2 - 6$ c) $y = -x^2 - 2x$

7. **Thinking/Inquiry/Problem Solving** One side of a parallelogram has slope $\frac{3}{4}$.

   a) Draw the parallelogram.

   b) How many different parallelograms are possible? Explain.

8. A month ago, Juan built a skateboard ramp with run 5 m, rise 4 m, and slope $\frac{4}{5}$. Juan wants to change the length of the run to 15 m. How much will he need to increase the rise of the ramp to preserve the $\frac{4}{5}$ slope?

Rise = 4 m

Run = 5 m

9. This diagram is part of a side view of a roller coaster. Segments AB and CD represent 2 uphill segments of the ride. Which segment is steeper? Justify your answer.

BANQUET STYLE
ROUND TABLES

BANQUET STYLE
OBLONG TABLES

THEATRE STYLE
CHAIRS ONLY

By the end of this chapter, you will:

- Use tables of values, graphs, and equations to represent linear relations and to solve problems.

- Describe how changes in situations affect graphs and equations.

- Graph lines by hand and using a graphing calculator.

- Find the equation of a line, given information about the line.

- Communicate solutions, and justify your reasoning.

- Identify $y = mx + b$ as a standard form for the equation of a straight line, including the special cases $x = a$, and $y = b$.

- Identify the significance of m and b in the equation $y = mx + b$.

Setting Up for a Banquet

People sometimes rent large room in hotels to hold a banquet or some other function. The number of guests depends on the area of the room and the way the tables and chairs are arranged. On page 190, there are 3 possible seating arrangements for one room.

In Section 5.8, you will use mathematical modelling to estimate the number of people that can be seated in each arrangement. You will apply the models to your classroom, your cafeteria, and some hotel rooms.

Necessary Skills

Slope of a Line Segment

The slope of a line segment is $\frac{\text{rise}}{\text{run}}$.

For AB, the rise is 5 and the run is 2.

So, the slope of AB is $\frac{5}{2}$.

For CD, the rise is −3 and the run is 1.

So, the slope of CD is $\frac{-3}{1}$, or −3.

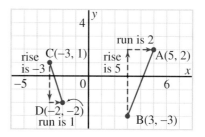

Exercises

1. Find the slope of each line segment.

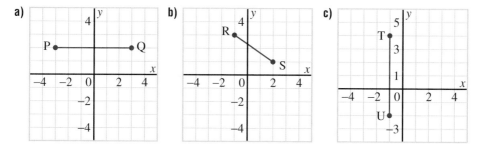

a)

b)

c)

2. Graph each line segment. Find its slope.

a) A(−2, 4), B(3, 2)　　　　　**b)** C(3, 1), D(0, −3)

c) E(−2, 1), F(−6, 1)　　　　　**d)** G(1, 2), H(1, 9)

e) I(−4, 10), J(−3, 4)　　　　　**f)** K(−5, 3), L(0, 0)

g) M(0, 5), N(0, −5)　　　　　**h)** P(−6, −2), Q(4, 3)

3. a) What is the slope of any horizontal line segment?

　　b) What is the slope of any vertical line segment?

Linear Relations

For a linear relation:

- The points on the graph lie on a straight line.

- When the x-coordinates increase by 1, the differences in the y-coordinates equal the slope of any segment of the graph.

For the graph of $y = 3x + 2$, the slope of any segment is 3.

x	y	Difference
−1	−1	
		3
0	2	
		3
1	5	
		3
2	8	

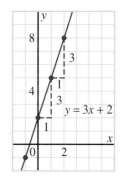

Exercises

1. For each relation:

   a) Copy and complete the table of values.

   b) Graph the equation.

   c) What is the slope of any segment of the graph?

   d) What do you notice about the slope and the numbers in the Difference column?

   i) $y = -3 + 4x$

x	y	Difference
1		
2		
3		
4		
5		

   ii) $y = 2x - 5$

x	y	Difference
1		
2		
3		
4		
5		

2. For each equation in exercise 1:

   a) Is the relation linear?

   b) Explain how the table of values shows whether the relation is linear.

   c) Explain how the slope shows whether the relation is linear.

5.1   Slope of a Line

In Chapter 4, we calculated the slope of a line segment. In this section, we will calculate the slope of a line.

Suppose several line segments with the same slope are connected.

For example, start at A(1, 3). Move 2 up and 3 right to B. Then move 2 up and 3 right to C. Continue in this way to D and E.

Observe that A, B, C, D, and E lie on a straight line.

Choose any 2 segments of this line, for example, AB and BD, or AD and CE. Find their slopes.

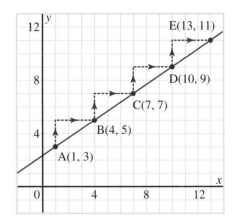

Slope of AB $= \dfrac{\text{rise}}{\text{run}}$ Slope of BD $= \dfrac{\text{rise}}{\text{run}}$

$\qquad\qquad = \dfrac{2}{3}$ $= \dfrac{4}{6}$

$\qquad\qquad\qquad\qquad\qquad\qquad\qquad\; = \dfrac{2}{3}$

Slope of AD $= \dfrac{\text{rise}}{\text{run}}$ Slope of CE $= \dfrac{\text{rise}}{\text{run}}$

$\qquad\qquad = \dfrac{6}{9}$ $= \dfrac{4}{6}$

$\qquad\qquad = \dfrac{2}{3}$ $= \dfrac{2}{3}$

The slope of the line through AE is $\dfrac{2}{3}$.

TAKE NOTE

Slope of a Line

The slopes of all segments of a line are equal.

The slope of a line is the slope of any segment of the line.

We can use these results to draw a line when we know its slope and the coordinates of a point on the line.

Example 1

On a grid, draw a line through A(2, 5) with slope 2.

Solution

Mark the point A(2, 5).

Write slope 2 as $\frac{2}{1}$.

The rise is 2 and the run is 1.

Move 2 up and 1 right. Mark a point.

Move 2 up and 1 right again. Mark another point.

Draw a line through the points.

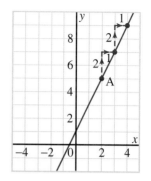

Discuss

Could you draw the line with slope 2 by marking points on the opposite side of A? Explain.

Example 2

On a grid, draw a line through K(4, −2) with slope $-\frac{1}{3}$.

Solution

Mark the point K(4, −2).

Write slope $-\frac{1}{3}$ as $\frac{-1}{3}$.

The rise is −1 and the run is 3.

Move 1 down and 3 right. Mark a point.

Move 1 down and 3 right again. Mark a point.

Draw a line through the points.

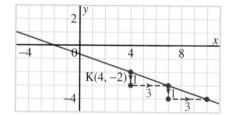

Discuss

Could you have drawn the line by using the slope as $\frac{1}{-3}$? Explain.

A   1. State the slope of each line.

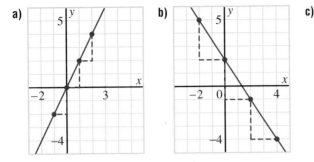 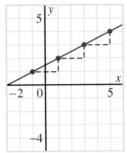

   a)   b)   c)

2. State the slope of each line.

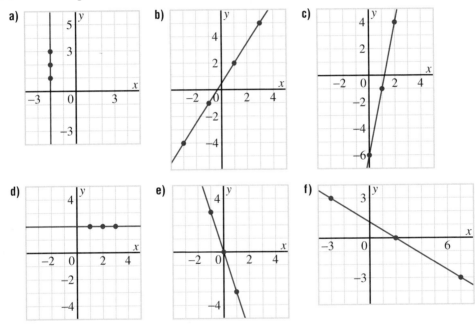

   a)   b)   c)

   d)   e)   f)

B   3. Draw a line through each point with each given slope.

   a) A(−2, 1), slope 3   b) B(4, 0), slope $\frac{3}{2}$

   c) C(0, 0), slope $-\frac{1}{4}$ d) D(−1, −3), slope −4

4. **Knowledge/Understanding** Draw a line through B(3, 2) with each slope.

   a) 2   b) $-\frac{1}{2}$ c) −3   d) 0

5. Draw a line through E(0, 4) with each slope. Find the coordinates of 2 more points on each line.

   a) 3   b) $\frac{1}{2}$ c) −2   d) $-\frac{1}{4}$

6. Draw a line with each slope. Find the coordinates of 2 points on the line.

a) 3   **b)** $\frac{4}{3}$ **c)** −2   **d)** $-\frac{2}{5}$

7. Communication Choose a slope from exercise 6. Compare your coordinates of the 2 points with a classmate's. Do your points lie on your classmate's line? Do your classmate's points lie on your line? Explain why the points lie on the same or different lines.

8. a) Draw a line through C(−2, 3) with slope 0.

b) Find the coordinates of 3 other points on this line. What do you notice about the coordinates of these points?

9. a) Draw a line through D(4, −3) with an undefined slope.

b) Find the coordinates of 3 other points on this line. What do you notice about the coordinates of these points?

✓ **10.** Draw the line through each pair of points. Find the coordinates of 2 more points on each line.

a) E(2, 3) and F(1, 7)   **b)** G(−4, 7) and H(1, 0)

c) J(−6, −2) and K(5, 8)   **d)** L(−3, −7) and M(−4, −6)

11. Graph each set of points.

   i) A(0, 1), B(3, 3), C(9, 7)

   ii) A(−6, 1), B(−2, −1), C(4, −4)

   iii) A(8, 5), B(−2, 1), C(3, 3)

a) Find the slopes of AB, BC, and AC. What do you notice? Explain whether this makes sense.

b) Suppose D is another point on the line. What is the slope of AD? How do you know?

12. Application Points that lie on the same line are *collinear* points. In the diagram, points A, B, and C appear to be collinear.

a) Find the slopes of AB, BC, and AC.

b) Are the 3 points collinear?

c) Find another way to determine whether the points are collinear.

13. Thinking/Inquiry/Problem Solving A line has slope −1. It passes through the points C(q, 3) and D(4, −2). What is the value of q? Explain how you got your answer.

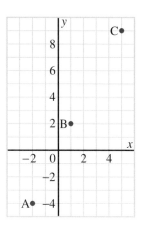

If you have a graphing calculator, complete *Investigation 1*.
If you do not have a graphing calculator, complete *Investigation 2*.

The Equation $y = mx$

Set-up

- Press [WINDOW]. Enter these settings.
- Press [Y=]. Use the scroll buttons and [CLEAR] to clear all equations.
- If Plot1, Plot2, and Plot3 are highlighted, use the scroll buttons and [ENTER] to remove the highlighting.

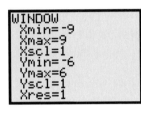

Graph $y = x$, $y = 2x$, and $y = 4x$ on the same screen.

1. To enter the equation $y = x$, make sure the cursor is beside $Y_1 =$. Press [X,T,θ,n].
   To enter $y = 2x$, make sure the cursor is beside $Y_2 =$. Press 2 [X,T,θ,n].
   To enter $y = 4x$, make sure the cursor is beside $Y_3 =$. Press 4 [X,T,θ,n].
   Press [GRAPH].

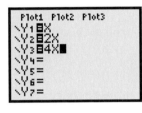

2. How are the graphs in exercise 1 alike? How are they different?

Graph $y = -x$, $y = -2x$, and $y = -4x$ on the same screen.

3. To enter $y = -x$, make sure the cursor is beside $Y_4 =$.
   Press [(-)] [X,T,θ,n].
   To enter $y = -2x$, make sure the cursor is beside $Y_5 =$.
   Press [(-)] 2 [X,T,θ,n].
   To enter $y = -4x$, make sure the cursor is beside $Y_6 =$.
   Press [(-)] 4 [X,T,θ,n].
   To differentiate the graphs of Y_4, Y_5, and Y_6, move the cursor to the left of $Y_4 =$, $Y_5 =$, and $Y_6 =$. Press [ENTER] to select the thick line. Press [GRAPH].

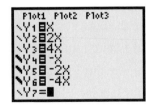

4. How are the thick-lined graphs alike? How are they different?

5. How are the thick-lined graphs similar to the thin-lined graphs? How are they different?

6. Press [2nd] [WINDOW] for TBLSET. Make sure TblStart = 0 and ΔTbl = 1.

```
TABLE SETUP
 TblStart=0
  ▵Tbl=1
Indpnt: Auto Ask
Depend: Auto Ask
```

7. Press [2nd] [GRAPH] for TABLE.

   a) To find the slope of $y = x$, calculate the differences in the Y_1 values.

   b) To find the slope of $y = 2x$, calculate the differences in the Y_2 values.

   c) Compare the slope of each line with its equation. What do you notice?

8. Each equation is in $y = mx$ form. What do you think m represents?

Using Grid Paper to Investigate $y = mx$

1. Copy and complete this table of values for each equation.

   a) $y = x$ **b)** $y = 2x$

   c) $y = -x$ **d)** $y = -2x$

x	y
−2	
0	
2	

2. a) Use the coordinates from each table. Graph each equation in exercise 1 on the same grid. Label each line.

   b) How are the graphs alike?

   c) How are the graphs different?

3. Find the slope of each line in exercise 1.

4. Compare the slope of each line with its equation. What do you notice?

5. Each equation in exercise 1 is in $y = mx$ form. What do you think m represents?

Each *Investigation* shows that for the line $y = mx$:

- m is the slope of the line.
- The line passes through the origin O(0,0).
- When m is positive, the line rises to the right. When m is negative, the line falls to the right.
- For positive slopes, the greater the slope, the steeper the line.
- The value of y *varies directly* with the value of x. For example, if x is doubled, y is doubled. If x is tripled, y is also tripled.

TAKE NOTE

The Line $y = mx$

- The graph of the equation $y = mx$ is a straight line with slope m.
- The value of m indicates the direction and steepness of the line.
- The line $y = mx$ passes through the origin O(0, 0).
- The equation $y = mx$ represents direct variation since y varies directly with x.

We can use these results to graph a line when its equation has the form $y = mx$.

Example 1

Graph each line.

a) $y = 3x$
b) $y = -\dfrac{2}{5}x$

Solution

Each equation has the form $y = mx$, so each line passes through the origin.

a) $y = 3x$

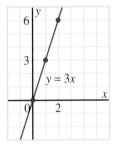

The slope is $\dfrac{3}{1}$.

The rise is 3 and the run is 1.
Mark a point at the origin.
Move 3 up and 1 right. Mark a point.
From that point, move 3 up and 1 right again.
Mark another point.
Draw a line through the points.

b) $y = -\frac{2}{5}x$

The slope is $-\frac{2}{5}$, or $\frac{-2}{5}$.

The rise is −2 and the run is 5.

Mark a point at the origin.

Move 2 down and 5 right. Mark a point.

From that point, move 2 down and 5 right again.

Mark another point.

Draw a line through the points.

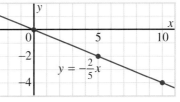

If we are given a line that passes through the origin, we can find its equation.

Example 2

Find the equation of each line.

a)

b)

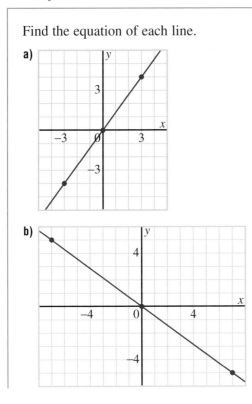

Solution

a) The line passes through the origin.

So, the equation has the form $y = mx$.

Find the slope, m, of the line.

Label any point A on the line.

The slope of segment OA is: $\dfrac{\text{rise}}{\text{run}} = \dfrac{4}{3}$

The slope of the line is equal to the slope of OA, $\dfrac{4}{3}$.

So, the equation of the line is $y = \dfrac{4}{3}x$.

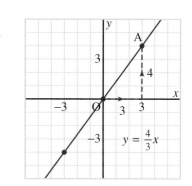

b) The line passes through the origin.

So, the equation has the form $y = mx$.

Find the slope, m, of the line.

Label point B.

The slope of segment OB is: $\dfrac{\text{rise}}{\text{run}} = \dfrac{-5}{7}$

The slope of the line is equal to the slope of OB, $-\dfrac{5}{7}$.

So, the equation of the line is $y = -\dfrac{5}{7}x$.

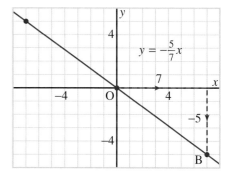

A special case of $y = mx$ occurs when $m = 0$.

The x-axis is a horizontal line. Its slope is 0.

When $m = 0$, $y = mx$ becomes $y = 0x$, or $y = 0$.

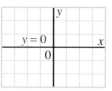

The y-axis is a vertical line. Its slope is undefined.

Each point on the y-axis has x-coordinate 0.

Its equation is $x = 0$.

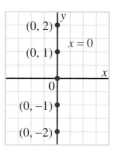

Equations of the Axes

The x-axis has equation $y = 0$.

The y-axis has equation $x = 0$.

A **1.** Each equation has the form $y = mx$. State each value of m.

    a) $y = 2x$ **b)** $y = -\frac{1}{5}x$ **c)** $y = -x$ **d)** $y = -\frac{4}{3}x$

2. State the slope of each line.

    a) $y = -2x$ **b)** $y = \frac{1}{4}x$ **c)** $y = 10x$

    d) $y = -\frac{4}{7}x$ **e)** $y = 0$ **f)** $x = 0$

3. Write the equation of a line through the origin with each slope.

    a) $m = 1$ **b)** $m = -1$ **c)** $m = -\frac{1}{4}$

    d) $m = \frac{1}{3}$ **e)** $m = 0$ **f)** $m = 10$

B **4.** Find the slope of each line, then write its equation.

a) 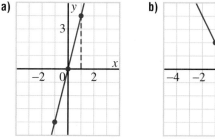 **b)** 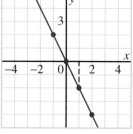 **c)**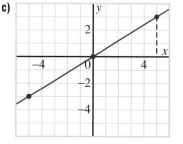

5. Find the equation of each line.

a) 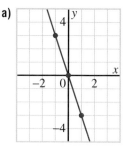 **b)** 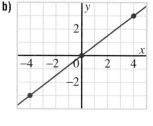 **c)**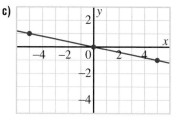

6. Knowledge/Understanding Graph each line.

    a) $y = 4x$ **b)** $y = \frac{7}{2}x$ **c)** $y = -\frac{1}{6}x$

    d) $y = -x$ **e)** $y = 0$ **f)** $x = 0$

7. a) Write the next 2 equations for each list. Graph the lines from each list on the same grid.

i) $y = 2x$

$y = 3x$

$y = 4x$

ii) $y = \dfrac{1}{2}x$

$y = \dfrac{1}{4}x$

$y = \dfrac{1}{6}x$

iii) $y = -x$

$y = -2x$

$y = -3x$

b) For each list, what do you notice about the lines represented by the equations?

8. Graph each line, then write its equation.

a) Every point on the line has x-coordinate 0.

b) Every point on the line has y-coordinate 0.

9. Communication Explain why a vertical line through the origin does not have the form $y = mx$.

10. Application The price of a ticket to a museum is \$6. The total cost is represented by the equation $y = 6x$, where y dollars represents the total cost and x represents the number of tickets.

a) Graph $y = 6x$.

b) State the slope of the graph.

c) What does the slope tell you about the tickets?

11. Thinking/Inquiry/Problem Solving Are the lines represented by the equations $y = 0$ and $x = 0$ perpendicular? Explain how you know.

12. • Enter these window settings.

• Use a graphing calculator to graph each line.

• Press TRACE and use the scroll buttons to move the cursor along the line.

• State the coordinates of two points on each line, other than the origin.

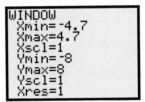

```
WINDOW
 Xmin=-4.7
 Xmax=4.7
 Xscl=1
 Ymin=-8
 Ymax=8
 Yscl=1
 Xres=1
```

a) $y = 6x$

b) $y = -\dfrac{4}{5}x$

c) $y = \dfrac{6}{5}x$

d) $y = -7x$

If you have a graphing calculator, complete *Investigation 1*.
If you do not have a graphing calculator, complete *Investigation 2*.

The Equation $y = mx + b$

Set-up

- Press WINDOW. Enter these settings.
- Press Y=. Use the scroll buttons and CLEAR to clear all equations.
- If Plot1, Plot2, and Plot3 are highlighted, use the scroll buttons and ENTER to remove the highlighting.

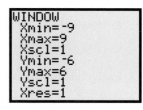

1. Make sure the cursor is beside $Y_1 =$.
   To enter the equation $y = x + 1$, press X,T,θ,n + 1.

   Graph each equation on the same screen.

   $y = 2x + 1$

   $y = -x + 1$

   $y = 3x + 1$

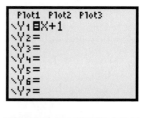

2. **a)** How are the graphs in exercise 1 alike?

   b) How are they different?

3. Each equation in exercise 1 has the form $y = mx + b$.

   a) What does m represent?

   b) What do you think b represents?

4. Press Y=. Clear all equations. Graph $y = x$.

5. Graph each equation on the same screen.

   $y = x + 1$　　　　　$y = x + 3$　　　　　$y = x - 2$

6. How are the graphs in exercises 4 and 5 similar? How are they different?

7. Each equation in exercise 5 has the form $y = mx + b$. Compare the equation and the graph of each line. What does b represent?

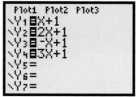

Using Grid Paper to Investigate $y = mx + b$

1. Copy and complete this table of values for each equation.

   a) $y = x + 1$ b) $y = 2x + 1$

   c) $y = -x + 1$ d) $y = 3x + 1$

x	y
–2	
0	
2	

2. Graph the equations in exercise 1 on the same grid. Label each line.

   a) How are the graphs alike?

   b) How are they different?

3. Each equation in exercise 1 has the form $y = mx + b$.

   a) What does m represent?

   b) What do you think b represents?

4. Copy and complete this table of values for each equation.

   a) $y = x + 1$ b) $y = x + 3$ c) $y = x - 2$

x	y
–2	
0	
2	

5. Graph each equation in exercise 4 on the same grid. Label each line.

   a) How are the graphs alike?

   b) How are they different?

6. Each equation in exercise 4 has the form $y = mx + b$. Compare the equation and the graph of each line. What does b represent?

Each *Investigation* shows that for the line $y = mx + b$:

- m is the slope of the line.
- b is the y-intercept; that is, the y-coordinate of the point where the line crosses the y-axis.
- The value of y *varies partially* with the value of x.
- The graph does not go through the origin.

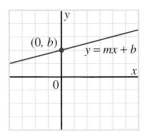

Consider the equation $y = 2x + 3$. The slope of the graph is 2.
The y-intercept is 3; so, the graph crosses the y-axis at $(0, 3)$.

$$y = 2x + 3$$

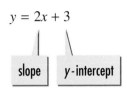

slope y-intercept

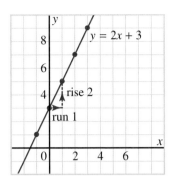

The equation $y = mx + b$ is called the *slope y-intercept form*
of the equation of a line.

TAKE NOTE

The Line $y = mx + b$

- The graph of $y = mx + b$ is a straight line with slope m and y-intercept b.
- The equation $y = mx + b$ represents *partial variation*.

We can graph an equation in this form without making a table of values.

Example 1

Graph each line.

a) $y = \frac{2}{3}x - 5$ **b)** $y = -2x + 4$

Solution

a) $y = \frac{2}{3}x - 5$

The slope is $\frac{2}{3}$. The rise is 2 and the run is 3.
The y-intercept is -5 with coordinates $(0, -5)$.
Begin at $(0, -5)$. Move 2 up and 3 right.
Mark a point. Find points on the line by continuing
2 up and 3 right or moving 2 down and 3 left.
Join the points.

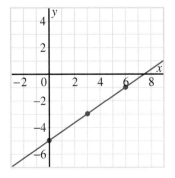

b) $y = -2x + 4$

The slope is -2, or $\frac{-2}{1}$. The rise is -2 and the run is 1.

The y-intercept is 4.

Begin at $(0, 4)$. Move 2 down and 1 right.

Mark a point. Find other points on the line by continuing 2 down and 1 right, or moving 2 up and 1 left. Join the points.

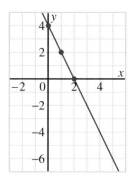

Discuss

In what direction do you move for a positive rise? a negative rise?
In what direction do you move for a positive run? a negative run?

We can also find the equation of a line in the slope y-intercept form when its graph is given.

Example 2

Find the equation of each line.

a)

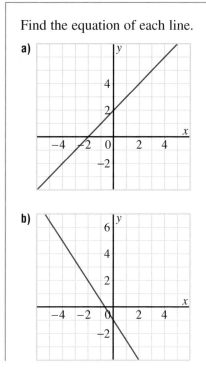

b)

Solution

Read the *y*-intercept and slope from the graph.
Each equation has the form $y = mx + b$.

a) The *y*-intercept is 2. Mark a point at $(0, 2)$.
Locate another point with integer coordinates.
The slope is 1.
The equation is $y = 1x + 2$, or $y = x + 2$.

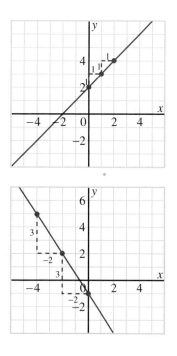

b) The *y*-intercept is -1. Mark a point at $(0, -1)$.
Locate another point with integer coordinates.
The slope is $-\dfrac{3}{2}$.
The equation is $y = -\dfrac{3}{2}x - 1$.

A special case occurs for $y = mx + b$ when $m = 0$.
When $m = 0$, $y = mx + b$ becomes $y = 0x + b$, or $y = b$.
The line $y = b$ is a horizontal line with *y*-intercept *b*.
For example, $y = 3$ is a horizontal line with *y*-intercept 3.
And, $y = -2$ is a horizontal line with *y*-intercept -2.

Another special case occurs for vertical lines.
A vertical line has a slope that is undefined.
So, its equation does not have the form $y = mx + b$.

For example, consider the vertical line with *x*-intercept 2.
Each point on the line has *x*-coordinate 2.
So, the equation of the line $x = 2$.

Similarly, a vertical line with *x*-intercept -3 has
equation $x = -3$.

Equations of Horizontal and Vertical Lines

A horizontal line has equation $y = b$,
where b is the y-intercept.

A vertical line has equation $x = a$,
where a is the x-intercept.

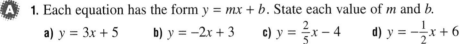

5.4　Exercises

A　**1.** Each equation has the form $y = mx + b$. State each value of m and b.

    a) $y = 3x + 5$　　**b)** $y = -2x + 3$　　**c)** $y = \frac{2}{5}x - 4$　　**d)** $y = -\frac{1}{2}x + 6$

✓　**2.** State the slope and y-intercept for each line.

    a) $y = -4x - 7$　　**b)** $y = \frac{3}{8}x - 5$　　**c)** $y = \frac{4}{3}x - 2$　　**d)** $y = \frac{9}{5}x + 1$

✓　**3.** Write the equation of the line with each slope and y-intercept.

    a) $m = 2, b = 3$　　　　**b)** $m = -1, b = 4$　　　　**c)** $m = \frac{2}{3}, b = -1$

    d) $m = -\frac{4}{5}, b = 8$　　　**e)** $m = -3, b = \frac{5}{2}$　　　**f)** $m = 0, b = 3$

B　**4.** State the y-intercept of each line.

✓　**a)**　　　　　　　**b)**　　　　　　　**c)**

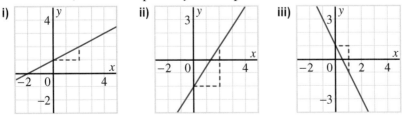

✓　**5. a)** For each line, find the slope and y-intercept.

    i)　　　　　　　**ii)**　　　　　　　**iii)**

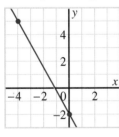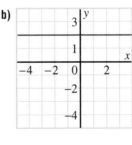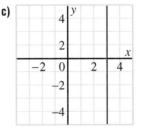

    b) State the equation of each line in part a.

6. Find the equation of each line.

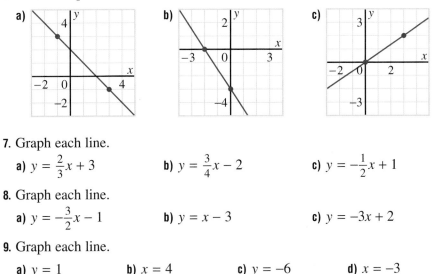

a)

b)

c)

7. Graph each line.

a) $y = \frac{2}{3}x + 3$ **b)** $y = \frac{3}{4}x - 2$ **c)** $y = -\frac{1}{2}x + 1$

8. Graph each line.

a) $y = -\frac{3}{2}x - 1$ **b)** $y = x - 3$ **c)** $y = -3x + 2$

9. Graph each line.

a) $y = 1$ **b)** $x = 4$ **c)** $y = -6$ **d)** $x = -3$

10. Knowledge/Understanding

a) Graph the line $y = -\frac{1}{2}x + 3$.

b) What are the coordinates of the point where the line intersects the x-axis?

11. a) Graph the lines $y = 2x + 4$ and $y = -x + 7$.

b) What are the coordinates of the point where the lines intersect?

12. Application The equations of the 3 sides of a triangle are $y = 2x - 4$, $y = -\frac{1}{2}x + 6$, and $y = -3x + 1$.

a) Graph the lines on the same grid.

b) Find the coordinates of the vertices of the triangle.

13. Graph each line, then write its equation.

a) Every point on the line has the x-coordinate 9.

b) Every point on the line has the y-coordinate -8.

14. Communication Maria graphed the equation $y = 3x - 2$ on a grid. When she checked with a classmate, she realized her graph was different. Is Maria's graph correct? If so, explain how you know. If not, explain what Maria did incorrectly.

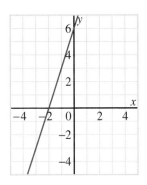

15. a) Identify the pattern in the values of m and b in each list.

    i) $y = 2x + 4$
        $y = x + 3$
        $y = 0x + 2$
        $y = -x + 1$
        $y = -2x + 0$

    ii) $y = 2x - 6$
        $y = x - 3$
        $y = 0.5x - 1.5$
        $y = -0.5x + 1.5$
        $y = -x + 3$
        $y = -2x + 6$

b) Graph the lines in each list on the same grid. Describe what you see.

16. a) Describe the patterns in the values of m and b in these equations.

    $y = x + 1$
    $y = 2x + 0.5$
    $y = 0.5x + 2$

    $y = -x - 1$
    $y = -2x - 0.5$
    $y = -0.5x - 2$

b) Plot the 6 graphs on the same grid. Describe what you see.

17. Use a graphing calculator. Set the window as shown. Graph each line on the same screen. Sketch the graphs.

    a) $y = -2x + 7$
    b) $y = \frac{2}{5}x - 1$
    c) $y = -\frac{4}{3}x - 5$
    d) $y = -3x + 4$

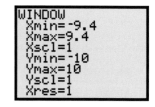

```
WINDOW
Xmin=-9.4
Xmax=9.4
Xscl=1
Ymin=-10
Ymax=10
Yscl=1
Xres=1
```

18. a) Thinking/Inquiry/Problem Solving The equation of a line is $y = 3x + b$. Determine the value of b when the line passes through each point.

    i) R(2, 1)
    ii) K(-1, 4)
    iii) A(3, -2)

b) Choose one point from part a. Explain how you determined the value of b.

19. Make a prediction about either the y- or x-intercept for the graphs of the equations in each list. Give reasons for your predictions. Use a calculator to check your predictions.

    a) $y = x + 3$
        $y = 2x + 3$
        $y = 3x + 3$
        $y = 4x + 3$

    b) $y = x$
        $y = 2x$
        $y = 3x$
        $y = 4x$

    c) $y = x + 3$
        $y = 2x + 6$
        $y = 3x + 9$
        $y = 4x + 12$

1. On a grid, draw a line through each point with each given slope.

   a) $O(0, 0)$, slope $\frac{1}{4}$

   b) $F(-4, -1)$, slope -3

2. Graph the line through each point with the given slope. Write the coordinates of 2 more points on each line.

   a) $C(-2, 3)$, slope $-\frac{4}{3}$

   b) $D(0, 1)$, slope 2

3. Draw a line through $J(-1, 3)$ with each slope. Find the coordinates of 2 more points on each line.

   a) $\frac{3}{2}$ b) -2 c) 1 d) $\frac{1}{5}$ e) $-\frac{2}{3}$

4. Write the equation of a line passing through the origin with each slope.

   a) $m = 3$ b) $m = -1$ c) $m = -\frac{1}{2}$ d) $m = 0$

5. Graph each line.

   a) $y = x$ b) $y = -\frac{4}{3}x$ c) $y = -5x$ d) $y = -\frac{1}{5}x$

6. Write the equation of a line with each slope and y-intercept.

   a) $m = -3$, $b = -1$ b) $m = \frac{1}{2}$, $b = 2$ c) $m = -\frac{3}{5}$, $b = -4$

7. Find the equation of each line.

   a)   b)   c)

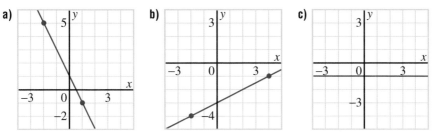

8. Graph each line.

   a) $y = -\frac{3}{4}x - 2$ b) $y = 3x + 3$ c) $y = -x - 1$ d) $y = \frac{1}{3}x - 5$

9. Which equation best represents this graph?

   a) $y = 2$

   b) $x = 2$

   c) $x = -2$

   d) $y = x + 2$

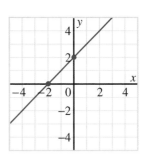

We can use the equation $y = mx + b$ to write the equation of a line if we know its slope, m, and its y-intercept, b.

The coordinates of all the points on a line satisfy its equation. That means we can substitute the x-coordinate and y-coordinate of a point into the equation. Once evaluated, the result for the left side equals the result for the right side.

For example, the point C(8, 5) lies on the line $y = \frac{1}{2}x + 1$.

Substitute $x = 8$ and $y = 5$ into the equation $y = \frac{1}{2}x + 1$.

Left side $= y$ 　　　　　Right side $= \frac{1}{2}x + 1$
$= 5$ 　　　　　$= \frac{1}{2}(8) + 1$
$= 4 + 1$
$= 5$

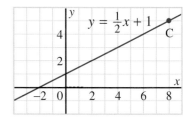

Since left side = right side, the coordinates (8, 5) satisfy the equation of the line.

We can graph a line and find its equation by using other information about the line.

Given the slope and a point on the line

For a given slope, there is only one line that passes through a given point.

Example 1

a) Graph the line with slope $-\frac{1}{2}$ that passes through the point A(4, 1).

b) Find the equation of the line.

c) Check that the coordinates of A satisfy the equation of the line.

Solution

a) The slope is $-\frac{1}{2}$, or $\frac{-1}{2}$.
So, the rise is -1 and the run is 2.
Plot point A(4, 1).
From A, move 1 down and 2 right. Mark point B.
Move 1 down and 2 right again. Mark point C.
Draw a line through the points.

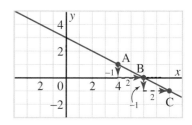

b) Let the equation of the line be $y = mx + b$.

To write the equation of the line, we need m, the slope, and b, the y-intercept.

Since the slope is $-\frac{1}{2}$, $m = -\frac{1}{2}$.

From the graph, the y-intercept is 3, so $b = 3$.

The equation of the line is $y = -\dfrac{1}{2}x + 3$.

c) Substitute $x = 4$ and $y = 1$ into the equation $y = -\dfrac{1}{2}x + 3$.

Left side $= y$ Right side $= -\dfrac{1}{2}x + 3$

$\qquad\quad = 1$ $= -\dfrac{1}{2}(4) + 3$

$\qquad\qquad\qquad\qquad\qquad\qquad = -2 + 3$

$\qquad\qquad\qquad\qquad\qquad\qquad = 1$

Since left side = right side, the coordinates of A satisfy the equation of the line.

Given two points on the line

There is only one line that passes through 2 given points.

Example 2

Find the equation of the line that passes through the points A(-2, -1) and C(2, 5).

Solution

Plot A and C. Join them with a line.

Let the equation of the line be $y = mx + b$.

Find the slope and y-intercept from the graph.

From the graph,

the slope is $\dfrac{\text{rise}}{\text{run}} = \dfrac{6}{4}$

$\qquad\qquad\qquad = \dfrac{3}{2}$

So, $m = \dfrac{3}{2}$

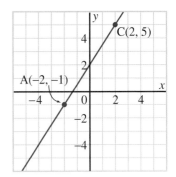

The y-intercept is 2, so $b = 2$.

Substitute for m and b in $y = mx + b$.

The equation of the line is $y = \dfrac{3}{2}x + 2$.

A   **1.** The slope, m, and y-intercept, b, of a line are given. Write the equation of each line.

a) $m = 4$

$b = 3$

b) $m = -2$

$b = \dfrac{1}{2}$

c) $m = -\dfrac{2}{3}$

$b = \dfrac{3}{4}$

d) $m = \dfrac{7}{4}$

$b = -\dfrac{1}{4}$

2. The coordinates of the y-intercept and the slope of a line are given. Write the equation of each line.

a) y-int $(0, -3)$, slope 5   **b)** y-int $(0, 4)$, slope -2 **c)** y-int $(0, -6)$, slope $\dfrac{2}{3}$

3. Point A is marked on each line.

a) Write the coordinates of A.

b) Find the slope of the line from the graph.

c) Find the y-intercept from the graph.

d) Write the equation of the line.

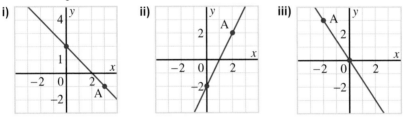

4. Points A and B are marked on each line.

a) Write the coordinates of A and B.

b) Find the slope of AB.

c) Find the y-intercept from the graph.

d) Write the equation of the line.

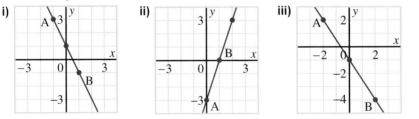

5. Find the equation of each line.

a)

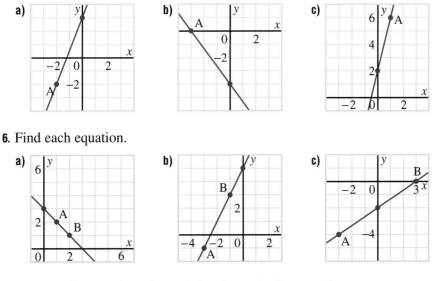

b)

c)

6. Find each equation.

a)

b)

c)

7. The coordinates of a point and the slope of a line are given.

   i) Graph each line.

   ii) Write each equation.

   a) A(2, 5), slope 3   **b)** R(−4, 2), slope $-\dfrac{1}{2}$ **c)** K(4, −6), slope −3

8. Which points lie on the line $y = 3x + 6$?

   a) A(3, 15)   **b)** B(−4, 0)   **c)** C(0, 6)

   d) E(−2, 0)   **e)** F(−2, 3)   **f)** G(−1, 3)

9. Which lines pass through the point (−4, 2)?

   a) $y = -x$ **b)** $y = x + 6$ **c)** $y = 3x + 14$ **d)** $y = -2x + 2$

10. The coordinates of a point and the slope of a line are given.

   i) Graph each line.

   ii) Write the equation of each line.

   iii) Check that the coordinates of the point satisfy the equation.

   a) G(1, 4), slope −2   **b)** H(−5, −6), slope 1   **c)** J(−2, 5), slope $\dfrac{1}{2}$

11. The coordinates of 2 points are given.

   i) Draw a line through the points.

   ii) Write the equation of the line.

   a) B(3, 0), C(−1, −8)   **b)** D(−2, 4), E(1, −5)   **c)** F(−3, −2), G(−1, 6)

12. Knowledge/Understanding The coordinates of 2 points are given.

   i) Draw a line through the points.

   ii) Write the equation of the line.

   a) H(2, 5), J(−2, −1)   **b)** K(0, −4), L(10, 0)   **c)** P(−2, 5), Q(2, −7)

✓ **13. Application** The equation $y = mx + b$ represents a line with slope m and y-intercept b. So, the line passes through $(0, b)$.

a) Graph the line through $(0, 5)$ with each slope.

    i) 3   **ii)** 2   **iii)** 1   **iv)** 0

    v) −1   **vi)** −2   **vii)** −3

b) Find the y-intercept of each line in part a.

c) Write the equation of each line in part a. When you notice a pattern, use it to write the remaining equations.

d) Describe the pattern in the equations.

14. Communication To find the equation of a line, you need 2 facts about it. List as many pairs of facts as you can that determine a line. Use examples and exercises in this chapter for ideas.

15. To visit the Ontario Science Centre and see one movie, the cost is $220 for 20 visitors and $330 for 30 visitors. These costs are represented by the points $(20, 220)$ and $(30, 330)$.

a) Draw the line through points $(20, 220)$ and $(30, 330)$.

b) Use the graph to estimate the cost for each group of visitors.

    i) 25   **ii)** 17   **iii)** 48

c) Let y dollars represent the cost and x represent the number of visitors. Write the equation for the cost of a group visit to the Science Centre.

d) Use the equation to calculate the cost for each group in part b.

e) Compare estimates from part b with calculations from part d. What are advantages of using the graph? What are advantages of using the equation? What are advantages of comparing results from both?

16. Thinking/Inquiry/Problem Solving

a) **i)** Graph the line through K$(-4, 4)$ with slope $-\frac{2}{3}$.

    ii) To find the approximate y-intercept, read the integer closest to the y-intercept on the graph. Write the equation of the line with the slope and approximate y-intercept.

    iii) Graph the line for your equation on the same grid. Does this line pass through K$(-4, 4)$ with slope $-\frac{2}{3}$? Is it close?

    iv) Check whether the coordinates of K satisfy your equation. Does your equation represent a line through K with slope $-\frac{2}{3}$? Does it represent a line that passes close to K with slope $-\frac{2}{3}$?

    v) Explain why your equation is an estimate of the equation of the line through K$(-4, 4)$ with slope $-\frac{2}{3}$.

b) Use a similar method as in part a to estimate the equation of a line through M$(-3, 0)$ and N$(5, 6)$.

Many relations in business and science are linear relations. The slope and intercepts of the graphs of these relations represent different things. Variables other than x and y may be used.

When graphing variables other than x and y, plot the *dependent variable* vertically. Plot the *independent variable* horizontally.

TAKE NOTE

Dependent and Independent Variables

Dependent Variable: the output of a relation; often denoted y

Independent Variable: the input of a relation; often denoted x

Example 1

Sam sells computers and earns 5% commission on her sales.
Her commission, C dollars, varies directly with her sales, s dollars.
The equation is $C = 0.05s$.

a) Make a table of values for the relation.

b) Graph the relation.

c) Use the graph.
   i) What is Sam's commission on sales of $8000?
   ii) Sam earns $200 commission. What are her sales?

d) Suppose Sam's commission increases to 10%.
   How would the graph change?

e) Suppose Sam's commission decreases to 3%.
   How would the graph change?

Solution

a) Substitute some values for s into the equation $C = 0.05s$.
   Calculate the corresponding values of C.

   When $s = 0$, $C = 0.05(0)$
   $ = 0$

   When $s = 3000$, $C = 0.05(3000)$
   $ = 150$

   When $s = 6000$, $C = 0.05(6000)$
   $ = 300$

s ($)	C ($)
0	0
3000	150
6000	300

b) Plot the data from the table. Since the variable C is used instead of y, plot C vertically. Extend the graph to include $s = 8000$ because that value is needed in part c.

c) i) From 8000 on the s-axis, draw a vertical line to the graph. Then draw a horizontal line to the C-axis. This line meets the C-axis at 400. Sam earns $400 commission on sales of $8000.

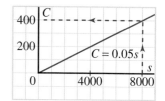

ii) From 200 on the C-axis, draw a horizontal line to the graph. Then draw a vertical line to the s-axis. This line meets the s-axis at 4000. Sam has sales of $4000 to earn a commission of $200.

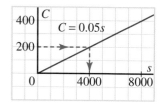

d) If Sam's commission increases to 10%, she will earn more commission. The graph would still pass through the origin, but all other points would be higher. The slope of the graph would be steeper.

e) If Sam's commission decreases to 3%, she will earn less commission. The graph would still pass through the origin, but all other points would be lower. The slope of the graph would be less steep.

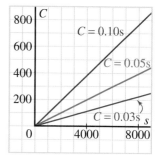

Discuss

Does the graph illustrate direct variation or partial variation? Explain. What are the slope and C-intercept for the line?

Example 2

When you exercise, your pulse should not exceed a maximum rate. The relation between the maximum rate and your age is represented by the equation $p = 220 - a$, where p is the number of beats per minute and a is your age in years.

a) Make a table of values for the equation $p = 220 - a$, for ages between 18 and 50.

b) Graph p against a.

c) Find the slope of the line. What does the slope represent?

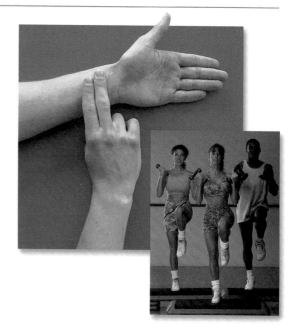

Solution

a) Substitute some values of a in the equation $p = 220 - a$.

Find the corresponding values of p.

When $a = 18$, $p = 220 - 18$
$\qquad = 202$

When $a = 25$, $p = 220 - 25$
$\qquad = 195$

When $a = 40$, $p = 220 - 40$
$\qquad = 180$

When $a = 50$, $p = 220 - 50$
$\qquad = 170$

Age, a (years)	Maximum pulse, p (beats/min)
18	202
25	195
40	180
50	170

b) Plot the data. Since the variable p is used instead of y, plot p vertically.

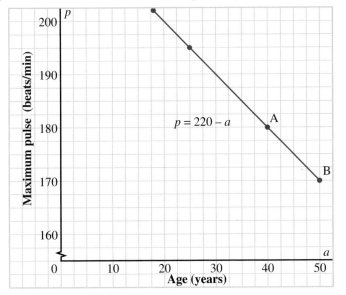

c) The graph is a straight line. Choose any 2 points on the line, such as A(40, 180) and B(50, 170).

$$\text{Slope of AB} = \frac{\text{rise}}{\text{run}}$$
$$= \frac{-10}{10}$$
$$= -1$$

The slope of the line is -1.

The slope is negative. So, as age increases, the maximum pulse decreases. Since the slope is -1, for each year increase in age, the maximum pulse decreases by 1 beat/minute.

Discuss

What would a positive slope show? Explain.

A 1. State the slope of each line.

a) $m = 60n$ b) $T = 1.15c$ c) $E = 16h$

2. State the slope and vertical intercept for each line.

a) $E = 19s + 15$ b) $C = 145 + 9t$ c) $m = 159 + 25n$

3. State whether each equation illustrates direct variation or partial variation. How do you know?

a) $C = 100 + 20n$ b) $C = 60n$ c) $C = 8n + 240$

d) $C = 315n$ e) $C = 1000n$ f) $C = 125n + 5$

4. State whether each graph illustrates direct variation or partial variation. How do you know?

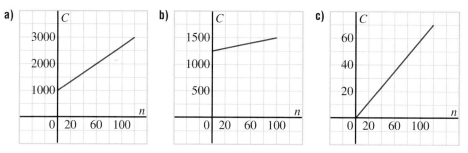

a)   b)   c)

B 5. **Knowledge/Understanding** A child receives a weekly allowance from age 6 to 16. The allowance is $1 per week the first year. It increases by $1 each year. The weekly allowance, a dollars, is related to the age, n years, by the equation $a = n - 5$.

a) Copy and complete this table.

n (years)	6	8	10	12	14	16
a ($)						

b) Graph the data. Plot n horizontally and a vertically.

c) Does it make sense to join the points? Explain why.

d) What is the slope? What does it represent?

e) Extend the graph to find the weekly allowance the child would receive at age 18.

6. This table shows the cost of processing a roll of film. The cost, C dollars, is related to the number of photos, n, by the equation $C = \frac{1}{4}n + 2$.

Numbers of photos, n	Cost, C ($)
12	5.00
24	8.00
36	11.00

a) Graph C against n.

b) Does it make sense to join the points? Explain why.

c) What is the slope? What does it represent?

d) Use the graph to find the cost to process 48 photos.

7. Turkeys are cooked at an oven temperature of 165°C. For turkeys between 3 kg and 8 kg, the cooking time is 30 min per kilogram. The time, t hours, is related to the mass, k kilograms, by this equation: $t = \frac{1}{2}k$.

a) Copy and complete this table.

k (kg)	3	4	5	6	7	8
t (h)						

b) Graph t against k.

c) Does it make sense to join the points? Explain why.

d) What is the slope? What does it represent?

e) Turkeys larger than 8 kg need less cooking time per kilogram. How would the graph change for these turkeys?

f) Turkeys with stuffing need more cooking time per kilogram. How would the graph change for stuffed turkeys?

8. Thinking/Inquiry/Problem Solving The yearbook club is choosing a company to print the school yearbook. Blue Heron Yearbooks charges $8000 for set-up and $4 per copy. The equation that represents this relation is $C = 8000 + 4n$, where C is the cost in dollars and n is the number of books printed. Miles Ahead Yearbooks charges $8400 for set-up and $3 per copy. The equation that represents this relation is $C = 8400 + 3n$. Which company charges less? Explain.

9. **Application** A car travels at an average speed of 80 km/h from Hearst to Nipigon. The towns are 400 km apart. The distance, d kilometres, from Nipigon after t hours of driving is given by the equation $d = 400 - 80t$.

a) Copy and complete this table.

t (h)	0	1	2	3	4	5
d (km)						

b) Graph d against t.

c) Does it make sense to join the points? Explain why.

d) What is the slope? What does it represent?

e) Suppose the average speed increased. How would the graph change?

f) Suppose the average speed decreased. How would the graph change?

g) What is the d-intercept? What does it represent?

h) Suppose a longer route was taken. How would the graph change?

i) Suppose a shorter route was taken. How would the graph change?

10. **Communication** Find an exercise in this section that illustrates direct variation and another that illustrates partial variation. Explain how the equations, tables, and graphs show whether each relation illustrates direct or partial variation.

11. The trip from Toronto to the cross-country running provincial finals in Ottawa costs $1940 for the bus and $80 per runner for meals and accommodation. The cost, C dollars, is modelled by the equation $C = 1940 + 80n$, where n represents the number of runners.

a) Copy and complete this table.

n	0	10	20	30	40	50
C ($)						

b) Graph the relation.

c) Does it make sense to join the points? Explain why.

d) What is the C-intercept? What does it represent?

e) What is the slope? What does it represent?

f) Use the graph to estimate the cost for each number of runners.
   i) 25   ii) 12   iii) 48

g) Suppose the runners stay with local families so the cost per runner is reduced to $32. How would the graph and equation change?

h) Suppose the cost of the bus is covered by fundraising. So, the only expense is $80 per runner. How would the graph and equation change?

We can use the description of a linear relation to write an equation to represent it.

Example 1

A banquet hall charges $40 per person for a reception. Let C dollars represent the total cost and n represent the number of people attending.

a) Write an equation to relate C and n.

b) Graph the relation.

c) Find the slope and the C-intercept.

d) What does the slope tell us?

Solution

a) In words, the equation is:
   Total cost = $40 × number of people
   Using algebra, the equation is:
   $C = 40n$

b) *Using a graphing calculator*
   Use the indicated window settings, which assume a maximum of 100 people will attend. To find the cost for 100 people, substitute $n = 100$ in the equation.
   When $n = 100$, $C = 40(100)$
                        $= 4000$

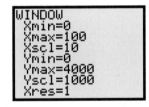

Press [Y=]. Use the scroll button and [CLEAR] to delete any previous equations.
Press: 40 [X,T,θ,n] [GRAPH]

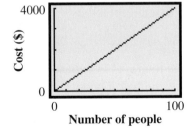

Using grid paper
Choose 2 values of n. Find each corresponding cost.
When $n = 0$, $C = 40(0)$
                    $= 0$
When $n = 100$, $C = 40(100)$
                      $= 4000$

Draw axes on grid paper. Label the horizontal axis n and the vertical axis C. Plot the points (0, 0) and (100, 4000). Join the points with a straight line. Label the graph with its equation.

c) For the equation $C = 40n$, the slope is 40 and the C-intercept is 0.

d) The slope tells us that the cost increases by $40 per person.

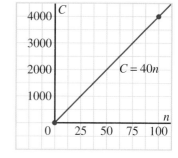

Discuss

How would the graph change if the cost per person decreased?

In *Example 1*, C varies directly with n. Recall that the graph of a direct variation relation is a straight line through the origin. The equation has the form $y = mx$; in this case, $C = 40n$.

Example 2

To hold a banquet, it costs $1000 to rent the hall, plus $25 for each person attending. Let C dollars represent the total cost. Let n represent the number of people attending.

a) Write an equation to relate C and n.

b) Graph the relation.

c) Find the slope and the C-intercept.

d) What do the rise, run, and slope represent?

e) What does the C-intercept tell us?

Solution

a) C represents the total cost in dollars and n represents the number of people attending. In words, the equation is:
Total cost = $25 × number of people + $1000
Using algebra, the equation is:
$C = 25n + 1000$.

b) *Using a graphing calculator*
Use the window settings from *Example 1*.
Press ⌷Y=⌷. Use the scroll buttons and ⌷CLEAR⌷ to delete any previous equations.
Press: 25 ⌷X,T,θ,n⌷ ⌷+⌷ 1000 ⌷GRAPH⌷

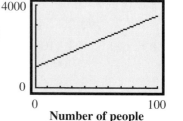

Using grid paper
Choose 2 values of n and find the corresponding costs.
When $n = 0$, $C = 25(0) + 1000$
$$= 1000$$
When $n = 100$, $C = 25(100) + 1000$
$$= 3500$$

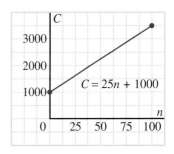

Draw and label axes as in *Example 1*. Plot the points $(0, 1000)$
and $(100, 3500)$. Join the points with a straight line. Label the
graph with its equation.

c) Use the equation $C = 25n + 1000$.
Compare the equation with $y = mx + b$.
The slope, m, is 25 and the C-intercept, b, is 1000.

d) The rise is the change in total cost in dollars.
The run is the change in the number of people attending the banquet.
The slope represents the cost increase of \$25 per person.

e) The C-intercept is the fixed cost; that is, the rent for the hall.
The fixed cost is \$1000.

Discuss
How would the graph change if the \$1000 rent increased? decreased?
How would the graph change if the \$25 per person increased? decreased?

In *Example 2*, C varies partially with n. Recall that the graph of a partial
variation relation is a straight line that does not pass through the origin.
The equation has the form $y = mx + b$; in this case, $C = 25n + 1000$.

5.7   Exercises

A

1. What does each variable in the equations below represent?

a) Paul earns 4% commission on his sales. The equation is $C = 0.04s$.

b) The federal government charges 7% GST on goods and services.
The equation is $T = 0.07c$.

c) A bus is travelling at a constant rate of 55 km/h. The equation is $d = 55t$.

d) The length of time to set up is 100 min. The time to paint each poster is
20 min. The equation is $t = 100 + 20n$.

2. Let T dollars represent the total cost and d days represent the rental time. Write an equation to relate the variables.

a) A rental agency charges $31/day for a small car.

b) A room in a hotel costs $134/day.

c) A room in a different hotel costs $239/day.

d) Renting a popcorn machine costs $90/day.

e) Renting a tent that is 6 m by 6 m costs $160 plus $305/day.

3. A car is driven on the highway at an average speed of 65 km/h. Let d kilometres represent the distance travelled in h hours. Write an equation to relate the variables.

4. Let C dollars represent the total cost and h hours represent the length of rental time. Write an equation for each situation.

a) At the least expensive times, the cost of renting Lakeside Arena is $86/h.

b) At the most expensive times, the cost of renting Lakeside Arena is $164/h.

c) Another arena charges a rental fee of $110 plus $95/h.

5. State whether each relation illustrates a direct variation or a partial variation. How do you know?

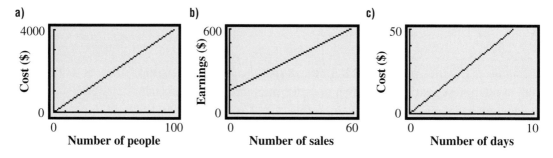

a)

b)

c)

6. **Knowledge/Understanding** The table shows the production of cans at a soft drink company. The number of cans produced, C, is related to d, the number of days of production.

a) Write an equation to relate C and d.

b) Graph this relation.

c) How many cans will be produced on day 10?

Day, d	Number of cans produced, C
1	4000
2	4200
3	4400
4	4600
5	4800

7. **Communication** Compare the costs to have a banquet in *Examples 1* and *2*. Which hall would you choose? Explain your choice.

8. The mass of each candy in a box is 5 g. The mass of the empty box is 20 g. Let t grams represent the total mass of the box and candies. Let n represent the number of candies.

a) Write an equation to relate t and n.

b) Graph the relation.

c) Find the slope and the t-intercept.

d) What does the t-intercept represent?

e) What does the slope represent? What are the units for the slope?

f) How would the graph change in each situation?
　i) The mass of each candy is 7 g.　**ii)** The mass of the box is 30 g.

g) Write the equation for each situation in part f.

9. A tanker truck contains crude oil. The mass of an empty truck is 14 000 kg. The mass of one barrel of oil is 180 kg. Let T kilograms represents the total mass of the truck and the oil. Let b represent the number of barrels of oil.

a) Write an equation to relate T and b.

b) Graph the relation.

c) Find the slope and the T-intercept.

d) What does the T-intercept represent?

e) What does the slope represent? What are the units for the slope?

f) How would the graph and the equation change for a heavier truck?

✓ **10. Application** The average temperature of Earth's surface is 20°C. For every kilometre below the surface, the temperature increases by 10°C. Let T°C represent the temperature at a depth of d kilometres.

a) Write an equation to relate T and d.

b) Graph the relation.

c) Find the slope and the T-intercept.

d) What does the T-intercept represent?

e) What does the slope represent? What are the units for the slope?

f) How would the graph change in each situation?
　i) The surface temperature is 5°C.　**ii)** The surface temperature is 40°C.

g) Write the equation for each situation in part f.

11. Thinking/Inquiry/Problem Solving The cost of organizing a concert in the park is $12 000. Each ticket costs $25. Let t represent the number of tickets sold, and P dollars represent the promoter's profit.

a) How many tickets must be sold to break even?

b) How is this shown on a graph of P against t?

12. The boiling point of water, $T°C$, depends upon h, the height in kilometres above sea level. The boiling point at sea level is $100°C$. For every kilometre above sea level, the boiling point decreases by approximately $3.4°C$.

a) Write an equation to relate T and h.

b) Use a graphing calculator to graph the relation.

c) Find the slope and the T-intercept.

d) What does the T-intercept represent?

e) What does the slope represent? What are the units for the slope?

f) The world's highest mountain is Mt. Everest at 8848 m. Use TRACE to find the temperature at which water boils at the top of Mt. Everest.

13. The amount of batter mix for pancakes varies directly with the number of people who eat breakfast. It takes 4 cups of batter mix to serve 6 people.

a) Create a table of values.

b) Graph the relation.

c) How many cups of batter mix are needed for 30 people?

d) How many people can be served with 12 cups of batter mix?

e) Suppose you use a mix that requires 5 cups of batter mix for 8 people. How would the graph change?

14. Riverdale Collegiate is planning an athletic banquet. The community centre charges a fixed cost of $200 plus $5 per guest. Let T dollars represent the total cost. Let g represent the number of guests.

a) Write an equation to relate T and g.

b) Graph the relation.

c) Find the slope and the T-intercept.

d) What does the slope represent?

e) What does the T-intercept represent?

f) Use the graph to estimate each cost.
   i) 45 guests attend   ii) 52 guests attend   iii) 81 guests attend

g) Use the equation to calculate each cost. Check by comparing your results with estimates from part f.
   i) 47 guests attend   ii) 50 guests attend   iii) 79 guests attend

h) Suppose the cost was $2 more per guest. How would the graph and the equation change?

i) Is this relation best represented by an equation, a table of values, a graph, or a description in words? Justify your opinion.

5.8   Setting Up for a Banquet

On page 190, you saw different arrangements for tables and chairs for a banquet or some other function. One company uses rules to estimate the number of chairs and tables needed. To use these rules, the area of the room must be in square feet. (One square metre is approximately 10 square feet.)

Gathering Data

1. Estimate or measure the area, in square metres, of these rooms in your school.

   a) your classroom   **b)** the cafeteria

2. The approximate dimensions of some rooms in the Royal York Hotel in Toronto are given. Assume each room is rectangular. Calculate the area of each room.

   a) Canadian Room   length: 187 ft   width: 71 ft

   b) Imperial Room   length: 96 ft   width: 63 ft

   c) Manitoba Room   length: 55 ft   width: 22 ft

3. Multiply the areas of the rooms in exercise 1 by 10.76 to convert the areas to square feet. Copy this table. Complete the *Area* column. You will complete the other columns in the exercises that follow.

Room	Area (sq. ft.)	Number of people		
		Theatre style	Oblong table	Round table
Classroom				
Cafeteria				
Canadian Room				
Imperial Room				
Manitoba Room				

The Theatre Style Model

The rule for theatre style:

For the number of people, divide the room area (in square feet) by 6.

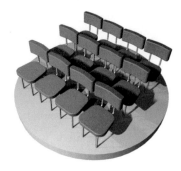

4. a) Let *x* represent the room area in square feet.
   Let *y* represent the number of people who can be seated.
   Use the rule to write an equation for *y* in terms of *x* for this model.

b) Graph the equation.

5. a) Determine how many people can be seated in each room in exercise 3. Enter the results in the 3rd column of the table.

b) Are the results for the rooms in your school reasonable? Explain.

The Oblong Table Model

The rule for oblong tables:

For the number of people, divide the room area (in square feet) by 8.

6. a) Write an equation for *y* in terms of *x* for this model.

b) Graph the equation.

7. a) Determine how many people can be seated at oblong tables in each room in exercise 3. Enter the results in the 4th column of the table.

b) Are the results for the rooms in your school reasonable? Explain.

The Round Table Model

The rule for round tables:

For the number of people, divide the room area (in square feet) by 10.

8. a) Write an equation for *y* in terms of *x* for this model.

b) Graph the equation.

9. a) Determine how many people can be seated at round tables in each room in exercise 3. Enter the results in the 5th column of the table.

b) Are the results for the rooms in your school reasonable? Explain.

10. Communication Explain how rules can be used to find the number of people who can be seated at a banquet.

MATHEMATICS TOOLKIT

Slope of a Line

- The slopes of all segments of a line are equal.
- The slope of a line is the slope of any segment on the line.

The Line $y = mx$

- Graph is a straight line with slope m.
- Passes through the origin O(0, 0).
- Represents *direct variation* since y varies directly with x.

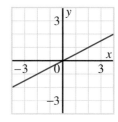

The Line $y = mx + b$

- Graph is a straight line with slope m and y-intercept b.
- Does not pass through the origin.
- Represents *partial variation* since y varies partially with x.
- Called slope y-intercept form.

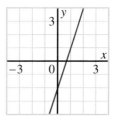

Horizontal and Vertical Lines

Horizontal line

- Has the equation $y = b$, where b is the y-intercept.

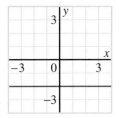

Vertical line

- Has the equation $x = a$, where a is the x-intercept.

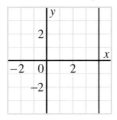

Equation of a Line

To find the equation of a line, one of the following is needed:

- slope and y-intercept
- slope and the coordinates of a point on the line
- the coordinates of two points on the line

5.1 **1.** Graph the line through each point with each given slope.

    a) C(−4, 2), slope −1   **b)** D(5, −3), slope $\frac{5}{2}$ **c)** E(−6, −1), slope undefined

  2. Draw a line with slope $-\frac{3}{4}$ through each point. Find the coordinates of 2 more points on each line.

    a) Q(1, −2)   **b)** R(3, 0)   **c)** S(0, 0)   **d)** T(−3, −1)

  3. Graph the line through each point with each given slope. Find the coordinates of 2 more points on each line.

    a) M(2, 5), slope $\frac{1}{4}$ **b)** N(−2, −4), slope $-\frac{2}{3}$ **c)** P(−1, 3), slope 0

5.2 **4.** Write the equation of each line.

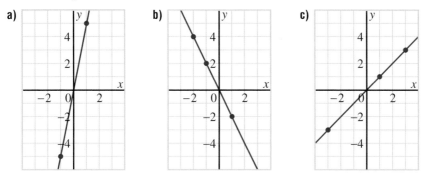

  5. Graph each line.

    a) $y = -\frac{3}{2}x$ **b)** $y = 4x$ **c)** $y = -x$ **d)** $y = \frac{1}{3}x$

5.4 **6.** Write the equation of the line with each slope and y-intercept.

    a) $m = -\frac{1}{4}$, $b = 3$ **b)** $m = 1$, $b = -2$ **c)** $m = \frac{2}{5}$, $b = -4$

  7. Match each line, right, with an equation.

    a) $y = -2$ **b)** $y = \frac{1}{2}x + 2$

    c) $y = -x + 2$ **d)** $y = \frac{1}{2}x - 2$

    e) $y = 2x + 2$ **f)** $y = -2x + 2$

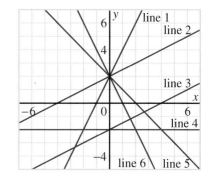

  8. Graph each line then write its equation.

    a) Every point on the line has the x-coordinate −3.

    b) Every point on the line has the y-coordinate 2.

  9. Graph each line.

    a) $y = -2x - 5$ **b)** $y = \frac{2}{3}x + 2$ **c)** $y = -\frac{1}{6}x - 1$

5.5 **10.** Write each equation.

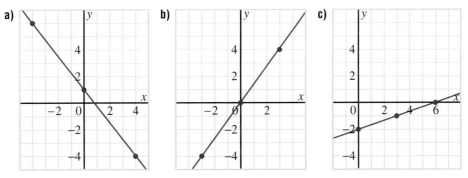

a) **b)** **c)**

11. The coordinates of a point on a line and the slope of the line are given.
　　i) Graph each line.　　　　　　　　**ii)** Write each equation.
　　a) J(1, 3), slope −3　　　**b)** K(−5, −2), slope $\frac{2}{5}$　　**c)** L(4, 0), slope −2

12. Find the equation of the line that passes through each pair of points.
　　a) A(3, 5) and B(−5, −3)　　　　　**b)** C(2, −7) and D(−1, −1)
　　c) G(4, 2) and H(−2, −1)　　　　　**d)** L(6, 0) and M(0, 5)

5.6 **13.** A car travels at an average speed of 65 km/h. The distance travelled, d kilometres, after t hours is given by the equation $d = 65t$.

　　a) Copy and complete this table.

t (h)	0	1	2	3	4	5
d (km)						

　　b) Graph d against t.
　　c) What is the d-intercept? What does it represent?
　　d) What is the slope? What does it represent?
　　e) Suppose the average speed increased. How would the graph change?

5.7 **14.** Olaf is paid \$75/day plus \$15 commission for each product he sells. Let T dollars represent Olaf's total pay and p represent the number of products he sells.

　　a) Write an equation to relate T and p.
　　b) Graph the relation. Should the points be joined? Explain why.
　　c) Find the T-intercept. What does it represent?
　　d) Is the relationship between T and p direct variation or partial variation? Explain how the equation and the graph show this.
　　e) How much would Olaf earn on a day he sells 6 products?
　　f) Suppose Olaf was paid \$95/day plus \$10 commission for each product he sells. Write an equation to relate T and p.

1. **Knowledge/Understanding** Graph each line.

   a) $y = \frac{1}{4}x$

   b) $y = -3x$

   c) $y = -\frac{5}{3}x$

   d) $y = 4x - 1$

   e) $y = 4$

   f) $y = -\frac{2}{3}x + 3$

2. Graph the line for each pair of points.

   a) S(4, 1), T(0, −3)   b) V(−2, 5), Z(−2, −6)   c) L(−5, −1), M(7, −1)

      i) State the slope.

      ii) Find the coordinates of 2 more points on each line.

      iii) Write the equation of each line.

3. **Application** For a business trip, Gina took a flight 450 km north, then rented a car and drove further north at a speed of 70 km/h. Let d kilometres represent the total distance travelled and h, the hours of driving.

   a) Write an equation to relate d and h.

   b) Graph the relation. Estimate the total distance Gina travelled after driving 3 h.

   c) What is the d-intercept? What does it represent?

   d) Suppose Gina drove at a faster speed. How would the graph and the equation change?

   e) Suppose the flight distance had been shorter. How would the graph and the equation change?

4. The coordinates of a point on a line and the slope of the line are given. Graph each line, then write its equation.

   a) D(5, −3), slope $-\frac{1}{5}$ b) E(−4, 1), slope −1   c) F(0, −6), slope $\frac{4}{3}$

5. **Communication**

   a) Describe the steps for substituting the coordinates of a point into an equation of a line to find out whether the point is on the line.

   b) Illustrate the steps from part a with a line from exercise 4.

6. **Thinking/Inquiry/Problem Solving** A line passes through D(−5, 4). The run is 3. The rise is either 2 or −2. When the line crosses the x-axis, the x-coordinate is positive. Write the equation of the line.

7. The graph below shows the number of hectares of trees remaining in a northern forest each year after the logging season.

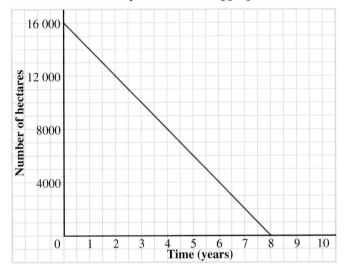

For the situation above, give the meaning of each number below.

- −2000, the slope of the line
- 16 000, the vertical intercept
- 8, the horizontal intercept

8. The graph below shows Yoshikatsu's walk in front of a motion detector.

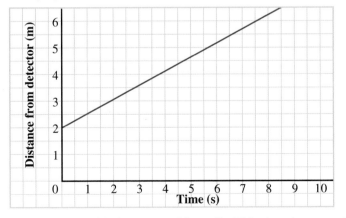

Yoshikatsu decided to repeat his walk. This time he started 1 m in front of the detector and walked at the same speed.

Copy the graph above. Draw a line for the second walk. Determine the equation of the line for the second walk.

CHAPTER 6

Polynomials

By the end of this chapter, you will:

- Substitute into and evaluate algebraic expressions with exponents.
- Use exponent rules for multiplying and dividing monomials, and the exponent rule for the power of a power.
- Add and subtract polynomials.
- Multiply a polynomial by a monomial.
- Expand and simplify polynomials.

Could a Giant Survive?

The Guinness Book of Records reports some real-life examples of exceptionally tall people. The tallest person ever, Robert Wadlow, was 272 cm tall. Wadlow died at age 22. The tallest woman, Zeng Jinlian, was 248 cm tall. She died at age 18.

In Section 6.7, you will develop a mathematical model to help you understand what happens to the body if all the body's dimensions become much larger than normal.

Exponent Laws for Multiplying and Dividing Powers

Recall the exponent law for multiplying powers: $a^n \times a^m = a^{n+m}$

Recall the exponent law for dividing powers: $\frac{a^n}{a^m} = a^{n-m}$

Example

Express as a single power, then evaluate.

a) $3^2 \times 3^3$ **b)** $\frac{5^3}{5^2}$

Solution

a) $3^2 \times 3^3 = 3^{2+3}$ Use a calculator.   **b)** $\frac{5^3}{5^2} = 5^{3-2}$

$\qquad\qquad = 3^5$ $\qquad\qquad\qquad\qquad\qquad\qquad\qquad = 5^1$

$\qquad\qquad = 243$ $\qquad\qquad\qquad\qquad\qquad\qquad\qquad = 5$

Exercises

1. Express as a single power, then evaluate.

   a) $2^3 \times 2^2$ **b)** $4^1 \times 4^3$

   c) $3^2 \times 3^5$ **d)** $10^2 \times 10^5$

   e) $6^4 \div 6^2$ **f)** $10^7 \div 10^3$

   g) $7^6 \div 7$ **h)** $4^9 \div 4^6$

2. Express as a single power, then evaluate.

   a) $\frac{3^8}{3^6}$ **b)** $\frac{10^8}{10^5}$

   c) $\frac{4^5}{4^2}$ **d)** $\frac{5^4}{5^2}$

   e) $\frac{6^4}{6^3}$ **f)** $\frac{2^9}{2}$

   g) $\frac{10^6}{10^2}$ **h)** $\frac{1^7}{1^3}$

Exponent Law for a Power of a Product

Sometimes we apply the exponent law for a power of a power to an algebraic term.

We raise an algebraic term to an exponent; for example, $(2x)^3$.

$(2x)^3$ means $(2x)(2x)(2x) = (2)(2)(2)(x)(x)(x)$
$$= (2^3)(x^3)$$
$$= 8x^3$$

The term, $2x$, is a product of 2 and x.

To raise a product to an exponent, raise each factor to that exponent.

TAKE NOTE

Exponent Law for a Power of a Product

$(ab)^n = a^n b^n$, where n is an integer

Example

Simplify.

a) $(4a)^3$

b) $(-3a)^3$

Solution

Use the power of a product law.

a) $(4a)^3 = 4^3 a^3$
$$= 64a^3$$

b) $(-3a)^3 = (-3)^3 a^3$
$$= -27a^3$$

Exercises

1. Simplify.

a) $(2a)^2$ **b)** $(2a)^3$ **c)** $(2a)^4$ **d)** $(2a)^5$

2. Simplify.

a) $(-3x)^2$ **b)** $(-5a)^3$ **c)** $(-2x)^4$ **d)** $(-2a)^5$

3. Simplify.

a) $(4b)^4$ **b)** $(-6z)^2$ **c)** $(-3c)^5$ **d)** $(5m)^4$

e) $(-2t)^6$ **f)** $(-7x)^3$ **g)** $(-4z)^7$ **h)** $(3q)^8$

Necessary Skills

The Distributive Law

Recall the distributive law: $a(b + c) = ab + ac$

Example

Expand.

a) $2(x + 4)$ **b)** $-3(2a - 5)$

Solution

a) $2(x + 4) = 2(x) + 2(4)$
$$= 2x + 8$$

b) $-3(2a - 5) = -3(2a) - 3(-5)$
$$= -6a + 15$$

Exercises

1. Expand.

   a) $3(2 + a)$ **b)** $3(2 - a)$ **c)** $4(2x + 1)$ **d)** $4(2x - 1)$

2. This diagram represents a parking lot. Use the distributive law. Write two expressions for the total area of the parking lot.

3. Expand.

   a) $6(4x + 9)$ **b)** $-3(5c + 3)$ **c)** $11(3 - 8z)$

   d) $-10(-2 + 7y)$ **e)** $5(6z + 2)$ **f)** $-(3y - 6)$

Jennifer has U.S. bills from a vacation in the United States and some Canadian bills.

To calculate the amount, Jennifer adds the U.S. money: $20 + $10 + $10 + $5 + $1 = $46 U.S. and the Canadian money: $10 + $5 + $5 = $20 Can

All the terms that represent Canadian money are like terms. They can be combined into a single value. Similarly, all the terms that represent U.S. money are like terms. However, a term that represents Canadian money and a term that represents U.S. money are unlike terms. They cannot be combined into a single value.

We can only say that Jennifer has $46 U.S. and $20 Can.

In Chapter 3, you worked with algebra tiles and like and unlike terms.

Recall:

This is a 1-tile.

It measures 1 unit on each side.
Its area is 1 square unit.

This is a variable tile, or x-tile.

It measures 1 unit by x units.
Its area is x square units.

This new algebra tile is a square measuring x units on each side.
Its area is $x \times x$, or x^2 square units.
It is an x^2-tile.

All three tiles represent unlike terms.

Forming Rectangles with Algebra Tiles

1. Arrange 4 green 1-tiles to form a rectangle.

   a) What is the length of the rectangle?

   b) What is the width of the rectangle?

   c) What is the area of the rectangle?

   d) What is the perimeter of the rectangle?

2. Arrange the tiles from exercise 1 to form a different rectangle. Repeat exercise 1a to d for the new rectangle.

3. Compare your answers to exercises 1 and 2. What do you notice about the perimeter and area?

4. a) Arrange 4 green *x*-tiles to form a rectangle. Repeat exercise 1 for this rectangle.

   b) Make as many different rectangles as possible. For each new rectangle, repeat exercise 1.

5. Use the tiles from exercises 1 and 4 together. Make as many different rectangles as possible. Repeat exercise 1 for each rectangle.

6. When you arrange algebra tiles to form different rectangles:

   a) What do you notice about the areas?

   b) What do you notice about the perimeters?

From the *Investigation*, for a fixed number of tiles, when the rectangle changed:

• The area remained constant.

• The perimeter changed.

Since x is a variable, we cannot combine the areas of a 1-tile, an x-tile, and an x^2-tile to form a single term. The tiles represent unlike terms.

To represent these tiles:

We think: 3 x^2-tiles + 2 x-tiles + 5 1-tiles

We write: $3x^2 + 2x + 5$

There are special names for terms and combinations of terms.
Terms are separated by plus or minus signs. The sign belongs to the term.

A term is a constant or a coefficient and one or more variables.
A coefficient is the number that precedes a variable.
The term $3x^2$ has coefficient 3 and variable x.

A *polynomial* is one term or the sum of two or more terms.
These are polynomials: $-3x$, $3a^2 - 5a - 14$, $11 - d^2$

A *monomial* is a polynomial with one term.
These are monomials: $3x^2$, $4x$, $-6m^3$

A *binomial* is a polynomial with two terms.
These are binomials: $3x + 7$, $4 - a^4$

A *trinomial* is a polynomial with three terms.
These are trinomials: $3x^2 + 7x - 6$, $a^2 - 2a + 1$

The trinomial $3x^2 - 2x + 5$ contains coefficients 3 and -2; 5 is a constant term.
The variable is x.

We can use algebra tiles to represent the polynomial $3x^2 + 2x + 5$. The terms in this polynomial have positive coefficients. We can also represent a polynomial such as $3x^2 - 2x + 5$, which has a term with a negative coefficient. We do this by flipping the two x-tiles.

We see: $3x^2 - 2x + 5$
We think: 3 x^2-tiles, 2 flipped x-tiles, and 5 1-tiles

We display:

Recall that we can evaluate an expression by substituting a number for a variable.

Example 1

a) Evaluate $2x - 3$ for $x = 4$.

b) Evaluate $-4a^2 + 3a + 3$ for $a = -2$.

Solution

a) Substitute $x = 4$ in $2x - 3$.

$$2x - 3 = 2(4) - 3$$
$$= 8 - 3$$
$$= 5$$

b) Substitute $a = -2$ in $-4a^2 + 3a + 3$.

$$-4a^2 + 3a + 3 = -4(-2)^2 + 3(-2) + 3 \qquad \text{Recall that } (-2)^2 = 4.$$
$$= -4(4) - 6 + 3$$
$$= -16 - 3$$
$$= -19$$

As you discovered in the *Investigation*, we can combine algebra tiles to form a rectangle. We can write the area and the perimeter of the rectangle as a polynomial.

Example 2

Write polynomials that represent the perimeter and area of each rectangle.

a)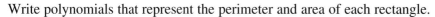

b)

Solution

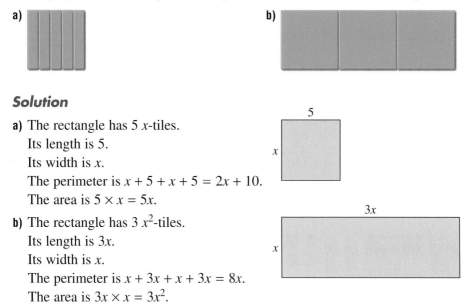

a) The rectangle has 5 x-tiles.
Its length is 5.
Its width is x.
The perimeter is $x + 5 + x + 5 = 2x + 10$.
The area is $5 \times x = 5x$.

b) The rectangle has 3 x^2-tiles.
Its length is $3x$.
Its width is x.
The perimeter is $x + 3x + x + 3x = 8x$.
The area is $3x \times x = 3x^2$.

A

1. How much money is represented?

10 Can	10 U.S.	1 U.S.
10 Can	5 Can	2 Can
10 U.S.	5 U.S.	1 U.S.
10 Can	5 U.S.	5 U.S.

2. Let x represent Canadian money.
Let y represent U.S. money.
Write an expression to represent the total money in exercise 1.

3. Is each expression a monomial, binomial, or trinomial? Give reasons.
a) $3x + 4$ b) $-x^2$ c) $-2 - y^2$ d) 10
e) $5 - 2x + 3x^2$ f) $4x$ g) $5x^2 + 4 + x$ h) $-3 - y$

4. For each, write a polynomial that represents the total area.

a)

b)

c)

d)

5. Use algebra tiles to represent each polynomial.
a) $x^2 + 3x + 2$ b) $2x^2 + x + 7$ c) $-2x^2 - 3$ d) $2x^2 - 5x - 4$
e) $-x^2 - 3x + 2$ f) $x^2 - 4x$ g) $6 - x$ h) 5

6. State the coefficient in each term.

   a) $14x$　　　**b)** $7y^2$　　　**c)** a　　　**d)** $-b^2$　　　**e)** $3r^2$

7. State the constant term in each polynomial.

   a) $5x^2 - 2x + 6$　　**b)** $-x^2 - 5$　　**c)** $7 - 3x - 2x^2$　　**d)** $7x^2 - 5x$

8. State the coefficient for each variable term.

   a) $6p + 2p^2 + 3$　　**b)** $6 - 2c + 9c^2$　　**c)** $1.8C + 32$

   d) $2r$　　　　　　**e)** $7y^2 - 3y - 9$　　**f)** $4s^3 - s^2 - 5s + 2$

9. State the like terms in each group.

   a) $5a, 3b, 5c, a^2, -a, 3d, 3e$　　　　**b)** $4x, 3y^2, 4z, 2y, y^2, 4w$

   c) $9g, 6h, 9g^2, \frac{1}{9}g, \frac{1}{6}h^2, g^2$　　　　**d)** $16, d^2, d, f, -8, 0.5d, 7d^3$

B **10.** Evaluate $3n + 4$ for each value of n.

   a) 1　　　　**b)** 3　　　　**c)** 4　　　　**d)** -1

11. Evaluate $3x - 5$ for each value of x.

   a) 0　　　　**b)** 1　　　　**c)** -1　　　　**d)** 7

12. Evaluate $2a^2 - 6a + 1$ for each value of a.

   a) 0　　　　**b)** -1　　　　**c)** 2　　　　**d)** -3

13. Knowledge/Understanding Write a polynomial to represent the perimeter of each rectangle.

   a)　　　　　**b)**　　　　　**c)**

14. Write a polynomial to represent the area of each rectangle in exercise 13.

15. Represent each rectangle using algebra tiles.

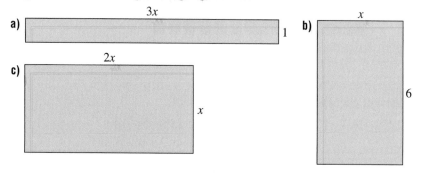

$3x$

a)　　　　　　　　　　　　　　　1　**b)**　x

$2x$

c)　　　　　　　　　　x　　　　　　6

16. For each rectangle in exercise 15, write a polynomial to represent its perimeter and a polynomial to represent its area.

17. Communication

   a) Is a binomial a polynomial? Explain.

   b) Is a monomial a binomial? Explain.

18. Write a polynomial to represent the perimeter of each rectangle.

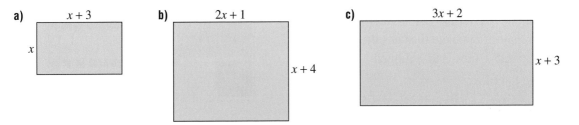

a) $x + 3$, x **b)** $2x + 1$, $x + 4$ **c)** $3x + 2$, $x + 3$

19. For exercise 18, determine the perimeter of each rectangle when $x = 4$ cm and when $x = 2$ m.

20. a) Write a polynomial to represent the area of a square with side length x.

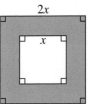

2x, x

   b) Write a polynomial to represent the area of:
   i) the large square
   ii) the small square
   iii) the shaded region

   c) Determine the area of each figure in part b when $x = 3$ cm.

21. Application The formula, $d = 0.20v + 0.015v^2$, gives the approximate stopping distance, d metres, for a car travelling at v kilometres per hour. Estimate the stopping distance for a speed of 50 km/h and a speed of 100 km/h.

22. Thinking/Inquiry/Problem Solving Use the variable x. Make up a trinomial, a binomial, and a monomial that result in -3 when $x = 2$.

6.2 Adding Polynomials

To add two polynomials, we combine like terms. We can use algebra tiles to add polynomials. We combined like terms in Section 3.2. Now we include x^2-tiles.

Suppose we add $2x^2 + 3x + 1$ and $-x^2 + 2x - 4$.
We write: $(2x^2 + 3x + 1) + (-x^2 + 2x - 4)$

We think:

Combine like terms. Use the Zero Principle. Each pair of opposite tiles has the sum 0.
1 x^2-tile, 5 x-tiles, and 3 flipped 1-tiles remain.

We display:

From the tiles,
$(2x^2 + 3x + 1) + (-x^2 + 2x - 4) = x^2 + 5x - 3$

To add polynomials algebraically, we group like terms, then simplify. When grouping like terms, the sign in front of the term belongs to the term. The sign should move with the term.

Example 1

Simplify $(-2x^2 + 6x - 7) + (3x^2 - x - 2)$.

Solution

$$
\begin{aligned}
(-2x^2 + 6x - 7) + (3x^2 - x - 2) &= -2x^2 + 6x - 7 + 3x^2 - x - 2 \\
&= -2x^2 + 3x^2 + 6x - x - 7 - 2 \\
&= x^2 + 5x - 9
\end{aligned}
$$

Remove brackets

Group like terms

Add like terms

Discuss

Explain how to use algebra tiles to add $(-2x^2 + 6x - 7) + (3x^2 - x - 2)$.

Some polynomials cannot be represented with algebra tiles. We use algebra to combine these polynomials.

Example 2

Simplify $(2x^4 - 3x^2 + x - 1) + (-x^4 - 3x + 3)$.

Solution

$$
\begin{aligned}
(2x^4 - 3x^2 + x - 1) + (-x^4 - 3x + 3) &= 2x^4 - 3x^2 + x - 1 - x^4 - 3x + 3 \\
&= 2x^4 - x^4 - 3x^2 + x - 3x - 1 + 3 \\
&= x^4 - 3x^2 - 2x + 2
\end{aligned}
$$

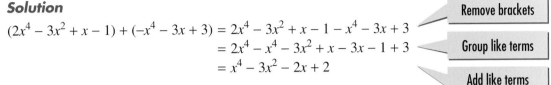

Remove brackets

Group like terms

Add like terms

Discuss

Why can we not represent these polynomials with algebra tiles?

When we evaluate the sum of two polynomials, we simplify first.

Example 3

a) Simplify $(-2x^3 + 3x + 1) + (x^3 - 4x - 2)$.

b) Evaluate the polynomial in part a for $x = -2$.

Solution

a)
$$
\begin{aligned}
(-2x^3 + 3x + 1) + (x^3 - 4x - 2) &= -2x^3 + 3x + 1 + x^3 - 4x - 2 \\
&= -2x^3 + x^3 + 3x - 4x + 1 - 2 \\
&= -x^3 - x - 1
\end{aligned}
$$

b) $-x^3 - x - 1$

Substitute $x = -2$.

$$
\begin{aligned}
-x^3 - x - 1 &= -(-2)^3 - (-2) - 1 \\
&= -(-8) + 2 - 1 \\
&= 8 + 2 - 1 \\
&= 9
\end{aligned}
$$

Note: $(-2)^3 = (-2) \times (-2) \times (-2)$

$= 4 \times (-2)$

$= -8$

Discuss

Suppose we evaluated $(-2x^3 + 3x + 1) + (x^3 - 4x - 2)$ for $x = -2$ without simplifying first. What would be the result? Why does this make sense? How can you check?

A **1.** Use algebra tiles to add.

    a) $(x^2 + 2x - 1) + (2x^2 + 3x + 3)$ **b)** $(3x^2 - x + 5) + (x^2 - 2x - 4)$

    c) $(-2x^2 - 3x - 4) + (-2x^2 - 5x - 1)$ **d)** $(x^2 - 2x - 4) + (-x^2 + 2x + 4)$

2. a) Use the variable x. What polynomials do these tiles represent?

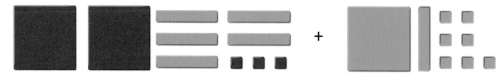

    b) Use algebra tiles to find the sum of the polynomials in part a.

3. Use the variable x. Add.

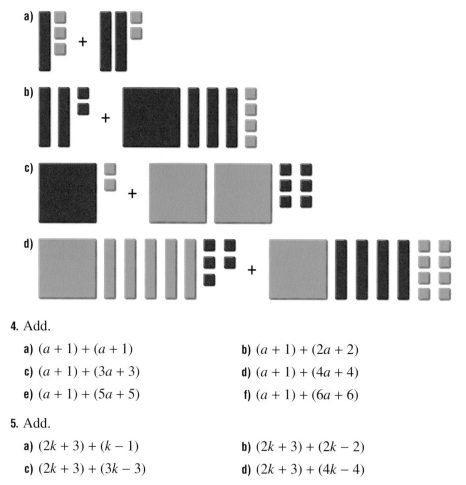

✓ **4.** Add.

    a) $(a + 1) + (a + 1)$ **b)** $(a + 1) + (2a + 2)$

    c) $(a + 1) + (3a + 3)$ **d)** $(a + 1) + (4a + 4)$

    e) $(a + 1) + (5a + 5)$ **f)** $(a + 1) + (6a + 6)$

✓ **5.** Add.

    a) $(2k + 3) + (k - 1)$ **b)** $(2k + 3) + (2k - 2)$

    c) $(2k + 3) + (3k - 3)$ **d)** $(2k + 3) + (4k - 4)$

B **6.** Add.

a) $(h^2 + 1) + (4h^2 + 5)$

b) $(h^2 - 1) + (4h^2 - 5)$

c) $(h^2 + h) + (4h^2 + 3h)$

d) $(h^2 - h) + (4h^2 - 3h)$

e) $(h^2 + h + 1) + (4h^2 + 3h + 5)$

f) $(h^2 - h - 1) + (4h^2 - 3h - 5)$

7. Add.

a) $(6x + 2) + (3x + 4)$

b) $(5a - 3) + (2a + 7)$

c) $(8 - 4m) + (-3 - 2m)$

d) $(-x + 4) + (7x - 2)$

8. Knowledge/Understanding Add.

a) $(4n^2 - 3n - 1) + (2n^2 - 5n - 3)$

b) $(3x^2 + 6x - 8) + (-5x^2 - x + 4)$

c) $(2 - 3c + c^2) + (5 - 4c - 4c^2)$

d) $(8 - 2n - n^2) + (-3 - n + 4n^2)$

e) $(b^3 + 3b - 5) + (2b^3 - 4b - 6)$

f) $(m^4 - 5m^2 + 6m - 2) + (-6m^4 + 3m^2 + 7)$

9. Add.

a) $(3x^2 + 2x + 4) + (x^2 + 3)$

b) $(3x^2 - 2x - 4) + (x^2 - 3)$

c) $(5m + 2m^2) + (m^2 + 6)$

d) $(5m - 2m^2) + (m^2 - 6)$

10. Add.

a) $(5c^4 + 2c^3 - 7) + (3c^4 - c^3 + 1)$

b) $(-4q^5 + 3q^2 - 5q - 7) + (-q^4 - 6q^3 + 2q)$

c) $(2t^3 - 6 + 2t^2) + (4t^3 + t - 1)$

d) $(3 + t + 4t^4) + (-7 - t - 5t^3 + t^4)$

11. a) Add $(2x^5 + 3x^4 + 4x^3 + 5x^2) + (-2x^3 + 3x^2 - 7)$.

b) Communication Explain why you cannot use algebra tiles to simplify the polynomial sum in part a.

12. Simplify. Then determine the value of the polynomial when $x = 1$.
$(1 - 2x^2 - x) + (2x - 3x^2 - 7)$

13. Simplify. Then determine the value of the polynomial when $x = -2$.
$(3 - 2x^2 - x) + (2x - 3x^2 - 7)$

14. Simplify. Then evaluate for $y = -3$.

a) $(y^2 + y + 2) + (3y^2 - y + 1)$

b) $(-2y^4 - y^3 + y - 1) + (3y^4 - y^3 - y^2 - 5)$

c) $(5y^3 + 2y^2 - 4y) + (-y^4 - y^3 + 4)$

15. Application Each rectangle is divided into squares and rectangles. Write one polynomial for the area of each section and one polynomial for the area of the entire rectangle.

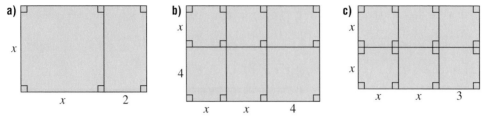

a)

b)

c)

16. Simplify.

a) $(3x^2 - 7x + 4) + (5x - 7x^2 + 6)$

b) $(6 - 3x + x^2) + (9 - x)$

c) $(1 - 7x^2 + 2x) + (x^3 - 3x^2 + 7)$

d) $(5x - x^2) + (3x + x^2 - 7)$

17. What hint would you give about using algebra tiles to represent the addition of polynomials?

18. Thinking/Inquiry/Problem Solving
Choose any month on a calendar.
Then choose a 3 by 3 square of 9 dates.
Let x represent the date at the centre
of the square.

a) Write a polynomial for:
   i) the date one week before x
   ii) the date one week after x
   iii) the sum of the dates in each column
   iv) the sum of all 9 dates

b) Suppose you know the sum of all 9 dates.
   How could you determine the value of x?

19. a) Write a polynomial expression for the perimeter of the triangle shown.

b) Find the perimeter when $x = 2$.

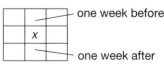
one week before
x
one week after

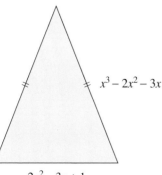
$x^3 - 2x^2 - 3x$

$2x^2 - 3x + 1$

Subtracting Polynomials

Polynomials can be subtracted. We can use algebra tiles to subtract polynomials.

Polynomials that have a sum of 0 are called *opposites*.
Flipping the tiles representing $-2x^2 + x - 9$ gives its opposite, $2x^2 - x + 9$.
We can use this to subtract one polynomial from another.

Suppose we subtract $-2x^2 + x - 9$ from $3x^2 + 5x - 6$.
We write: $(3x^2 + 5x - 6) - (-2x^2 + x - 9)$

We think:

Flip the tiles representing $(-2x^2 + x - 9)$.
Combine like terms.
Use the Zero Principle.
5 x^2-tiles, 4 x-tiles, and 3 1-tiles remain.
From the tiles,
$(3x^2 + 5x - 6) - (-2x^2 + x - 9) = 5x^2 + 4x + 3$

When we subtract a polynomial from itself,
we get zero.
For example, $(x^2 - 2x - 4) - (x^2 - 2x - 4) = 0$

We display:

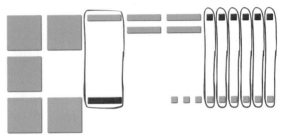

We get the same result if we add the polynomial and its opposite.
For example, $(x^2 - 2x - 4) + (-x^2 + 2x + 4) = 0$

So, to subtract a polynomial, we add its opposite.

Example 1

Simplify $(3x^2 + 5x - 6) - (-2x^2 + x - 9)$.

Solution
$$\begin{aligned}
(3x^2 + 5x - 6) - (-2x^2 + x - 9) &= (3x^2 + 5x - 6) + (2x^2 - x + 9) \\
&= 3x^2 + 5x - 6 + 2x^2 - x + 9 \\
&= 3x^2 + 2x^2 + 5x - x - 6 + 9 \\
&= 5x^2 + 4x + 3
\end{aligned}$$

Add the opposite of
$-2x^2 + x - 9$

Remove brackets

Group like terms

Add like terms

We can subtract polynomials using algebra.

Example 2

Simplify $(3x^4 - 2x^2 + 3x - 9) - (x^2 - 4x + 2)$.

Solution

$(3x^4 - 2x^2 + 3x - 9) - (x^2 - 4x + 2)$
$= (3x^4 - 2x^2 + 3x - 9) + (-x^2 + 4x - 2)$
$= 3x^4 - 2x^2 + 3x - 9 - x^2 + 4x - 2$
$= 3x^4 - 2x^2 - x^2 + 3x + 4x - 9 - 2$
$= 3x^4 - 3x^2 + 7x - 11$

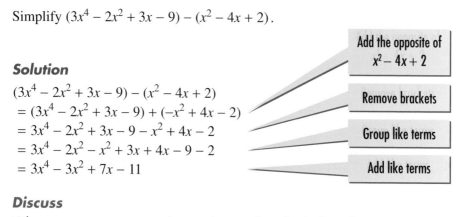

Add the opposite of $x^2 - 4x + 2$

Remove brackets

Group like terms

Add like terms

Discuss

Why can we not represent these polynomials with algebra tiles?

When we evaluate the difference of two polynomials, we simplify first.

Example 3

a) Simplify $(2x^3 - 3x^2 + x - 1) - (-x^2 + 2x - 1)$.

b) Evaluate the polynomial in part a for $x = 3$.

Solution

a) $(2x^3 - 3x^2 + x - 1) - (-x^2 + 2x - 1) = 2x^3 - 3x^2 + x - 1 + x^2 - 2x + 1$
$= 2x^3 - 3x^2 + x^2 + x - 2x - 1 + 1$
$= 2x^3 - 2x^2 - x$

b) $2x^3 - 2x^2 - x$

Substitute $x = 3$.
$2x^3 - 2x^2 - x = 2(3)^3 - 2(3)^2 - 3$ Note: $3^3 = 27$ and $3^2 = 9$
$= 2(27) - 2(9) - 3$
$= 54 - 18 - 3$
$= 33$

6.3   Exercises

1. Show each polynomial using algebra tiles. Then flip the tiles and state
its opposite.

    a) $3x^2 + 7$ **b)** $2x^2 - 5x + 3$ **c)** $-4n^2 + 3n - 5$

2. a) Use the variable x. What polynomials do these tiles represent?

b) Use algebra tiles to find the difference of the polynomials in part a.

3. Use the variable m. Subtract.

a)

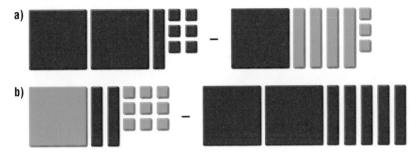

b)

4. Use algebra tiles to subtract.

a) $(-x^2 + 5x + 4) - (2x^2 + 3x + 3)$ **b)** $(3x^2 + 4) - (x^2 + 2)$

5. State the opposite of each polynomial.

a) $5x + 2$ **b)** $2 - 3a$ **c)** $7x^2 - 5x + 4$

d) $5 - 2m - 4m^2$ **e)** $6n^2 - 3n + 1$ **f)** $-2x^3 - 5$

6. Write each subtraction statement as an addition statement.

a) $(3x^2 + 5) - (2x^2 + 1)$

b) $(x^2 + 2x) - (-x - 1)$

c) $(x^2 + 3x - 2) - (-x^2 - x + 1)$

7. Communication Explain why the two polynomials in each pair are not opposites.

a) $5x^2 - 3x - 2$ **b)** $x^2 + 7x - 9$ **c)** $-4y + y^2 + 11$ **d)** $x^3 - 4x^2 + 9$

$5x^2 + 3x + 2$ $-x^3 - 7x + 9$ $4y - y^2 + 11$ $-x^3 + 4x^2 - x$

8. Subtract.

a) $(8s + 8) - (s + 1)$ **b)** $(8s^2 + 8s + 8) - (s^2 + s + 1)$

c) $(8s + 8) - (-s - 1)$ **d)** $(8s^2 + 8s + 8) - (-s^2 - s - 1)$

9. Simplify.

a) $(-2x + 3) - (3x + 2)$ **b)** $(4 - 5n) - (-6n + 2)$

c) $(8a^2 + 2a - 3) - (-6a^2 + 4a + 7)$ **d)** $(-6x^2 + 5x + 1) - (4x^2 + 5 - 2x)$

10. **Knowledge/Understanding** Simplify.
   a) $(3 - 2n - n^2) - (7 - 6n + n^2)$ b) $(2 + 6x^2) - (7 - 3x^2)$
   c) $(5 - 6t^2) - (3 - t^2)$ d) $(5x^2 - 3x) - (-3x + 5x^2)$

11. a) What is the sum of a polynomial and its opposite? Explain.
    b) Is there a polynomial that is equal to its opposite? Explain.

12. Simplify.
   a) $(3x - 2) - (x - 1)$ b) $(2a + 3) - (6a - 1)$
   c) $(5x^2 - 3x) - (x^2 + 2x)$ d) $(5t - 4) - (3t - 1)$
   e) $(3 - 4x + x^2) - (2x - x^2)$ f) $(3n^2 - 6n + 5) - (3n^2 - 2n - 1)$

13. Simplify.
   a) $(5x^2 + 7x + 9) - (3x^2 + 4x + 2)$ b) $(11m^2 - 5m + 8) - (7m^2 + m - 3)$
   c) $(4a^2 - 3a^3 - 7) - (a^2 - 2a^3 - 13)$ d) $(-6x^2 + 17x - 4) - (3x^2 + 12x + 8)$

14. Simplify. Then find the value of the polynomial when $x = 3$.
   $(3x^2 - 8x + 6) - (-2x^2 + 7x + 3)$

15. Simplify. Then find the value of the polynomial when $x = -2$.
   $(x^2 - 4x + x^3) - (3x + 5 - x^3)$

16. a) Simplify.
      i) $(5 - 2m - m^2) - (7m + 4 - 5m^2)$ ii) $(2m^2 - 5m + 3) - (4 - 3m)$
    b) Determine the value of each polynomial in part a when $m = 0$ and
       when $m = -2$.

17. a) Simplify.
      i) $(y^2 - 2y) - (5 - 2y)$ ii) $(8y - 5) - (y - 4) + (3y + 1)$
    b) Determine the value of each polynomial in part a when $y = 4$ and
       when $y = 1$.

18. **Application** When the terms of a polynomial in x are arranged from the
    highest to the lowest powers of x, the polynomial is in *descending* powers of x.
    a) Simplify. Write the polynomial in descending powers of x.
       $7 - (3x^2 + 2x) - (5x + x^2 - 6) - (3x + 3x^2 - 12)$
    b) Determine the value of the polynomial in part a when $x = 2$.

19. **Thinking/Inquiry/Problem Solving**
    a) Plan a method of adding to check subtraction with polynomials. Show
       your method with an example.
    b) Plan a method of subtracting to check addition with polynomials. Show
       your method with an example.
    c) Explain whether your methods in parts a and b are related.

6.4 Multiplying Monomials

In Sections 6.2 and 6.3, we added and subtracted polynomials.

We now multiply one-term polynomials, called monomials.

Recall the exponent laws for multiplying powers.
We apply this to multiply monomials.

$$(a^m)(a^n) = a^{m+n}$$

Consider this product:

$$(3a^2)(5a^3) = (3 \times a \times a)(5 \times a \times a \times a)$$ Write each term as a product of factors.
$$= (3)(5)(a \times a \times a \times a \times a)$$ Rearrange the factors.
$$= 15a^5$$ Write $a \times a \times a \times a \times a$ as a^5.

The above example illustrates this rule for multiplying monomials:

TAKE NOTE

Multiplying Monomials

To multiply two monomials, multiply their coefficients and multiply their variables.
If the variables are the same, add their exponents.

We use this rule to multiply $3a^2$ by $5a^3$.
Multiply the coefficients: $3 \times 5 = 15$
To multiply the variables, write the variable and add the exponents: $a^2 \times a^3 = a^{2+3}$
$$= a^5$$

$$(3a^2)(5a^3) = 15a^5$$

Example

Simplify $(3x^2)(-2x^3)$.

Solution

$$(3x^2)(-2x^3) = (3)(-2)(x^2)(x^3)$$
$$= -6x^{2+3}$$
$$= -6x^5$$

A 1. Simplify.

   a) $(2)(5)(x^4)(x^2)$ b) $(5)(2)(x^2)(x^4)$ c) $(-2)(5)(x^3)(x^3)$

   d) $(2)(-5)(x)(x^5)$ e) $(-9)(4)(t^6)(t^2)$ f) $(-7)(-6)(z)(z^6)$

2. Simplify.

   a) $(3x^2)(4x^3)$ b) $(-x^2)(2x^6)$ c) $(a^2)(a^4)$ d) $(-5a)(6a^2)$

3. Simplify.

   a) $(6x)(6x)(x^3)$ b) $(3z^2)(3z^2)(3z^2)(-z)(-z)$

   c) $(-4a^3)(-4a^3)(-a^2)(-a^2)(-a^2)$ d) $(-2n)(-2n)(-2n)(-2n)(n^2)(n^2)$

B 4. Simplify.

   a) $4(3b)$ b) $(-7)(2k)$ c) $5(4t)$ d) $(-2)(8p)$

   e) $a(5a)$ f) $p(-3p)$ g) $n(4n)$ h) $x(-2x)$

5. **Knowledge/Understanding** Simplify.

   a) $(3a)(2a)$ b) $(-2c)(5c)$ c) $(-2a)(-5a)$

   d) $(7x)(3x)$ e) $(8y)(-7y)$ f) $(-x)(-5x)$

6. Simplify.

   a) $(12x)^2$ b) $(-3y)^3$ c) $-(5b)^2$

   d) $-(9m^5)^2$ e) $(-5b^2)^3$ f) $-(3n^4)^2$

7. Simplify.

   a) $(x^3)(-x^2)$ b) $(2p^2)(3p^3)$ c) $(6y^3)(-2y)$ d) $(3b)(2b^2)$

8. Simplify.

   a) $(3m^4)(7m^5)$ b) $(2x^2)(4x^3)$ c) $(8a^3)(7a^{11})$

   d) $(-5b^3)(2b^4)$ e) $(6x^5)(-3x^3)$ f) $(-8p^4)(-6p^2)$

9. **Application**

   a) Write the area of the square as a product of monomials.

   b) Write the area of the square as a monomial.

10. **Communication** When is the product of two monomials a monomial?
    Explain using an example.

11. **Thinking/Inquiry/Problem Solving** Name a pair of monomials that will
    satisfy each equation. Is there only one possible answer for each equation?
    Explain.

   a) $\square \times \square = 3x^6$ b) $\square \times \square = -5b^3$ c) $\square \times \square = -6x$

To divide two monomials, use the exponent law for dividing powers.

Consider this quotient:

$$\frac{a^m}{a^n} = a^{m-n}$$

$$\frac{18a^6}{3a^2} = \frac{2 \times 3 \times 3 \times a \times a \times a \times a \times a \times a}{3 \times a \times a}$$ Write each term as a product of factors.

$$= \frac{2 \times 3 \times 3^1 \times a \times a \times a \times a \times a^1 \times a^1}{3^1 \times a^1 \times a^1}$$ Reduce by dividing common factors.

$$= 6a^4$$ Write $a \times a \times a \times a$ as a^4.

The above example illustrates this rule for dividing monomials:

TAKE NOTE

Dividing Monomials

To divide two monomials, divide their coefficients and divide their variables.
If the variables are the same, subtract their exponents.

We use this rule to divide $18x^6$ by $3x^2$.

Divide the coefficients: $18 \div 3 = 6$

To divide the variables, write the variable

and subtract the exponents: $x^6 \div x^2 = x^{6-2}$

$$= x^4$$

$$\frac{18x^6}{3x^2} = 6x^4$$

Example

Simplify $8a^4 \div 2a^2$.

Solution

$$8a^4 \div 2a^2 = \frac{8a^4}{2a^2}$$

$$= \frac{8}{2} \times \frac{a^4}{a^2}$$ Note: $\frac{8}{2} = 4$

$$= 4a^{4-2}$$

$$= 4a^2$$

A **1.** Divide.

   a) $\dfrac{6x}{3}$ **b)** $\dfrac{12x^2}{4}$ **c)** $\dfrac{20x^3}{5}$

   d) $\dfrac{32x^4}{8}$ **e)** $\dfrac{x^3}{x}$ **f)** $\dfrac{x^5}{x^2}$

2. Simplify.

   a) $\dfrac{2x^2}{x}$ **b)** $\dfrac{2x^3}{x^2}$ **c)** $\dfrac{4x^2}{2x}$ **d)** $\dfrac{4x^3}{2x^2}$

3. Simplify.

   a) $\dfrac{-3x^2}{x}$ **b)** $\dfrac{-3x^3}{x^2}$ **c)** $\dfrac{-9x^2}{3x}$ **d)** $\dfrac{-9x^3}{3x^2}$

4. Simplify.

   a) $\dfrac{(3x)(3x)(3x)(3x)}{(-x)(-x)}$ **b)** $\dfrac{(-4d)(-4d)(-4d)(-4d)(-4d)}{(2d)(2d)(2d)(2d)}$

   c) $\dfrac{(-10a)(-10a)(-10a)}{(-5a)}$ **d)** $\dfrac{(6t)(6t)(6t)(6t)}{(3t)(3t)(3t)}$

B **5.** Simplify.

   a) $\dfrac{5m^5}{2m^3}$ **b)** $\dfrac{-25x^5}{10x^2}$ **c)** $\dfrac{30x^6}{-6x^2}$

6. Knowledge/Understanding Simplify.

   a) $\dfrac{12x^3}{3}$ **b)** $\dfrac{32y^4}{16}$

   c) $\dfrac{27m^3}{-9m}$ **d)** $(-45y^6) \div (-5y^4)$

   e) $3n^6 \div 5n^4$ **f)** $25x^4 \div (-5x^4)$

7. Simplify.

   a) $15x^3 \div 3x$ **b)** $(-6y^2) \div 2y$

   c) $20a^3 \div (-4a^2)$ **d)** $\dfrac{6b^3}{2b^2}$

   e) $\dfrac{15m^5}{3m^2}$ **f)** $\dfrac{21x^2}{7x^2}$

8. Simplify.

   a) $\dfrac{-28a^7}{4a^2}$ **b)** $\dfrac{20s^3}{-5s}$

   c) $\dfrac{-32c^8}{-8c^2}$ **d)** $45x^9 \div 9x^3$

   e) $18y^4 \div 3y^2$ **f)** $12b^3 \div 4b^2$

9. Simplify.

a) $42m^{12} \div 6m^4$

b) $36k^4 \div 9k^3$

c) $25w^3 \div 5w^3$

d) $\dfrac{49z^7}{7z^4}$

e) $\dfrac{56a^4}{8a^3}$

f) $\dfrac{60x^3}{15x^3}$

10. Simplify.

a) $\dfrac{(-10v)^6}{(5v^2)^2}$

b) $\dfrac{(4p)^6}{(2p)^2}$

11. **Communication** Javier's solution to the exercise $\dfrac{6x^{10}}{3x^2}$ is $2x^5$. Is his solution correct? Explain why.

12. Multiply or divide.

a) $(2m^3)(5m^2)$

b) $(-x^4)(3x)$

c) $\dfrac{2x^5}{3x^3}$

d) $\dfrac{-9m^8}{12m^5}$

e) $(3b^3)(2b^4)$

f) $\dfrac{15x^3}{-5x}$

13. Multiply or divide.

a) $(2d^3)(5d^4)$

b) $(-30m^2) \div (-6m)$

c) $(-x^2)(5x)$

d) $(-3a)(-10a^3)$

e) $\dfrac{12x^3}{2x}$

f) $\dfrac{-25a^7}{15a^2}$

14. When is the quotient of two monomials a monomial? Explain using an example.

15. **Thinking/Inquiry/Problem Solving** Name a pair of monomials that will satisfy each equation. Is there only one possible answer for each equation? Explain.

a) $\square \div \square = 2x^2$

b) $\square \div \square = 6x^3$

c) $\square \div \square = 4$

16. **Application** Evaluate each expression for $x = 2$.

a) $\dfrac{12x^5}{3x^2}$

b) $\dfrac{-9x^7}{2x^3}$

c) $\dfrac{-10x^4}{-5x}$

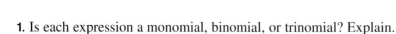
1. Is each expression a monomial, binomial, or trinomial? Explain.

   a) $x^2 - 5$ **b)** $y - 1 + 4y^2$ **c)** $6x^2$ **d)** $4 - c$

2. Write the polynomial these algebra tiles represent.

3. Simplify.

   a) $(6x + 3) + (3x - 1)$ **b)** $(x^2 - 2x + 4) + (2x^2 - 3x - 4)$

   c) $(5n - 3n^2 - 7) + (-3n + 2n^2 - 5)$ **d)** $(6 - 5a + a^2) + (2 - 7a^2)$

4. Simplify.

   a) $(-3x - 5) - (4x + 3)$ **b)** $(3x^2 + 5x - 6) - (x^2 - x + 4)$

   c) $(2g^2 + 1) - (5g^2 - 2)$ **d)** $(-5b^2 - 3b + 2) - (b^3 - 2b^2 + 7)$

5. Simplify. Find the value of each polynomial when $x = -4$.

   a) $(-3x^2 + 2x - 3) - (-4x^2 - x + 1)$ **b)** $(2x^4 - 4x + x^3) - (x^4 + 5 - x^3)$

6. Simplify.

   a) $(6f)(-2f)$ **b)** $(-5)(-3r)$ **c)** $(-4t)(9t)$

   d) $(-p^3)(-7p^5)$ **e)** $(2w^4)(8w^3)$ **f)** $(6)(-8x^2)$

7. Simplify.

   a) $(4x)^3$ **b)** $(-5y^3)^5$ **c)** $(-2t^5)^2$

   d) $(-6f^5)^4$ **e)** $(-w^3)^6$ **f)** $(3g^6)^4$

8. Simplify.

   a) $16x^2 \div 4x$ **b)** $28h^3 \div (-7h)$ **c)** $(-54y^5) \div (-9y^3)$

   d) $\dfrac{-15b^7}{5b^4}$ **e)** $\dfrac{-6s^6}{-s^2}$ **f)** $\dfrac{30c^8}{-6c^5}$

Preparation for Ontario Testing

9. Simplify $\dfrac{-15x^6}{3x^2}$.

   a) $-5x^4$ **b)** $-5x^3$ **c)** $5x^8$ **d)** $-5x^8$

6.6 Multiplying a Polynomial by a Monomial

In Section 3.1, you expanded a product such as $3(x + 4)$ using the distributive law. We can represent this product by combining these 3 sets of algebra tiles:

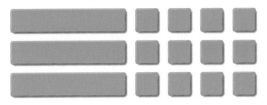

We can represent the product 3×5:

with a rectangle and...   with algebra tiles arranged in a rectangle

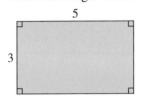

The area is $3 \times 5 = 15$.

Similarly, we can represent the product $2(x + 4)$ with algebra tiles in a rectangle.

The area is $2(x + 4) = 2x + 8$.

Instead of writing the length and width as algebraic terms, we use algebra tiles.

length

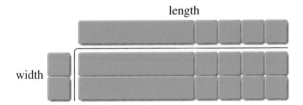

width

To represent the product $2x(x + 4)$ with algebra tiles, we make a rectangle $2x$ units wide and $(x + 4)$ units long. We use tiles to represent the length and the width.

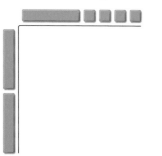

We fill in the rectangle with 2 x^2-tiles and 8 x-tiles. The total area of the rectangles is $2x^2 + 8x$. We write: $2x(x + 4) = 2x^2 + 8x$

The Distributive Law in Arithmetic and in Algebra

To multiply in arithmetic, we use the distributive law.

$3 \times 27 = 3(20 + 7)$
$\qquad = 3(20) + 3(7)$
$\qquad = 60 + 21$
$\qquad = 81$

To multiply in algebra, we use the distributive law.

$2x(x + 4) = 2x(x) + 2x(4)$
$\qquad = 2x^2 + 8x$

When we use the distributive law to multiply a polynomial by a monomial, we are *expanding* the product of the monomial and polynomial.

Example 1

Expand $8x(x - 3)$.

Solution

$8x(x - 3) = 8x(x) - 8x(3)$ Use the distributive law.
$\qquad = 8x^2 - 24x$

Discuss

Can we use algebra tiles to expand this product? Explain.

We apply the same method when a polynomial has more than two terms.
When polynomials cannot be represented with algebra tiles, we use the distributive law.

Example 2

Expand $(-5a)(a^2 - 4a - 7)$.

Solution

$(-5a)(a^2 - 4a - 7) = (-5a)(a^2) - (-5a)(4a) - (-5a)(7)$ Use the distributive law.
$= -5a^3 + 20a^2 + 35a$

Discuss

Can we use algebra tiles to expand this product? Explain.

6.6   Exercises

A   **1.** What product does each diagram represent?

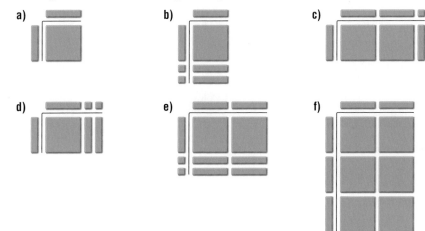

2. Use algebra tiles to expand each product.

    a) $x(x + 1)$ **b)** $x(3x + 2)$ **c)** $2(x^2 + x + 3)$ **d)** $2x(x + 2)$

3. Expand.

    a) $2(x + 3)$ **b)** $(-2)(x + 3)$ **c)** $3(x - 2)$ **d)** $(-3)(x - 2)$

    e) $4(2x + 1)$ **f)** $(-4)(2x + 1)$ **g)** $5(4 - x^2)$ **h)** $(-5)(4 - x^2)$

4. Expand.

    a) $x(x + 3)$ **b)** $(-x)(x + 3)$ **c)** $x(x - 2)$ **d)** $(-x)(x - 2)$

    e) $x(2x + 1)$ **f)** $(-x)(2x + 1)$ **g)** $x(4 - x^2)$ **h)** $(-x)(4 - x^2)$

5. Expand.

    a) $5(x - 3)$ **b)** $7(a + 1)$ **c)** $(-3)(2 + n)$

    d) $(-4)(-x - 2)$ **e)** $3(6x - 4)$ **f)** $5(x^2 - 6x + 3)$

6. Match each product with a set of algebra tiles.

   a) $2x(x + 1)$ b) $2x(2x + 3)$ c) $2x(x + 5)$

   d) $3x(x + 1)$ e) $x(x + 3)$ f) $x(2x + 2)$

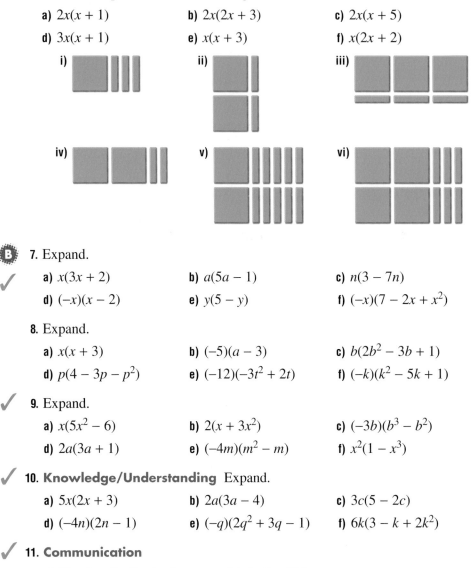

B 7. Expand.

   a) $x(3x + 2)$ b) $a(5a - 1)$ c) $n(3 - 7n)$

   d) $(-x)(x - 2)$ e) $y(5 - y)$ f) $(-x)(7 - 2x + x^2)$

8. Expand.

   a) $x(x + 3)$ b) $(-5)(a - 3)$ c) $b(2b^2 - 3b + 1)$

   d) $p(4 - 3p - p^2)$ e) $(-12)(-3t^2 + 2t)$ f) $(-k)(k^2 - 5k + 1)$

9. Expand.

   a) $x(5x^2 - 6)$ b) $2(x + 3x^2)$ c) $(-3b)(b^3 - b^2)$

   d) $2a(3a + 1)$ e) $(-4m)(m^2 - m)$ f) $x^2(1 - x^3)$

10. **Knowledge/Understanding** Expand.

   a) $5x(2x + 3)$ b) $2a(3a - 4)$ c) $3c(5 - 2c)$

   d) $(-4n)(2n - 1)$ e) $(-q)(2q^2 + 3q - 1)$ f) $6k(3 - k + 2k^2)$

11. **Communication**

   a) Use the distributive law to multiply 7×236.

   b) Use the distributive law to expand $7(2x^2 + 3x + 6)$. Evaluate this polynomial for $x = 10$.

   c) Compare your answers in parts a and b. Explain any relationship you discover.

12. **Application** The dimensions of a cereal box, in centimetres, are $5x - 1$, $3x$, and x.

a) Write an expression for each measurement:
  i) the area of the base of the box
  ii) the height of the box
  iii) the volume, V, of the box
  iv) the area of the top of the box
  v) the area of the front of the box
  vi) the area of a side of the box
  vii) the surface area, A, of the box

b) Determine the volume and surface area of the box when $x = 7$ cm.

13. **Thinking/Inquiry/Problem Solving** The height of any television screen is about $\frac{3}{4}$ of its width.

a) Write an expression for the height of a television screen x units wide.

b) Write an expression for the height of a television screen that is 4 units wider than the screen in part a.

c) Write an expression for the area of the screen in part a.

6.7 Could a Giant Survive?

See page 239 for some examples of fantasy giants and exceptionally tall people. In the book, *Gulliver's Travels*, the giants in the land of Brobdingnag were 12 times as tall as a normal adult. Could these giants survive?

To model this situation, think about a sequence of cubes like this:

  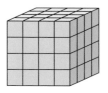

1. Make and complete a table for larger and larger cubes.

Edge length, x (cm)	Volume, V (cm³)	Surface area, A (cm²)	$\dfrac{\text{Volume, } V}{\text{Surface area, } A}$
1			
2			
3			
:			
10			

2. a) As the edge length increases, which grows more rapidly, surface area or volume?

b) As the edge length increases, what happens to the value of $\dfrac{\text{Volume}}{\text{Surface area}}$?

3. a) Use the data in the completed table.

    i) Graph Volume, V, against Edge length, x.

    ii) Graph Surface Area, A, against Edge length, x.

    iii) Graph $\dfrac{\text{Volume}}{\text{Surface area}}$ against Edge length, x.

b) Explain how the graphs in part a support your answers to exercise 2.

4. Suppose you multiply each dimension of a person by 12.

a) Approximately how many times as great would the surface area and the volume be for the giant than for the person?

b) How would the value of $\dfrac{\text{Volume}}{\text{Surface area}}$ for a giant compare with this value for a person?

5. In the movie *Honey, I Blew Up the Kid*, an inventor accidentally enlarges his child. The child eventually grows from 1 m to 32 m tall. Suppose you multiply each dimension of a person by 32. Repeat parts a and b of exercise 4.

6. Choose one of the biological systems described below. What health problems might the giants in the land of Brobdingnag have, or the giant child in the movie *Honey, I Blew Up the Kid*?

    Respiratory system All the cells in your body require oxygen. The number of cells in your body depends on your volume, but the amount of oxygen absorbed by your lungs depends on the surface area of your lungs.

    Skeletal system Your mass depends on your volume, but the strength of your bones depends on the area of their cross-section.

7. See page 239 for two real-life examples of the gigantic. Jinlian suffered from severe scoliosis, or curvature of the spine. Wadlow died of an infected blister on his ankle, caused by a poorly fitting brace.

    a) Do you think that Jinlian's and Wadlow's ailments might have been related to their size? Explain.

    b) How do you think their exceptional heights may have contributed to their early deaths?

8. **Communication** What is your answer to the question "Could a Giant Survive?" Explain how mathematical modelling supports your answer.

Exponent Law for a Power of a Product

- $(xy)^n = x^n y^n$, where n is an integer

Polynomials

- A term is a constant or a coefficient and one or more variables.
- A *polynomial* is one term or the sum of two or more terms.
- A *monomial* is a polynomial with one term.
- A *binomial* is a polynomial with two terms.
- A *trinomial* is a polynomial with three terms.

Adding Polynomials

- To add polynomials, group like terms. Simplify by adding the coefficients of like terms.

Zero Principle

- Polynomials with a sum of 0 are opposites.

Subtracting Polynomials

- To subtract a polynomial, add its opposite.

$$(4x + 2) - (2x - 5) = 4x + 2 + (-2x + 5)$$
$$= 4x + 2 - 2x + 5$$
$$= 2x + 7$$

Multiplying Monomials

- To multiply two monomials, multiply their coefficients and multiply their variables. If the variables are the same, add their exponents.

$$5a \times 3a^2 = 15a^3$$

Dividing Monomials

- To divide two monomials, divide their coefficients and divide their variables. If the variables are the same, subtract their exponents.

$$\frac{6x^7}{3x^2} = 2x^5$$

The Distributive Law

- Use the distributive law to multiply a polynomial by a monomial.

1. Use algebra tiles to represent each polynomial.

    a) $2x^2 + 5x + 3$ **b)** $x^2 - 3x + 2$ **c)** $4x^2 - 2x - 3$ **d)** $-3x^2 - 4x$

2. Write a polynomial to represent the perimeter and a polynomial to represent the area of each rectangle.

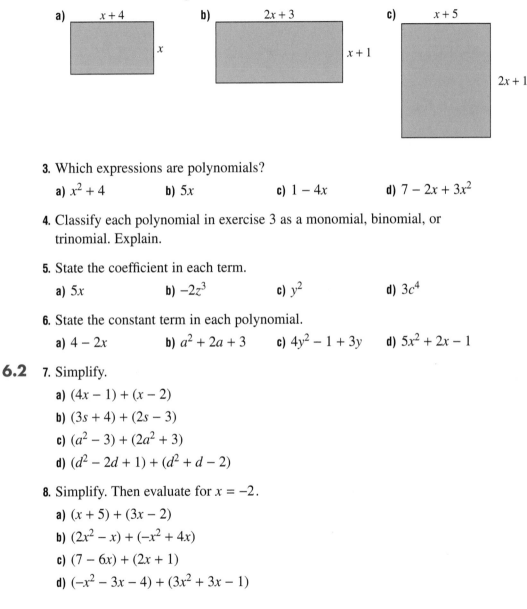

    a) $x + 4$ x **b)** $2x + 3$ $x + 1$ **c)** $x + 5$ $2x + 1$

3. Which expressions are polynomials?

    a) $x^2 + 4$ **b)** $5x$ **c)** $1 - 4x$ **d)** $7 - 2x + 3x^2$

4. Classify each polynomial in exercise 3 as a monomial, binomial, or trinomial. Explain.

5. State the coefficient in each term.

    a) $5x$ **b)** $-2z^3$ **c)** y^2 **d)** $3c^4$

6. State the constant term in each polynomial.

    a) $4 - 2x$ **b)** $a^2 + 2a + 3$ **c)** $4y^2 - 1 + 3y$ **d)** $5x^2 + 2x - 1$

7. Simplify.

    a) $(4x - 1) + (x - 2)$

    b) $(3s + 4) + (2s - 3)$

    c) $(a^2 - 3) + (2a^2 + 3)$

    d) $(d^2 - 2d + 1) + (d^2 + d - 2)$

8. Simplify. Then evaluate for $x = -2$.

    a) $(x + 5) + (3x - 2)$

    b) $(2x^2 - x) + (-x^2 + 4x)$

    c) $(7 - 6x) + (2x + 1)$

    d) $(-x^2 - 3x - 4) + (3x^2 + 3x - 1)$

9. Simplify.

   a) $(u^2 - 4u + 1) + (5u^2 - 3u)$

   b) $(r^3 + r - 2) + (r^3 - 5r + 6)$

   c) $(6 - 2j^4) + (2 - 3j^2 + 3j^4)$

   d) $(-3k^4 - 2k^3 - 1) + (2k^3 + 6k^2 + k)$

   e) $(4t^3 - 5t^2 + 4) + (-2t^3 + 7t - 3)$

   f) $(p^4 + 5p - 6) + (-p^4 - 3p + 1)$

6.3 10. Simplify.

   a) $(q - 3) - (2q + 3)$

   b) $(2r - 1) - (4r - 5)$

   c) $(x^2 - 4x + 1) - (5x^2 + 2x - 6)$

   d) $(8 - 3h^2) - (2 + 4h - 5h^2)$

   e) $(6t^4 + 3t^3 - 2t) - (t^3 + 3t - 4)$

   f) $(4d^2 + 2 - 3d^4) - (2d^2 + 1 - 2d^4 - 5d^3)$

11. Simplify.

   a) $(5y - 3y^2) - (y + 4y^2)$ b) $(-2x - 7) - (-14x - 6)$

   c) $(9a^2 + 2a - 3) - (-6a^2 + 4a + 7)$ d) $(5z^2 - 3z - 2) - (2z^4 + 3z^2 - z - 1)$

   e) $(4x^2 - 3x) - (x^2 + 2x)$ f) $(3c^2 + 5c + 7) - (2c^2 - 4c + 9)$

12. Simplify. Evaluate when $x = 2$ and when $x = -3$.

   a) $(5 - 2x) - (3 - x)$ b) $(5x^2 - 5x + 7) - (2x^2 - 3x - 5)$

6.4 13. Simplify.

   a) $(2y)(2y)(2y)(y^2)(y^2)$ b) $(-a^2)(-a^2)(-4a)(-4a)(-4a)$

   c) $(-3m^3)(m^4)(m^4)(m^4)(m^4)$ d) $(c)(c)(c)(c)(2c^3)(2c^3)$

14. Simplify.

   a) $(-3)(3r)$ b) $6(-y)$ c) $(-2)(-5k)$ d) $7(4q)$

   e) $(-8x)(-2x)$ f) $(-5b)(7b)$ g) $(4a)(6a)$ h) $(c)(-9c)$

15. Simplify.

   a) $(7m)^3$ b) $(-2d)^4$ c) $-(4q)^2$ d) $(-5p)^3$

   e) $(-g^2)^5$ f) $(-4y^2)^3$ g) $(3w^5)^4$ h) $-(2t^3)^2$

16. Simplify.

   a) $(-3n^2)(6n^2)$ b) $(-4c^3)(-4c^2)$ c) $(7x^2)(5x^3)$

   d) $(-8n)(5n^3)$ e) $(2j^2)(-3j^4)$ f) $(-t^4)(-6t^5)$

17. Simplify.

a) $(-2a^2)^2(a^3)$ **b)** $(-4q^4)(-6q)^2$ **c)** $(2x^4)^2(2x)^5$

6.5 **18.** Simplify.

a) $12a^3 \div a$ **b)** $(-8b^2) \div 4$ **c)** $21h^7 \div (-3h^2)$

d) $(-18x^4) \div 3x$ **e)** $(-54y^6) \div 9y^5$ **f)** $(-32z^8) \div (-8z^5)$

19. Simplify.

a) $\dfrac{-45y^8}{-5y^4}$ **b)** $\dfrac{36n^6}{4n^2}$ **c)** $\dfrac{25x^7}{-5x^3}$

d) $\dfrac{-24a^5}{6a^3}$ **e)** $\dfrac{-54m^9}{-9m^8}$ **f)** $\dfrac{72b^6}{8b^3}$

20. Simplify.

a) $\dfrac{(12k^2)^3}{(-4k)^2}$ **b)** $\dfrac{(16s^2)^4}{(4s^2)^3}$ **c)** $\dfrac{(-15d)^4}{(-5d)^2}$

6.6 **21.** What product does each diagram represent?

a) 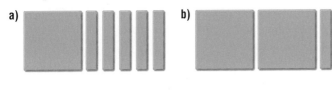   **b)   c)**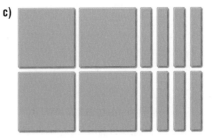

22. Expand.

a) $4(y - 2)$ **b)** $8(a - 3)$ **c)** $(-4)(x + 2)$

d) $3x(5 - x)$ **e)** $2y(y - 6)$ **f)** $(-5x)(3 - x)$

23. Expand.

a) $(-4d)(3d + 2)$ **b)** $5h(7 - 2h)$ **c)** $3t(6t^2 + 2t + 1)$

d) $(-p)(p^2 - 5p + 3)$ **e)** $2w(2 - w + 6w^2)$ **f)** $6x^2(2x^2 - 3x - 4)$

Self-Test

1. **Knowledge/Understanding** Simplify. Then evaluate for $x = -1$.

   a) $(4x - 2) + (3x + 1)$

   b) $(5x^2 + 3x + 2) - (x^2 - 4x - 5)$

   c) $(x^2 + 5x - 1) - (x^2 + 2x - 4)$

   d) $(2x^4 - 6x^2 - 2) + (3x^4 + x^2 - 3)$

2. Simplify.

   a) $6(-5j)$

   b) $(-a)(8a)$

   c) $(-7y)(4y)$

   d) $(-8g)(-2g)$

   e) $(-4f^2)(-6f^3)$

   f) $(5e^4)(e^3)^3$

   g) $(6k^5)(-3k^4)$

   h) $(-5p^6)(4p^2)^2$

3. Simplify.

   a) $(5r^6)^2$

   b) $(-3d^3)^3$

   c) $(-2s^4)^4$

   d) $(4a^2)^3$

4. Simplify.

   a) $16t^3 \div (-t)$

   b) $(-6w^8) \div (-3w^5)$

   c) $(-28b^7) \div 4b^6$

   d) $\dfrac{54m^9}{9}$

   e) $\dfrac{48k^4}{-8k^2}$

   f) $\dfrac{-42n^7}{-6n^5}$

5. a) Simplify.

   i) $\dfrac{8m^5}{2m}$

   ii) $\dfrac{-15x^4}{5x^2}$

   iii) $\dfrac{-20s^8}{-4s^7}$

   iv) $\dfrac{27h^6}{-h^3}$

   b) **Communication** For each expression in part a, write a related multiplication equation using the quotient. Explain the relationship between the multiplication equation and your results from part a.

6. **Thinking/Inquiry/Problem Solving**

   a) Find the mean of $6x$, $-2x$, and $5x$.

   b) Check whether your answer is the mean for the monomials $6x$, $-2x$, and $5x$ when $x = 2$, $x = -4$, and $x = 0$. Check for any two other values of x.

   c) Repeat parts a and b to find and check the mean of x, $-8x$, $-x$, and $-4x$.

   d) Draw a conclusion about whether your method of finding the mean of monomials always works. Justify your conclusion.

7. a) **Application** The area of a rectangle is $36x^2$ and the length is $4x$. What is the width? Show the dimensions on a diagram.

   b) State the dimensions of 2 other rectangles with an area of $36x^2$. Label the dimensions on a diagram of each rectangle.

8. Expand.

   a) $(-5r)(2r - 2)$

   b) $x(x + 1)$

   c) $3g(6 - 4g^2)$

   d) $(-4y)(1 - 3y + 2y^2)$

   e) $(-2h)(-5h^2 + 3h)$

   f) $4q^2(q^2 + 2q - 3)$

9. Volume of a rectangular solid = lwh

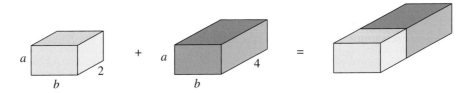

Write an algebraic statement that represents the sum of the two volumes as indicated in the diagram.

10. The algebra tile that represents x^2 is shown.

Create a diagram of algebra tiles to represent $\dfrac{6x^2}{3}$.

1. Draw a graph for this situation:

   Lavita left for school on her bike. She cycled at a constant speed for 4 min. She approached a hill and cycled up the hill at a slower speed for 2 min. When she reached the top of the hill, she realized she was late for school and cycled at a very fast speed for 2 min until she reached her school.

2. Describe a situation each graph below could represent. State the labels of each axis.

   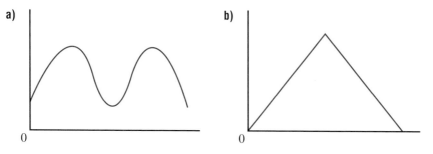

   a)

   b)

3. Write as a single power.

   a) $3^2 \times 3^4$
   b) $\dfrac{(-6)^5}{(-6)^2}$
   c) $(-8)^{-2}(-8)^{-3}$
   d) $\dfrac{5^4}{5^{-3}}$

4. The volume of Earth is about 1.1×10^{12} km³.

   a) The volume of the sun is about 1.3×10^6 times as great as the volume of Earth. Calculate the volume of the sun.

   b) The volume of Earth is about 49 times the volume of the moon. Calculate the volume of the moon.

5. Solve.

   a) $3x = 36$
   b) $4a - 5 = 3$
   c) $3(a + 2) = 12$
   d) $2(y - 2) = 6$

6. Expand.

   a) $4(3y - 6)$
   b) $-5(m - 7)$
   c) $4d(d + 2)$
   d) $-6x(2x - 3)$

7. Simplify.

   a) $(5x)(5x)$
   b) $\dfrac{4y^3}{2y}$
   c) $(3m)(3m^2)^2$
   d) $\dfrac{-6w^5}{3w}$

8. Graph each line segment. Find its slope.

a) A(2, 7), B(−5, −5) **b)** C(−1, 6), D(8, −3)

9. Graph each line segment. State the slope of a parallel line segment and a perpendicular line segment.

a) A(0, 4), B(2, 0) **b)** C(−1, 1), D(3, 3) **c)** E(4, −2), F(−1, 3)

d) G(0, 1), H(−5, −1) **e)** J(2, 3), K(−1, 3) **f)** K(3, 5), M(3, −2)

10. a) Copy and complete each table of values.

i) $y = -5x$

x	y
0	
1	
2	
3	

ii) $y = 2 - x$

x	y
0	
2	
4	
6	

iii) $y = 3x - 1$

x	y
0	
1	
2	
3	

b) Graph each equation.

c) Find the slope of each line.

11. Graph each equation. Decide if the relation is linear or non-linear. Explain how you know.

a) $y = 4x + 1$ **b)** $y = 1 - 3x^2$ **c)** $y = -5x - 5$

d) $y = \dfrac{2}{x}$ **e)** $y = 2x^2 - x$ **f)** $y = -x$

12. Are the points in each set collinear? Explain how you know.

a) A(1, 1), B(3, 0), C(7, −2) **b)** G(2, 7), H(4, 16), I(0, −2)

13. State the slope and y-intercept for the line represented by each equation.

a) $y = -x + 1$ **b)** $y = \dfrac{2}{3}x - 8$ **c)** $y = -1$

14. a) Graph the line represented by each equation.

i) $y = 2x - 1$ **ii)** $y = -\dfrac{1}{2}x + 3$

iii) $y = x + 4$ **iv)** $y = -3$

b) Choose an equation from part a. Explain how you graphed the line.

15. The coordinates of a point and the slope of a line are given. Graph each line, then find its equation.

a) A(−5, 0), −1 **b)** B(3, −1), $\dfrac{3}{2}$ **c)** C(−6, 2), $-\dfrac{1}{3}$

16. The coordinates of 2 points are given. Plot the points. Draw a line through the points. Find each equation.

a) J(−2, 1), K(4, 4) **b)** Q(−3, 0), R(0, −4) **c)** E(−5, 6), F(2, 6)

CHAPTER

NEW RELIEF *for*

MIGRAINE

SUFFERERS

By the end of this chapter you will:

- Demonstrate an understanding of sampling and surveying.
- Carry out experiments to investigate relationships between variables.
- Collect data using technology.
- Organise and analyse data, create scatter plots, and draw the line of best fit.
- Determine the equation of the line of best fit.
- Make predictions from data based on the line of best fit or its equation.
- Describe any trends or relationships in data.
- Communicate the findings of experiments.

PainGon
Relief. Fast.

Our study shows that with **Paingon**, people have a 15% reduction in migraine headaches.

Good News for Migraine Sufferers

We see advertisements like the one on page 280 in newspapers, on billboards, and on television. What does it mean? Can we believe the claims made?

You will investigate these questions in Section 7.6.

Mean, Median, and Mode

The *mean* is the sum of all the numbers, divided by the number of numbers.

The *median* is the middle number when the numbers are arranged in order. If there is an even number of numbers, the median is the mean of the two middle numbers.

The *mode* is the number that occurs most often. There may be more than one mode. There may be no mode.

Example

Calculate the mean, median, and mode of this set of numbers:
4, 5, 7, 3, 7, 9, 9, 1, 3, 9

Solution

There are 10 numbers in the set.
For the mean, add the numbers, then divide by 10.

$$\text{Mean} = \frac{4+5+7+3+7+9+9+1+3+9}{10} \qquad \text{Use a calculator.}$$

$$= \frac{57}{10}$$

$$= 5.7$$

For the median, arrange the numbers in order, beginning with the smallest.
1, 3, 3, 4, $\underline{5}$, $\underline{7}$, 7, 9, 9, 9
Since there are 10 numbers, the median is the mean of the two middle numbers.

$$\text{Median} = \frac{5+7}{2}$$

$$= \frac{12}{2}$$

$$= 6$$

The mode is the number that occurs most often. The mode is 9.

Exercises

Calculate the mean, median, and mode of each set of numbers.

a) 1, 6, 6, 2, 9

b) 7, 7, 8, 1, 2, 2, 0

c) 10, 18, 16, 11, 12, 13, 16, 13

d) 21, 21, 22, 20, 28, 27, 29, 24, 20, 29

People collect data because they need information. Often, instead of surveying the entire *population*, a small portion, called a *sample*, is studied.

TAKE NOTE

Principles of Sampling

Population: all the things or people considered
Sample: the portion studied

For example:

- To test how hot a bowl of soup is, you may sip a spoonful. This is *sampling*. Based on the temperature of the soup in your spoon, you decide if it is too hot to eat. The spoonful of soup is the sample. The bowl of soup is the population.

- Sampling is used for product testing. A manufacturer may wish to test the lifespan of its bulbs. It cannot test each bulb because testing destroys the product. So, a sample of bulbs is tested.

Example 1

Identify the population.

a) A citywide volleyball league wants to know if team members want long- or short-sleeve uniforms.

b) The marketing team at a North Bay shopping mall wants to know how to attract more people between the ages of 13 and 19.

c) A chocolate-bar packager wants to determine the actual mass of 55-g chocolate bars.

d) An office cafeteria wants to determine if soup should be served daily.

Solution

a) All team members belonging to the volleyball league

b) People in North Bay between the ages of 13 and 19

c) All 55-g chocolate bars packaged by the company

d) All office workers that use the cafeteria

Samples

A *representative sample* truly represents a population. It must:

- Reflect the population. This means that all parts of the population are fairly represented.
- Ensure all members of the population have an equal chance of being selected. That is, the sample members should be chosen at *random*.

Example 2

A company is hired to find out who Canadians think will win the next World Cup in soccer. To collect the data, the company considers sampling Canadians in one of the following ways.

a) Conducting phone-in surveys on radio talk shows

b) Putting an advertisement in the sports section of all major newspapers asking people to vote for their choice

c) Sending questionnaires to 500 major businesses to be completed by employees selected at random

Describe a weakness in each method.

Solution

a) Only people who are listening to the radio talk shows would be asked. The sample is not random.

b) Only people who read the sports section of major newspapers would be asked. The sample is not random.

c) This sample ignores people such as students, homemakers, senior citizens, self-employed people, and those who do not work for major businesses. So, the sample is not random.

B 1. Identify the weakness in each method.

 a) A shoe store conducts a survey of the most popular brands of athletic shoes. It asks the first 200 people in the mall who are wearing athletic shoes to respond.

 b) You want to know whether students will attend another dance this month at your school. You ask your friends whether they want another dance this month.

 c) A company is hired to find out which team Canadians think will win the Stanley Cup this year. The company polls people in Alberta by attending 10 NHL games and asking the first 100 people entering the stadium their opinion.

2. **Knowledge/Understanding** Identify the population for each situation in exercise 1.

3. Explain the weakness in each method.

 a) A sample of your classmates is used to estimate the average age of students in your school.

 b) A sample of senior citizens is used to find the music that Canadians like best.

 c) To determine which movie teenagers like best, 12 of your closest friends are interviewed.

4. A TV program chooses its Movie of the Week according to the votes cast by viewers. They phone one of two 1-900 phone numbers at $0.75 per call. Is this a random sample? Why?

5. A school cafeteria wants to know what food students would like the cafeteria to serve. Which of these methods gives a representative sample? Why?

 a) The first 100 people to enter the school that morning are interviewed.

 b) All grade 11 students are asked to fill out a questionnaire.

 c) Teachers are asked what foods they want the cafeteria to serve.

 d) A school computer randomly generates names of 300 students. These students are asked to fill out a questionnaire.

6. Which of these methods gives a representative sample? Why?

   a) The editors of a health-food magazine want to know if organic foods make people feel better. They ask readers to write in their experiences.

   b) A computer manufacturer wishes to check a shipment of 10 000 RAM chips from a supplier. The manager selects one carton at random, then selects five chips at random from the carton.

   c) A light-bulb company wants to know how long light bulbs will burn before failure. It selects the first 100 bulbs manufactured on Monday morning.

7. For each situation, identify what you think the population is.

   a) The quality of flash bulbs

   b) The number of Canadians who watch television daily

   c) The cost of ski equipment

   d) The percentage of North Americans with each blood type

8. In each situation, why would data be collected from a sample and not from the population?

   a) To find the average age of drivers when they get their drivers' licences

   b) To find the number of hours a high-efficiency light bulb will burn

   c) To find the average volume of milk in a 4-L bag

9. Communication Wine buyers often sample a small amount of wine for taste, flavour, and bouquet. Is a mouthful a suitable random sample? Explain why.

10. A baker engages in sampling when he tests a cake with a toothpick. Is this a reliable random sample? Explain why.

11. Application How would you collect data to find the following information? Give reasons for your answers.

   a) The popularity of a TV program

   b) The most popular breakfast cereal

   c) The average number of CDs owned by high-school students

   d) The average weekly fast-food budget for a teenager

A critical part of survey design is the method of selecting the sample. Recall that the sample must reflect the population. Sample members should be chosen at random.

Example

These are the surnames of the 36 students in a mathematics class. Use a random sample of 6 surnames. Estimate the mean, median, and mode for the number of letters in a surname in the population.

Balfour	Gillis	Majic	Sinclair
Barnett	Hood	Ng	Stelzer
Borshay	Karpenko	Norris	Tabori
Burt	Kennedy	Peressini	Thompson
Dunlop	Keyes	Perkins	Triantafylido
Durocher	Kilbank	Reardon	Veerman
Forsyth	King	Richardson	Walker
Francesconi	Lee	Rucker	Willoughby
Gianelia	MacPherson	Sarraude	Zimnicki

Solution

Method 1 Choosing names from a bag

Write each name on a piece of paper. Fold up each piece of paper and place it into a bag. Choose six names at random.

For example, these names may have been chosen:

Reardon   Kilbank   Hood   Richardson   Gianelia   Lee

The numbers of letters in these names are: 7, 7, 4, 10, 8, 3

The mean is $\frac{7 + 7 + 4 + 10 + 8 + 3}{6} = 6.5$

For the median, arrange the numbers in order: 3, 4, 7, 7, 8, 10
The median is the mean of 7 and 7, which is 7.

The mode is 7.

Method 2 Using a graphing calculator

Number the surnames as follows:

01	Balfour	10	Gillis	19	Majic	28	Sinclair
02	Barnett	11	Hood	20	Ng	29	Stelzer
03	Borshay	12	Karpenko	21	Norris	30	Tabori
04	Burt	13	Kennedy	22	Peressini	31	Thompson
05	Dunlop	14	Keyes	23	Perkins	32	Triantafylido
06	Durocher	15	Kilbank	24	Reardon	33	Veerman
07	Forsyth	16	King	25	Richardson	34	Walker
08	Francesconi	17	Lee	26	Rucker	35	Willoughby
09	Gianelia	18	MacPherson	27	Sarraude	36	Zimnicki

Use a TI-83 calculator to generate random numbers from 1 to 36.

- Press [MATH] [▶] [▶] [▶] **5** to display randInt(.
- Press 1 [,] 36 [ )] [ENTER] to display a
  random number from 1 to 36.

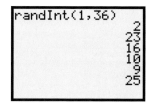

- Continue pressing [ENTER] until 6 *different*
  numbers are displayed.

The screen shows this sample:

Barnett   Perkins   King   Gillis   Gianelia   Richardson

The numbers of letters in these names are: 7, 7, 4, 6, 8, 10

The mean is $\dfrac{7 + 7 + 4 + 6 + 8 + 10}{6} = \dfrac{42}{6}$
$$= 7$$

For the median, arrange the numbers in order: 4, 6, 7, 7, 8, 10

The median is the mean of 7 and 7, which is 7.

The mode is 7.

The results of the *Example* are only estimates of the actual mean, median, and mode of the population of 36 names. The actual values are:

mean = 7.2

median = 7

mode = 7

As this example indicates, when the sample is chosen randomly, the mean, median, and mode will usually be close to the true mean, median, and mode of the population.

There is an extremely small chance that the random sample contains the 6 shortest names or the 6 longest names. In this rare situation, the mean, median, and mode will be very different from those of the population.

B 1. Refer to the *Example*.

    a) Use a random sample of 6 surnames. Estimate the mean, median, and mode for the number of letters in a surname in the population.

    b) Suppose your sample had consisted of the 6 shortest surnames. What are the mean, median, and mode for this sample?

    c) Suppose your sample had consisted of the 6 longest surnames. What are the mean, median, and mode for this sample?

2. **Investigation: What Is the Average Surname Length in Your Class?** Obtain a list of surnames for the students in your class. Investigate the average surname length.

    a) Decide how large a sample you need.

    b) Decide how you will ensure that the sample is random.

    c) Obtain your sample.

    d) Estimate the mean, median, and mode for the population.

3. **Investigation: What Is the Average Hand Span?** Have everyone in your class measure her or his hand span to the nearest half-centimetre. Your hand span is the greatest possible distance between the tips of your thumb and your 5th finger. Record each hand span measurement and the student's name. Investigate the average hand span for your class by repeating exercise 2a to d.

4. **Investigation: What Is the Average Pulse?** Have everyone in your class measure her or his pulse. To measure your pulse, press a finger on your wrist just below your hand. Count the number of beats in 15 s, then multiply by 4 to get the number of beats per minute. Investigate the average pulse for your class by repeating exercise 2a to d.

5. Choose one of the investigations below. Work in a group of 3 or 4 students to collect the data.

    a) Describe the population.

    b) Decide how large a sample you need.

    c) Decide how you will ensure that the sample is random.

    d) Estimate the mean, median, and mode for the population.

The average age of the students in your school	The average amount spent on lunch in the cafeteria
The average time spent waiting in line in the cafeteria	The average number of letters in English words

1. Identify the population in each situation.

   a) The favourite weekly school cafeteria special is to be determined. A survey is distributed to students whose names are randomly generated by a computer.

   b) The most popular type of car in a particular city is to be determined. The make of every 5th car at a busy intersection is recorded.

   c) To determine the favourite coffee flavour, a survey is given to every customer between the hours of 9:00 A.M. and 11:00 A.M. at a coffee shop.

2. Identify the weakness in each method in exercise 1.

3. A car manufacturer wants to find out what features of its cars are superior to other makes. It offers free movie tickets to customers who fill out a survey. Explain any weaknesses in the sampling.

4. **Investigation: What Is the Average Foot Length of Your Class?**
   Have everyone in your class measure her or his foot length in centimetres.

   a) Decide how large a sample you need.

   b) Decide how you will ensure the sample is random.

   c) Obtain your sample.

   d) Estimate the mean, median, and mode for the population.

Preparation for Ontario Testing

5. Neil is reporting on the upcoming student elections in the school newspaper. To report on preliminary poll results, he will take a sample survey. Which sample best represents the population? Explain your choice.

   a) He polls all students in the library at lunch.

   b) He puts up a checklist in the cafeteria on which students anonymously check off who they will vote for.

   c) He polls all grade 10 and 11 students because they are in the "middle" grades.

   d) He randomly generates a list of student numbers from the school database and polls these students.

Arm Span and Height Relationships

Work with a partner. You will need a tape measure or metre stick.

1. How do you think arm span and height are related?

2. Measure and record your arm spans and your heights.

3. Combine your data with those of other students. Record the data in a table.

Student's name	Arm span (cm)	Height (cm)

4. Plot the data on a grid. Plot *Arm span (cm)* horizontally and *Height (cm)* vertically. This graph is a *scatter plot*. A scatter plot is any graph consisting of a set of points.

5. Describe any patterns or trends in the data. What appears to be the relationship between arm span and height? How does this relationship compare with your prediction in exercise 1?

6. Place a ruler so that it passes as close as possible to all the plotted points (use a transparent ruler, if possible). Draw a straight line along the ruler. This line is a *line of best fit*.

7. Use the line of best fit.

   a) Predict the height of someone whose arm span is 1.4 m.

   b) Predict the arm span of someone whose height is 1.6 m.

8. How did the way you collected your data affect the results of the experiment? Suppose you were to repeat the experiment. What would you do differently?

Save your data for use in 7.4 Exercises.

In *Investigation 1*, you drew a line of best fit for the data. A line of best fit is useful for predicting unknown values.

Olympic Discus Records

The table shows the winning distances for the discus event at the Olympic Summer Games since 1948. The data are rounded to the nearest metre.

Year	Men's distance (m)	Women's distance (m)
1948	53	42
1952	55	51
1956	56	54
1960	59	55
1964	61	57
1968	65	58
1972	64	67
1976	68	69
1980	67	70
1984	67	65
1988	69	72
1992	65	70
1996	69	70
2000	69	68

You will look for trends in the data. If there is a trend, you can use it to predict the winning distances in future Olympics, such as the 2012 Olympic Games.

1. Create a scatter plot for the men's distances. Plot *Year* on the horizontal axis and *Men's distance (m)* on the vertical axis.

2. Use a ruler to draw a line of best fit.

3. Use the line of best fit. Estimate the winning distance for the men's discus event in the 2012 Olympic Games. Compare your estimate with other students' estimates.

Save your graph for use in 7.4 Exercises.

In this section, you will plot data and draw lines of best fit and make predictions from the graphs. You will also determine the equation of a line of best fit, and use the equation to make predictions.

Recall that drawing a line of best fit is useful for predicting and estimating.

Example 1

a) Create a scatter plot and draw a line of best fit for the women's Olympic discus records.

b) Use the line of best fit to predict the winning distance for the women's discus in 2012.

Year	Women's distance (m)	Year	Women's distance (m)
1948	42	1976	69
1952	51	1980	70
1956	54	1984	65
1960	55	1988	72
1964	57	1992	70
1968	58	1996	70
1972	67	2000	68

Solution

a)

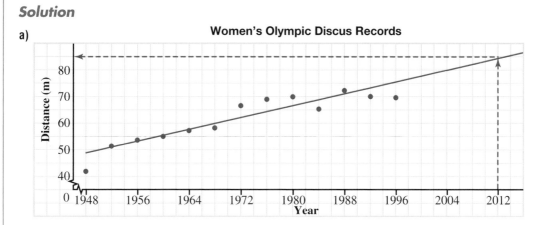

b) Start with 2012 on the horizontal axis. Draw a vertical line to the line of best fit, then draw a horizontal line to the vertical axis. The distance is 85 m. In 2012, the winning distance for the women's discus might be about 85 m.

Discuss

Why are the zigzag marks used near the origin in the graph? What do they represent?

When data points lie close to a line of best fit, we can use the line to predict data at points for which measurements were not taken. However, the more widely scattered the data points are around a line of best fit, the less reliable the predictions.

Example 2

a) Determine the equation of the line of best fit in *Example 1*.

b) Use the equation to predict the winning distance for the women's discus in 2012.

Solution

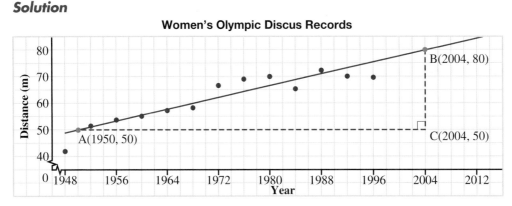

a) Mark two points on the line of best fit whose coordinates are easy to read.
For example, the points could be A(1950, 50) and B(2004, 80).

Mark and label a point, C, to form a right triangle.
The rise is $80 - 50 = 30$
The run is $2004 - 1950 = 54$
Slope of AB $= \dfrac{80 - 50}{2004 - 1950}$
$ = \dfrac{30}{54}$
$ \doteq 0.5556$

Let the equation of the line be $y = mx + b$.
The slope of the line is approximately 0.5556. Substitute $m = 0.5556$.

$$y \doteq 0.5556x + b$$

We cannot read the y-intercept from the graph since there is a break in the axes values.

Since A(1950, 50) lies on the line, its coordinates satisfy the equation.
Substitute $x = 1950$ and $y = 50$. Then solve for b.

$$50 \doteq 0.5556(1950) + b$$
$$ \doteq 1083.42 + b$$
$$b \doteq 50 - 1083.42$$
$$ \doteq -1033.42$$

Therefore, the vertical intercept of the line is about -1033.42.
The equation of the line of best fit is approximately $y = 0.5556x - 1033.42$.

b) Substitute 2012 for x in the equation.

$$y \doteq (0.5556)(2012) - 1033.42$$
$$\doteq 84.45$$

The winning distance for the women's discus in 2012 might be about 84 m.

Discuss

Do you think the women's gold medalist in 2012 will achieve this distance? Explain your thinking.

7.4   Exercises

1. Communication Look at the scatter plots below. Which line of best fit do you think would provide the most reliable predictions? Why?

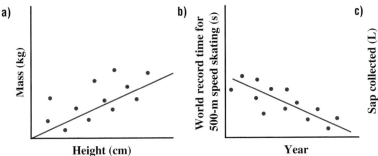

a) Mass (kg) / Height (cm)

b) World record time for 500-m speed skating (s) / Year

c) Sap collected (L) / Height of a sugar maple tree (m)

2. This scatter plot shows the number of bottles of pop sold by a street vendor versus the temperature outside.

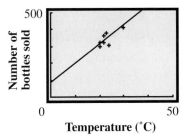

a) Predict the number of bottles sold when the temperature outside is 15°C.

b) Predict the number of bottles sold when the temperature outside is 5°C.

c) Do you think this is reasonable? Why?

3. Knowledge/Understanding This scatter plot shows the value of a certain model of car versus the age of the car.

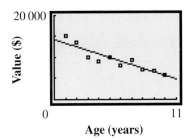

a) What is the value of the car when it is new?

b) Predict the value of the car after 11 years.

4. Investigation: Foot Length and Height Relationships Work with a partner. Measure and record your foot lengths. Combine your data with those of other students in your group or class. Use the heights from *Investigation 1*, page 291.

a) How do you think foot length and height are related?

b) Record the data in a table.

Student's name	Foot length (cm)	Height (cm)

c) Create a scatter plot of the data. Decide which measurement is graphed horizontally and which is graphed vertically.

d) Draw a line of best fit for the data.

e) Describe any trends in the data. What appears to be the relationship between foot length and height? How does this relationship compare with your prediction in part a?

f) Use the line of best fit.
  i) Predict the foot length of someone whose height is 1.6 m.
  ii) Predict the height of someone whose foot length is 20 cm.

5. Examine this scatter plot.

a) Would it be appropriate to draw a line of best fit?

b) Should a line of best fit pass through the origin? Explain.

c) Should we always construct a line of best fit by connecting the first and last points? Explain.

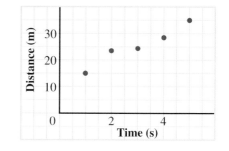

6. a) Application Use the line of best fit you drew in *Investigation 2*, page 292. Find the equation of the line of best fit.

b) Use the equation. Predict the winning distance for the men's discus in 2012.

c) Compare the answer to part b with the estimate in exercise 3, page 292.

7. Thinking/Inquiry/Problem Solving Would it be appropriate to construct a line of best fit for the data in this scatter plot? Explain.

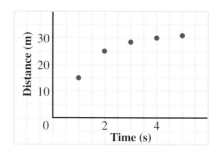

8. **Investigation: Foot Length and Arm Span Relationships**
   Work with a partner. Use the foot length data from exercise 4
   and the arm span data from *Investigation 1*, page 291.

   a) How do you think foot length and arm span are related?

   b) Record the data in a table.

Student's name	Foot length (cm)	Arm span (cm)

   c) Create a scatter plot of the data.

   d) Draw a line of best fit for the data.

   e) Describe any trends in the data. What appears to be the relationship
      between foot length and arm span? How does the relationship compare
      with your prediction in part a?

   f) Use the line of best fit.
      i) Predict the foot length of someone whose arm span is 1.4 m.
      ii) Predict the arm span of someone whose foot length is 22 cm.

   g) Use the line of best fit in part d. Determine the equation of the line of best fit.

   h) Use the equation.
      i) Predict the foot length of someone whose arm span is 1.4 m.
      ii) Predict the arm span of someone whose foot length is 22 cm.

   i) Compare your answers to parts f and h.

9. The table shows the population of Ontario
   from 1977 to 1997.

   a) Create a scatter plot of year versus
      population. Plot *Year* on the horizontal axis.

   b) Determine the equation of the line of best fit.

   c) Predict the population of Ontario in 2010.

   d) What assumptions are you making in part c?

Year	Population (in thousands)	Year	Population (in thousands)
1977	8526	1988	9884
1978	8613	1989	10 151
1979	8686	1990	10 341
1980	8770	1991	10 472
1981	8838	1992	10 647
1982	8951	1993	10 814
1983	9073	1994	10 937
1984	9206	1995	11 098
1985	9334	1996	11 258
1986	9477	1997	11 408
1987	9685		

In Section 7.4, you graphed lines of best fit. In earlier chapters, you used a graphing calculator to graph data in a table, and also to graph an equation. You can combine these skills to graph a line of best fit on a graphing calculator using estimation.

INVESTIGATION

Length of a Row of Coins

You will need 15 pennies and a ruler.

1. a) Put some pennies in a row and measure its length in millimetres.

b) Repeat with other numbers of pennies until you have four sets of results. Record the results in a table (the data shown below are for a different coin).

Number of coins	Length (mm)
14	297
11	233
9	190
6	127

2. Use a graphing calculator to graph the data. Follow these steps.

Step 1. Enter the data.

- Press [STAT] **1**. Clear lists L1 and L2 if necessary.
- Enter the numbers of pennies in list L1 and the lengths in list L2.

Step 2. Set up the scatter plot.

- Press [2nd] [Y=] **1** to select Plot1. Press [ENTER].
- Select the first plot type, and make sure that L1 and L2 are beside Xlist and Ylist, respectively.

Step 3. Set up the window.

- Press [WINDOW]. Enter appropriate values.

Step 4. Graph the data.

- Press [GRAPH].

Your graph should look similar to this. The graph shows a linear relation between the length of the row of coins and the number of coins. If a line of best fit were drawn, it would pass through the origin. So, it has the form $y = mx$, where m is the slope of the line.

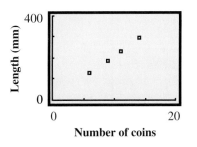

3. a) Press [Y=] and clear any equations. Move the cursor beside Y_1=.

b) Press [____] [X,T,θ,n] [ENTER] [GRAPH], where [____] represents a number that you think is close to the slope of the line.

To estimate the value of m, visualize where the line of best fit should lie. Count the rise and run between any two points along this line. Repeat part b using other values of m until your line passes through the plotted points.

For the first screen below, the value of m was too small. For the second screen, it was just right.

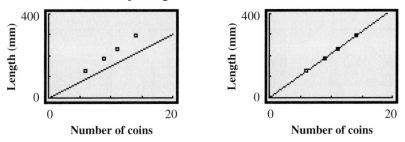

c) What is the equation of the line of best fit?

d) Explain what the slope of the line represents.

4. You can use your line of best fit to estimate the lengths of rows formed by other numbers of pennies not plotted on the screen. Use each method below to estimate the lengths of two other rows of pennies.

a) *Using trace*

With the graph on the screen, press [TRACE]. Press [▼] to move the cursor to the line, and not the plotted points. To estimate the length for other numbers of pennies, enter the number you want then press [ENTER].

b) *Using a table*

Press [2nd] [WINDOW] to select TBLSET. Make sure that your screen looks like the one on page 300, left. Then press [2nd] [GRAPH] to select TABLE. You will get a table of values like the one shown on page 300, right. Scroll down the table to see as many values as you want.

5. Compare your graph in exercise 3 with the graphs given on page 299. What coin do you think was used to create these graphs? Explain.

In exercise 3 in the *Investigation,* you estimated the equation of the line of best fit. You will encounter similar situations in the exercises, but the data may not fit the line as closely as they did in the *Investigation.*

7.5   Exercises

B

1. Estimate the slope of each line of best fit.

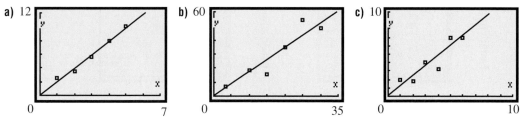

a) 12   b) 60   c) 10

2. The table shows the heights of several seedlings after various growing times.

Time (days)	1	3	2	3	3	2	1	2
Height (mm)	6	13	11	14	15	10	4	7

a) What relationship would you expect between growing time and height?

b) Enter the data into a graphing calculator. Enter the times in list L1 and the heights in list L2.

c) Use the calculator to create a scatter plot.

d) Describe any trends in the data. What appears to be the relationship between growing time and height? How does this relationship compare with your prediction in part a?

e) Use the calculator to estimate the equation of the line of best fit. Display the line of best fit on the scatter plot.

f) Sketch the graph you obtained. Show the plotted points, the line of best fit, and its equation.

g) What does the slope of the line of best fit represent? Explain.

3. **Investigation: Your Pulse**

   a) Count the number of pulse beats in each time:
   7 s, 17 s, 38 s, 52 s
   Record the results in a table.

Time (s)	Number of beats
7	
17	
38	
52	

   b) Enter the data into a graphing calculator. Enter the times in list L1 and the number of beats in list L2.

   c) Use the calculator to create a scatter plot.

   d) Use the calculator to estimate the equation of the line of best fit. Display the line of best fit on the scatter plot.

   e) Sketch the graph you obtained. Show the plotted points, the line of best fit, and its equation.

   f) What does the slope of the line of best fit represent? Explain.

4. **Investigation: Lengths of Shadows**
   Work in a group or with a partner. You will need a table or other horizontal surface in sunshine. You will also need some objects with different heights and a ruler.

   a) Place one object vertically on the table so that its shadow is cast on the table. Measure the height of the object and the length of its shadow.

   b) Repeat part a for the other objects.

   c) Enter the data into a graphing calculator. Enter the heights in list L1 and the shadow lengths in list L2.

   d) Use the calculator to create a scatter plot.

   e) Use the calculator to estimate the equation of the line of best fit, and display the line of best fit on the scatter plot.

   f) Use the equation to predict the height of your own shadow at the time the other measurements were made.

g) Sketch the graph you obtained. Show the plotted points, the line of best fit, and your result for part f. Record the equation of the line of best fit.

h) Is the line of best fit a reasonable model for the data? Explain.

i) What factors affected the outcome of this investigation? Suppose you were to repeat the investigation. What would you do differently to account for these factors?

5. The standard measure for tree size is the diameter at breast height (DBH). The table shows the DBH of 16 red pine trees at various ages. Red pine is a coniferous tree found throughout Eastern Canada.

Age (years)	DBH (cm)	Age (years)	DBH (cm)
9	8	27	30
20	12	5	5
11	6	16	9
4	1	22	12
16	20	3	4
18	9	29	19
12	9	23	19
23	14	21	13

a) What relationship do you expect between age and DBH?

b) Use a graphing calculator to create a scatter plot.

c) i) Describe any trends in the data.
  ii) What appears to be the relationship between age and DBH?
  iii) How does the relationship compare with your prediction in part a?

d) Estimate the equation of the line of best fit.

e) Suggest some reasons why a line does not fit the data points closely.

7.6 Good News for Migraine Sufferers

On page 281, you considered an advertisement for pain medication.

Research was conducted on 72 migraine sufferers. For six months, the people recorded the number of migraines they experienced.

During the same 6-month period the following year, the people took a pill regularly and recorded the number of migraines they experienced. Unknown to them, half the pills contained the medication being tested, while the other half contained no medication. These pills, called "placebos," have no effect.

Here are the data:

People who received the medication

Number of migraines during first 6 months	Number of migraines by same person during second 6 months
18	16
24	20
15	14
19	17
15	13
25	23
21	18
19	16
21	18
17	15
25	21
21	17
23	21
18	17
18	15
23	21
22	19
17	14
21	18
19	17
18	16
25	23
18	16
23	21
17	15
21	17
24	19
27	22
20	19
23	21
25	22
25	23
15	14
23	20
18	16
17	16

People who received the placebo

Number of migraines during first 6 months	Number of migraines by same person during second 6 months
16	15
22	24
15	16
12	12
21	23
13	14
13	12
17	19
22	22
17	16
15	15
16	16
20	22
14	13
21	23
18	19
20	19
17	18
21	19
21	20
21	22
13	12
12	12
18	20
13	12
22	23
17	17
15	14
21	21
13	13
16	16
14	13
14	14
20	19
22	22
20	21

Graphing the results for samples of people who received the medication

Create a random sample of the people who received the medication. The size of your sample should be approximately 20% of the population. To ensure randomness, use the following method.

1. *Using a graphing calculator*

   - Press MATH ▶ ▶ ▶ 5 to display randInt(.
   - Press 1 , 36) ENTER to display a random number from 1 to 36. This will indicate which row to take data from.
   - To repeat, continue pressing ENTER. Press CLEAR to delete the information.

2. Graph the data from your sample. Label the axes as shown.

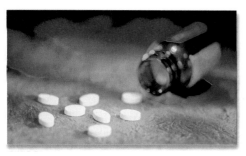

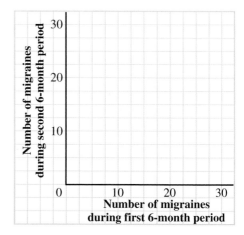

Graphing the results for samples of people who received the placebo

3. Repeat exercises 1 and 2 for people who received the placebo. Use a different graph.

4. a) Do you think your sample size is large enough? Explain why.

   b) What other methods are there to select your random samples?

The graphs below were obtained from all people in the study, not just samples.

5. The screen below left shows the results for everyone who received the placebo. The equation of the line of best fit is $y = 1.10x - 1.65$. Suppose the placebo had no effect. What would you expect the equation of the line of best fit to be?

People who received the placebo

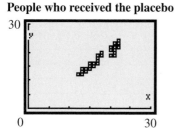

People who received the medication

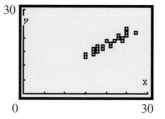

6. The screen above right shows the results for everyone who received the medication. The equation of the line of best fit is $y = 0.83x + 1.06$. How does the equation show that the medication was effective?

7. Can the advertising company reasonably claim a reduction in the number of headaches? Explain why.

MATHEMATICS TOOLKIT

- Population—all things or people considered
- Sample—the portion studied

In a representative sample:
- All parts of the population are fairly represented.
- Sample members are chosen at random.

The line of best fit passes through as many plotted points as possible. It is useful for predicting values.

To estimate the equation of the line of best fit:
- Mark 2 points whose coordinates are easy to read.
- Mark a third point to form a right triangle.
- Determine the slope (by finding the rise and run).
- Use the equation or the graph to determine the y-intercept.

To estimate the equation of the line of best fit (through the origin) using a graphing calculator:
- Visualise where the line of best fit should lie.
- To determine the slope, count the rise and run to go from any point on the line to another point on the line.
- Enter the slope, m, in the form $y = mx$ beside $Y_1=$.
- If the line does not go through the majority of plotted points, repeat the process with another value of m.

7.1 1. Identify the population in each situation.

  a) A sporting-goods store wants to determine the Canadian teenager's favourite brand of running shoe. It puts a questionnaire on the Internet.

  b) A cola company wants to determine the favourite brand of cola of Ontarians. It sets up a booth at all university and college campuses.

  c) A car manufacturer wants to test the safety of cars it manufactures. Cars are chosen at random from one factory, and safety tests are conducted.

  2. Identify the weakness (if any) in each situation in exercise 1.

3. A radio station wishes to compile a list of the top 10 songs in Canada for the year. Listeners call to vote for their favourite song. Will the results truly compile the top 10 songs in Canada? Explain.

7.2 **4. Investigation: What Is the Average Height of Students in Your Class?**
Measure the height of each student in your class.

a) Decide how large a sample you need.

b) Decide how you will ensure that the sample is random.

c) Obtain your sample.

d) Estimate the mean, median, and mode of the population.

7.3 **5.** The table at right shows the DBH (diameter at breast height) of white pine trees at various ages.

a) Create a scatter plot of age versus DBH. Plot *Age (years)* on the horizontal axis.

b) Estimate the DBH of a tree that is 110 years old.

c) Estimate the age of a tree that has a DBH of 20 cm.

Age (years)	White pine DBH (cm)
13	6.0
20	12.5
28	17.8
42	22.3
54	29.6
63	39.5
83	44.3
88	46.8
99	50.0
104	53.6
120	57.1
130	60.9

6. These data from Statistics Canada show the number of unemployed people in Canada from 1995 to 2000.

Year	Number of unemployed
1995	1 393 100
1996	1 436 900
1997	1 378 600
1998	1 277 300
1999	1 190 100
2000	1 089 600

a) Create a scatter plot of year versus number of unemployed. Plot *Year* on the horizontal axis.

b) Estimate the number of unemployed people in Canada in 2010.

c) Do you think this is reasonable? Why?

7.4 **7.** The table at right shows the winning times for the 800-m race at the Olympic Summer Games.

a) Estimate a line of best fit for each set of data. Predict the winning times in the year 2024.

b) In approximately what year would the men's and women's winning times be about the same?

Year	Men's time (s)	Women's time (s)
1960	106.30	124.30
1964	105.10	121.10
1968	104.30	120.90
1972	105.90	118.55
1976	103.50	114.94
1980	105.40	113.42
1984	103.00	117.60
1988	103.45	116.10
1992	103.66	115.54
1996	102.58	117.73

8. In Ontario, a driver who has more than 0.08 mL of alcohol per 100 mL of blood is legally impaired. The amount of alcohol in a person's blood (called the blood-alcohol level) is found using a breathalyser.

Researchers conducted a test to determine how the amount of alcohol in a person's bloodstream decreased over time. These data were collected:

Time (h)	0.0	0.5	1.0	1.5
Blood-alcohol level (mL per 100 mL)	0.094	0.090	0.085	0.080

One evening, a reckless driver was stopped by police and the breathalyser indicated a reading of 0.06. The driver had been driving for 2.5 h.

a) Graph the data. Determine the equation of the line of best fit.

b) Use the model in part a. Determine what the blood-alcohol level was when the driver started driving.

c) What assumptions are you making in part b? Explain your thinking.

9. Estimate the equation of the line of best fit for each scatter plot.

a)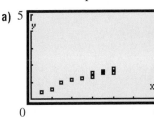

b)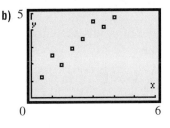

7.5 10. The data show the age and height of a tree.

Age (years)	1	2	3	4	5	6	7	8	9
Height (cm)	11	16	15	39	46	63	75	79	94

a) Enter the data into a graphing calculator.

b) Estimate the equation of the line of best fit.

c) Sketch the graph you obtained. Show the plotted points, the line of best fit, and its equation.

d) What does the slope of the line of best fit represent?

1. **Communication** Explain the weakness: To determine the favourite sport in her school, Anise put a checklist up in the gym. Students were instructed to check off their favourite sport.

2. **Knowledge/Understanding** The following data represent the sales of a store in millions of dollars for a 10-year period.

Year	1	2	3	4	5	6	7	8	9	10
Sales ($ millions)	1.36	1.44	1.69	1.84	2.14	2.59	2.75	2.89	2.95	3.15

a) Draw a scatter plot of the data. Represent the year along the x-axis and the sales on the y-axis. Choose suitable scales.

b) Use a clear ruler to draw an estimated line of best fit for the data.

3. **Thinking/Inquiry/Problem Solving** What is the least number of points you need to determine a line of best fit? Explain your answer.

4. This table shows the number of points scored versus the time played for a basketball player last season.

Time played (min)	25	30	22	15	40	38	35	42
Points scored	23	32	20	13	34	40	28	35

a) Use the calculator to create a scatter plot. Enter the time played in list L1 and the points scored in L2.

b) Use the calculator to estimate the equation of the line of best fit. Display the line of best fit on the scatter plot.

c) Sketch the graph you obtained. Show the plotted points, the line of best fit, and its equation.

d) What does the slope of the line of best fit represent?

5. **Application** These data are from Statistics Canada. They show the percent of Canadian homes with telephones from 1965 to 1995.

Year	1965	1970	1975	1980	1985	1990	1995
Homes with telephones (%)	89.4	93.9	96.4	97.6	98.2	98.5	98.7

a) Plot the data in a scatter plot.

b) Draw the line of best fit.

c) Determine the equation of the line of best fit.

d) Use the equation to determine when 100% of Canadian homes will have a telephone. Is this a reasonable answer? Explain.

6. The graph shows the temperature of water as it is heated. A line of best fit has been drawn. Determine the equation of the line of best fit.

Temperature of Water versus Time

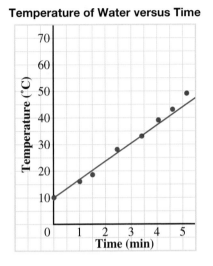

7. A grade nine class made a scatter plot of each student's height versus the length of each student's foot. In the scatter plot, many points overlapped and were bunched together. This made it difficult to draw a line of best fit.

Jaime suggested the problem was due to the fact that the sample considered only students from grade nine.

Explain how a good, random sample of students could be obtained.

8 Measurement

By the end of this chapter, you will:

- Calculate sides in right triangles, using the Pythagorean Theorem.
- Construct a variety of rectangles for a given perimeter and find the maximum area for a given perimeter.
- Construct a variety of square-based prisms for a given volume and find the minimum surface area for a square-based prism with a given volume.
- Construct a variety of cylinders for a given volume and find the minimum surface area for a cylinder with a given volume.
- Find applications in which it would be important to know the maximum area for a given perimeter or the minimum surface area for a given volume.

- Solve problems involving the area of composite plane figures.
- Solve simple problems, using the formulas for the surface area of prisms and cylinders and for the volume of prisms, cylinders, cones, and spheres.
- Solve problems involving perimeter, area, surface area, volume, and capacity in applications.
- Judge the reasonableness of answers to measurement problems by considering likely results within the situation described in the problem.
- Judge the reasonableness of answers found by a calculator or pencil and paper, using mental mathematics and estimation.

Designing a Cooler

Mathematics can be used to make a system or object as efficient as possible. This is called *optimization*.

Your task at the end of this chapter is to find the best shape and dimensions for a portable cooler. This cooler must maintain the temperature of its contents for as long as possible.

You will design a cooler in Section 8.11.

Perimeters of Figures

Rectangle
The perimeter of a rectangle is
length + width + length + width.
That is, $P = 2l + 2w$ or $P = 2(l + w)$

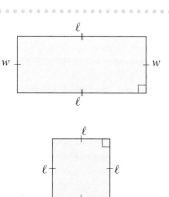

Square
A square is a rectangle with all sides equal.
The perimeter of a square is
length + length + length + length.
That is, $P = 4l$

Circle
The perimeter of a circle is its circumference.
Circumference is $\pi \times$ diameter.
That is, $C = \pi d$
The diameter is $2 \times$ radius.
That is, $d = 2r$
So, $C = \pi(2r)$, or $C = 2\pi r$

Example

Find the perimeter or circumference of each figure.

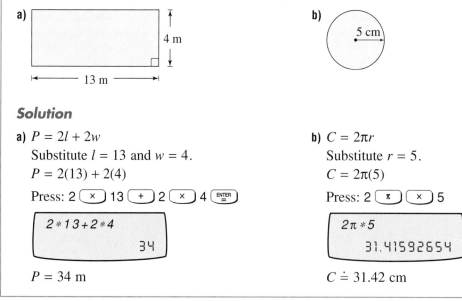

a)

4 m

13 m

b)

5 cm

Solution

a) $P = 2l + 2w$
   Substitute $l = 13$ and $w = 4$.
   $P = 2(13) + 2(4)$
   Press: 2 ⨯ 13 + 2 ⨯ 4 ENTER

   $$2*13+2*4$$
   $$34$$

   $P = 34$ m

b) $C = 2\pi r$
   Substitute $r = 5$.
   $C = 2\pi(5)$
   Press: 2 π ⨯ 5

   $$2\pi*5$$
   $$31.41592654$$

   $C \doteq 31.42$ cm

Exercises

1. Calculate the perimeter or circumference of each figure.

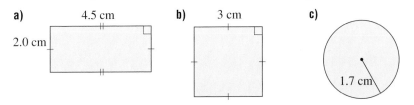

a) 4.5 cm, 2.0 cm

b) 3 cm

c) 1.7 cm

2. Calculate the perimeter of each figure.

a) a rectangle with length 5.6 cm and width 2.1 cm

b) a square with side length 3.7 cm

c) a circle with radius 1.8 cm

d) a circle with diameter 1.8 cm

Areas of Figures

Rectangle
The area of a rectangle is length × width.
That is, $A = lw$

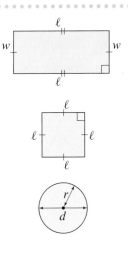

Square
The area of a square is length × length.
That is, $A = l^2$

Circle
The area of a circle is π × radius × radius.
That is, $A = \pi r^2$

Parallelogram
The area of a parallelogram is base × height.
The height is the perpendicular distance between
two sides, where one of these sides is the base.
That is, $A = bh$

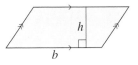

Triangle

The area of a triangle is $\frac{1}{2} \times$ base $\times$ height.

The height is the perpendicular distance from one vertex to the opposite side, which is the base.

That is, $A = \frac{1}{2}bh$

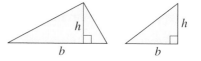

Trapezoid

The area of a trapezoid is $\frac{1}{2} \times$ (sum of parallel sides) $\times$ (perpendicular distance between them).

That is, $A = \frac{1}{2}(a + b)h$, or $A = \frac{h(a + b)}{2}$

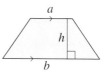

Example

Find the area of each figure.

a)

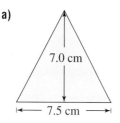

7.0 cm

7.5 cm

b)

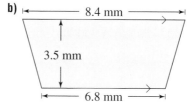

8.4 mm

3.5 mm

6.8 mm

Solution

a) $A = \frac{1}{2}bh$

Substitute $b = 7.5$ and $h = 7.0$.

$A = \frac{1}{2}(7.5)(7.0)$

Press: 1 ÷ 2 × 7.5 × 7 ENTER =

```
1/2*7.5*7
            26.25
```

$A = 26.25$ cm^2

b) $A = \frac{h(a + b)}{2}$

Substitute $h = 3.5$, $a = 8.4$, and $b = 6.8$.

$A = \frac{3.5(8.4 + 6.8)}{2}$

Press: 3.5 (8.4 + 6.8) ÷ 2 ENTER =

```
3.5(8.4+6.8)/2
            26.6
```

$A = 26.6$ mm^2

Discuss

Why do we use units squared for area?

Exercises

1. Calculate the area of each figure.

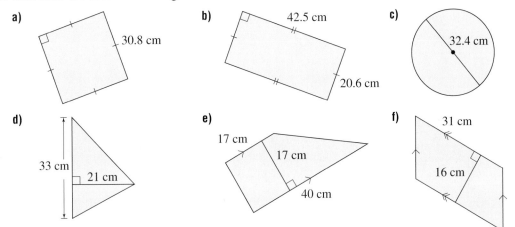

a) 30.8 cm

b) 42.5 cm, 20.6 cm

c) 32.4 cm

d) 33 cm, 21 cm

e) 17 cm, 17 cm, 40 cm

f) 31 cm, 16 cm

2. Calculate the area of each figure.

a) a parallelogram with base 10.9 cm and height 3.9 cm

b) a square with side length 12.1 cm

c) a triangle with base 12.3 cm and height 4.7 cm

d) a rectangle with length 20.5 cm and width 15.6 cm

e) a circle with radius 4.4 cm

f) a circle with diameter 4.4 cm

g) a trapezoid with parallel sides 9.8 cm and 12.6 cm, and a perpendicular distance between them of 6.2 cm

3. Calculate the area of each figure in exercise 1, page 313.

4. Calculate the area of each rectangle in exercise 2, page 313.

5. Calculate the area of each circle in exercise 2, page 313.

Necessary Skills

The Pythagorean Theorem

Recall that for any right triangle,
(length of hypotenuse)^2 = (one side)^2 + (other side)^2.
So, for $\triangle ABC$, $(AC)^2 = (AB)^2 + (BC)^2$

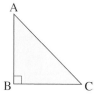

Example

Determine the length x in each triangle.

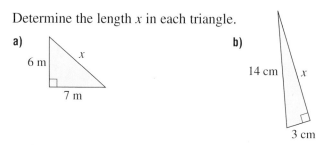

a)

6 m
x
7 m

b)

14 cm
x
3 cm

Solution

a) $x^2 = 6^2 + 7^2$
$ = 36 + 49$
$ = 85$
$ x = \sqrt{85}$
$ \doteq 9.22$

b) $3^2 + x^2 = (14)^2$
$ 9 + x^2 = 196$
$ x^2 = 196 - 9$
$ = 187$
$ x = \sqrt{187}$
$ \doteq 13.67$

Exercises

1. Determine the measure of each unknown side.

a)

C
5 cm
A
4 cm
B

b)

A
5.1 cm
B
12.3 cm
C

c)

A
B
6.8 cm
9.2 cm
C

2. Determine the measure of each unknown side.

a)

A
16.1 cm
11.7 cm
B
C

b)

X
8.3 cm
Z
6.4 cm
M

c)

L
12.1 cm
M
2.4 cm
N

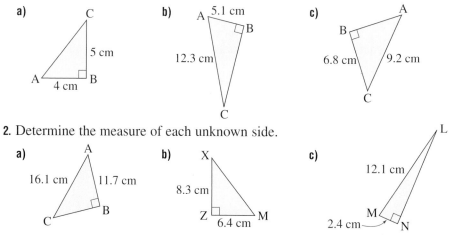

Many figures are combinations or *composites* of geometric figures.

INVESTIGATION

Figures in a Tangram

Recall the tangram you used in earlier grades.

Copy this diagram on grid paper.
Draw a 20-cm square.
Draw one diagonal.
Draw part of the second diagonal, as shown in the diagram.
Complete the construction, using the fact that all indicated segments are equal.

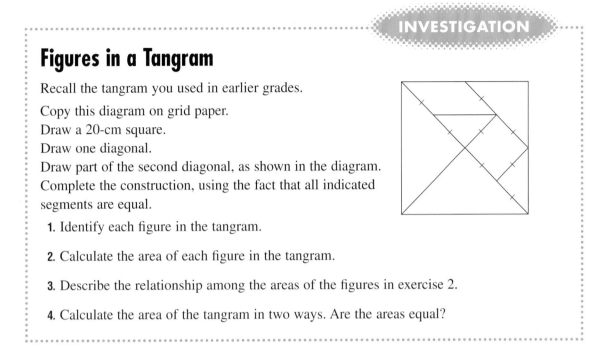

1. Identify each figure in the tangram.

2. Calculate the area of each figure in the tangram.

3. Describe the relationship among the areas of the figures in exercise 2.

4. Calculate the area of the tangram in two ways. Are the areas equal?

The front view of a house is a composite of a rectangle and a triangle.
A window could be a composite of a rectangle and a semicircle.

We can use the formulas we reviewed on pages 312–314 to solve problems involving the perimeter and area of composite figures.

Example 1

Determine the approximate length of wood frame needed for this Roman window.

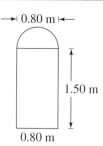

0.80 m

1.50 m

0.80 m

Solution

The window is made up of a rectangle and a semicircle.
The length of frame = perimeter of the rectangle + circumference of the semicircle

For the rectangle:
$P = 2(l + w)$
Substitute $l = 1.50$ and $w = 0.80$.
$P = 2(1.50 + 0.80)$
$ = 2(2.30)$
$ = 4.60$

For the semicircle:
Since the circumference of a circle is $C = 2\pi r$, the circumference of a semicircle is $C_{semicircle} = \frac{2\pi r}{2}$ or $C_{semicircle} = \pi r$.

The radius is one-half the width of the rectangle.
Substitute $r = 0.40$.
$C_{semicircle} = \pi(0.40)$
$\phantom{C_{semicircle}} \doteq 1.26$

The total length of wood needed is:
$P_{rectangle} + C_{semicircle} = 4.60 + 1.26$
$\phantom{P_{rectangle} + C_{semicircle}} = 5.86$

So, approximately 5.86 m of wood is needed to frame the window.

Example 2

The lobby of an office has the measurements shown. The lobby is to be retiled. Calculate the area of the lobby to the nearest square metre.

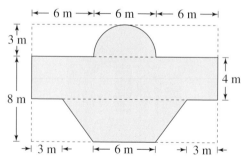

6 m — 6 m — 6 m

3 m

8 m

4 m

3 m — 6 m — 3 m

Solution

The lobby is made up of a semicircle, a rectangle, and a trapezoid.
The area of a circle is $A = \pi r^2$. So, the area of a semicircle is $A_{semicircle} = \frac{\pi r^2}{2}$.

From the diagram, the diameter of the semicircle is 6 m. So, the radius is $r = 3$ m.
Substitute $r = 3$.

$A_{semicircle} = \frac{\pi(3)^2}{2}$
$\phantom{A_{semicircle}} \doteq 14.14$

6 m

The area of a rectangle is $A = lw$.

$l = 6\text{ m} + 6\text{ m} + 6\text{ m}$ $w = 4\text{ m}$
  $= 18\text{ m}$

Substitute $l = 18$ and $w = 4$.

$A_{\text{rectangle}} = 18 \times 4$
         $= 72$

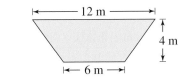

The area of a trapezoid is $A_{\text{trapezoid}} = \dfrac{h(a + b)}{2}$,

where a and b represent the parallel sides, and h is the distance between them.

From the diagram,

$a = 6\text{ m}$ $b = 18\text{ m} - 3\text{ m} - 3\text{ m}$ $h = 8\text{ m} - 4\text{ m}$
                  $= 12\text{ m}$ $= 4\text{ m}$

Substitute $a = 6$, $b = 12$, and $h = 4$.

$A_{\text{trapezoid}} = \dfrac{4(6 + 12)}{2}$
         $= 36$

$A_{\text{lobby}} = A_{\text{semicircle}} + A_{\text{rectangle}} + A_{\text{trapezoid}}$
       $= 14.14 + 72 + 36$
       $= 122.14$

The area of the lobby is approximately 122 m^2.

Example 3

Calculate the perimeter of the lobby in *Example 2*.

Solution

Label the diagram with letters and known measurements.
We know all measurements except the circumference of the semicircle with diameter BC, and the two lengths FG and IH.
The circumference of the semicircle is $C_{\text{semicircle}} = \pi r$.

Substitute $r = 3$.

$C_{\text{semicircle}} = \pi(3)$
          $\doteq 9.42$

Triangle IKH and $\triangle$FLG are congruent, so IH = FG.

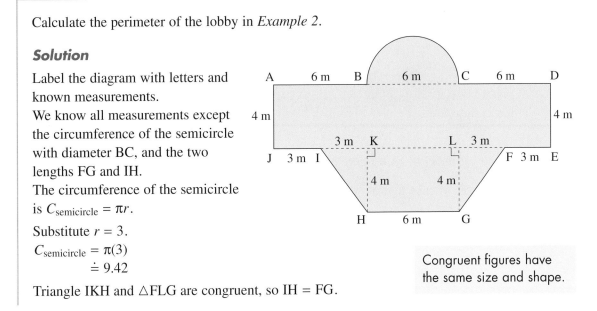

Congruent figures have the same size and shape.

Use the Pythagorean Theorem in $\triangle$IKH.

$$(IH)^2 = (IK)^2 + (KH)^2$$
$$= 3^2 + 4^2$$
$$= 25$$
$$IH = \sqrt{25}$$
$$= 5$$

So, IH = FG = 5

The perimeter is AB + semicircle + CD + DE + EF + FG + GH + HI + IJ + JA.

$$P \doteq 6 + 9.42 + 6 + 4 + 3 + 5 + 6 + 5 + 3 + 4$$
$$\doteq 51.42$$

The perimeter of the lobby is approximately 51 m.

8.1   Exercises

A   **1.** Calculate the area of each figure.

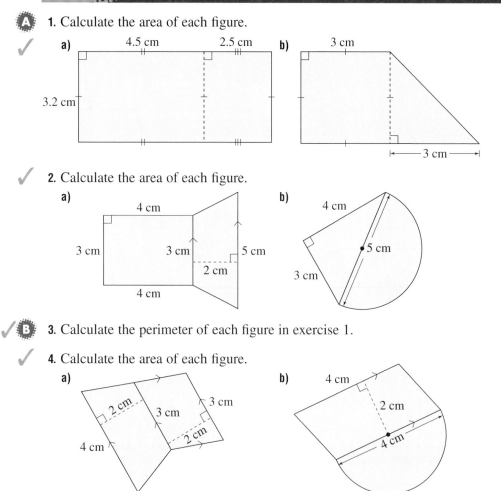

2. Calculate the area of each figure.

B   **3.** Calculate the perimeter of each figure in exercise 1.

4. Calculate the area of each figure.

c)

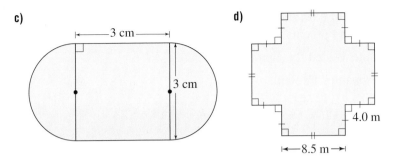

d)

✓ **5. Knowledge/Understanding**

  a) Calculate the diameter of each circle.

  b) Calculate the area of each circle.

  c) Calculate the area of the square or triangle (in white).

  d) Determine the shaded area of each figure.

   i)

   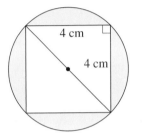

   ii)

   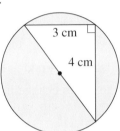

6. Calculate the shaded area of each figure.

   a)

   b)

   c)

   d)

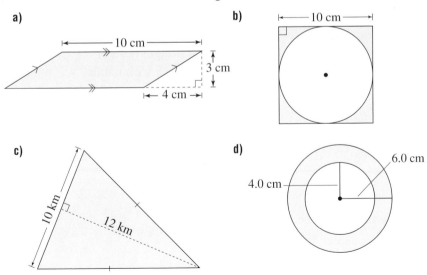

7. A Roman window is a composite of a rectangle and a semicircle (below left). The dimensions of the rectangle are 60 cm by 100 cm.

a) Calculate the length of frame needed for this window.

b) Is the answer in part a reasonable? Explain.

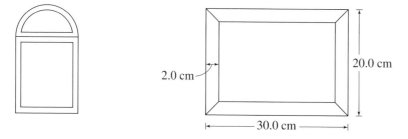

8. **Application** A picture frame measures 30.0 cm by 20.0 cm (above right). The four trapezoids that comprise this frame are cut from one piece of wood 2.0 cm wide.

a) Determine the area of a picture that fills this frame.

b) Determine the minimum length of wood needed to make the frame.

c) How would your answer to part b change if the framing material was wider? Explain.

9. **Communication** Values have been substituted into area formulas below. Examine each formula. Describe the figure suggested by each.

a) $A = \pi(5.2)^2 - \pi(4.8)^2$

b) $A = 4 \times 3 + \dfrac{\pi(1.5)^2}{2}$

10. The field inside a 400-m running track is to be seeded. Each straight portion of the track is 100 m. Each curved part of the track is a semicircle with radius approximately 31.8 m. One 1.5-kg bag of grass seed will seed an area of 80 m².

a) Calculate the width of the field.

b) Calculate the area of the field to the nearest 10 m².

c) Is the answer in part b reasonable? Explain.

d) Calculate the number of bags of seed required.

e) One 1.5-kg bag of grass seed costs $12.64. How much does it cost to seed the field?

11. Thinking/Inquiry/Problem Solving

a) Describe *two* methods to find the area of the shaded region in each figure.

b) Check your answers in part a by using each method.

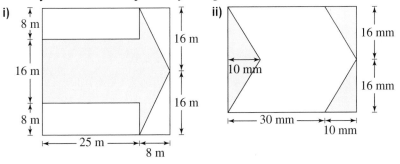

i)

ii)

12. a) How many triangles are in this figure? Name them.

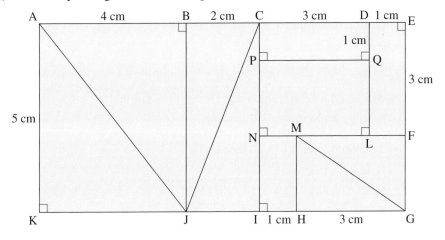

b) How many rectangles are in the figure above? Name them.

c) Calculate the area of each rectangle and triangle you named in parts a and b.

13. Grain elevators are common on the prairies. The front of this grain elevator is to be painted.

a) Determine the area of the front of the grain elevator.

b) One can of paint covers an area of 14 m². Determine how many cans of paint need to be purchased.

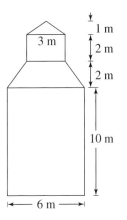

In this section, you will investigate different rectangles with the same perimeter.

Area for a Given Perimeter: Part I

You will need grid paper.

Suppose you have 40 m of fencing. You want to make a rectangular dog pen. What is the maximum area you can provide for a dog?

We will model this problem using 1 cm to represent 1 m.

1. On grid paper, draw a rectangle with perimeter 40 cm.

a) What is the length of the rectangle?

b) What is the width?

c) What is the area?

2. Repeat exercise 1. Draw as many different rectangles as you can that have perimeter 40 cm. Copy and complete this table.

Length (cm)	Width (cm)	Area (cm^2)

3. Look at the table.

a) What is the greatest area?

b) What are the dimensions of the rectangle with the greatest area?

By using grid paper, you were probably only able to draw rectangles with dimensions that are whole numbers. We can use a spreadsheet to calculate areas of rectangles with dimensions that are rational numbers.

Area for a Given Perimeter: Part II

We will use a spreadsheet to calculate areas of rectangles with rational number dimensions. We will use a perimeter of 40 cm.

1. Set up this spreadsheet.
   Enter the text and formulas shown.

	A	B	C
1	Maximum area with perimeter 40		
2			
3	Width	Length	Area
4	0.5	=20-A4	=A4*B4
5	=A4+0.5		
6			

2. a) Explain what the formula in each cell does.
      i) Cell A5   ii) Cell B4   iii) Cell C4

   b) Highlight cell A5. Fill Down:

   For *Excel* and *Quattro Pro*, move the pointer to the bottom right of the
   highlighted cell. The pointer should change to crosshairs (a plus sign).
   Drag down to row 42.

   For *Claris Works*, drag down from the bottom right corner of the
   highlighted cell, A5. Highlight down to row 42. Under the Calculate
   menu, click on Fill Down.

   Highlight cells B4 and C4 and Fill Down to row 42.
   What is the maximum area of the rectangle?

3. What are the dimensions of the rectangle with the maximum area? Explain.

4. Use the results of *Investigations 1* and *2*. Describe the rectangle that has the
   greatest area for a perimeter of 40 cm.

Designing an Enclosure

Workers at a resort set up a rectangular area to store outdoor equipment
and furniture. They use metal stands. They have 26 stands, each 3 m long.
The rectangles they make can have different shapes.

The length could be much longer
than the width.

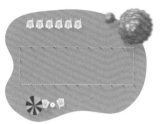

The length and width could be
almost equal.

1. Suppose 3 metal stands are used for the width.

   a) How many stands could be used for the length?

   b) What are the dimensions of this enclosure, in metres?

   c) What is the enclosed area?

2. Repeat exercise 1 for each condition given.

   a) The workers use 4 stands for the width.

   b) They use 5 stands for the width.

3. **a)** Record your results from exercises 1 and 2 in a table.

Number of stands along the width	Number of stands along the length	Width of enclosure (m)	Length of enclosure (m)	Area enclosed (m²)
3				
4				
5				

   b) Extend your table to show the results for greater widths.

   c) How many stands should be used for the width and length to make the largest possible enclosure? What are the dimensions of this enclosure?

4. **Communication** Use the results of exercises 1 to 3. The stands have a fixed length. Describe the rectangle that has the greatest area for a given perimeter of these stands.

From the results of *Investigations 1* and *2*, Section 8.2, you should have discovered that, for a perimeter of 40 cm, the rectangle with the greatest area is a square with side length 10 cm. The side length 10 cm is the *optimal value* of measurement when maximizing area. The optimal value is the maximum or minimum area for a particular figure.

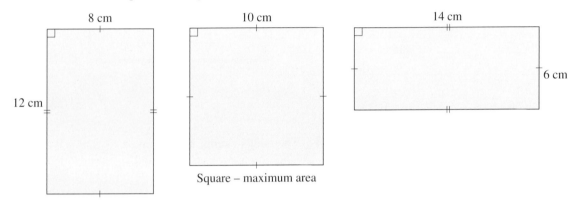

Square – maximum area

In general, for any given perimeter, the rectangle with the greatest area is a square.

Rectangles—Maximum Area for a Given Perimeter

For a given perimeter, the rectangle with the maximum area is a square.

There are many applications where a square is not possible. In *Investigation 3*, Section 8.2, the perimeter was made from a fixed number of stands with a fixed length. In this case, for any given perimeter, the rectangle with the greatest area has a shape that is closest to a square.

Example 1

A rectangle is formed using 24 metre sticks. The sticks cannot be broken. Calculate the greatest possible area of the rectangle.

Solution

The area is greatest when the rectangle is closest to a square.

A square has 4 equal sides.

Divide the number of sticks by 4
to find the length of each side.

$\frac{24}{4} = 6$

Each side is 6 m long.

$A_{\text{rectangle}} = 6 \times 6$
$\qquad\quad = 36$

The greatest possible area is 36 m².

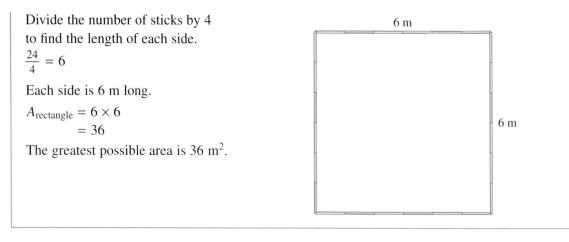

Example 2

A rectangle is formed using 26 metre sticks. The sticks cannot be broken.
Calculate the greatest possible area of the rectangle.

Solution

The area is greatest when the rectangle
is closest to a square.

When we calculate $\frac{26}{4}$, the quotient is
not a whole number.

That is, $\frac{26}{4} = 6.5$

We cannot break the sticks.

This means that 2 sides of the rectangle have 6 sticks.
So, the total length of the other two sides is:

$26 - 2(6) = 26 - 12$
$\qquad\qquad = 14$

So, each of the other sides is 7 m.

$A = 6 \times 7$
$\quad = 42$

The greatest possible area is 42 m².

8.3   Exercises

1. Find the maximum rectangular area for each given perimeter.

   a) 4 cm   **b)** 8 cm   **c)** 12 cm   **d)** 16 cm   **e)** 20 cm

2. Find the maximum rectangular area for each given perimeter.

   a) 36 cm   **b)** 32 cm   **c)** 28 cm   **d)** 40 cm   **e)** 200 cm

B **3. Knowledge/Understanding** A rectangle is formed using 1-m sticks.
Calculate the maximum area for each number of 1-m sticks.

a) 10   b) 20   c) 40   d) 66   e) 98

4. There are thirty 3-m metal stands like those in *Investigation 3*, page 325.
They are used to make a rectangular enclosure.

a) What are the dimensions of the enclosure with the greatest area?

b) Can the enclosure have an area of 50 m²? If so, what are its dimensions?

5. Melanie has 36 patio tiles, each 0.6 m square.

a) Suppose she uses the patio tiles to form a path. What are the dimensions
of the narrowest rectangular path?

b) Suppose Melanie uses all the patio tiles to form a square patio. What are
the dimensions of the patio?

6. Campbell has 10 railroad ties, each 1.8 m long. He uses the ties to enclose a
rectangular garden.

a) What are the dimensions of the different rectangles he could form?

b) What is the area of each rectangle in part a?

7. Communication Steve wants to fence a rectangular garden. The fencing material
comes in 1-m long units that cannot be cut. Suppose Steve has 20 m of fencing.
Explain how Steve can calculate the dimensions of the largest possible garden.

8. Application A lifeguard has 400 m of rope
to enclose a rectangular swimming area at a
beach. The diagrams show different ways she
can do this.

a) Do you think the area of the enclosed region
depends on the way the rope is arranged?
Explain.

b) Suppose the side parallel to the beach
measures 300 m. How long is the other side
of the rectangle? Calculate the area of water
enclosed by the rope.

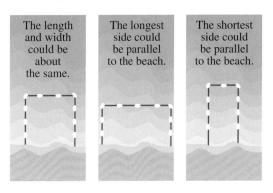

c) Repeat part b if the side parallel to the beach measures:

i) 250 m   ii) 200 m   iii) 150 m   iv) 100 m

d) Record your results in a table.

Length of side parallel to beach (m)	Length of side perpendicular to beach (m)	Total length of rope (m)	Area enclosed (m²)
300			
250			

e) What are the dimensions of the largest possible rectangular swimming area? How are these dimensions related?

9. A storeowner wants to create a rectangular area for a store display. He has 6 m of rope. What are the dimensions of the largest area he can enclose in each situation? Explain your answers.

   a) The rope encloses the entire area.

   b) There is a wall on one side.

   c) There are walls on 2 sides.

10. Consider the twenty-six 3-m stands in *Investigation 3*, page 325. Calculate the dimensions of the largest enclosure for each situation.

   a) Use metal stands for 3 sides of the enclosure, with a wall on the remaining side.

   b) Use metal stands for 2 sides of the enclosure, with walls on two adjacent sides.

11. Twenty-six 3-m metal stands are used to make two enclosures with equal area and a common side. The diagram shows one way to do this.

   a) Calculate the combined area of the two enclosures.

   b) Find some other ways to arrange the metal stands to make the two enclosures. Calculate the combined area for each. Record your results in a table.

Number of the stands along each of the 3 sides	Number of the stands along each of the other 2 sides	Overall width (m)	Overall length (m)	Combined area (m²)
6	4			

   c) How should the stands be arranged to make the largest possible enclosure? What are the dimensions and the area of this enclosure?

12. **Thinking/Inquiry/Problem Solving** Suppose you have several rectangles with the same area. How could you tell, just by looking, which one has the *least* perimeter?

C 13. You will need some string and a sheet of 1-cm grid paper. Cut a piece of string and tie the ends together to form a loop.

   a) Describe the shape of the largest region on the grid paper you can enclose with the string. Experiment using different shapes.

   b) What is the area of the largest region?

   c) Suppose the string is 42.5 cm long. What are the dimensions of the largest region?

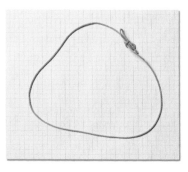

Many items that we see and use everyday, such as CD jewel cases and refrigerators, are rectangular prisms. A die is a special rectangular prism in which all edges have the same length; this prism is a cube.

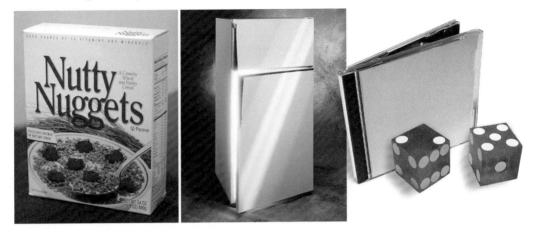

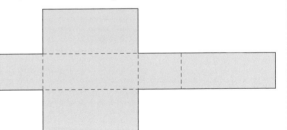

INVESTIGATION

Surface Area and Volume of a Rectangular Prism

You will need 1-cm grid paper, a pencil, a ruler, scissors, and tape.

1. On grid paper, create a net for a rectangular prism that is not a cube. Recall that a net is a 2-dimensional diagram of the faces of a hollow solid.

2. Check that the opposite sides of each face of the prism are equal.

3. Measure the net. Calculate the area of the net.

4. Cut, fold, and tape the net to form a rectangular prism, with the grid on the outside surface.

5. One grid square represents 1 face of a 1-cm cube. Calculate the number of 1-cm cubes that would fit inside your prism.

6. a) What is the surface area of the rectangular prism? Explain.

   b) What is the volume of the rectangular prism? Explain.

In the *Investigation*, you constructed a rectangular prism, then calculated its surface area and volume.

For any rectangular prism:

- Its volume is the number of unit cubes needed to fill it.
  Volume = base area × height or Volume = length × width × height

- Its surface area is the sum of the areas of its 6 rectangular faces.
  There are 3 pairs of faces with equal areas.
  Surface area = (2 × length × width) + (2 × length × height) + (2 × width × height)

The algebraic formulas for volume and surface area are shown below.

TAKE NOTE

Rectangular Prism

Volume, V = base area × height, or

$$V = lwh$$

Surface area, $SA = 2(lw + lh + wh)$

Two triangular prisms are formed
by cutting a rectangular prism in half
along a diagonal of a base.

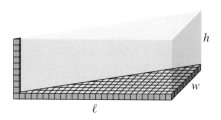

Therefore, the volume of a triangular prism is one-half the volume of the corresponding rectangular prism.

To calculate the volume of a triangular prism, we use the general formula for the volume of a prism.

Volume = base area × height

The surface area of a triangular prism is the sum of the areas of its 5 faces.

Triangular Prism

Volume, V = base area × height, where base area is the area of the triangle.

Surface area, SA = the sum of the areas of the faces

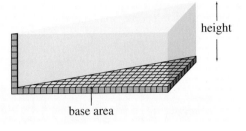

height

base area

Note that for any prism, the base is the shape that has a consistent cross-sectional area throughout the length or height of the figure.

Example 1

Determine the surface area of this carton.

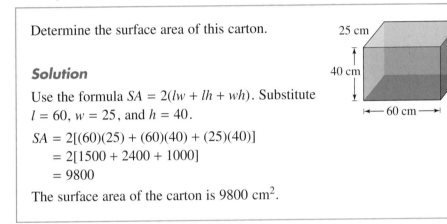

25 cm

40 cm

60 cm

Solution

Use the formula $SA = 2(lw + lh + wh)$. Substitute $l = 60$, $w = 25$, and $h = 40$.

$SA = 2[(60)(25) + (60)(40) + (25)(40)]$
$\quad = 2[1500 + 2400 + 1000]$
$\quad = 9800$

The surface area of the carton is 9800 cm^2.

Example 2

A railway car approximates a rectangular prism. It has a volume of 82.5 m^3. The car is 3 m wide and 11 m long. Determine the height of the railway car.

Solution

Use the formula $V = lwh$.
Substitute $V = 82.5$, $l = 11$, and $w = 3$.

$82.5 = 11 \times 3 \times h$
$82.5 = 33h$ Solve for h.
$\dfrac{82.5}{33} = h$
$\quad h = 2.5$

The height of the railway car is 2.5 m.

Example 3

A large Toblerone® bar has the approximate dimensions shown.

a) Calculate the volume of this prism.

b) Calculate the surface area of this prism.

Solution

a) Volume, V = base area × height

For a triangular prism:

The base of the prism is the triangular face.

The height of the prism is the length of the bar.

The area of the triangular face = $\frac{1}{2}bh$

Substitute $b = 6.0$ and $h = 5.2$.

The area of the triangle = $\frac{1}{2}(6.0)(5.2)$

$= 15.6$

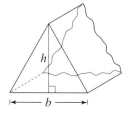

So, V = base area × height

$= 15.6 \times 30.5$

$= 475.8$

The volume of the prism is approximately 476 cm^3.

b) Consider a net of the prism.

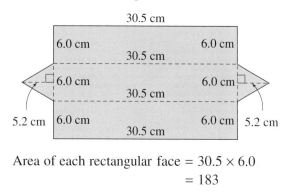

Area of each rectangular face = 30.5×6.0

$= 183$

From part a, the area of each triangular face is 15.6.

The surface area of the prism = sum of the areas of all the faces

There are 2 triangular faces, each with area 15.6.

There are 3 rectangular faces, each with area 183.

So, $SA = 2(15.6) + 3(183)$

$\qquad = 580.2$

The surface area of the prism is approximately 580 cm^2.

Discuss

Why is the base of the prism a triangle, and not the rectangle it sits on?

8.4   Exercises

1. Calculate the volume of each prism.

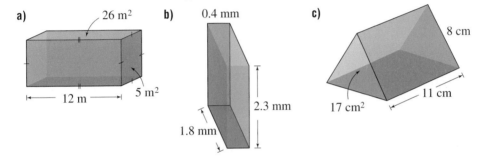

a) 26 m^2 12 m   5 m^2

b) 0.4 mm   2.3 mm   1.8 mm

c) 8 cm   11 cm   17 cm^2

2. Calculate the surface area of each prism in exercise 1.

3. Calculate the surface area of each rectangular prism.

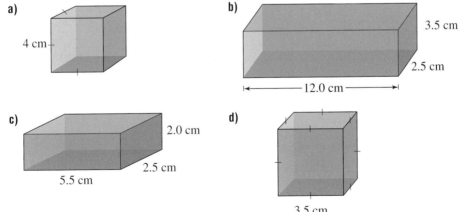

a) 4 cm

b) 3.5 cm   2.5 cm   12.0 cm

c) 2.0 cm   2.5 cm   5.5 cm

d) 3.5 cm

4. Knowledge/Understanding Calculate the volume of each prism in exercise 3.

5. Calculate the surface area of each triangular prism.

a)

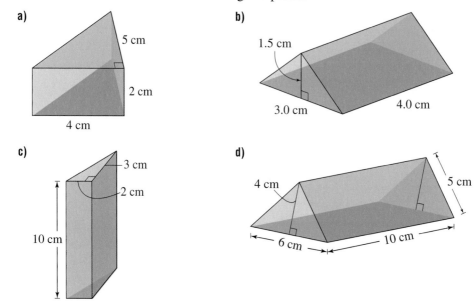

5 cm

2 cm

4 cm

b)

1.5 cm

3.0 cm

4.0 cm

c)

3 cm

2 cm

10 cm

d)

4 cm

6 cm

10 cm

5 cm

6. Calculate the volume of each prism in exercise 5.

7. For some triangular prisms, only the edge lengths are known. We use the Pythagorean Theorem to calculate the height of the triangular face.

a)

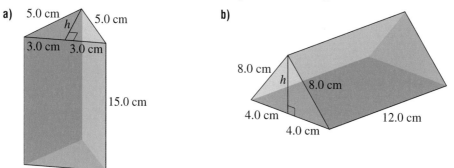

5.0 cm   5.0 cm

h

3.0 cm   3.0 cm

15.0 cm

b)

8.0 cm

h 8.0 cm

4.0 cm

4.0 cm

12.0 cm

For each prism:
i) Calculate the height h of the triangular face.
ii) Calculate the surface area.
iii) Calculate the volume.

8. Communication The box of a dump truck has dimensions 1 m by 2 m by 4 m. Explain how this truck was able to carry 9 m³ of soil.

9. Determine the minimum amount of packaging needed to completely cover a Toblerone® bar with these dimensions: length 20.7 cm; triangular face edges 3.5 cm; and height 3.0 cm. Express the surface area to the nearest square centimetre.

10. **Application** For each prism, several measurements are given. Calculate each unknown measure.

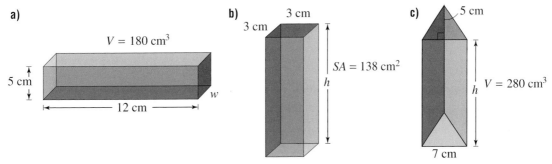

a)
$V = 180 \text{ cm}^3$
5 cm
12 cm
w

b)
3 cm
3 cm
$SA = 138 \text{ cm}^2$
h

c)
5 cm
h
$V = 280 \text{ cm}^3$
7 cm

11. **Thinking/Inquiry/Problem Solving** Volumes of fluids are measured in millilitres or litres. One millilitre equals 1 cm^3. There are 1000 mL in 1 L. A 2-L carton of milk approximates a rectangular prism.

a) Find 3 sets of possible dimensions for a 2-L carton of milk.

b) Which set of dimensions is most likely? Why?

12. A manufacturer lists the capacity of one cooler as 50 L. The inside dimensions are 31 cm by 32 cm by 50 cm. Was the manufacturer's information correct? Explain.

13. a) How many cubic centimetres fit in 1 m^3? Explain.

b) What percent of the space in one cubic metre would 250 000 cm^3 fill?

14. A packing crate is a rectangular prism. Its surface area is 24 m^2.

a) Determine some possible dimensions for this crate.

b) What is the volume of this crate?

c) Suppose each dimension of the crate was reduced by 50%. How much material would be saved?

d) What would the new volume be?

15. Explain how the volume of a rectangular prism changes in each case.

a) The length of the prism is doubled.

b) Both the length and width of the prism are doubled.

c) The length, width, and height of the prism are doubled.

16. Explain how the surface area of a rectangular prism changes in each case.

a) The length of the prism is doubled.

b) Both the length and width of the prism are doubled.

c) The length, width, and height of the prism are doubled.

In this section, you will investigate different square-based prisms with the same volume.

Square-Based Prisms with a Fixed Volume: Part I

You will need 36 1-cm cubes.

1. Use all the cubes to make a rectangular prism with a square base.
Copy and complete this table for the prism you constructed.

Length (cm)	Width (cm)	Height (cm)	Surface area (cm²)	Volume (cm³)

2. Repeat exercise 1 several times until you have constructed all possible square-based prisms. How many prisms did you construct?

3. Look at the table.

a) What is the minimum surface area?

b) What are the dimensions of the prism with the minimum surface area?

Square-Based Prisms with a Fixed Volume: Part II

Suppose you used millimetre cubes instead of centimetre cubes to make a square-based prism with a volume of 36 cm³.

Could you construct a square-based prism with a surface area smaller than that in *Investigation 1*?

You can use a spreadsheet to find out.

1. Set up a spreadsheet document. Enter the information shown.

	A	B	C	D
1	Surface area of a square-based prism			
2				
3	Length/width	Height	Area of base	Surface area
4	0.1	=36/A4^2	=A4^2	=2*C4+4*A4*B4
5	=A4+0.1			

2. **a)** Explain what the formula in each cell does.

   i) Cell B4   **ii)** Cell C4   **iii)** Cell D4   **iv)** Cell A5

   b) Highlight cell A5. Fill Down. Highlight and fill down cells B4, C4, and D4. For detailed instruction of how to fill down, refer to *Investigation 2*, Section 8.2.
   What is the minimum surface area of the prism?

3. What are the dimensions of the prism with the minimum surface area?

Square-Based Prisms with a Fixed Volume: Part III

You will need 3 sheets of grid paper, a ruler, scissors, and tape. You will construct three square-based rectangular prisms each with a volume of 125 cm³.

1. **a)** Choose any measurement between 3.5 cm and 8.0 cm as the side length for the square base.

   b) Calculate the area of the base.

   c) Divide the volume (125 cm³) by the base area to calculate the height of the prism.

2. **a)** Draw the net of your prism on grid paper. If there is no room for the top, the top can be omitted.

   b) Use the net to determine the surface area of the prism.

   c) Cut out the net and tape it together to form the prism.

3. Repeat exercises 1 and 2 (using different side lengths than in exercise 1a) to create three prisms.

4. Each of your prisms should have a square base and a volume of 125 cm³.

   a) Compare the surface areas of the three prisms.

   b) Compare the heights of the prisms with the side lengths of their bases.

   c) Choose the prism that has the least surface area. How does its height compare with the base side length?

5. **Communication** Use the results of *Investigations 1, 2,* and *3*. Describe the square-based prism that has the least surface area for a volume of 125 cm³.

From the results of *Investigation 3*, Section 8.5, you should have discovered that, for a volume of 125 cm^3, the square-based prism with the least surface area is a cube with side length 5 cm. This is the optimal dimension when minimizing surface area.

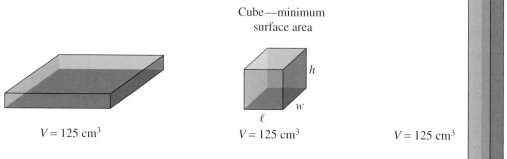

Cube—minimum
surface area

$V = 125$ cm^3 $V = 125$ cm^3 $V = 125$ cm^3

In general, for any given volume, the square-based prism with the least (minimum) surface area is a cube.

The same principle applies to rectangular prisms.

TAKE NOTE

Rectangular Prism—Minimum Surface Area for a Given Volume

These rectangular prisms have the same volume and different surface areas. The prism that has the minimum surface area is a cube.

minimum
surface area

Example

A square-based prism is formed from 45 1-cm cubes. Calculate the minimum surface area of the prism.

Solution

The minimum surface area is produced when the prism is closest to a cube.

The prism has a square base.

List possible dimensions of the prism with a square base. The product of the 3 dimensions is 45 cm³.

Length, l (cm)	Width, w (cm)	Height, h (cm)
1	1	45
2	2	not possible
3	3	5
4	4	not possible
5	5	not possible
6	6	not possible

This is because 45 is not divisible by 2 × 2, or 4.

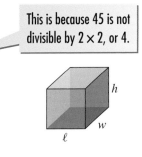

The prism that is closest to a cube is 3 cm by 3 cm by 5 cm.

Use the formula for the surface area of a prism.
$SA = 2(lw + lh + wh)$
Substitute $l = 3$, $w = 3$, and $h = 5$.
$SA = 2[(3)(3) + (3)(5) + (3)(5)]$
$\quad = 2(9 + 15 + 15)$
$\quad = 2(39)$
$\quad = 78$
The minimum surface area is 78 cm².

8.6　　Exercises

A

1. Minimum surface area is needed. Find the dimensions for a square-based prism made with each number of 1-cm cubes.

   a) 8　　　　　　　　**b)** 27　　　　　　　　**c)** 64

2. Calculate the surface area of each prism in exercise 1.

3. **Knowledge/Understanding** Minimum surface area is needed. Find the dimensions for a square-based prism made with each number of 1-cm cubes.

   a) 20　　　　　　　　**b)** 48　　　　　　　　**c)** 52

4. Calculate the surface area of each prism in exercise 3.

B

5. Find the minimum surface area for a rectangular prism made with each number of 1-cm cubes.

   a) 12　　　　　　　　**b)** 60　　　　　　　　**c)** 15

6. **a)** List several possible sets of dimensions for a rectangular prism with volume 24 cm³. Each dimension should be a whole number.

   b) Which prism has the least surface area?

7. a) List several possible sets of whole-number dimensions for a rectangular prism with volume 32 cm³.

   b) Which prism has the least surface area?

✓ **8. a)** List several possible sets of whole-number dimensions for a rectangular prism with volume 100 m³.

   b) Which prism has the least surface area?

9. Here are two designs for a flat-roof building.

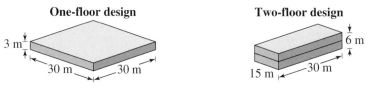

One-floor design   Two-floor design

3 m   30 m   30 m   6 m   15 m   30 m

   a) Check that each building has 900 m² of floor space and a volume of 2700 m³.

   b) For each design, calculate the total area of the roof and the four outside walls. Which building do you think is cheaper to heat in the winter? Explain.

✓ **10. Communication** Suppose you have several rectangular prisms, all with the same volume. Explain how you could tell, just by looking, which one has the least surface area. Illustrate your answer with some examples.

11. A company has been hired to design boxes to hold popcorn. Each box has a volume of 4000 cm³. The boxes have an open top and a square base.

   a) Suppose the base is 10 cm long and 10 cm wide. What is the height for a volume of 4000 cm³? Calculate the surface area of this box.

   b) Repeat part a for each base described.
      i) 12 cm by 12 cm   **ii)** 14 cm by 14 cm

   c) Record your results from parts a and b in a table.

Length (cm)	Width (cm)	Height (cm)	Volume (cm³)	Surface area (cm²)
10	10			
12	12			
14	14			

   d) Determine the dimensions of the box that requires the minimum amount of cardboard. Describe the box. Do you think it would be a good idea for movie theatres to use this shape? Explain.

12. **Thinking/Inquiry/Problem Solving** The company in exercise 11 needs to design a larger box with a volume of 8000 cm^3. The box is to be made with the least amount of cardboard. Would the dimensions of the new box be double the dimensions of the box in exercise 11d? Explain.

13. a) Measure a juice box. Calculate its total surface area.

  b) Determine some dimensions of boxes that contain the same volume of juice, but have a smaller surface area.

  c) Do you think it would be a good idea for juice box manufacturers to change the dimensions of their boxes? Explain.

14. **Application** Sugar cubes come in boxes of 144 cubes. There are 2 layers of cubes. Each layer forms a 12 by 6 rectangle. The company wants to design a box that uses less cardboard and still holds 144 sugar cubes.

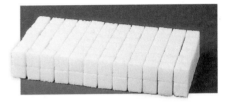

  a) Calculate the surface area of the box, in square units, that would enclose the cubes shown.

  b) Determine three other ways to arrange 144 sugar cubes in a box. Calculate the surface area of each box.

  c) How would you arrange 144 sugar cubes to use the least amount of cardboard?

  d) Do you think it would be a good idea for sugar-cube boxes to be redesigned? Why?

15. Suppose you have an 8-cm cube.

The 8-cm cube can be divided into 4-cm cubes.

These 4-cm cubes can be divided further into 2-cm cubes.

Step 1

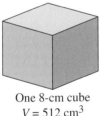

One 8-cm cube
$V = 512$ cm^3

Step 2

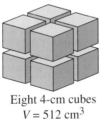

Eight 4-cm cubes
$V = 512$ cm^3

Step 3

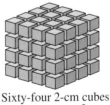

Sixty-four 2-cm cubes
$V = 512$ cm^3

  a) Calculate the total surface area of the cubes in each step above.

  b) Suppose you divided the 2-cm cubes in a fourth step. Determine the total surface area of the 1-cm cubes.

  c) Describe a pattern in the total surface area from step to step.

16. Mary bought some caramels at the bulk-food store. She wants to pack them in a box. The caramels are 2 cm by 2 cm by 1 cm.

   a) Mary found a box measuring 8 cm by 5 cm by 4 cm. What is the maximum number of caramels she can pack in this box? Explain your answer.

   b) Mary found another box whose dimensions are double the dimensions of the box in part a. What is the maximum number of caramels she can pack in it?

17. A company makes boxes from pieces of cardboard 28.0 cm long and 21.6 cm wide. Equal squares are cut from each corner and the sides are folded up. Plain copy paper measures approximately 28.0 cm by 21.6 cm. On a piece of paper like this, draw lines 6 cm from each side. Cut a 6-cm square from each corner. Fold up the sides to make an open box.

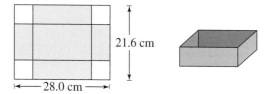

21.6 cm

28.0 cm

   a) Calculate the volume of the box.

   b) Suppose you change the size of the cutout square. Predict what will happen to the volume. Will it be the same, greater, or smaller?

   c) To check your prediction, copy and complete the table below. Use lengths of the cutout square from 1 cm to 9 cm.
   i) The length of the cutout square increases from 1 cm to 9 cm. What happens to the volume of the box?
   ii) Suppose the length of the cutout square increases beyond 9 cm. What would happen to the volume of the box? What would happen if the length of the cutout square were less than 1 cm?

Length of the cutout square (cm)	Length of the box (cm)	Width of the box (cm)	Height of the box (cm)	Volume of the box (cm³)

   d) Graph the *Volume of the box (cm³)* against the *Length of the cutout square (cm)*. Use the graph to answer these questions.
   i) What is the volume of the largest box that could be made from this size of cardboard? What size of square should be cut from the corners to make this box?
   ii) Suppose the company wanted to use the cardboard to make a box with a volume of 900 cm³. What size of square should be cut from the corners to make this box?

1. Calculate the amount of fencing needed (perimeter) for each yard.

   a)

   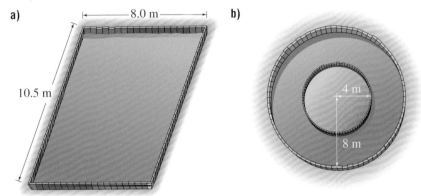

   b)

   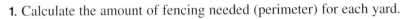

2. Calculate the area of the yard in exercise 1b.

3. Meena wants to create a garden with a border. There are 40 border tiles. What layout of border tiles creates the largest possible garden?

4. A rectangular patio is to be made with concrete. The patio measures 4.5 m by 2.3 m. The concrete will be 0.2 m deep. How much concrete is required?

5. A trough in the shape of a triangular prism has the dimensions shown. Determine the amount of water to fill the trough.

   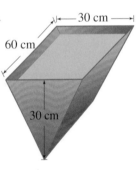

6. Find the surface area of the trough in exercise 5.

7. **a)** List several whole-number dimensions for a rectangular prism with volume 36 cm^3.

   b) Which prism has the least surface area?

8. Appliances such as refrigerators, freezers, and microwave ovens have volumes measured in cubic feet (cu. ft., or ft^3). A fridge has a volume of 24 cu. ft. Determine at least 6 sets of possible dimensions for the inside of this fridge. Which dimensions are the most likely?

Preparation for Ontario Testing

9. A triangular prism has volume 72 cm^3. The area of the triangular face is 12 cm^2. What is the length of x?

   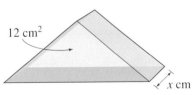

   a) 3

   b) 432

   c) 864

   d) 6

Everyday objects, such as tin cans, mugs, and paper towel rolls, are *cylinders*.

The total surface area of a cylinder is the area of its curved surface and the two bases.

INVESTIGATION

Total Surface Area of a Cylinder

You will need some tin cans with labels attached and a millimetre ruler.
Cut off the label.

Choose one can. What do you think *total surface area* means?
Devise a plan to calculate the total surface area of this can. Then use your
plan to calculate the total surface area.

1. **a)** What do you notice about the shape of the label?

   b) How do you calculate the area of the label? What does this tell you
   about the area of the curved surface of the can?

2. How do you calculate the area of the bottom of the can?

3. What is the total surface area of the can?

Look at the cylinder, below left. Imagine there is a paper label on the cylinder.
When you unroll the label, it forms a rectangle. The length of the rectangle is
equal to the circumference of the cylinder.
The width of the rectangle is equal to the height of the cylinder.
So, the area of the curved surface of the cylinder is equal to the area of the rectangle.
The total surface area includes the two circles at the ends.

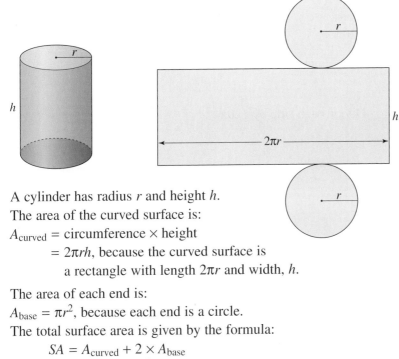

A cylinder has radius r and height h.
The area of the curved surface is:
A_{curved} = circumference × height
$\qquad$ = $2\pi rh$, because the curved surface is
$\qquad\qquad$ a rectangle with length $2\pi r$ and width, h.

The area of each end is:
$A_{base} = \pi r^2$, because each end is a circle.
The total surface area is given by the formula:
$\qquad SA = A_{curved} + 2 \times A_{base}$
or $\qquad SA = 2\pi rh + 2\pi r^2$

Example 1

A can of baked beans has the dimensions shown. Calculate its surface area.

Solution

Use the formula $SA = 2\pi rh + 2\pi r^2$.
Substitute $r = 3.7$ and $h = 11.0$.
$SA = 2\pi(3.7)(11.0) + 2\pi(3.7)^2$
$\qquad \doteq 341.742$
The surface area is approximately 341.7 cm^2.

3.7 cm

11.0 cm

Discuss

What calculator key strokes were used to calculate the surface area?

Example 2

A 60-cm cardboard tube is open at both ends.
Its curved surface area is 950 cm².
Determine its diameter to the nearest centimetre.

Solution

Since the cylinder is open at both ends, use
the formula for the curved surface area.
Use the formula $A = 2\pi rh$.
Substitute $A = 950$ and $h = 60$.

$950 = 2\pi r(60)$

$950 = 120\pi r$ Solve for r. Divide each side by 120π.

$$\frac{950}{120\pi} = \frac{120\pi r}{120\pi}$$

$\dfrac{950}{120\pi} = r$ Press: 950 $\boxed{\div}$ $\boxed{(}$ 120 $\boxed{\pi}$ $\boxed{)}$ $\boxed{\text{ENTER} \atop =}$

$2.520 \doteq r$

$d = 2r$

   $= 2(2.520)$

   $= 5.04$

```
950/(120π)
         2.519953266
```

The diameter is approximately 5 cm.

Discuss

Why did we use a formula different from that in *Example 1*?

Why do we use brackets to key in $\dfrac{950}{120\pi}$?

Imagine that a cylinder is filled with a liquid. The amount of liquid needed
to cover the base is equal to the area of the base. If you multiply this by the
height, the result is the amount of liquid that fills the cylinder. This is the
volume of the cylinder.

TAKE NOTE

Total Surface Area and Volume of a Cylinder

The surface area, *SA*, and volume, *V*, of a cylinder with
radius, *r*, and height, *h*, are given by the formulas:

    V = area of base × height $SA = 2\pi rh + 2\pi r^2$
or $V = \pi r^2 h$

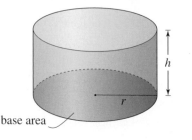

base area

Example 3

A building must have a certain number of air changes per hour. To plan a building's ventilation system, an engineer needs to know the volume of space each floor of the building encloses.

The Peachtree Westin Plaza in Atlanta features a cylindrical hotel with base diameter 60 m. Each floor of the hotel has an interior height of 3.5 m. Calculate the volume of space occupied by each floor of the hotel.

Solution

Use the formula $V = \pi r^2 h$.
The base radius is 30 m. Substitute $r = 30$ and $h = 3.5$.

$V = \pi r^2 h$
$\quad = \pi \times 30^2 \times 3.5$
$\quad \doteq 9896.02$

The volume of space occupied by each floor of the hotel is about 9900 m³.

8.7 Exercises

Round answers to 1 decimal place where necessary.

1. Calculate the area of each circle.

a)
10 cm

b)
8 cm

c)
6.7 cm

2. Calculate the surface area of the curved region of each cylinder.

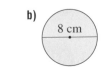

a)
1 cm
2 cm

b)
10 cm
20 cm

c)

4 cm
3 cm

d)
2.2 cm
12.4 cm

3. Calculate the total surface area of each cylinder in exercise 2.

4. Calculate the volume of each cylinder in exercise 2.

B **5.** Calculate the total surface area of each cylindrical solid.

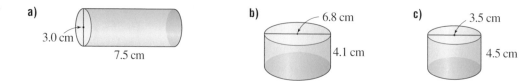

a) 3.0 cm   7.5 cm

b) 6.8 cm   4.1 cm

c) 3.5 cm   4.5 cm

6. Knowledge/Understanding Calculate the volume of each cylinder in exercise 5.

7. A cylinder has a radius of 10 cm and a height of 40 cm.

   a) Calculate the total surface area.

   b) Calculate the volume.

8. Thinking/Inquiry/Problem Solving One cylinder has a base radius of 3 cm and a height of 4 cm. Another cylinder has a base radius of 4 cm and a height of 3 cm. Do you think their total surface areas are equal? Why?

9. Calculate the total surface area of each cylinder.

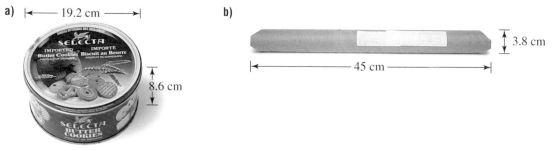

a) |←——— 19.2 cm ———→| 8.6 cm

b) 3.8 cm |←——————— 45 cm ———————→|

10. Application The label on a can of pineapple indicates a volume of 540 mL. The diameter of the can is measured as 6.5 cm. Calculate the height of the can.

11. A juice can has a cardboard curved surface and two metal ends.

   a) What area of cardboard is needed to make the can?

   b) What is the area of each metal end?

   c) What is the total surface area of the juice can?

6.6 cm |←——— 11.6 cm ———→|

12. A refinery has five cylindrical storage tanks each measuring 12.2 m in diameter and 24.4 m high. The tanks are full.

   a) What is the total storage capacity of the refinery?

   b) Tanker trucks have cylindrical tanks 11 m long and 1.8 m in diameter. How many truckloads are needed to empty all the tanks?

✓ 13. **Application** Three tennis balls are packaged in a cylindrical container. The diameter of each ball is 7.5 cm. Calculate the total surface area of the cylinder.

14. Newsprint is one of Canada's major exports. It is shipped in cylindrical rolls. The rolls have a diameter of 102 cm and a length of 137 cm. What is the area of the outer wrapping of the roll?

✓ 15. **Communication** Describe how you calculate the total surface area of a cylinder when you know its dimensions. Include an example in your description.

16. A cylindrical hot-water tank has a diameter of 56 cm and a height of 132 cm.

   a) Calculate the volume of the tank to the nearest cubic centimetre. What is the capacity of the tank in litres?

   b) Calculate the surface area of the tank to the nearest square centimetre.

17. The reticulated python of Southeast Asia is the world's longest snake. Use a cylinder as a model for a snake. Determine the length of a python with a surface area of 25 000 cm² and an average radius of 5 cm.

18. A square piece of cardboard measuring 20 cm on a side is used to form the curved surface of a cylinder. Circles cut from another piece of cardboard are used for the top and the bottom.

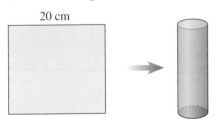

   a) Calculate the radius of the cylinder to 2 decimal places.

   b) Calculate the total surface area of the cylinder.

19. What happens to the total surface area of a cylinder in each case? Explain.

   a) Its radius stays the same, but its height is multiplied by two.

   b) Its height stays the same, but its radius is multiplied by two.

   c) Both the height and the radius are multiplied by two.

In this section, you will investigate different cylinders with the same volume.

Cylinders with a Fixed Volume: Part I

You will need some paper, a ruler, scissors, and tape or glue. You will construct three different paper cylinders, each with a volume of 125 cm^3.

1. a) Choose any measurement between 1.6 cm and 4.0 cm as the radius of the cylinder.

   b) Calculate the area of the base.

   c) To calculate the height of the cylinder, divide the volume (125 cm^3) by the area.

2. a) Use the radius in exercise 1a to calculate the circumference of the base.

   b) Construct a rectangle whose length is equal to the circumference of the base, and whose width is equal to the height you found in exercise 1c.

   c) Calculate the area of the rectangle.

   d) Cut out the rectangle, and tape it to form the curved part of the cylinder.

   e) Visualize the circular base and top of your cylinder. Calculate the total surface area of the cylinder.

3. Repeat exercises 1 and 2 (using different radii than in exercise 1a) to create three cylinders.

4. All your cylinders should have a circular base and a volume of 125 cm^3.

   a) Compare the surface areas of the three cylinders.

   b) Calculate the diameters of the bases of the three cylinders.

   c) Compare the heights of the cylinders with the diameters of their bases.

   d) Choose the cylinder that has the least surface area. How does its height compare with the diameter of its base?

Cylinders with a Fixed Volume: Part II

Recall what you did in *Investigation 1*, exercises 1 and 2:

- You started with a radius for the base.
- You calculated the area of the base.
- You divided 125 by the area to calculate the height.
- You constructed a rectangle and used it to form the cylinder.
- You calculated the area of the rectangle, and the areas of the top and the bottom to determine the total surface area.

1. Set up a spreadsheet similar to the one below. Copy the formulas in cells B3, C3, and D3 into row 4. Then fill down the formulas in row 4 until the areas in column D begin to increase. For detailed instructions on how to fill down, see *Investigation 2*, Section 8.2.

	A	B	C	D
1	Minimizing the Surface Area of a Cylinder			
2	Base Radius	Base Area	Height	Surface Area
3	1.6	= PI( )*A3^2	=125/B3	=2*B3+2*PI( )*A3*C3
4	=A3+0.5			

a) Explain how the formulas in row 3 represent the steps in exercises 1 and 2, *Investigation 1*.

b) What is the minimum surface area? For what radius does it occur?

2. Consider the cylinder that has the minimum surface area.

a) What is the base diameter of this cylinder?

b) How does its height compare with its base diameter?

3. Up to now, you have been using a cylinder with a volume of 125 cm^3. Suppose the volume were different.

a) Predict how the height of the cylinder with minimum surface area would be related to the base diameter.

b) Choose a volume that is much larger or much smaller than 125 cm^3. Make the appropriate change to the formula in cell C3. Fill Down the new formula in column C.

c) Do the results confirm your prediction? Explain.

4. Communication Use the results of *Investigations 1* and *2*. Describe the cylinder that has the least surface area for a volume of 125 cm³.

In *Investigations 1* and *2*, you should have found that the height of the cylinder with the minimum surface area is equal to the diameter of the base, which is approximately 5.4 cm.

In general, for the minimum surface area of any cylinder, the height of the cylinder is equal to the diameter of the base.

TAKE NOTE

Cylinders—Minimum Surface Area for a Given Volume

These cylinders have the same volume and different surface areas. For the minimum surface area, the height of the cylinder equals the base diameter.

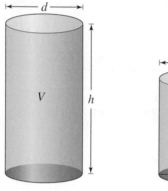
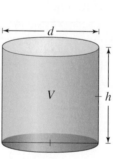

minimum surface area

8.9 Volume of a Cone

Everyday objects, such as an ice cream cone and some fireworks, have the shape of a *cone*.

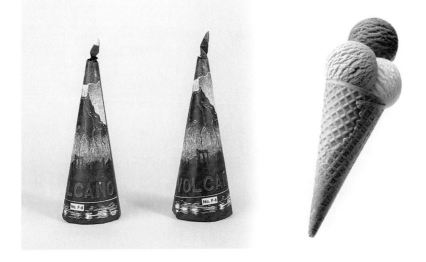

When a cone just fits inside a cylindrical can, you can fill the cone three times and pour its contents into the can. Then the can will be full.

These three volumes taken together ...　　　　**... are equal to this volume.**

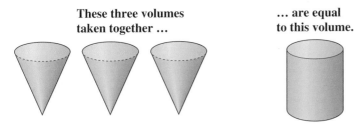

This is because the volume of a cylinder is exactly three times the volume of a cone with the same height and the same base radius. That is, the volume of the cone is one-third the volume of the cylinder with the same base area and height as the cone.

TAKE NOTE

Volume of a Cone

The volume of a cone with radius, r, and height, h, is given by the formula:

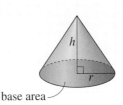

base area

$$V = \frac{1}{3} \times \text{area of base} \times \text{height}$$

so, $V = \frac{1}{3}\pi r^2 h$ or $V = \frac{\pi r^2 h}{3}$

Example 1

Coke is a fuel that is stored in large, cone-like piles. Suppose a coke pile has a base diameter of 20 m and a height of 8 m. Calculate the volume of coke in the pile.

Solution

The base radius is 10 m.
Substitute $r = 10$ and $h = 8$.
Use the formula $V = \frac{1}{3}\pi r^2 h$.

$V = \frac{1}{3} \times \pi \times 10^2 \times 8$ Press: 1 ÷ 3 × π × 10 x^2 × 8 ENTER =
$\doteq 837.76$

The volume of the pile is approximately 838 m^3.

Example 2

Starburst Fireworks wants to package one of their cone-shaped fireworks. It has a base radius of 3.3 cm and a volume of 205 cm^3.
Calculate the height of the firework.

Solution

The volume of the firework is 205 cm^3.
The base radius is 3.3 cm.
Let the height of the firework be h centimetres.
Use the formula $V = \frac{1}{3}\pi r^2 h$.

Substitute $V = 205$ and $r = 3.3$.   Use a calculator for the right side.

$205 = \frac{1}{3} \times \pi \times (3.3)^2 \times h$ Press: 1 ÷ 3 × π × 3.3 x^2 ENTER =

$205 \doteq 11.404h$

Divide each side by 11.404.

$\frac{205}{11.404} \doteq \frac{11.404h}{11.404}$

$h \doteq 17.98$

The firework is approximately 18 cm high.

A   **1.** Calculate the volume of each cone.

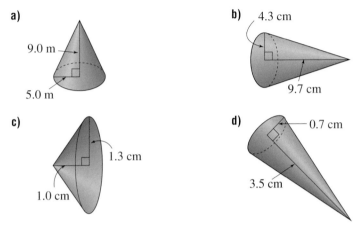

a) 9.0 m 5.0 m

b) 4.3 cm 9.7 cm

c) 1.3 cm 1.0 cm

d) 0.7 cm 3.5 cm

✓ **2.** Calculate the volume of each cone. Give the answers to 1 decimal place.

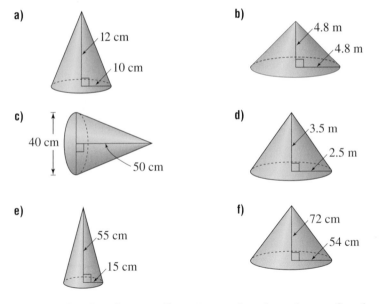

a) 12 cm 10 cm

b) 4.8 m 4.8 m

c) 40 cm 50 cm

d) 3.5 m 2.5 m

e) 55 cm 15 cm

f) 72 cm 54 cm

B   **3. Knowledge/Understanding**   Determine the volume of each cone,
✓   to 2 decimal places.

     a) base radius 1.6 cm, height 3.5 cm   **b)** base radius 0.35 m, height 1.8 m

     c) height 27 cm, base radius 8 cm   **d)** height 57 cm, base radius 42 cm

4. A cylinder has volume 96 cm^3. What is the volume of a cone that just fits inside the cylinder?

5. A cone has volume 54 cm^3. What is the volume of a cylinder that just holds the cone?

6. A cone-shaped funnel has radius 5.7 cm and height 4.3 cm. How much can the funnel hold? Express your answer to 1 decimal place.

7. Application One litre is represented by a cube measuring 10 cm along each edge.

    a) Calculate the volume of a cylinder that just fits inside the cube.

    b) Calculate the volume of a cone that just fits inside the cube.

8. A farmer stores feed in a cone-shaped storage unit. The storage unit has base diameter 14.3 m and height 27.4 m. How much feed can this unit store?

9. Cone A has base radius 25 cm and height 10 m. Cone B has height 25 cm and base radius 10 m. Which cone has the greater volume? Explain.

10. Thinking/Inquiry/Problem Solving A cone and a cylinder have the same base. Suppose they also have the same volume. How are their heights related? Explain.

11. A cone has volume 376 m^3. The diameter of its base is 12 m. Determine the height of the cone, to 1 decimal place.

12. An engineer is designing a cone-shaped storage unit to hold 5000 m^3 of sand. The unit has base radius 15 m. What is its height, to 1 decimal place?

13. Communication What information is needed about a cone before you can calculate its volume? Explain your reasoning.

This photograph of Mars shows features of its surface. Mars approximates a sphere. A sphere is like a ball. All the points on the sphere are the same distance from the *centre*. A line segment joining the centre to any point on the sphere is called its *radius*, *r*. The *diameter*, *d*, of a sphere is twice as long as its radius.

Volume of a Sphere

You will need an empty 355-mL frozen juice can, a millimetre ruler, an old tennis ball, masking tape, some water, and an overflow container.

Step 1

Measure the diameter of the tennis ball. Carefully cut the can so its inside height is equal to the diameter of the ball.

Step 2

Place the can in the overflow container. Fill the can to the top with water, but do not allow it to overflow. Make sure there is no water in the overflow container.

Step 3

Soak the ball with water. Then slowly place it in the can, allowing the water to overflow into the container. Push the ball to the bottom of the can.

Step 4

Take the can out of the overflow container, remove the ball, and empty the can. Then pour the water from the overflow container into the can. Measure the depth of the water.

1. How do you think the volume of the water in the can at the end of *Step 4* compares with the volume of the ball?

2. At the end of *Step 4*, what fraction of the can is filled with water?

3. In this *Investigation*, the diameter of the cylinder is equal to its height. The sphere has the same diameter as the cylinder. What conclusion can you make about the volume of the sphere compared with the volume of the cylinder?

In the *Investigation*, you probably discovered that the volume of a sphere is approximately $\frac{2}{3}$ the volume of the cylinder into which it just fits. Using more advanced mathematics, it can be shown that the volume of the sphere is exactly $\frac{2}{3}$ the volume of the cylinder. If the sphere has radius r, then the cylinder has base radius r and height $2r$. Hence, the volume of the sphere is:

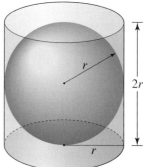

$$V = \frac{2}{3} \times \text{volume of a cylinder}$$
$$= \frac{2}{3} \times \pi r^2 h$$
$$= \frac{2}{3} \times \pi r^2 \times 2r$$
$$= \frac{4}{3}\pi r^3$$

The volume of a sphere with radius, r, is $V = \frac{4}{3}\pi r^3$.

Volume of a Sphere

Volume, $V = \frac{4}{3}\pi r^3$

Example

The mean radius of Earth is approximately 6365 km. Calculate the volume of Earth.

Solution

Visualize Earth as a sphere. Substitute $r = 6365$ in the formula for the volume of a sphere.

$V = \frac{4}{3}\pi r^3$

$\quad = \frac{4}{3} \times \pi \times 6365^3$

$\quad \doteq 1.1 \times 10^{12}$

Press: 4 ⌈÷⌉ 3 ⌈×⌉ ⌈π⌉ ⌈×⌉ 6365 ⌈^⌉ 3 ⌈ENTER =⌉

```
4/3*π*6365^3
     1.080 1494 11 ×10¹²
```

The volume of Earth is approximately 1.1×10^{12} km^3.

Discuss

Suppose you use the decimal approximation, 3.14, instead of the ⌈π⌉ key on a calculator. How would this affect the final answers?

8.10   Exercises

A

1. Calculate the volume of each sphere. Give the volumes to the nearest whole unit. The radius is given.

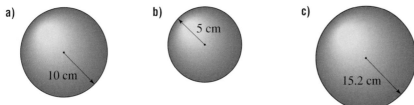

a) 10 cm

b) 5 cm

c) 15.2 cm

2. Knowledge/Understanding Calculate the volume of each ball.

	Sport	Diameter of ball (cm)
a)	Baseball	7.4
b)	Golf	4.3
c)	Table tennis	3.7
d)	Volleyball	20.9

B

3. The radius of Uranus is almost 4 times as great as the radius of Earth. The radius of the moon is approximately $\frac{1}{4}$ that of Earth. Use the information in the *Example*. Calculate the volume of:

 a) Uranus   b) the moon

4. Application Earth is not spherical. It is flattened at the poles. Its polar radius is 8 km less than its mean radius. Its equatorial radius is 13 km more than its mean radius.

 a) Calculate Earth's volume using the polar radius and the equatorial radius.

 b) Would the actual volume be closer to the volume obtained using the polar radius or the volume obtained using the equatorial radius? Explain.

5. A spherical balloon is blown up from a diameter of 20 cm to 60 cm. By how many times has its volume increased?

6. A basketball has a circumference of 75 cm.

 a) Calculate its radius.   b) Calculate its volume.

7. A sphere just fits inside a cube with edge length 10.0 cm. Calculate the volume of the sphere.

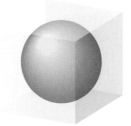

8. Communication Explain what happens to the volume of a sphere when its radius is doubled. Include an example in your explanation.

9. Which has the greater volume: a sphere with radius 10 cm or a cube with edge length 10 cm? Explain.

10. Thinking/Inquiry/Problem Solving A sphere has volume 45.7 m^3. What is its radius? Explain.

11. a) Graph the equation $V = \frac{4}{3}\pi r^3$ for the volume of a sphere against its radius.

 b) Use the ⌐TRACE⌐ key. Determine the volume of a sphere with radius 5 cm.

 c) Use the ⌐TRACE⌐ key. Estimate the radius of a sphere with volume 100 cm^3.

 d) Trace to check your answers for exercise 2.

8.11   Designing a Cooler

On page 311, you considered the problem of finding the best shape and dimensions for a portable cooler. We will assume the cooler has a certain capacity. This means the volume is known. Let us assume the volume is 50 L or 50 000 cm^3.

The cooler must maintain the temperature of its contents for as long as possible. Since heat from outside enters the cooler from its top, sides, and bottom, we would like its total surface area to be a minimum. So, we have to design a cooler with a volume of 50 000 cm^3 and a minimum surface area.

Earlier in the chapter, you looked at rectangular prisms and cylinders that had a minimum surface area. The optimal prism is a cube. The optimal cylinder is as close to a cube as it can be.

Rectangular Prism Model

The optimal prism is a cube with edges about 36.8 cm.

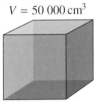

$V = 50\,000 \text{ cm}^3$

|←36.8 cm→|

Cylinder Model

The optimal cylinder has both height and diameter about 39.9 cm.

$V = 50\,000 \text{ cm}^3$

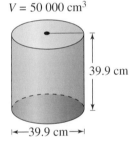

39.9 cm

|←39.9 cm→|

1. Verify that the volumes of the optimal prism and the optimal cylinder are each approximately 50 000 cm^3.

2. a) Calculate the surface area of the optimal prism and the optimal cylinder.

   b) Which model is more efficient? Explain.

   c) Calculate the difference in the surface areas of the two models.

The Sphere Model

Suppose the portable cooler has the shape of a sphere. Recall that the formula for the volume of a sphere is $V = \frac{4}{3}\pi r^3$. If we substitute 50 000 for V, we obtain the equation $\frac{4}{3}\pi r^3 = 50\,000$.

3. a) Solve the equation $\frac{4}{3}\pi r^3 = 50\,000$ using any method. The result is the radius of a sphere that has a volume of 50 000 cm^3.

   b) Calculate the surface area of the sphere.

4. Compare the surface area of the sphere with the surface areas of the optimal prism and the optimal cylinder. Which model is most efficient? Explain.

A sphere has the smallest surface area for any given volume. This is the reason why it is the most efficient shape for a cooler. The most efficient rectangular prism is a cube because a cube is as close to a sphere as a rectangular prism can be. Similarly, the most efficient cylinder is one whose height equals its diameter, because this is as close to a sphere as a cylinder can be.

5. Why might the spherical model not be the best choice for a portable cooler?

Combination Models

A cooler might be designed as a combination of a sphere and a cylinder whose height equals its diameter. Here are two possible models.

Cylinder with hemisphere at each end   *Cylinder with hemisphere on top*

$V = 50\,000 \text{ cm}^3$

$V = 50\,000 \text{ cm}^3$

Choose one of the two models above. Use it to complete exercises 6 and 7.

6. Let r centimetres represent the base radius of the cylinder.
   a) Write an expression for the volume of the model.
   b) Since you know that the volume is 50 000 cm^3, use your expression in part a to write an equation in r.
   c) Solve the equation using any method.

7. a) Write an expression for the surface area of the model.
   b) Use your answer to exercise 6c to calculate the surface area of the model.
   c) How does the surface area of your model compare with the surface areas of the previous models?

MATHEMATICS TOOLKIT

- Perimeter—To find the perimeter, add the lengths of all sides.
- Circumference—The circumference, C, of a circle is $C = \pi d$ or $C = 2\pi r$.

Area Formulas				
rectangle	triangle	parallelogram	trapezoid	circle
$A = \ell w$	$A = \frac{1}{2}bh$	$A = bh$	$A = \frac{h(a+b)}{2}$	$A = \pi r^2$

- For a given perimeter, the rectangle with the maximum area is a square.

Figure	Volume	Surface Area
	$V = $ Area of base $\times$ Height $\\ = \ell wh$	$SA = $ Sum of area of faces or $SA = 2(\ell w + \ell h + wh)$
	$V = $ Area of base $\times$ Height $\\ = \pi r^2 h$	$SA = 2\pi rh + 2\pi r^2$
Isosceles triangle prism	$V = \frac{1}{2}(bh)\ell$	$SA_{\text{triangle}} = \frac{1}{2}bh$ (for each triangle) $SA_{\text{rectangles}} = \ell s + \ell b + \ell s$ $SA_{\text{total}} = SA_{\text{rectangles}} + 2(SA_{\text{triangle}})$
	$V = \frac{4}{3}\pi r^3$	
	$V = \frac{1}{3} \times $ Area of base $\times$ Height $\\ = \frac{1}{3}\pi r^2 h$	

- In general, for any given volume, the rectangular prism with minimum surface area is a cube.
- In general, for any given volume, the cylinder whose height is equal to its base diameter has minimum surface area.

8.1 **1.** Find the perimeter of each figure.

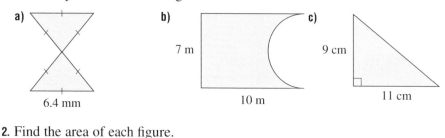

a)

6.4 mm

b)

7 m

10 m

c)

9 cm

11 cm

2. Find the area of each figure.

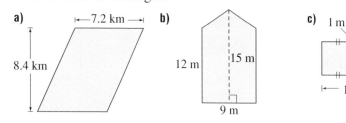

a)

—7.2 km—

8.4 km

b)

12 m   15 m

9 m

c)

1 m   5 m

7 m

10 m

3. A garden is to be planted in the shape shown.
A stone border will be placed around the garden.
Soil and bedding plants will be placed in the garden.

a) What is the length of the stone border?

b) What is the area of the lawn?

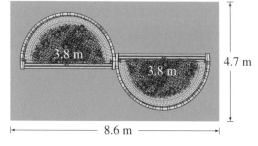

3.8 m

3.8 m

4.7 m

8.6 m

8.3 **4.** Find the maximum area for each rectangle with the
given perimeter.

a) 64 m   **b)** 50 m

5. Mario wants to fence-in a play area for his dog. He has 18 m of fencing.
What dimensions should he make the play area so that the area is a maximum?

6. Suppose Mario (from exercise 5) has 18 1-m fence units that cannot be cut.
Would the area of his dog's play area change? If so, what would the dimensions be?

8.4 **7.** Calculate the surface area of each figure.

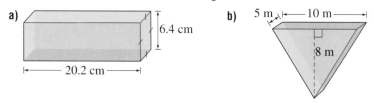

a)

6.4 cm

20.2 cm

b)

5 m   —10 m—

8 m

8. A CD jewel case is approximately 14 cm by 12.5 cm by 0.7 cm.

a) Find the volume of a box that could hold 50 CD cases.

b) What is the surface area of the box in part a?

9. A triangular prism has a volume of 350 mm^3.
Find the value of x.

$A_{\text{triangle}} = 70$ mm^2

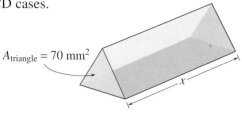

x

8.6 **10.** A square-based prism is formed from 75 1-cm cubes. Calculate the minimum surface area of the prism.

11. A chest freezer is advertised as being 18 cubic feet. State 3 sets of possible whole-number dimensions for the freezer.

8.7 **12.** Calculate the volume of each cylinder.

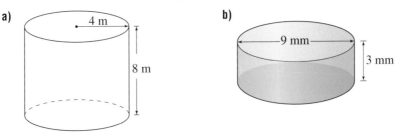

a) 4 m, 8 m

b) 9 mm, 3 mm

13. Calculate the surface area of each cylinder in exercise 12.

14. A cylindrical oil tank has a diameter of 2.25 m and height of 3.5 m.

a) Calculate the volume of the tank in litres.

b) Calculate the surface area of the tank.

$1000 \text{ cm}^3 = 1\text{L}$

8.8 **15.** A juice can has volume 355 mL. The height of the can is 12 cm and the diameter is 6.25 cm. Is the surface area of the can a minimum for a volume of 355 mL? How do you know?

8.9 **16.** A cone has volume 36 mL. What is the volume of a cylinder with equal height and equal diameter as the cone?

17. Calculate the volume of each cone.

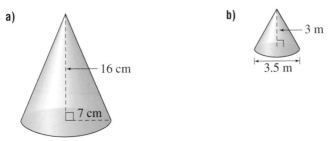

a) 16 cm, 7 cm

b) 3 m, 3.5 m

18. Paper cones for drinking water are 9.5 cm high and have a 7-cm diameter. What is the maximum volume, in millilitres, of each cone?

8.10 **19.** Calculate the volume of each sphere with the given dimensions.

a) $r = 13$ cm   **b)** $d = 6$ m   **c)** $C = 45$ mm

20. A volleyball has a diameter of 18 cm. Calculate the volume of the ball.

1. **Knowledge/Understanding** Find the perimeter and area of each figure.

a)

4.8 cm

2.3 cm

b)

0.6 m

7.5 m

2. Calculate the volume of each figure.

a)

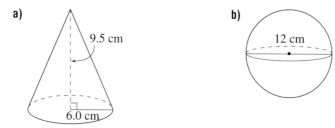

9.5 cm

6.0 cm

b)

12 cm

3. **Communication** Both cylinders shown have a volume of 100 mm³. Without calculating, which cylinder has the minimum surface area? How do you know?

5.1 mm

2.5 mm

3.25 mm

3.0 mm

4. **Application** An in-ground rectangular pool is 10.5 m by 5.8 m. A 1.5 m concrete deck will be constructed around the pool. The concrete will be 25 cm thick. Calculate the volume of concrete required.

5. **Thinking/Inquiry/Problem Solving** Calculate the surface area (excluding the floor) of the tent shown.

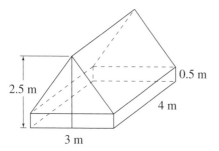

0.5 m

2.5 m

4 m

3 m

6. Ahmed needs to buy an air conditioner for his new house. The air conditioners come in sizes of 20 000 BTUs, 60 000 BTUs, and 80 000 BTUs. He knows the following facts:

   - The floor space of his house is 245 m^2.
   - The height of the inside walls is 4.5 m.
   - 50 BTUs are needed to cool 1 m^3 of air in the house.

   What is the best air conditioner for Ahmed to buy? Give exact mathematical reasons for your answer.

7. Anita wished to know the surface area of an open-ended pipe shown in the diagram below. She calculated the area as follows:

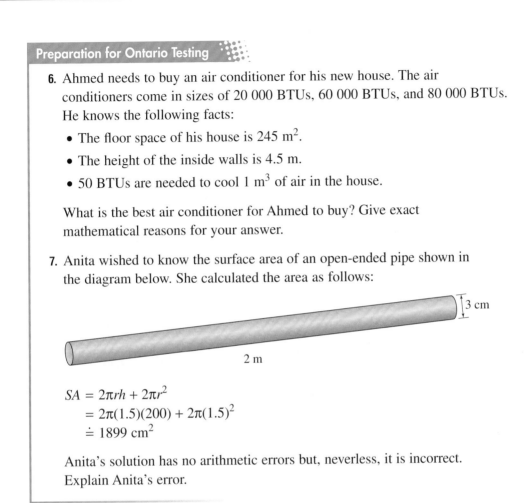

2 m

3 cm

$$SA = 2\pi rh + 2\pi r^2$$
$$= 2\pi(1.5)(200) + 2\pi(1.5)^2$$
$$\doteq 1899 \text{ cm}^2$$

Anita's solution has no arithmetic errors but, neverless, it is incorrect. Explain Anita's error.

9 Geometry

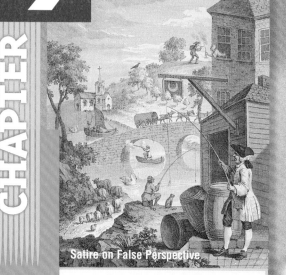

Satire on False Perspective

Paradise Garden

By the end of this chapter, you will:

- Determine the properties of angle bisectors, medians, and altitudes in various types of triangles through investigation.

- Illustrate and explain the properties of the interior and exterior angles of triangles and quadrilaterals.

- Illustrate and explain the properties of angles related to parallel lines.

- Determine some properties of the sides and the diagonals of quadrilaterals.

- Communicate the findings of investigations, using appropriate language and mathematical form.

The Annunciation

Representing 3-Dimensional Objects in 2 Dimensions

In word processors, you can create 3-D letters. The letters are on a flat surface but they appear to have depth.

Some artists do not give depth to their pictures. Objects and figures often look distorted, and those in the background are frequently too large. Geometry produces a 3-dimensional effect. The appearance of reality in paintings is achieved. We say these paintings have "perspective." A painting has perspective when you can see lines that appear to meet at one or more distant points.

Which painting on these pages has perspective? In this painting, find some examples of lines that would meet if they were extended.

An artist sometimes intentionally goes against the laws of perspective to create an amusing scene or object.

Examine the engraving *Satire on False Perspective*. Find as many examples as possible of things that are wrong with this engraving.

After exploring properties of geometric figures using *The Geometer's Sketchpad*, you will extend your skills to construct 2-dimensional representations of 3-dimensional objects.

You will revisit this topic in Section 9.14.

Necessary *Skills*

Identifying Figures and Angles

Example

Identify each figure.

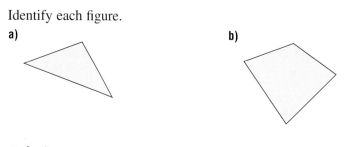

a)

b)

Solution

a) The figure is a triangle. A triangle is a figure with 3 sides.

b) The figure is a quadrilateral. A quadrilateral is a figure with 4 sides.

Exercises

Match each figure below with its name. Use each figure only once. Explain.

a) acute triangle   **b)** equilateral triangle   **c)** isosceles triangle

d) kite   **e)** obtuse triangle   **f)** parallelogram

g) rectangle   **h)** rhombus   **i)** right triangle

j) square   **k)** trapezoid

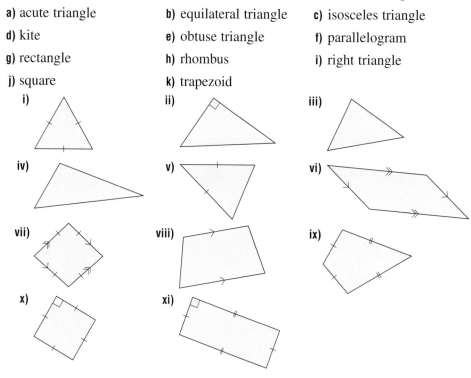

9.1 Introduction to *The Geometer's Sketchpad*

Dynamic geometry software, such as *The Geometer's Sketchpad*, allows us to explore geometry in a new way. This section introduces you to *The Geometer's Sketchpad*.

You may use the software to complete the Investigations in this chapter.

If you choose to complete the chapter Investigations using pencil and paper, go to Section 9.3.

INVESTIGATION 1

The Toolbox

From the File menu, choose New Sketch.

1. On the left of the screen is the Toolbox. To work with *The Geometer's Sketchpad*, you must select one of these tools.

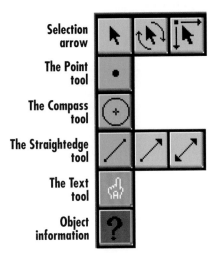

There are 3 Selection arrows. Click on the Selection arrow, hold down the mouse button, and drag to the right. Beside the Translation arrow is a Rotation arrow and a Dilatation arrow. To choose either, drag to highlight the tool you want, then release the mouse button.

There are 3 Straightedge tools. To see them, click on the Straightedge tool, hold down the mouse button, and drag to the right. Beside the Segment tool, there is a Ray tool and a Line tool.

2. Follow the instructions below to explore some features of the Toolbox.

Click on this tool ...   ... and do this:

a) Draw 4 points by clicking anywhere on the screen. Notice that a point appears with a black outline. The outline disappears when the second point is drawn.

b) Click on one point. Hold down the mouse button and drag to an adjacent point. Click on this point. Hold down the mouse button and drag it to the next point. Repeat until a quadrilateral is drawn. Notice the little black squares on each segment as it is completed. These show when a segment is *selected*.

c) Click on one vertex. Notice that the black outline appears. This shows that the point is selected. Hold down the mouse button and drag the figure. By dragging different vertices, you can make the figure a square, a parallelogram, or even a straight line.

d) As you move closer to a point or line, the hand turns black. Click, and the object will be labelled. Click again and the label disappears.

e) Labels can be changed to other letters or even words. Use the Text tool to double-click on the label, not on the object. A dialog box appears and a new label can be typed.

f) Use the Compass tool to draw a circle. Hold down the mouse button anywhere on the screen. Move the mouse to draw a circle. Notice the four little black squares. These appear when the circle is selected.

g) The circle has a point called the *control point*. Drag this point to make the circle larger or smaller.

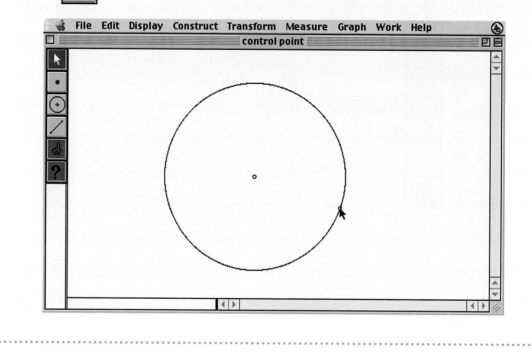

Sketchpad Tip

When a segment or a circle has black squares on it, or when a point is outlined in black, the object is selected. You may not be able to carry out a procedure if the wrong objects are selected. To *deselect* an object, click on the Selection tool, then click anywhere on the screen.

The Measure Menu

From the File menu, choose New Sketch.

There are nine menus at the top of the screen. Click on each menu to view its contents.

	File Edit Display Construct Transform Measure Graph Work Help
	Untitled #1

Many options are grey. They cannot be chosen unless the correct objects have been selected.

In this Investigation, you will explore the Measure menu and learn some special geometry features of *The Geometer's Sketchpad*.

Measuring Circles

Click on this tool ...   ... and do this:

a) Ensure the measurements are in centimetres. From the Display menu, choose Preferences. Under Distance Unit, select cm, then click OK. Draw a circle. Go to the Measure menu. Several items are now black. Choose Radius. The radius will be measured and the measure displayed on the screen.

b) Check that the circle is still selected. From the Measure menu, choose Area. The area measure is displayed. From the Measure menu, choose Circumference. Its measure is displayed.

c) Drag the control point of the circle. Observe how the measurements change.

d) To move a measurement, click on it, hold down the mouse button, then drag the measurement to a new location.

Measuring Length

Click on this tool ...   ... and do this:

a) Draw a segment. Two black squares show that the segment is selected.

b) From the Measure menu, choose Length. The length of the segment will appear on the screen.

c) Click on an endpoint of the segment. Drag by holding down the mouse button. Notice that the measurement changes.

Measuring Area and Perimeter

Click on this tool ...   ... and do this:

Draw five points on the screen. Do not connect them.
We will use a different technique to complete a pentagon.

a) Hold down the shift key, then click on each point. From the Construct menu, choose Segment. A pentagon is constructed.

b) Click anywhere on the screen to deselect everything.

c) Hold down the shift key, then click on each side of the pentagon. Go to the Measure menu. Notice that you cannot select Perimeter and Area because they are grey.

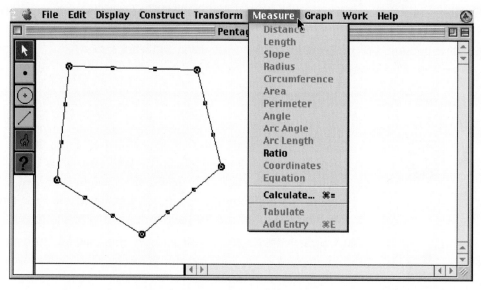

d) Click anywhere on the screen to deselect everything.

e) Hold down the shift key, then click on each vertex of the pentagon.

f) From the Construct menu, choose Polygon Interior. The pentagon interior is now striped. This shows that it is selected.

g) From the Measure menu, choose Area.

h) Drag a vertex of the pentagon. Watch the area measurement change as the figure changes.

i) Select the pentagon interior. From the Display menu, choose Color, then pick your favourite colour. Click anywhere on the screen.

Explore More

In this Investigation, you will learn to use some commands in the Construct menu and the Graph menu.

From the File menu, choose New Sketch.

Constructing Parallel Lines

1. Draw a line segment and a point above the segment.

2. Select the segment. Shift-click to also select the point. From the Construct menu, choose Parallel Line.

3. Drag an endpoint of the original segment. What do you notice? Note: If you *draw* two lines that look parallel, dragging one line will not affect the other line. If you use the Construct menu to *construct* two parallel lines, dragging one line will cause the other line to move.

Constructing a Perpendicular Line

1. Draw a line segment.

2. Select the segment. From the Construct menu, choose Point on Object.

3. Select the segment. Shift-click to also select the point. From the Construct menu, choose Perpendicular Line.

4. Drag an endpoint of the original segment. What do you notice?

5. To replace the perpendicular line with a segment:
- Select the perpendicular line.
- From the Construct menu, choose Point on Object.
- Deselect all objects.
- Select the perpendicular line again. From the Display menu, choose Hide Line.
- Select the two constructed points. From the Construct menu, choose Segment.

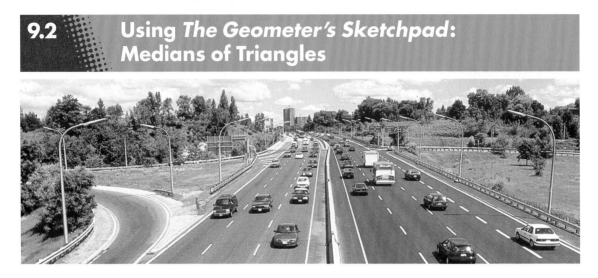

9.2 Using *The Geometer's Sketchpad*: Medians of Triangles

A highway is often separated by a median. This is a concrete barrier or a strip of land that divides the road in half.

In the triangle at the right, line segment AM is a median.

In the diagram, M is the midpoint of side BC.
The line segment AM is a median of △ABC.

A *median* of a triangle is the line segment
that joins a vertex to the midpoint of the opposite side.

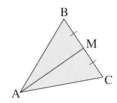

Use *The Geometer's Sketchpad*.

SETUP

From the File menu, choose New Sketch.

1. To construct △ABC:

Click on this tool ...	... and do this:
⬛ (point tool)	**a)** Draw 3 points.
⬛ (label tool)	**b)** Click on each point to display its label. To change a label, double-click and type a new letter. Make sure the letters are A, B, and C.
⬛ (arrow tool)	**c)** Hold down the shift key and click on each point. This selects the points. When a point is outlined in black, it is selected.
	d) From the Construct menu, choose Segment.
	e) Click anywhere on the screen to deselect segments and points.

2. To construct the midpoint of AB:

Click on this tool ...   *... and do this:*

a) Click on side AB to select it. The two black squares on the line segment show that it has been selected.

b) From the Construct menu, choose Point At Midpoint.

c) Click on the midpoint to display its label, D. Double-click on D, then change it to M.

3. To construct the median CM:

Click on this tool ...   *... and do this:*

a) Hold down the shift key and click on points C and M.

b) From the Construct menu, choose Segment.

Sketchpad Tips

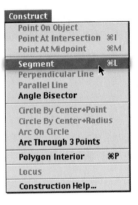

- To construct: always use the Construct menu.
- To select multiple objects: hold down the shift key while clicking on each object.
- To construct segment AB: select points A and B, then from the Construct menu choose Segment.
- To label: choose the Text tool. Click on the object to display its label. To change a label: double-click on the label and type a new letter.
- To hide an object: click on the object. Then from the Display menu choose Hide.
- If you make a mistake and want to delete a construction, click on it. Then from the Edit menu, select Undo.
- After labelling, ensure you click on the Selection arrow before the next construction.
- Ensure you know what is selected before you choose from the Construct menu.
- Ensure you deselect after each construction.

In *Investigations 1* and *2*, you will observe the properties of the medians in a triangle. These properties will be used in Section 9.3.

Medians and Area

1. Construct △ABC and median CM as in *Setup*.

2. Select points A, C, and M. From the Construct menu, choose Polygon Interior. From the Display menu, choose Color and pick red. Click anywhere on the screen to deselect △ACM.

3. Select points B, C, and M. Construct the interior as in exercise 2. Colour it blue.

4. Click on the red triangle to select it. (It is striped when it is selected.) From the Measure menu, choose Area. Record the area measurement. Click anywhere on the screen to deselect the red triangle.

5. Repeat exercise 4 for the blue triangle.

6. Click on any vertex and drag it across the screen. Observe the area measurements. What do you notice? Record your observations.

7. Write a statement about a median of a triangle and the area of the triangle.

Construct	
Point On Object	
Point At Intersection	⌘I
Point At Midpoint	⌘M
Segment	⌘L
Perpendicular Line	
Parallel Line	
Angle Bisector	
Circle By Center+Point	
Circle By Center+Radius	
Arc On Circle	
Arc Through 3 Points	
Polygon Interior	⌘P
Locus	
Construction Help...	

Three Medians

1. Construct △ABC and median CM as in *Setup*.

2. Select segment AC. From the Construct menu, choose Point At Midpoint. Label the midpoint N.

3. Select B and N. Construct segment BN.

4. Construct the midpoint of side BC. Label it P. Construct the median AP.

5. What do you notice about the medians?

6. Drag a vertex of the triangle to see if what you noticed is true for other triangles.

7. Write a statement about this property of medians in a triangle.

8. Select two medians. From the Construct menu, choose Point At Intersection. Label this point, O. The point O is the *centroid* of a triangle.

Construct	
Point On Object	
Point At Intersection	⌘I
Point At Midpoint	⌘M
Segment	⌘L
Perpendicular Line	
Parallel Line	
Angle Bisector	
Circle By Center+Point	
Circle By Center+Radius	
Arc On Circle	
Arc Through 3 Points	
Interior	
Locus	
Construction Help...	

If you completed *Investigations 1* and *2* from Section 9.2, skip this *Investigation*.

In the triangle at the right, line segment AM is a median.

In the diagram, M is the midpoint of side BC.
The line segment AM is a median of △ABC.

A *median* of a triangle is the line segment that joins a vertex to the midpoint of the opposite side.

INVESTIGATION

Triangle Medians

Work on your own.
You will need grid paper, a ruler, and a pencil.

1. Draw △ABC on grid paper with AB along a grid line.

2. Find the length of the base AB and the height of the triangle.

3. Use the formula Area $= \frac{1}{2}bh$ to calculate the area of △ABC.

4. Measure AB, then mark the midpoint, M. What is the measure of AM?

5. Draw a segment from M to the opposite vertex, C.

6. What is the height of △CAM? △CBM?

7. Use an appropriate formula to find the areas of △CAM and △CBM.

8. Compare your answers for exercises 3 and 7. Compare your findings with those of several classmates.

9. Write a statement about the relationship between the median of a triangle and the area of a triangle.

10. Find the midpoint of AC and label it N. Draw a segment from N to the opposite vertex, B.

11. Find the midpoint of BC and label it P. Draw a segment from P to the opposite vertex, A.

12. What do you notice about the medians?

13. Compare your findings with those of several classmates.

14. Label the point of intersection the *centroid*.

Here is a summary of the properties you observed in the *Investigations*.

Median Properties

1. A median divides the area of a triangle in half.

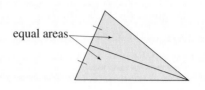
equal areas

2. The three medians of a triangle meet at one point. This point is the *centroid*.

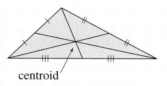
centroid

These properties can be used to solve problems.

Example

The area of $\triangle$PQM is 56 cm^2. Calculate the area of $\triangle$PQR.

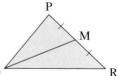

Solution

From the diagram, PM = MR
Thus, QM is a median.
From Median Property 1, area $\triangle$PQR = 2(area $\triangle$PQM)
$$= 2(56)$$
$$= 112$$
The area of $\triangle$PQR is 112 cm^2.

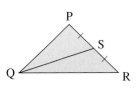

1. **Knowledge/Understanding** The area of △PQR is 72 cm².
Calculate the area of △PQS.

2. **Thinking/Inquiry/Problem Solving** On grid paper or using *The Geometer's Sketchpad*, plot △ABC with vertices A(1, 7), B(3, 1), and C(11, 7). To display a grid and axes using *The Geometer's Sketchpad*, click Show Axes then Show Grid, under the Graph menu.

   a) Find the midpoints of AB, BC, and AC.

   b) Find the coordinates of the centroid of △ABC.

3. **Application** Draw a triangle on cardboard. Cut out the triangle. Construct one median.

   a) Try to balance the triangle on the thin edge of a ruler aligned with the median. Explain why the triangle should balance on the ruler.

   b) The centroid is sometimes called the *point of balance* of a triangle. Find the centroid of your cardboard triangle. Try to balance the triangle on a pencil point at the centroid.

4. **Communication** In *Investigation 1*, page 380, you found that a median divides the area of a triangle in half. Cut out a scalene triangle. Draw a median. Cut along the median to divide the triangle into two parts.

   a) Do the two parts have the same shape? Explain.

   b) Do the two parts have the same area? Explain.

   c) Draw a triangle so that when you cut along a median, the two parts are congruent.

   d) Can you draw a triangle so that when you cut along a median, the two parts are isosceles triangles? Explain.

9.4 Using *The Geometer's Sketchpad:* Altitudes of Triangles

The altimeter in an airplane is an instrument that measures the height of the plane above sea level. Jets, such as the B-747, fly at altitudes between 30 000 and 40 000 feet. The height of a triangle is also called the altitude.

In the diagram, line segment AD is an altitude of △ABC.

An *altitude* of a triangle is the line segment drawn from a vertex perpendicular to the opposite side.

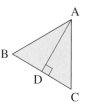

Use *The Geometer's Sketchpad.*

SETUP

From the File menu, choose New Sketch.

1. To construct △PQR:

Click on this tool …	*… and do this:*
✏	**a)** Draw a horizontal line segment by clicking on the screen, then dragging the mouse. The segment is selected.
▸	**b)** From the Construct menu, choose Point on Object.
	c) Click anywhere on the screen to deselect the segment and point.
	d) Click on the segment again to construct a second point.
●	**e)** Construct a point on one side of the segment.
☞	**f)** Click on the point on one side of the segment. Double-click on the label and change it to R.

g) Repeat this procedure to label the points P and Q you constructed on the segment.

h) Click on P and R. From the Construct menu, choose Segment.

i) Click on Q and R, then construct segment QR.

j) Drag a vertex of △PQR until all the angles are acute.

2. To construct the altitude from R:

Click on this tool …   *… and do this:*

a) Hold down the shift key, and select segment PQ and vertex R.

b) From the Construct menu, choose Perpendicular Line.

c) Hold down the shift key and select segment PQ and the perpendicular line. From the Construct menu, choose Point At Intersection.

d) Click on the intersection point. Double-click the label and change it to T.

In *Investigations 1* to *3*, you will observe the properties of altitudes in a triangle. These properties will be used in the exercises.

INVESTIGATION 1

Measuring Angles

1. Construct △PQR and altitude RT as in *Setup*.

2. Drag vertex R of △PQR. Observe the change in the altitude and the position of T.

3. Select P, then R, then Q. From the Measure menu, choose Angle. The measure of ∠PRQ is shown on the screen.

4. Repeat exercise 3 to measure ∠PQR and ∠RPQ. Deselect the vertices.

5. Drag R so that T is between P and Q. Record the measurements of ∠PQR, ∠RPQ, and ∠PRQ. Repeat this for another position of T between P and Q.

6. Drag R so that T is not between P and Q. We say that T is on PQ (or QP) *extended*. For two different positions of T, record the measurements of ∠PQR, ∠RPQ, and ∠PRQ.

7. How does the type of triangle affect the position of T?

Determining Area

1. Construct △PQR and altitude RT as in *Setup*.

2. Select P, Q, and R. From the Construct menu, choose Polygon Interior. From the Measure menu, choose Area. The area of △PQR is displayed.

3. Measure PQ by selecting its endpoints. From the Measure menu, choose Distance. Repeat for the measure of RT.

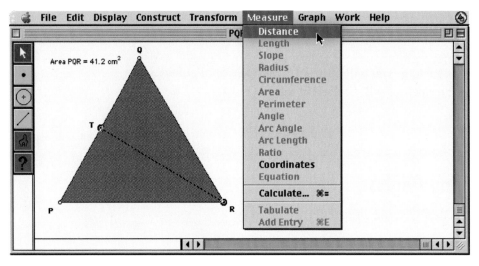

4. Select the measurements of PQ and RT. From the Measure menu, choose Calculate.

5. In the calculator, click on 1 ⬚ 2 ⬚. From the Values menu, select Distance (P to Q). Click on ⬚. Then from the Values menu, select Distance (R to T).

6. Your answer will be displayed on the screen. What did you calculate in exercise 5?

7. To find the area of △PQR, we use the formula Area = $\frac{1}{2}bh$. When PQ is the base, what is the altitude RT?

Constructing Three Altitudes

For this Investigation, we construct a triangle using lines instead of line segments.

1. Use the Point tool  to construct 3 points. Label these points A, B, and C.

2. Click on the Straightedge tool and drag to the right. You will see three icons: Segment—two endpoints, Ray—one endpoint and one arrow, and Line—two arrows. Choose the Line icon.

3. Select A, B, and C. From the Construct menu, choose Line. You now have a triangle with extended sides.

4. Change the colour for your construction. From the Display menu, select Color and choose red.

5. To construct the altitude from A to BC, select A and line BC. From the Construct menu, choose Perpendicular Line.

6. Repeat the method in exercise 5 to construct the altitudes from B and from C. What do you notice about the altitudes?

7. The point of intersection of the altitudes is the *orthocentre*. Drag a vertex of the triangle. Observe the orthocentre in other triangles. Record your observations.

8. How does the type of triangle affect the position of the orthocentre?

In the *Investigations*, you should have discovered that in an obtuse triangle, the altitudes from two vertices do not intersect the opposite sides. In this case, the opposite sides must be extended so that these altitudes can be drawn.

In a right triangle, two altitudes coincide with the sides of the triangle.

If you completed *Investigations 1–3* from Section 9.5, skip this *Investigation*.

Altitudes of Triangles

Work in a group of three.
You will each need 1-cm grid paper, a ruler, a protractor, and a pencil.
A plastic right triangle is optional.

Each student chooses a different type of △PQR:

- acute △PQR

- △PQR with a right ∠PQR

- obtuse △PQR with an obtuse ∠PQR

1. Draw a large △PQR on 1-cm grid paper with PQ along a grid line.

2. Measure ∠PRQ, ∠PQR, and ∠RPQ. Record the measurements on your diagram.

3. Draw a perpendicular from R to PQ, or to PQ extended, along or parallel to a grid line. Label the point where the perpendicular meets PQ or PQ extended, T.

4. Compare your diagrams with those of your group members as well as with those of other groups. How does the type of triangle affect the position of T?

5. Estimate the area of each triangle by counting squares and part squares. Write your estimate below the triangle.

6. Measure the lengths of PQ and RT. Record the lengths on your diagram.

7. Multiply $\frac{1}{2}$ × length of PQ × length of RT. Record your result under the estimated area.

8. To find the area of △PQR, we can use the formula Area $= \frac{1}{2}bh$. When PQ is the base, what is the altitude RT?

9. Use a protractor or plastic right triangle to draw an altitude from P to RQ or RQ extended. Draw an altitude from Q to PR.

10. Compare your diagrams with those of group members as well as with those of other groups. What do you notice about the altitudes in each triangle?

11. The point of intersection is called the *orthocentre*. How does the type of triangle affect the position of the orthocentre?

Here is a summary of the properties you observed in the *Investigations*.

Altitude Properties

1. The length of an altitude is a height of the triangle. It is used to calculate the area of the triangle.

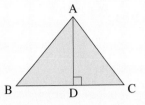

Base, BC = 8
Altitude, AD = 5
Area of △ABC = $\frac{1}{2}$(8)(5)
= 20

2. The three altitudes of a triangle meet at the orthocentre.

In an acute triangle, the orthocentre is inside the triangle.

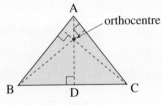

In a right triangle, the orthocentre is on a vertex of the triangle.

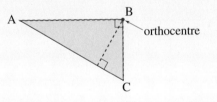

In an obtuse triangle, the orthocentre is outside the triangle.

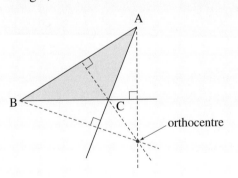

These properties can be used to solve problems.

Example 1

In $\triangle PQR$, the altitude $RT = 8$ cm and the base $PQ = 11$ cm.
Calculate the area of $\triangle PQR$.

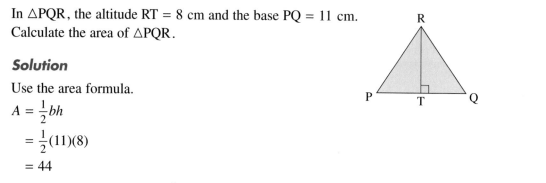

Solution

Use the area formula.

$A = \frac{1}{2}bh$

$ = \frac{1}{2}(11)(8)$

$ = 44$

The area of $\triangle PQR$ is 44 cm^2.

Example 2

The area of $\triangle ABC$ is 12 cm^2.
Altitude $BD = 4$ cm
What is the length of AC?

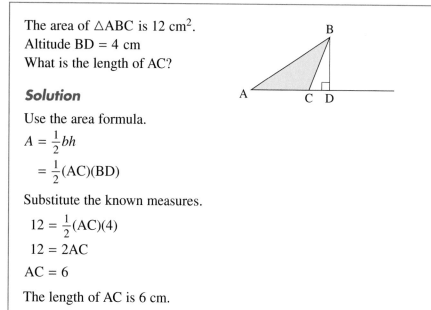

Solution

Use the area formula.

$A = \frac{1}{2}bh$

$ = \frac{1}{2}(AC)(BD)$

Substitute the known measures.

$12 = \frac{1}{2}(AC)(4)$

$12 = 2AC$

$AC = 6$

The length of AC is 6 cm.

A **1.** Calculate the area of each triangle.

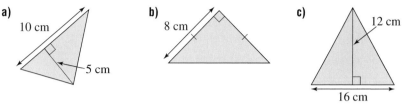

a)
10 cm
5 cm

b)
8 cm

c)
12 cm
16 cm

2. Knowledge/Understanding The area of △ABC (right) is 27 cm² and BC = 9 cm. Calculate the length of altitude AD.

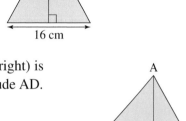

A
B   D   C

B **Estimating Roofing Materials**

Use this information to complete exercises 3 to 5.
Denise and Jack are planning to put new shingles on their roof. Before purchasing the materials they must:

- Determine the area of the roof.

- Calculate how many shingles they need.

The *hip roof* on their house has two triangular sections and two trapezoidal sections. Denise and Jack made these measurements.

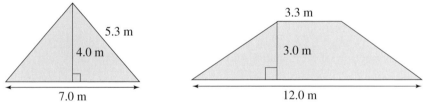

5.3 m
4.0 m
7.0 m

3.3 m
3.0 m
12.0 m

3. a) Use the formulas for the area of a triangle and the area of a trapezoid. Calculate the area of each section.

b) The roof has 2 triangular sections and 2 trapezoidal sections. What is the area of the roof?

4. To allow for waste, 10% of the area must be added to get the total area.

a) Calculate 10% of the area of the roof.

b) What is the total area, including the allowance for waste?

5. Application Shingles are sold in bundles. One bundle covers 3 m² (this includes allowances for overlap). Use the area from exercise 4b. How many bundles are needed?

Using *The Geometer's Sketchpad*: Angle Bisectors of Triangles

Have you ever tried to draw a circle that fits perfectly inside a triangle?
It isn't easy because you don't know where the centre of the circle is.
Studying the angle bisectors of a triangle will help you solve this problem.

In the diagram, line segment CD is an angle bisector of
△ABC because it bisects ∠C.

An *angle bisector* is a line that divides an angle into two
equal angles.

In *Investigations 1* to *3*, you will observe the properties of
the angle bisectors in a triangle.

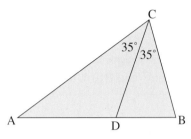

Use *The Geometer's Sketchpad*.

Constructing an Angle Bisector

From the File menu, choose New Sketch.

1. Construct △ABC, as described in *Setup*, page 378.

2. Hold down the shift key. Select point A, then B, then C. From the Construct menu,
choose Angle Bisector. This produces a ray from B that cuts ∠ABC in half.

3. Construct the point of intersection of the bisector and side AC. Label this point D.

4. Select the angle bisector. From the Display menu, choose Hide Ray.
The angle bisector is hidden.

5. Construct segment BD.

Angle Bisectors and Distance

1. Construct △ABC and BD, the bisector of ∠B, as in *Investigation 1*.

2. Select BD. From the Construct menu, choose Point on Object. Move the point so that it is easily visible. Label this point P.

3. Measure the distance from P to BA:
- Select P and BA. From the Construct menu, choose Perpendicular Line.
- Select the perpendicular line and side BA. From the Construct menu, choose Point At Intersection. Label this point Q.
- Hide the perpendicular line. Construct segment PQ.
- Measure the length of PQ.

4. Measure the distance from P to BC:
- Construct a line through P perpendicular to BC.
- Construct the Point At Intersection of the perpendicular and side BC. Label this point R.
- Hide the perpendicular line. Construct segment PR.
- Measure the length of PR.

5. What do you notice about the lengths of PQ and PR?

6. Move point P along BD. Observe the measurements.

7. Drag a vertex of △ABC. Observe the measurements.

8. Write a statement about any point on an angle bisector.

INVESTIGATION 3

Constructing Three Angle Bisectors

1. Construct △ABC and BD, the bisector of ∠B, as in *Investigation 1*.

2. Bisect ∠BAC. Bisect ∠ACB. What do you notice about the angle bisectors?

3. Select two angle bisectors. Construct their intersection point. From the Construct menu, choose Point at Intersection. Label it O.

4. Drag a vertex of △ABC. Observe how the angle bisectors change position as the shape of △ABC changes.

5. Write a statement about the three angle bisectors of a triangle.

If you completed *Investigations 1–3* from Section 9.6, skip this *Investigation*.

Angle Bisectors of Triangles

Work in a group of three.

You will need a ruler, a protractor, and 2 coloured pencils or pens.
A plastic right triangle is optional.

Each student chooses a different type of △ABC:

- acute △ABC

- △ABC with a right ∠ABC

- △ABC with an obtuse ∠ABC

1. Draw a large △ABC.

2. Measure ∠ABC. Record this angle measure on the diagram.

3. Divide the angle measurement in half. Use a protractor. Draw the angle
   bisector for ∠ABC. Label point D where the angle bisector intersects AC.

4. Measure ∠ABD and ∠DBC and record these measurements on the diagram.

5. Compare your results with those of your group members as well as with
   those of other groups. What do you notice about the angle measures of
   ∠ABD, ∠DBC, and ∠ABC?

Use a coloured pencil or pen for exercises 5 and 6.

6. Label any point P on BD. Use a plastic right triangle or a protractor
   to draw a line segment from P to AB perpendicular to AB. Label the
   point Q where this segment meets AB.

7. Draw segment PR perpendicular to BC. Measure PQ
   and PR. Record the measurements on the segments.

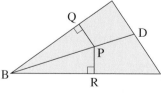

8. Share your results with your group. Compare your
   results with other groups. Write a statement about P.
   Is the statement true for any point on an angle bisector?

Use a different coloured pencil or pen for exercises 9–11.

9. In your triangle, draw angle bisectors for ∠BAC and ∠BCA.

10. Share your results with your group and with other groups. What do you notice about the three angle bisectors of a triangle?

11. Label the point of intersection the *incentre*.

Here is a summary of the properties you observed in the *Investigations*.

TAKE NOTE

Angle Bisector Properties

1. Each point on an angle bisector is *equidistant* from the arms of the angle.
Since ∠ABD = ∠DBF, then ED = DF

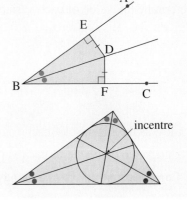

2. The three angle bisectors in a triangle meet at a single point. This intersection point is the *incentre*. It is the centre of the circle that just touches each side of the triangle.

incentre

These properties can be used to solve problems.

Example

The centre of the circle, O, is the incentre of isosceles △PQR. Determine the measure of ∠PRO.

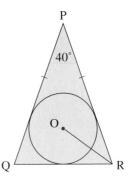

Solution

Since △PQR is isosceles,
∠PQR = ∠PRQ

Since the sum of the angles in the triangle is 180°,

∠PQR + ∠PRQ + 40° = 180°
∠PQR + ∠PRQ = 140°

Two equal angles have a sum of 140°.

So, each angle is $\frac{140°}{2}$ = 70°
∠PRQ = 70°

Since O is the incentre, RO is an angle bisector.

Therefore, $\angle PRO = \frac{1}{2}\angle PRQ$

$$\angle PRO = \frac{1}{2}(70°)$$
$$= 35°$$

Discuss

How can you tell from the diagram that △PQR is isosceles?

9.7 Exercises

A 1. **Knowledge/Understanding** Point P is on the bisector of each angle.
Determine the value of each variable. Explain your reasoning.

a)

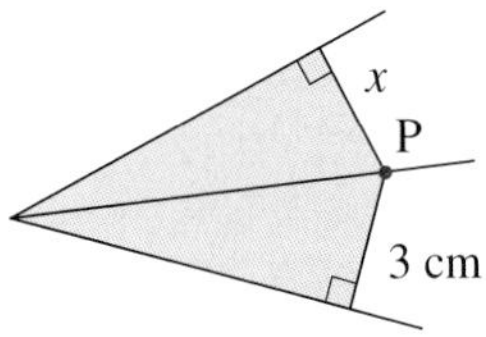

3 cm

b)

P

x 62°

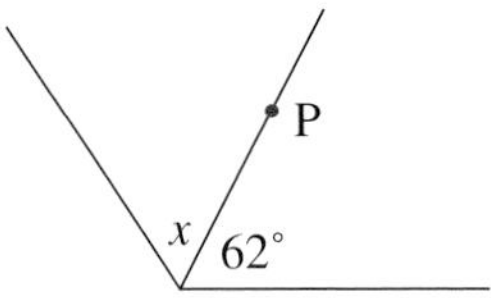

B 2. Point O is the incentre of each triangle.

a) Determine the value of each variable.

b) **Communication** Explain your reasoning.

i)

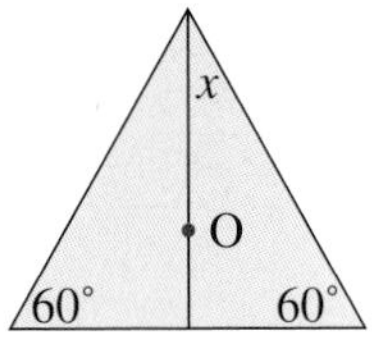

x

O

60° 60°

ii)

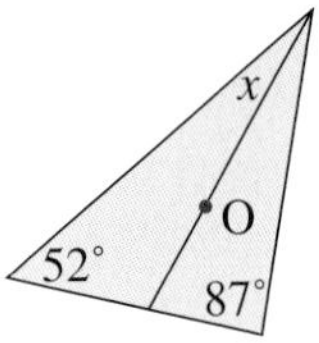

x

O

52° 87°

iii)

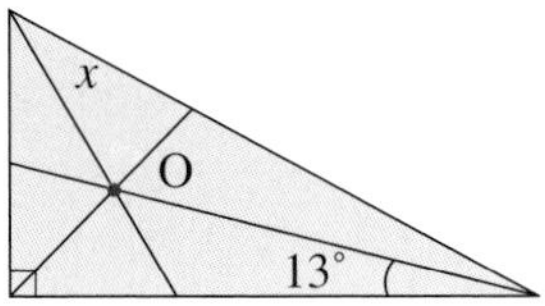

x

O

13°

iv)

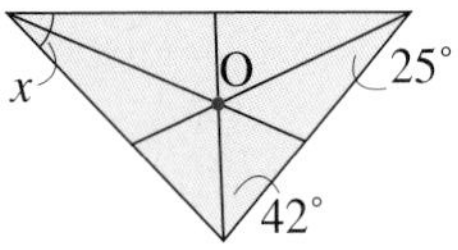

O

x

25°

42°

v)

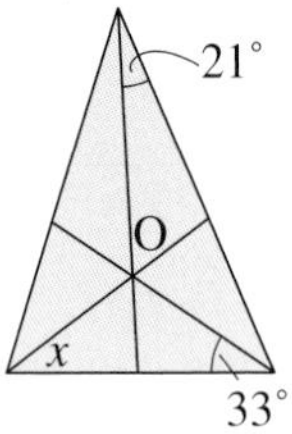

21°

O

x

33°

vi)

58°

O

x y

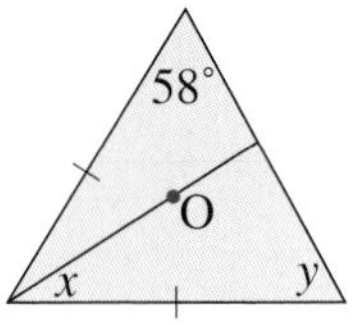

3. **Application** Point O is the incentre of the triangle.
Determine the value of x. Explain your reasoning.

O x

50°

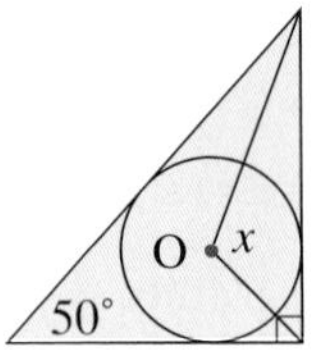

4. **Thinking/Inquiry/Problem Solving** Triangle ABC
is isosceles with AB = AC. Segment AP is the bisector
of ∠BAC. What is the sum of the two marked angles?
Explain your reasoning.

A

B P C

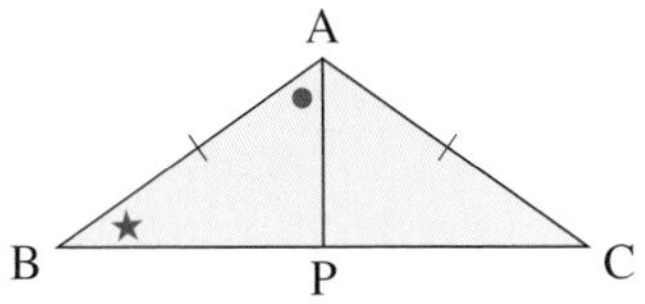

1. The area of △PQR is 25 mm². Point O is the centroid of △PQR. Calculate the area of △PQS.

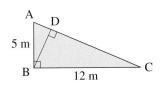

2. Construct equilateral △ABC with sides 10 cm. Construct medians AP, BN, and CM.

   a) Measure and record all the angles and sides of the six small triangles formed by the medians. What do you notice?

   b) What statement can you make about the medians of equilateral triangles?

   c) Check your answer in part b by repeating the construction using *The Geometer's Sketchpad*.

3. a) Calculate the area of △ABC.

   b) Calculate the length of AC.

   c) Calculate the length of altitude BD to the nearest tenth of a metre.

4. Draw the triangle with vertices A(3, 1), B(5, 7), and C(8, 1). Draw the altitude from B to meet AC at D.

   a) State the coordinates of point D.

   b) Determine the equation of the altitude.

5. Point O is the incentre of equilateral △ABC. Determine the measure of ∠APC and ∠PAC. Explain your reasoning.

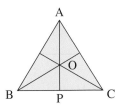

Preparation for Ontario Testing

6. Which statement about △ABC is true?

   a) CM is an angle bisector.

   b) O is the orthocentre, where the altitudes meet.

   c) △ABC is an equilateral triangle.

   d) O is the centroid, where the medians meet.

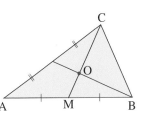

9.8 Using *The Geometer's Sketchpad*: Interior and Exterior Angles

The interior angles of △ABC are ∠ABC, ∠BCA, and ∠CAB.

To construct the exterior angles, we extend each side.

The exterior angles of △ABC are ∠ACD, ∠EAB, and ∠FBC.

Similarly, the interior angles of quadrilateral PQRS are ∠PQR, ∠QRS, ∠RSP, and ∠SPQ.

To construct the exterior angles, we extend each side.

The exterior angles of quadrilateral PQRS are ∠APQ, ∠BQR, ∠CRS, and ∠DSP.

You will investigate some properties of interior and exterior angles in triangles and quadrilaterals.

Use *The Geometer's Sketchpad.*

Measuring and Tabulating the Angles in a Triangle

1. Construct △ABC as in *Setup*, page 378.

2. Hold down the shift key. Click on point A, then B, then C.

3. From the Measure menu, choose Angle. The measure of ∠ABC is displayed.

4. Follow a procedure similar to exercise 3 to display the measures of ∠BAC and ∠BCA.

5. Hold down the shift key. Click on the three angle measures. From the Measure menu, choose Calculate.

6. Use the calculator to find the sum of the angle measures:
   - From the Values menu, choose one angle, then click on $\boxed{+}$.
   - From the Values menu, choose a second angle, then click on $\boxed{+}$.
   - From the Values menu, choose the third angle, then click OK.

   The screen displays the sum of the angle measures.

7. Select the four measurements. From the Measure menu, choose Tabulate. The screen displays the measurements in a table.

8. Drag a vertex of the triangle. The angle measurements change, but the table does not. A table gives a permanent record of your measurements.

9. Select the table. From the Measure menu, choose Add Entry. The table will extend to include your new measurements.

The Sum of Interior Angles

1. Construct △ABC and a table of measurements as in *Investigation 1*. Add entries to the table until you have recorded 5 sets of measurements. Write a statement about the sum of the angles in a triangle.

2. Start a New Sketch. Construct quadrilateral ABCD.

3. Measure the angles. Use the calculator to find their sum.

4. Set up a table to record the measurements.

5. Drag a vertex of the quadrilateral. Observe the change in the measurements.

6. What happens when you drag a vertex so the quadrilateral contains a reflex angle (an angle greater than 180°)?

7. Drag a vertex so that all the angles are less than 180°. Add entries to the table until you have recorded 5 sets of measurements. Write a statement about the sum of the angles in a quadrilateral.

8. Construct a diagonal of the quadrilateral. What is the sum of the interior angles of the two triangles formed by the diagonal? How does this construction explain the sum of the angles in a quadrilateral?

Constructing and Measuring Exterior Angles

The angle marked with a star is an *exterior* angle of △ABC. This exterior angle is created by extending side BC beyond vertex C. Angle BAF and ∠EBC are two other exterior angles of △ABC.

In this Investigation, construct triangles using rays instead of segments.
- Construct and label three points A, B, and C. Click on the Segment tool and drag to the right. Select the Ray tool.
- Select the three points. From the Construct menu, choose Ray.

To measure exterior angles:

- Construct a point on each ray outside the triangle. Look at the diagram on page 400. Construct D on the ray from B. Then select D, C, and A to measure the exterior angle at C.

1. Start a New Sketch. Construct △ABC using rays, as instructed above.

2. Construct the exterior points as explained above. Measure ∠ACB and ∠ACD. Use the calculator to find their sum.

3. Drag a vertex of △ABC and observe the results. Explain what you notice. Make a prediction about the measure of an exterior angle of a triangle.

4. Check your prediction by measuring ∠ABC and its exterior angle ∠CBE, then checking their sum.

5. Write a statement about a property of an exterior angle of a triangle.

6. Measure ∠ABC and ∠CAB. Use the calculator to find their sum.

7. Measure ∠ACD. What do you notice?

8. Drag a vertex of △ABC and observe the results.

9. Make a prediction about one of the other exterior angles. Check your prediction. If your prediction was false, re-examine your results and revise your prediction.

10. Find the sum of the exterior angles and tabulate the measurements. (See the instructions on page 399.)

11. Record 5 sets of measurements in the table. Examine the results. What is the sum of the exterior angles of a triangle?

12. Make the triangle as small as a point by dragging the vertices toward one another. What do you notice?

13. Predict the sum of the exterior angles of a quadrilateral. Construct a quadrilateral using rays. Measure the exterior angles. Was your prediction correct? If not, revise your prediction. Remember to recalculate if the quadrilateral contains a reflex angle.

14. Make the quadrilateral very small by dragging the vertices toward one another. What do you notice?

15. Write a statement about the exterior angles of a triangle and of a quadrilateral.

9.9 Interior and Exterior Angles

If you completed *Investigations 1–3* from Section 9.8, skip *Investigations 1* and *2*.

Interior and Exterior Angles of Triangles

Work in a group of three.
You will need a pencil, a protractor, a ruler, and paper.

Each student chooses a different type of △ABC:

- acute △ABC
- right △ABC
- obtuse △ABC

1. Draw a large △ABC.

2. Measure each angle in △ABC. Record the measurements on the diagram. These are the interior angles of the triangle.

3. Calculate the sum of the interior angles in each triangle. Record the sum below each triangle.

4. Compare your findings with those of your group. What do you notice about the sum of the interior angles in each triangle?

5. Extend each side of △ABC. Label each extension. AB is extended to E, BC is extended to D, and CA is extended to F, as shown.

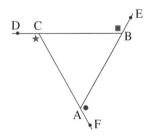

6. Measure ∠ACD. Record the measurement on the diagram.

7. What is the sum of ∠ACD and ∠ACB? What prediction can you make about the measure of an exterior angle of a triangle? Measure the angles with a protractor to check your prediction.

8. Find the sum of the exterior angles. Write a statement about the sum of the exterior angles of a triangle.

9. Compare your results with those in your group. What do you notice about the sum of the exterior angles of a triangle?

10. Compare your results with those from other groups. Write a statement about the sum of the exterior angles of a triangle.

Interior and Exterior Angles of Quadrilaterals

Work in a group of three.
You will need a pencil, a protractor, a ruler, and paper.

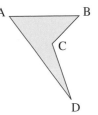

1. With your group, draw two quadrilaterals ABCD with each side a different length and with one quadrilateral having a reflex angle (greater than 180°). In the quadrilateral shown, ∠BCD is a reflex angle.

2. Measure the interior angles in each quadrilateral. Record the measurements on the diagrams.

3. Calculate the sum of the interior angles for each quadrilateral. Record the sum below each quadrilateral. Are there any similarities between the sums?

4. Draw a diagonal of one quadrilateral. That is, draw a line from one vertex to the opposite vertex. What is the sum of the angles of the two triangles formed by the diagonal? How does this help you understand the sum of the angles in a quadrilateral?

5. Predict the sum of the exterior angles in a quadrilateral. Extend each side of one quadrilateral and measure the exterior angles. Repeat this step for the other quadrilateral.

6. Share your results with your group. What is the sum of the exterior angles of a quadrilateral? Was this the same for each quadrilateral?

7. Compare your results with those from other groups. Write a statement about the exterior angles of a quadrilateral.

Here is a summary of the properties you observed in the *Investigations*.

Properties of Interior and Exterior Angles in Triangles and Quadrilaterals

1. The interior angles in a triangle add to 180°.

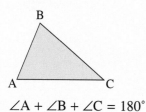

$$\angle A + \angle B + \angle C = 180°$$

2. The interior angles in a quadrilateral add to 360°.

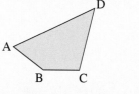

$$\angle A + \angle B + \angle C + \angle D = 360°$$

3. In a triangle and a quadrilateral, an exterior angle is supplementary to the interior adjacent angle.

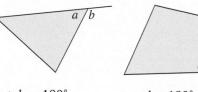

$$a + b = 180° \qquad c + d = 180°$$

4. An exterior angle of a triangle is equal to the sum of the interior opposite angles.

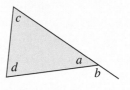

$$b = c + d$$

5. The exterior angles of a triangle and a quadrilateral add to 360°.

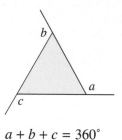

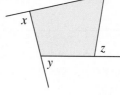

$$a + b + c = 360° \qquad w + x + y + z = 360°$$

These properties can be used to solve problems.

Example

Find the measure of each indicated angle.

a)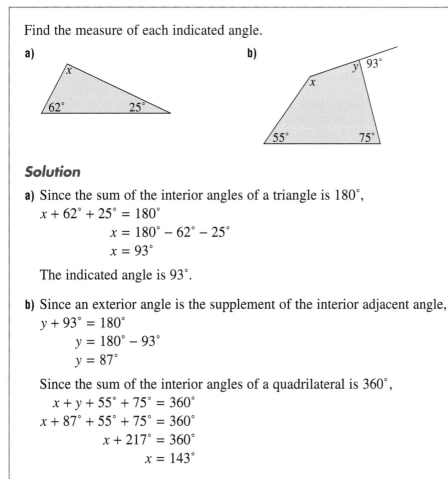

b)

Solution

a) Since the sum of the interior angles of a triangle is 180°,

$$x + 62° + 25° = 180°$$
$$x = 180° - 62° - 25°$$
$$x = 93°$$

The indicated angle is 93°.

b) Since an exterior angle is the supplement of the interior adjacent angle,

$$y + 93° = 180°$$
$$y = 180° - 93°$$
$$y = 87°$$

Since the sum of the interior angles of a quadrilateral is 360°,

$$x + y + 55° + 75° = 360°$$
$$x + 87° + 55° + 75° = 360°$$
$$x + 217° = 360°$$
$$x = 143°$$

9.9   Exercises

A   **1. Knowledge/Understanding** Find the measure of each angle x.

a)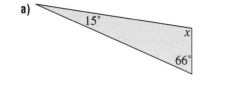

b)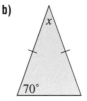

c)

d)

2. Communication Find the measure of each angle x.
Explain your reasoning.

a)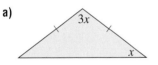

b)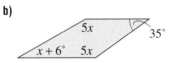

c)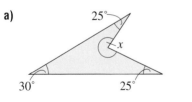

d)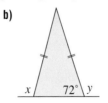

3. Application Find the measure of each indicated angle.
Explain your reasoning.

a)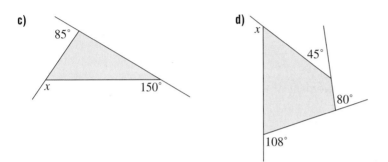

b)

4. Find the measure of each indicated angle. Explain your reasoning.

a)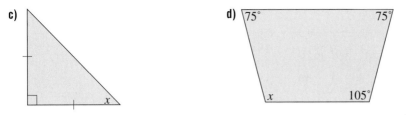

b)

Trina Raynes is a carpenter. When she hangs a door, she makes sure the sides of the frame are parallel and the top and sides of the frame are square. She uses a tool called a square, as shown.

Trina often deals with parallel lines. She uses a level to make sure work is true horizontal (level) or true vertical (plumb).

In this section, you will investigate the geometric properties Trina uses.

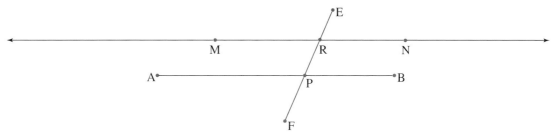

 Use *The Geometer's Sketchpad*.

SETUP

From the File menu, choose New Sketch.

  1. To construct AB and EF:

Click on this tool ...	*... and do this:*
	a) Draw a horizontal line segment.
	b) Draw a second line segment that intersects the first segment. This segment is a transversal.
	c) Label the two segments AB and EF, as shown on page 407.
	d) Select AB and EF. From the Construct menu, choose Point At Intersection.
	e) Click on the intersection point of AB and EF. Label it P.

2. To construct a line MN parallel to AB:

Click on this tool ...	*... and do this:*
	a) Draw a point above AB and to the left of segment EF.
	b) Click on the point. Label it M.
	c) Select point M and segment AB. From the Construct menu, choose Parallel Line.
	d) Click on the parallel line. From the Construct menu, choose Point On Object.
	e) Drag the new point to the right of EF.
	f) Select the parallel line and segment EF. From the Construct menu, choose Point At Intersection.
	g) Click on the two constructed points. Label the intersection point R and the point on the parallel line N.

In the *Investigation*, you will observe properties of parallel lines.

Angles Formed by a Transversal

In the *Setup*, transversal EF intersects AB and MN. Four angles are
formed at each intersection point.

1. Construct AB, MN, and EF as in *Setup*.

2. Measure the four angles at each point R and P. (If necessary, refer to
page 385 to review measuring an angle.)

3. Drag point A. If you have constructed the diagram correctly, the line
through M and N should move, too. It should remain parallel to AB.
If it does not, reconstruct the parallel line.

4. Hold down the mouse button and move each angle measurement until
it is visible. Line up the measurements for the four angles at P by
clicking on them and dragging. Repeat for the angles at R.

$$m\angle APE = \qquad m\angle APF = \qquad m\angle BPE = \qquad m\angle BPF =$$
$$m\angle MRE = \qquad m\angle MRF = \qquad m\angle NRE = \qquad m\angle NRF =$$

5. Examine the measures of the four angles at each point. What do you notice?

6. Drag point A. Describe the effect on the angle measures at R.

7. Write a statement about the angles formed by a transversal intersecting
two parallel lines.

If you completed the *Investigation* from Section 9.10, skip this *Investigation*.

Angles Formed by a Transversal

Work in pairs.

You will each need a pencil, a ruler, a protractor, and paper.

1. Place a ruler on a piece of paper. Trace along the bottom of the ruler to create line segment AB. Trace along the top of the ruler to create line segment MN.

2. Move the ruler below AB and turn it slightly so that it is not parallel to AB. Trace along the bottom of the ruler to create segment CD.

3. Draw segment EF to intersect MN at R, AB at P, and CD at Q.

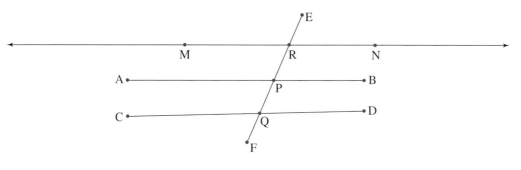

4. Measure the four angles at each point: R, P, and Q.
   Record each measure on each angle. What do you notice about the measures of the angles?

5. Share your results with your group and with other groups. Write a statement about the angles formed by a transversal intersecting two non-parallel lines.

6. Write a statement about the angles formed by a transversal intersecting two parallel lines.

Here is a summary of the properties you observed in the *Investigations*.

Properties of Angles Formed by a Transversal

A transversal that intersects two parallel lines creates eight angles.

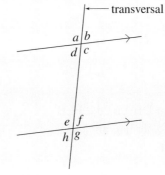

1. There are 2 pairs of *alternate angles*.

   - $c = e$
   - $d = f$

2. There are 4 pairs of *corresponding angles*.

   - $b = f$
   - $c = g$
   - $a = e$
   - $d = h$

3. There are 2 pairs of *interior angles*.

   - $c + f = 180°$
   - $d + e = 180°$

4. The angles at each intersection point form patterns.

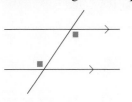

- The two angles in each pair of alternate angles are equal.

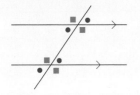

- The two angles in each pair of corresponding angles are equal.

- The interior angles are supplementary.

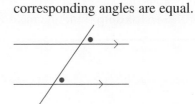

These angles add to 180°.   These angles add to 180°.

These properties can be used to solve problems.

Example

Find the angle measure of x and y.

a)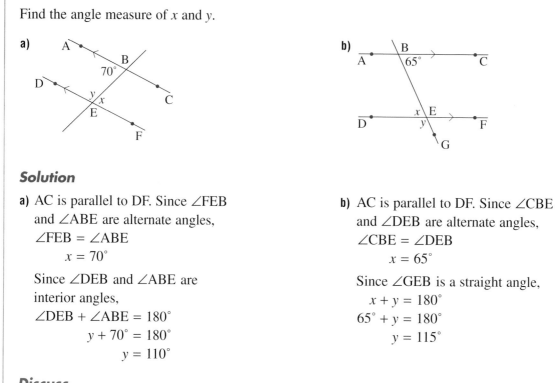

b)

Solution

a) AC is parallel to DF. Since ∠FEB and ∠ABE are alternate angles,
∠FEB = ∠ABE
x = 70°

Since ∠DEB and ∠ABE are interior angles,
∠DEB + ∠ABE = 180°
y + 70° = 180°
y = 110°

b) AC is parallel to DF. Since ∠CBE and ∠DEB are alternate angles,
∠CBE = ∠DEB
x = 65°

Since ∠GEB is a straight angle,
x + y = 180°
65° + y = 180°
y = 115°

Discuss

Suggest another way to determine the values of x and y in part a.

9.11   Exercises

1. Knowledge/Understanding Find the measure of each angle at P, Q, and R.

2. Name:

  a) a pair of acute alternate angles

  b) a pair of obtuse corresponding angles

  c) a pair of interior angles

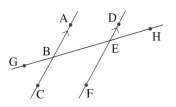

3. Application Sometimes lines that look parallel are not parallel. Which of the lines ℓ_1, ℓ_2, and ℓ_3 are parallel? Explain your reasoning.

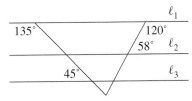

4. Communication Find the measure of each indicated angle. Explain your reasoning.

a)

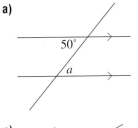

b)

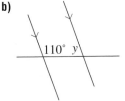

c)

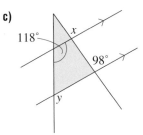

d)

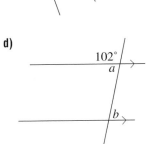

5. Determine the measure of each indicated angle.

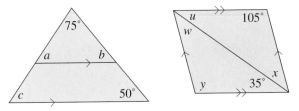

6. Thinking/Inquiry/Problem Solving Can two intersecting lines both be parallel to a third line? Draw a diagram to support your answer.

9.12 Using *The Geometer's Sketchpad*: Sides and Diagonals of Quadrilaterals

Many games are played on four-sided fields and courts. Tennis, racquetball, volleyball, basketball, and football use rectangular playing areas.

We refer to a baseball field as a diamond, but it is actually a square with each side 27.4 m. The pitcher is 18.4 m from the batter.

In this section, you will investigate some properties of quadrilaterals.

Quadrilaterals are four-sided figures, such as rectangles and squares.

Use *The Geometer's Sketchpad*.

SETUP

From the File menu, choose New Sketch.

1. To construct quadrilateral ABCD:

Click on this tool …   … and do this:

a) Draw 4 points.

b) Label the points clockwise as A, B, C, and D.

c) Select all 4 points in order. From the Construct menu, choose Segment.

2. To construct parallelogram PQRS:

Click on this tool …   … and do this:

a) Draw a horizontal line segment.

b) Label the endpoints P and S.

c) Draw a point above segment PS.

d) Label the point Q.

e) Select P and Q. From the Construct menu, choose Segment.

f) Select Q and segment PS. From the Construct menu, choose Parallel Line.

g) Select S and segment PQ. From the Construct menu, choose Parallel Line.

h) Select the two constructed lines. From the Construct menu, choose Point At Intersection.

i) Label the intersection point R.

j) Select lines QR and SR. From the Display menu, choose Hide Lines.

k) Select Q and R. From the Construct menu, choose Segment.

l) Select S and R. From the Construct menu, choose Segment.

3. To construct rectangle KLMN:

Click on this tool ...   *... and do this:*

a) Draw a segment.

b) Label the endpoints of the segment K and N.

c) Select K and segment KN. From the Construct menu, choose Perpendicular Line.

d) Select the perpendicular line. From the Construct menu, choose Point On Object.

e) Label the point L.

f) Select the line KL. From the Display menu, choose Hide Line.

g) Select K and L. From the Construct menu, choose Segment.

h) Select L and segment KN. From the Construct menu, choose Parallel Line.

i) Select N and segment KL. From the Construct menu, choose Parallel Line.

j) Select the two constructed lines. From the Construct menu, choose Point At Intersection.

k) Label the intersection point M.

l) Select lines LM and MN. From the Display menu, choose Hide Lines.

m) Select L and M. From the Construct menu, choose Segment.

n) Select M and N. From the Construct menu, choose Segment.

Save your sketches.

Diagonals and Their Lengths

1. For quadrilateral ABCD:

   a) Construct quadrilateral ABCD, as in *Setup*.

   b) Construct diagonals AC and BD.

   c) Select AC and BD. From the Construct menu, choose Point At Intersection. Label the intersection point E.

   d) Measure AE and EC, BE and ED. What do you notice?

   e) Drag the vertices until the measures of AE and EC are equal. What do you notice about the shape of ABCD?

   f) Drag the vertices until AE, EC, BE, and ED are equal. What do you notice about the shape of ABCD?

   g) Write a statement about the diagonals in a quadrilateral.

2. For parallelogram PQRS:

   a) Construct parallelogram PQRS as in *Setup*.

   b) Construct diagonals PR and QS.

   c) Select PR and QS. From the Construct menu, choose Point At Intersection. Label the intersection point T.

   d) Measure PT, TR, QT, and TS. What do you notice?

   e) Drag vertex S to see if your observations are true for other parallelograms.

   f) Measure PQ and QR.

   g) Drag vertex P until the lengths PQ and QR are equal. A parallelogram with equal sides is a *rhombus*. What do you notice about the lengths of PT, TR, QT, and TS in a rhombus?

   h) Write a statement about the diagonals in a parallelogram.

3. For rectangle KLMN:

   a) Construct rectangle KLMN as in *Setup*.

   b) Construct diagonals KM and LN.

   c) Select KM and LN. From the Construct menu, choose Point At Intersection. Label the intersection point O.

   d) Measure KO and OM. What do you notice?

   e) Drag vertex K to see if your observations are true for other rectangles.

   f) Measure LO and ON. What do you notice?

   g) How are your results for the rectangle different from the parallelogram results?

   h) Write a statement about the diagonals in a rectangle.

Diagonals and Angle Measures

1. For quadrilateral ABCD:

   a) Use quadrilateral ABCD from *Investigation 1*.

   b) Measure ∠AEB, ∠CEB, ∠AED, and ∠CED. What do you notice?

   c) Drag vertex B. Name any angles that are always equal. Explain why they are equal.

   d) Drag the vertices until ∠AEB = ∠CEB = ∠AED = ∠CED. What is the measure of these four angles?

   e) Measure AB, BC, CD, and DA. What do you notice?

   f) Drag the vertices until ∠AEB = ∠CEB = ∠AED = ∠CED, AD = AB, and CB = CD. A quadrilateral with adjacent sides equal is a *kite*.

   g) Write a statement about the angles formed by the diagonals in a quadrilateral. Include a statement about the special case of a kite.

2. For parallelogram PQRS:

   a) Use parallelogram PQRS from *Investigation 1*.

   b) Measure ∠PTQ, ∠RTQ, ∠PTS, and ∠RTS. What do you notice?

   c) Drag vertex Q. Name any angles that are always equal. Explain why they are equal.

   d) Drag vertex Q until ∠PTQ = ∠RTQ = ∠PTS = ∠RTS. What do you notice about the shape of PQRS?

   e) Measure PQ and QR. Does this confirm your observation in part d? Explain.

   f) Write a statement about the angles formed by the diagonals in a parallelogram. Include a statement about the special case of a rhombus.

3. For rectangle KLMN:

   a) Use rectangle KLMN from *Investigation 1*.

   b) Measure ∠KOL, ∠MOL, ∠KON, and ∠MON. What do you notice?

   c) Drag vertex L to see if your observations are true for other rectangles.

   d) Drag vertex L until KL = LM. What is the shape of KLMN?

   e) Write a statement about the angles formed by the diagonals in a rectangle. Include a statement about the special case of a square.

If you have completed *Investigations 1* and *2* from Section 9.12, skip *Investigations 1* and *2*.

Diagonals and Their Lengths

Work in pairs.

You will need grid paper, a ruler, and a pencil.

Each student chooses a different type of quadrilateral ABCD:

- quadrilateral ABCD with each side the same length and vertices 90° (a square)
- quadrilateral ABCD with each side a different length

1. On grid paper, draw a large quadrilateral, ABCD.

2. Draw diagonals AC and BD and label the point of intersection E.

3. Measure AE and EC, BE and ED. What do you notice?

4. Compare your results with those of several classmates. Write a statement about the diagonals in a quadrilateral.

5. Draw parallelogram PQRS and *rhombus* PQRS on grid paper. A rhombus is a parallelogram with equal side lengths.

6. Draw diagonals PR and QS for each figure. Label each point of intersection T.

7. Measure PT, TR, QT, and TS. Record the measurements on the diagonals. What do you notice?

8. Draw rectangle KLMN on grid paper. Draw and label diagonals KM and LM. Label the point of intersection O.

9. Measure KO and OM. What do you notice? Measure LO and ON. What do you notice?

10. How are your results for the rectangle different from the results of the parallelogram?

11. Compare your results with those of several classmates. Write a statement about the diagonals of a rectangle.

Diagonals and Angle Measures

Work in pairs.

You will need grid paper, a protractor, a ruler, and a pencil.

1. Use quadrilateral ABCD from *Investigation 1*. For quadrilateral ABCD:

   a) Measure ∠AEB, ∠CEB, ∠AED, and ∠CED. What do you notice?

   b) Trace *kite* ABCD. A kite is a quadrilateral with two pairs of adjacent equal sides.

   c) Draw diagonals AC and BD. Mark the point of intersection E.

   d) Measure ∠AEB, ∠CEB, ∠AED, and ∠CED. What do you notice? Compare your results with those of several classmates.

   e) Write a statement about the angles formed by the diagonals in a quadrilateral. Include a statement about the special case of a kite.

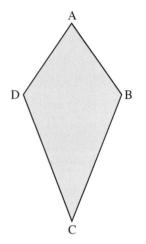

2. Use parallelogram PQRS and rhombus PQRS from *Investigation 1*.

   a) Measure ∠PTQ, ∠RTQ, ∠PTS, and ∠RTS in the parallelogram. What do you notice?

   b) Measure ∠PTQ, ∠RTQ, ∠PTS, and ∠RTS in the rhombus. What do you notice? Compare your results with those of several classmates.

   c) Write a statement about the angles formed by the diagonals in a parallelogram. Include a statement about the special case of a rhombus.

3. Use rectangle KLMN from *Investigation 1*. For rectangle KLMN:

   a) Measure ∠KOL, ∠MOL, ∠KON, and ∠MON. What do you notice?

   b) Draw square KLMN with diagonals KM and LN intersecting at O.

   c) Measure ∠KOL, ∠MOL, ∠KON, and ∠MON. What do you notice? Compare your results with those of several classmates.

   d) Write a statement about the angles formed by the diagonals in a rectangle. Include a statement about the special case of a square.

Here is a summary of the properties you observed in the *Investigations*.

Properties of Quadrilaterals

A parallelogram has:

* diagonals that bisect each other

A rectangle has:

* diagonals that bisect each other
* equal diagonals

A rhombus has:

* diagonals that bisect each other
* diagonals that are perpendicular

A square has:

* diagonals that bisect each other
* equal diagonals
* diagonals that are perpendicular

A kite has:

* diagonals that are perpendicular

We can use the properties of quadrilaterals to solve problems.

Example

A tile has the shape of a quadrilateral. Its length is twice its width. The diagonals of the tile are 15.0 cm long. Determine the dimensions of the tile.

Solution

Since the diagonals are equal, the tile is a rectangle.
A diagonal divides the rectangle into two right triangles.

Let the width of the rectangle be w centimetres. Then the length of the rectangle is $2w$ centimetres.

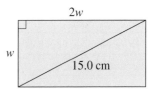

Use the Pythagorean Theorem in one right triangle.

$$w^2 + (2w)^2 = 15^2$$
$$w^2 + 4w^2 = 225$$
$$5w^2 = 225$$
$$w^2 = 45$$
$$w = \sqrt{45}$$
$$\doteq 6.708$$

The width is approximately 6.7 cm and the length is 2×6.708 cm, or approximately 13.4 cm.

9.13 Exercises

A **1. Communication** Name each quadrilateral. Explain how you identified it.

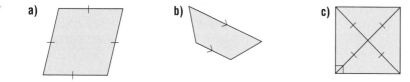

a)　　　b)　　　c)

B **2. Knowledge/Understanding** Determine the length of AC in each rectangle.

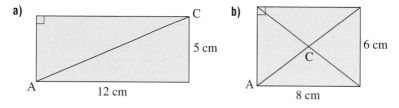

a)　C 5 cm　A 12 cm　b) 6 cm　A 8 cm　C

3. a) Is a square a parallelogram? Explain.

b) Is a square a rhombus? Explain.

4. Application Copy and complete this table. Sort the quadrilaterals.
A quadrilateral may be listed under more than one heading.
rectangle, square, rhombus, parallelogram, kite, trapezoid

a)	All sides equal	
b)	2 pairs of opposite sides equal	
c)	1 pair of opposite sides parallel	
d)	2 pairs of opposite sides parallel	
e)	Equal diagonals	
f)	Diagonals bisect each other	
g)	Perpendicular sides	
h)	Perpendicular diagonals	

9.14 Representing 3-Dimensional Objects in 2 Dimensions

We know that the two rails in a set of tracks never meet but, when they disappear into the distance, it appears that they do!

To create a realistic painting of railway tracks, an artist must know the rules of perspective drawing. One rule is that parallel lines appear to meet at a single point in the distance.

In this activity, you will examine perspective by constructing a box with one-point perspective.

Start a New Sketch in *The Geometer's Sketchpad*.

1. To construct a square:

   - Draw a short horizontal line segment, then label the two endpoints A and B.

   - Double-click on point A. Point A is now a centre of rotation.

   - Select segment AB and point B. From the Transform menu, choose Rotate. When the dialog box appears, type 90 and click OK. There will now be two segments at right angles. Label the new endpoint D.

   - Construct segment BD.

   - Double-click on segment BD. Segment BD is now a line of reflection.

   - Select segments AB and AD. From the Transform menu, choose Reflect.

   - Hide segment BD. Select the new vertex and label it C.

   - Drag point A and observe that the figure remains a square.

2. To construct a point in the distance:

   - Draw a long line segment as far away from the square as possible.

   - Click on the line segment. From the Construct menu, choose Point On Object. Label the point O.

   - Construct segments AO, BO, CO, and DO.

3. To complete the box:

- Click on segment AO. From the Construct menu, choose Point On Object. Label the point E.

- Select point E and segment AB. From the Construct menu, choose Parallel Line.

- Select the new line and segment BO. From the Construct menu, choose Point At Intersection. Label the intersection point F.

- Hide the line through E and F, then construct segment EF.

- Select point F and segment BC. From the Construct menu, choose Parallel Line.

- Select the new line, and segment CO. From the Construct menu, choose Point At Intersection. Label the intersection point G.

- Hide the line through F and G, then construct segment FG.

- Select point G and segment DC. From the Construct menu, choose Parallel Line.

- Select the new line and segment DO. From the Construct menu, choose Point At Intersection. Label the intersection point H. Hide the line through GH, then construct segments GH and EH.

- Drag point O to observe the box from different angles.

- Hide the perspective lines, then join corresponding vertices of the box with segments. Then move point O.

4. From exercises 1 to 3, explain how you know that ABCD is a square.

5. a) What is the relationship between $\angle$OHG and $\angle$ODC? Explain.

   b) Find an angle equal to $\angle$OEF.

   c) Find an angle equal to $\angle$OBA.

6. a) Find an angle equal to $\angle$DAO.   b) Find an angle equal to $\angle$BAO.

7. The construction in exercises 1 to 3 introduces perspective. You can use the same ideas to create drawings of other 3-dimensional objects. Try drawing your initials in 3 dimensions.

MATHEMATICS TOOLKIT

- **Median Properties**

   1. A median divides the area of a triangle in half.

   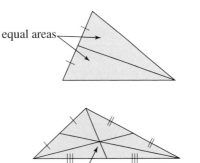

   equal areas

   2. The three medians of a triangle meet at one point. This point is the *centroid*.

   centroid

- **Altitude Properties**

   1. The length of an altitude is a height of the triangle. It is used to calculate the area of the triangle.

   A

   B   D   C

   2. The three altitudes of a triangle meet at the orthocentre. In an acute triangle, the orthocentre is inside the triangle. In a right triangle, the orthocentre is on a vertex. In an obtuse triangle, the orthocentre is outside the triangle.

   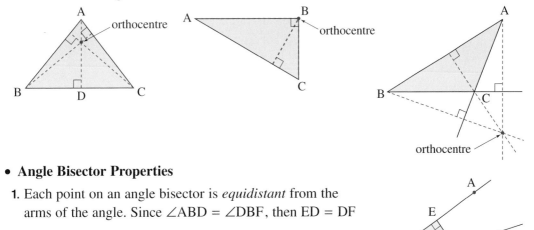

- **Angle Bisector Properties**

   1. Each point on an angle bisector is *equidistant* from the arms of the angle. Since $\angle ABD = \angle DBF$, then $ED = DF$

   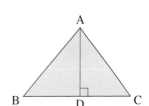

2. The three angle bisectors in a triangle meet at a single point. This intersection point is the *incentre*. It is the centre of the circle that just touches each side of the triangle.

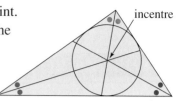
incentre

- **Properties of Interior and Exterior Angles in Triangles and Quadrilaterals**

   1. The interior angles in a triangle add to 180°.

   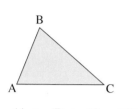

   $\angle A + \angle B + \angle C = 180°$

   2. The interior angles in a quadrilateral add to 360°.

   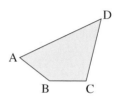

   $\angle A + \angle B + \angle C + \angle D = 360°$

   3. In a triangle and a quadrilateral, an exterior angle is supplementary to the interior adjacent angle.

   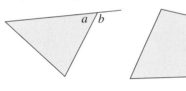

   $a + b = 180°$ $c + d = 180°$

   4. An exterior angle of a triangle is equal to the sum of the interior opposite angles.

   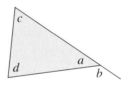

   $b = c + d$

   5. The exterior angles of a triangle and a quadrilateral add to 360°.

   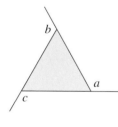

   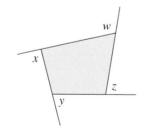

   $a + b + c = 360°$ $w + x + y + z = 360°$

- **Properties of Angles Formed by a Transversal**

   When a transversal intersects two parallel lines, the angles at each intersection point form patterns.

   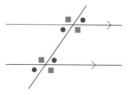

- The two angles in each pair of alternate angles are equal.

- The two angles in each pair of corresponding angles are equal.

- The interior angles are supplementary.

These angles add to 180°. These angles add to 180°.

- **Properties of Quadrilaterals**

A parallelogram has:

- diagonals that bisect each other

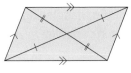

A rectangle has:

- diagonals that bisect each other
- equal diagonals

A rhombus has:

- diagonals that bisect each other
- diagonals that are perpendicular

A square has:

- diagonals that bisect each other
- equal diagonals
- diagonals that are perpendicular

A kite has:

- diagonals that are perpendicular

9.2, 9.3

1. Explain what medians of triangles are. Why is the word "median" appropriate?

2. In △PQR, O is the centroid. The area of △QMR is 9 mm². Calculate the area of △QPR.

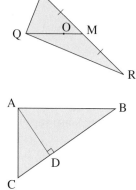

9.4, 9.5

3. The area of △ABC is 36 cm². BC is 9 cm. Calculate AD.

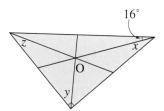

4. Name the type of triangle in each situation.

a) The orthocentre is inside the triangle.

b) The orthocentre is outside the triangle.

9.6, 9.7

5. Point O is the incentre of the triangle shown. Determine the value of each variable.

6. O is the incentre of equilateral △PQR. Determine the value of each variable. Explain your answer.

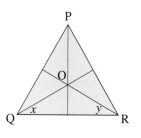

9.8, 9.9

7. Determine the value of each variable.

a)

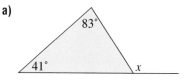

b)

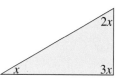

8. Determine the measure of each variable. Explain your reasoning.

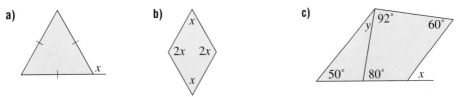

a)

b)

c)

9. Copy this figure. Replace 1–6 with the symbol ● or ■, based on the angle properties of parallel lines.

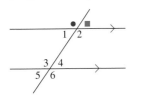

9.10, 9.11 **10.** Determine the measure of each indicated angle. Explain your reasoning.

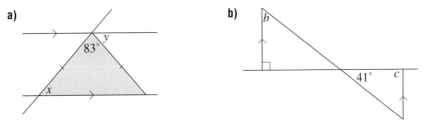

a)

b)

11. Determine the measure of each indicated angle. Explain your reasoning.

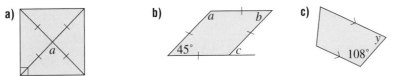

a)

b)

c)

9.12, 9.13 **12.** Sketch and label rectangle ABCD. Draw the diagonals to intersect at E. Which segments in ABCD are equal?

13. Sketch and label kite PQRS. Draw the diagonals to intersect at T. Which segment and angles in PQRS are equal?

14. Refer to the dimensions of a baseball diamond on page 414. Is the pitcher the same distance from each base?

1. In △ABC, N is the centroid. The area of △ABF is 21 cm². Determine the area of △BCD. Explain how you got your answer.

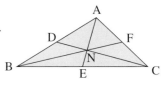

2. a) Determine the values of a, b, and $a + b$ in each diagram.

b) Communication Explain the results in part a. Write a statement about the exterior angles of a right triangle formed by extending the legs.

3. Knowledge/Understanding Determine the angle measure of x and y.

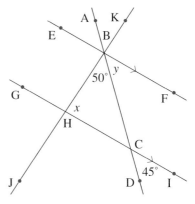

4. In what type of triangle does the orthocentre lie on a vertex of the triangle?

5. Thinking/Inquiry/Problem Solving What is the special name for each quadrilateral?

a) It has two diagonals, 6 cm and 14 cm, that bisect each other at right angles.

b) It has four sides, each 43 cm, and equal diagonals.

c) It has two adjacent sides 5 cm and two adjacent sides 13 cm.

d) It has two parallel sides. The other two sides are not parallel.

6. Application Explain why a square is a rectangle.

7. A carpenter is building a rectangular box. He is sure that the opposite sides are the same length but is not sure if all the corners are 90°. Explain what property of quadrilaterals he can use to ensure that the box is a rectangle.

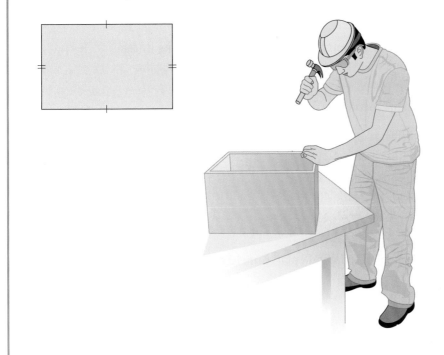

8. Quadrilateral ABCD is a parallelogram. Angle EBC is 72°. Randa looked at the diagram. She correctly stated that ∠BCD is also 72°, and therefore ∠ADC is 108°.

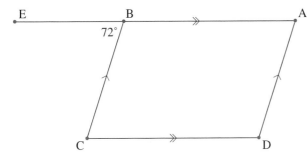

Explain Randa's reasoning.

1. a) Copy and complete this table.

Regular Hexagons						
Side length (m)	1	2	3	4	5	6
Perimeter (m)	6	12	18	24		

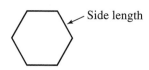

Side length

b) Graph the data in the table. Plot *Side length (m)* horizontally. Explain whether you should join the points.

c) Describe patterns in the table. Relate the patterns to the graph.

d) Is the relation between the side length and perimeter of hexagons linear or non-linear? Explain how the table and the graph show whether the relation is linear or non-linear.

e) Pose and solve a problem about the graph.

2. a) Graph each pair of line segments with these endpoints.

   i) A(−5, 4), B(−4, 1) and C(−7, 0), D(2, 3)
   ii) E(2, −2), F(−1, −5) and G(2, −6), H(7, −1)
   iii) W(−5, 2), X(6, 2) and Y(−3, 2), Z(−3, −2)
   iv) P(−4, 3), Q(0, 0) and R(−3, −2), S(1, −6)

b) Find the slope of each line segment.

c) Are the line segments parallel, perpendicular, or neither? How do you know?

3. Graph each table of values.

a)

x	y
0	10
1	9
2	8
3	7
4	6

b)

x	y
−2	1
−1	2
0	3
1	4
2	5

4. Rohinton bought 120 g of candies at the bulk-food store for $1.65.

a) How much would 70 g of candies cost?

b) How much candy could he buy for $3.80?

5. Write the equation of the line with each slope, *m*, and *y*-intercept, *b*.

  a) $m = 2, b = -1$ **b)** $m = \frac{4}{3}, b = 3$ **c)** $m = -\frac{1}{2}, b = -5$

6. Graph each line.

  a) $y = 3x - 4$ **b)** $y = \frac{5}{2}x$ **c)** $y = -\frac{2}{3}x + 3$

7. Graph the line through each point with each given slope.

a) C(−3, −1), slope $\frac{5}{3}$ b) D(2, −4), slope −1   c) E(−5, 0), slope 0

8. The cost, C dollars, for a school basketball team to play in a tournament is given by $C = 300 + 20n$, where n is the number of players.

a) Graph the relation.

b) What is the slope of the line? What does the slope represent?

c) What is the C-intercept? What does the C-intercept represent?

9. Evaluate. Express each answer as a fraction, if necessary.

a) 5^2 b) 6^{-1} c) 1^0 d) 4^{-2}

10. Find the square roots of each number.

a) 16   b) 25   c) 64   d) 81   e) 144

11. Calculate the value of x for each triangle.

a)   5 m, 7 m, x

b)   9 cm, 22 cm, x

12. Simplify.

a) $(x + 2) + (x + 7)$ b) $(x^2 − 4x + 1) + (x^2 + 6x − 4)$

c) $(4x − 3) − (2x + 1)$ d) $(3x^2 − 2x − 1) − (x^2 − x + 7)$

13. For each table of data, construct a scatter plot and a line of best fit. Determine the equation of the line of best fit.

a)

Amount spent on advertising ($1000s)	100	200	400	700	140	300	400	600	850	700	800	900
Number of new customers	10	16	28	40	15	25	32	29	49	35	52	58

b)

Distance to school (km)	0.8	1.5	1.2	0.9	1.4	0.9	1.2	0.5	1.3	1.5	0.9	1.5
Time to travel (min)	15	25	22	20	25	10	24	12	23	12	21	30

14. Calculate the volume of each solid.

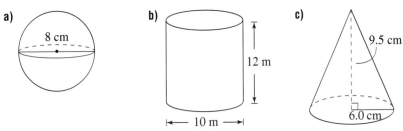

a)   8 cm

b)   12 m, 10 m

c)   9.5 cm, 6.0 cm

15. The table shows the dimensions used in square-based birdhouses.

Species	Entrance diameter (cm)	Side length (cm)	Wall height (cm)
House wren	2.5	6	15
Chickadee Downy woodpecker	3.1	8	20
Bluebird Tree swallow English sparrow	3.8	10	26
Hairy woodpecker Crested flycatcher Starling	5.0	12	31
Common flicker	6.3	15	38
Kestrel	7.5	18	43

a) Why do different birds require different sizes of entrances?

b) Plot a graph of *Side length (cm)* against *Entrance diameter (cm)*.

c) Construct a line of best fit.

d) A red-headed woodpecker needs an entrance hole with a diameter of 4.4 cm. Estimate the side length for a red-headed woodpecker's house.

e) Determine the equation of the line of best fit.

f) Use the equation to estimate the side length for a red-headed woodpecker's house.

g) Compare your answers to parts d and f. Explain any differences.

16. Determine the measure of each indicated angle. Explain your reasoning.

a)   **b)**

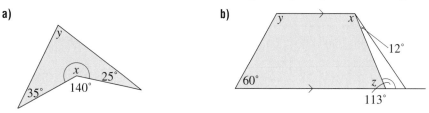

17. Point O is the incentre. Calculate the value of each variable. Explain your reasoning.

a)   **b)**

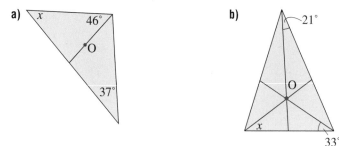

Numeracy Skills Appendix

In this appendix, you will:

- Plan and apply mental mathematics strategies.

- Plan and apply estimation strategies.

- Add, subtract, multiply, and divide with integers.

- Calculate with percent, ratio and rate, and rational numbers.

- Use a scientific calculator.

- Consider whether answers to problems are reasonable.

- Use mental mathematics to decide whether answers obtained from using a calculator and from using pencil and paper are reasonable.

Factors

The *factors* of a number divide into the number with no remainder.

Example

Find all factors of 12.

Solution

To find all the factors, use rectangles.
All the possible rectangles for 12 show all the factors.

$1 \times 12 = 12$ $2 \times 6 = 12$ $3 \times 4 = 12$

The factors of 12 are 1, 2, 3, 4, 6, and 12.

The factors of 9 are 1, 3, and 9.

$1 \times 9 = 9$ $3 \times 3 = 9$

The *common factors* of 12 and 9 are 1 and 3.

The *greatest common factor* of 12 and 9 is 3.

Exercises

1. List all the factors of each number. Draw rectangles if necessary.

   a) 10   **b)** 16   **c)** 6   **d)** 7   **e)** 2   **f)** 15

2. List all the factors of each number.

   a) 24   **b)** 100   **c)** 25   **d)** 8

3. List all the factors of each number. Underline the common factors. Circle the greatest common factor.

   a) 4, 12   **b)** 16, 20   **c)** 8, 12   **d)** 3, 9

4. Find the greatest common factor.

   a) 6, 8   **b)** 12, 24   **c)** 20, 100   **d)** 18, 24

Multiples

Example

List the multiples of 2 and 3.

Solution

The *multiples* of 2 are 2, 4, 6, 8, 10, 12, 14, 16, 18, 20, 24, … .
That is, the results of multiplying 2 by 1, 2 by 2, 2 by 3, and so on.

The multiples of 3 are 3, 6, 9, 12, 15, 18, 21, 24, … .
That is, the results of multiplying 3 by 1, 3 by 2, 3 by 3, and so on.

The *common multiples* of 2 and 3 are 6, 12, 18, 24, … .
The *least common multiple* of 2 and 3 is 6.

Exercises

1. List the first five multiples of 6.

2. Write the next 5 multiples for each pattern.

a) 5, 10, 15, …   **b)** 4, 8, 12, …   **c)** 7, 14, 21, …

d) 10, 20, 30, …   **e)** 100, 200, 300, …   **f)** 25, 50, 75, …

g) 12, 24, 36, …   **h)** 9, 18, 27, …

3. List the first 5 multiples for each number in the pair. Underline the least common multiple.

a) 6, 2   **b)** 3, 4   **c)** 2, 10   **d)** 4, 6

4. Find the least common multiple.

a) 2, 4   **b)** 4, 5   **c)** 4, 8   **d)** 2, 12

e) 3, 8   **f)** 10, 100   **g)** 6, 9   **h)** 8, 2

5. Muffins are sold in packages of a half dozen. How many muffins are in each of these?

a) 1 package   **b)** 2 packages

c) 3 packages   **d)** 4 packages

6. Veggie burgers are sold in packages of 12. Buns are sold in packages of 8. What is the least number of packages you can buy to have the same number of veggie burgers and buns?

The area of Canada is approximately 9 975 360 km^2. The value of each *digit* in this number depends on its position in a place-value chart.

Hundred Billions	Ten Billions	Billions	Hundred Millions	Ten Millions	Millions	Hundred Thousands	Ten Thousands	Thousands	Hundreds	Tens	Ones		Tenths	Hundredths	Thousandths	Ten Thousandths
					9	9	7	5	3	6	0	•				

Example

a) Round 9 975 360 to the nearest thousand.   **b)** Round 0.198 to the nearest hundredth.

Solution

a) Round 9 975 360 to the nearest thousand.

↑ The digit to the right of the thousands place is 3.
Since 3 is less than 5, round down to 9 975 000.

b) Round 0.198 to the nearest hundredth, or 2 decimal places.

↑ The digit to the right of the hundredths place is 8.
Since 8 is 5 or greater, round up to 0.020.

> Record 0 thousandths since the number is rounded to the nearest hundredth.

Exercises

1. In 2001, the population of Canada was approximately 31 081 900. Write the digit in each place value for this population of Canada.

    a) thousands   **b)** ten millions   **c)** hundreds   **d)** millions

2. The length of the largest flea is 1.25 cm. Write the digit in each place value for the length of this flea.

    a) tenths   **b)** ones   **c)** hundredths

3. Round to the nearest whole number.

    a) 19.3   **b)** 127.8   **c)** 14 299.19   **d)** 9.52   **e)** 153.099 8

4. The distance from the sun to Pluto is 5 906 376 200 km. Write the digit in each place value for the distance.

    a) ten thousand   **b)** million   **c)** billion   **d)** hundred million

5. The click beetle has a mass of about 0.009 69 g. Write the digit in each place value for the mass of the click beetle.

    a) thousandth   **b)** hundredth   **c)** ten thousandth

Estimating Sums and Differences

We can use rounding to estimate when we add or subtract.

Example

Estimate each sum and difference.

a) $\begin{array}{r} 44\ 538 \\ +\ 26\ 124 \\ \hline \end{array}$

b) $\begin{array}{r} 0.932 \\ -\ 0.450 \\ \hline \end{array}$

Solution

a) Round to the nearest 10 000.

$\begin{array}{r} 44\ 538 \\ +\ 26\ 124 \\ \hline \end{array}$ Rounds to $\begin{array}{r} 40\ 000 \\ +\ 30\ 000 \\ \hline 70\ 000 \end{array}$

The estimated sum is 70 000.

b) Round to the nearest tenth.

$\begin{array}{r} 0.932 \\ -\ 0.450 \\ \hline \end{array}$ Rounds to $\begin{array}{r} 0.9 \\ -\ 0.5 \\ \hline 0.4 \end{array}$

The estimated difference is 0.4.

In the *Example* part a, we could have rounded to the nearest 1000 or the nearest 100 to estimate the sum.

When you use a calculator, you can use rounding to check.

Exercises

1. Estimate by rounding.

a) $\begin{array}{r} 76\ 384 \\ -\ 55\ 193 \\ \hline \end{array}$
b) $\begin{array}{r} 2719 \\ +\ 5832 \\ \hline \end{array}$
c) $\begin{array}{r} 4047 \\ -\ 1504 \\ \hline \end{array}$
d) $\begin{array}{r} 54.01 \\ -\ 13.42 \\ \hline \end{array}$
e) $\begin{array}{r} 51.6 \\ +\ 52.59 \\ \hline \end{array}$

2. Estimate by rounding.

a) $\begin{array}{r} \$27\ 802 \\ +\ \$60\ 342 \\ \hline \end{array}$
b) $\begin{array}{r} 49.81 \\ -\ 5.45 \\ \hline \end{array}$
c) $\begin{array}{r} 0.62 \\ +\ 0.572 \\ \hline \end{array}$
d) $\begin{array}{r} \$7.70 \\ -\ \$5.05 \\ \hline \end{array}$
e) $\begin{array}{r} 9051 \\ +\ 884 \\ \hline \end{array}$

3. Estimate the amount of each grocery bill. An amount less than $1 is not written with a leading zero.

a)
1% MILK 1L	2.06
STONE GR BRD	2.09
STONE GR BRD	2.09
0.480 kg @ 3.73 /kg	
HH TOMATOES	1.79
JP HAMB BUNS	1.79
PINK SALMON	1.39
MUFFINS CARRI	2.97
ENG CUCUMBER	1.49

b)
0.725 kg @ 2.84 /kg	
WT POTATOES RED	2.06
0.360 kg @ 4.39 /kg	
WT SQUASH ZUCCH	1.58
0.600 kg @ 1.52 /kg	
WT BANANAS	.91
.010 kg @ 3.28 /kg	
WT NAVEL ORANGE	3.31
DELI CHEESE	3.64

Example

a) Add mentally. $5 + 7 + 3 + 100 + 4 + 900 + 1$

b) Add mentally. $296 + 7$

c) Subtract mentally. $104 - 6$

Solution

a) $5 + 7 + 3 + 100 + 4 + 900 + 1$

The sum is 1020.

Think: $5 + 4 + 1 = 10$

$7 + 3 = 10$

$100 + 900 = 1000$

Then: $1000 + 10 + 10 = 1020$

b) $296 + 7$

The sum is 303.

Think: $296 + 4 = 300$

Then: $296 + 7 = 296 + 4 + 3$

$= 300 + 3$

$= 303$

c) $104 - 6$

The difference is 98.

Think: $104 - 4 = 100$

Then: $104 - 6 = 104 - 4 - 2$

$= 100 - 2$

$= 98$

When we find sums of 10, 100, or 1000, as in part a, adding mentally is easy.

To add or subtract a number close to a 100, break the number into parts so that the addition or subtraction is easier.

Exercises

1. Add mentally by first finding sums of 10, 100, or 1000.

   a) $8 + 2 + 4 + 6$ **b)** $5 + 1 + 9 + 5$ **c)** $3 + 2 + 5$

   d) $800 + 200 + 4 + 6$ **e)** $50 + 10 + 90 + 50$ **f)** $300 + 200 + 500$

2. Add or subtract mentally.

   a) $96 + 4$ **b)** $96 + 8$ **c)** $205 - 5$

   d) $205 - 7$ **e)** $103 - 6$ **f)** $689 + 14$

3. Add or subtract mentally.

   a) $610 + 101$ **b)** $405 - 402$ **c)** $7912 - 2301$

   d) $1873 - 412$ **e)** $50\ 002 + 10\ 451$ **f)** $35\ 192 - 12\ 002$

Estimating Products and Quotients

Example

Estimate by rounding.

a) 4.07×5.5

b) $58\,041 \div 82$

Solution

a) 4.07×5.5 Round to the nearest whole number. $4 \times 6 = 24$

The estimated product is 24.

b) $\dfrac{58\,041}{82}$ Round to the nearest 1000. $\longrightarrow$ $\dfrac{58\,000}{80}$ Round to a multiple of 80. $\dfrac{56\,000}{80}$

Round to the nearest 10.

Think: $\dfrac{56}{8} = 7$, so $\dfrac{56\,000}{80} = 700$

The estimated quotient is 700.

Exercises

1. Estimate by rounding.

   a) 75×51 **b)** 58.24×80 **c)** 61.2×4.2 **d)** 705×38

2. Estimate by rounding.

   a) $612 \div 32$ **b)** $437.2 \div 56$ **c)** $81\,735 \div 75$ **d)** $125.81 \div 63$

3. To compensate for rounding one factor up, you can round the other factor down. Estimate by compensating.

   a) 85×65 **b)** 756×57

   c) 1.93×95 **d)** 4.3×7.4

   Round up. $\left(\begin{array}{c} 85 \times 65 \\ 90 \times 60 \end{array} \right)$ Round down.

4. In one second, Earth travels approximately 29.8 km as it orbits the sun. About how far does Earth travel in 1 min?

Example

Evaluate mentally.

a) 80×900

b) $72\,000 \div 80$

Solution

a) Think:

$$80 \times 900 = 8 \times 10 \times 9 \times 100$$
$$= 72 \times 1000$$
$$= 72\,000$$

b) Think:

$$\frac{72\,000}{80} = \frac{72 \times 1000}{8 \times 10}$$
$$= \frac{72}{8} \times \frac{1000}{10}$$
$$= 9 \times 100$$
$$= 900$$

Exercises

1. Use mental math and patterns to find each product.

a) 10×1
100×10
1000×100
$10\,000 \times 1000$

b) 6×7
60×70
600×700
6000×7000

c) 9×30
9×3
9×0.3
9×0.03

2. Use mental math and patterns to find each quotient.

a) $100 \div 10$
$1000 \div 10$
$10\,000 \div 10$
$100\,000 \div 10$

b) $56 \div 8$
$560 \div 8$
$5600 \div 8$
$56\,000 \div 8$

3. Use mental math to evaluate.

a) $64 \times 30 \times 0$ **b)** $1 \times 1 \times 1 \times 1$ **c)** $0 \div 512$ **d)** $0 \div 41 \div 25$ **e)** $823 \times 0 \times 0.734$

4. Use $36 \times 792 = 28\,512$ to evaluate mentally.

a) 792×36 **b)** $28\,512 \div 36$ **c)** 360×792 **d)** $285\,120 \div 36$ **e)** $285\,120 \div 792$

5. Use $25\,434 \div 54 = 471$ to evaluate mentally.

a) $2543.4 \div 54$ **b)** $254.34 \div 54$ **c)** $25.434 \div 54$ **d)** $2.5434 \div 471$ **e)** $254.34 \div 471$

6. Think of the number of quarters in $1 to calculate mentally.

a) 4×25 **b)** 4×0.25 **c)** 8×25 **d)** $100 \div 25$ **e)** $1.50 \div 25$

7. Bamboo can grow 40 cm in a day. Giant bamboo can grow 90 cm in a day. How tall can each type of bamboo grow in a week?

1 m = 100 cm

Integers

Integers are the numbers … −5, −4, −3, −2, −1, 0, +1, +2, +3, +4, +5, …

$$\leftarrow \overset{\;\;-5\;\;-4\;\;-3\;\;-2\;\;-1\;\;\;\;0\;\;\;+1\;\;+2\;\;+3\;\;+4\;\;+5}{|\;\;\;|\;\;\;|\;\;\;|\;\;\;|\;\;\;|\;\;\;|\;\;\;|\;\;\;|\;\;\;|\;\;\;|}\rightarrow$$

Negative integers are less than 0.   *Positive* integers are greater than 0.

−3 and +3 are *opposite* integers.

Example

The highest recorded temperature in Sudbury was 37 degrees above 0°C.
The lowest recorded temperature in Sudbury was 43 degrees below 0°C.
Express each temperature as an integer.

Solution

37 degrees above 0°C is 37 units to the right of 0 on the number line.
So, the highest recorded temperature in Sudbury was 37°C.
43 degrees below 0°C is 43 units to the left of 0 on the number line.
So, the lowest recorded temperature in Sudbury was −43°C.

Exercises

1. Write an integer for each temperature.

a) 8 degrees above 0°C   **b)** 6 degrees below 0°C   **c)** 35 degrees above 0°C

2. Express each as an integer.

a) a decrease of 16°C   **b)** an increase of 1°C

c) a rise of 7°C   **d)** a drop of 9°C

e) Isura earned $25.   **f)** Max spent $109.

3. Write the opposite of each integer.

a) +8   **b)** −2   **c)** −1

d) +24   **e)** +9   **f)** −15

4. Suppose red counters are positive, and blue counters are negative.
Write each integer.

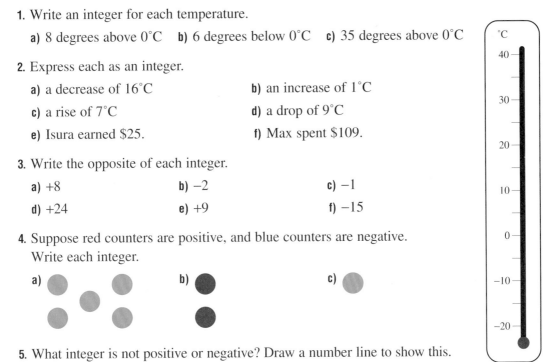

a)   **b)**   **c)**

5. What integer is not positive or negative? Draw a number line to show this.

Adding Integers

Example

Add.

a) $(-5) + (-3)$ **b)** $(-5) + (+3)$

Solution

a) $(-5) + (-3)$

Start at −5. Draw an arrow to represent −3. The arrow ends at −8.

$(-5) + (-3) = -8$

Both integers are negative, so the sum is negative.

b) $(-5) + (+3)$

Start at −5. Draw an arrow to represent +3. The arrow ends at −2.

$(-5) + (+3) = -2$

The integer −5 is farther from 0 than +3, so the sum is negative.

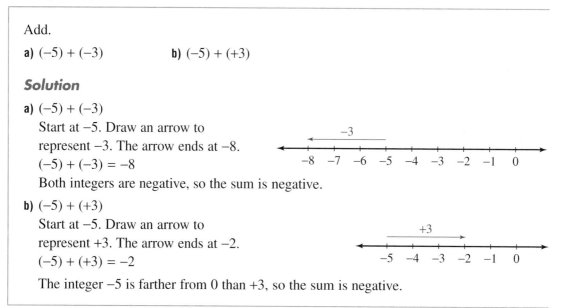

You can check with a calculator.

For $(-5) + (+3)$, press: (−) 5 + 3 (ENTER =)

⌐ ‾5+3

            ‾2 ⌐

Exercises

1. Add. Draw a number line if necessary.

  a) $(+6) + (+2)$ **b)** $(-6) + (-2)$ **c)** $(-6) + (+2)$ **d)** $(+6) + (-2)$

  e) $(+3) + (-3)$ **f)** $(-7) + (+7)$ **g)** $(+2) + (-2)$ **h)** $(-1) + (+1)$

2. Add.

  a) $(+2) + (+5)$ **b)** $(-4) + (+9)$ **c)** $(+8) + (-1)$ **d)** $0 + (-2)$

  e) $(-3) + (-6)$ **f)** $(-7) + (+7)$ **g)** $(-9) + (-5)$ **h)** $(+4) + (-8)$

3. Is each sum positive or negative?

  a) a positive integer + 0

  b) a negative integer + 0

  c) a positive integer + a positive integer

  d) a negative integer + a negative integer

  e) a positive integer + a negative integer, when the negative integer is farther from 0

  f) a positive integer + a negative integer, when the positive integer is farther from 0

Subtracting Integers

Example

Subtract.

a) $(+7) - (-2)$ **b)** $(-7) - (-2)$

Solution

a) $(+7) - (-2)$

Draw an arrow from −2 to +7.
The arrow represents the
difference between +7 and −2.
$(+7) - (-2) = +9$

The arrow shows $(+7) - (-2) = (+7) + (+2)$, or +9.
To subtract integers, add the opposite. The opposite of −2 is +2.

b) $(-7) - (-2)$

Draw an arrow from −2 to −7.
The arrow represents −5.
$(-7) - (-2) = -5$

The arrow shows $(-7) - (-2) = (-7) + (+2)$, or −5.
Check by adding. $(-5) + (-2) = -7$ and $(-2) + (-5) = -7$

You can check with a calculator.
For $(-7) - (-2)$, press: (−) 7 − (−) 2 ENTER =

```
-7--2

        -5
```

Exercises

1. Subtract. Draw a number line if necessary.

  a) $(+3) - (+4)$ **b)** $(+3) - (-4)$ **c)** $(-3) - (-4)$ **d)** $(-3) - (+4)$

2. Subtract by adding the opposite.

  a) $(-1) - (-7)$ **b)** $(-1) - (+7)$ **c)** $(+1) - (-7)$ **d)** $(+1) - (+7)$

3. Subtract.

  a) $(-1) - (+8)$ **b)** $(-4) - (-6)$ **c)** $(+1) - (+3)$ **d)** $(+8) - (-2)$

4. Subtract.

  a) $0 - (-8)$ **b)** $0 - (+4)$ **c)** $(-1) - 0$ **d)** $0 - 0$

5. Temperatures recorded in Australia range from 51°C on January 2, 1960 to −23°C on June 29, 1994. What is the difference between the highest and lowest temperatures?

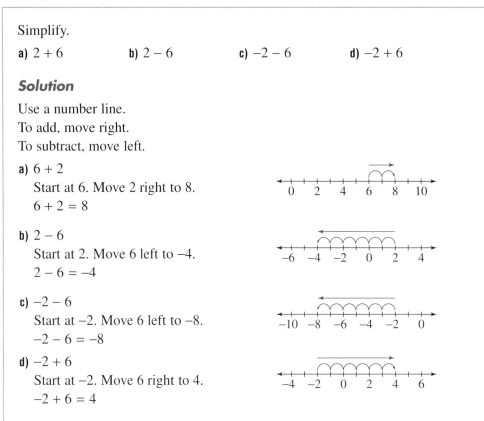

Adding and Subtracting Integers

Example

Simplify.

a) $2 + 6$ **b)** $2 - 6$ **c)** $-2 - 6$ **d)** $-2 + 6$

Solution

Use a number line.
To add, move right.
To subtract, move left.

a) $6 + 2$
   Start at 6. Move 2 right to 8.
   $6 + 2 = 8$

b) $2 - 6$
   Start at 2. Move 6 left to −4.
   $2 - 6 = -4$

c) $-2 - 6$
   Start at −2. Move 6 left to −8.
   $-2 - 6 = -8$

d) $-2 + 6$
   Start at −2. Move 6 right to 4.
   $-2 + 6 = 4$

Exercises

1. Simplify.

   a) $1 + 2$ **b)** $1 - 2$ **c)** $-1 - 2$ **d)** $-1 + 2$

   e) $3 + 1$ **f)** $-3 - 1$ **g)** $-3 + 1$ **h)** $3 - 1$

2. Simplify.

   a) $4 - 5$ **b)** $4 + 5$ **c)** $-4 + 5$ **d)** $-4 - 5$

   e) $5 - 4$ **f)** $-5 + 4$ **g)** $-5 - 4$ **h)** $5 + 4$

3. Simplify.

   a) $5 - 3$ **b)** $-6 + 9$ **c)** $3 - 10$

   d) $-7 - 3$ **e)** $4 + 2$ **f)** $10 - 5$

Multiplying Integers

Recall the rules for multiplying integers.

- When two integers have the same sign, their product is positive.
- When two integers have different signs, their product is negative.

$$(+3) \times (+3) = +9$$
$$(-3) \times (-3) = +9$$
$$(+3) \times (-3) = -9$$
$$(-3) \times (+3) = -9$$

Example

Multiply.

a) $(3) \times (-6)$

b) $(-3) \times (-6)$

Solution

a) $(3) \times (-6)$

The integers have opposite signs, so their product is negative.
$(3) \times (-6) = -18$

b) $(-3) \times (-6)$

The integers have the same sign, so their product is positive.
$(-3) \times (-6) = 18$

You can check with a calculator.

For $(-3) \times (-6)$, press: [(-)] 3 [×] [(-)] 6 [ENTER =]

```
-3*-6
            18
```

A product of integers may be written without a × sign. For example, $(3) \times (-6)$ is written $(3)(-6)$; the brackets indicate multiplication.

Exercises

1. Is each product positive or negative?

a) $(3)(-3)$ **b)** $(-4)(-4)$ **c)** $(-2)(5)$ **d)** $(1)(7)$

2. Multiply.

a) $(1) \times (2)$ **b)** $(-2) \times (1)$ **c)** $(-1) \times (-2)$ **d)** $(-1) \times (2)$

e) $(-10)(3)$ **f)** $(3)(2)$ **g)** $(-1)(-1)$ **h)** $(0)(9)$

3. Write each product. Write the next 3 rows of each pattern.

a) $(-7)(-2)$ **b)** $(4)(1)$ **c)** $(-9)(3)$ **d)** $(4)(-4)$

$(-7)(-1)$ $(3)(1)$ $(-9)(2)$ $(3)(-3)$

$(-7)(0)$ $(2)(1)$ $(-9)(1)$ $(2)(-2)$

4. Use a calculator. Record only the negative answers.

a) $(16)(-32)$ **b)** $(-48)(-25)$ **c)** $(-57)(62)$ **d)** $(-94)(0)$

5. Multiply.

a) $(5)(-7)(-2)$ **b)** $(-8)(0)(-24)$ **c)** $(-3)(-3)(-3)$ **d)** $(-6)(-1)(-9)(1)$

Dividing Integers

The rules for division are similar to those for multiplication.

- When two integers have the same sign, their quotient is positive.
- When two integers have different signs, their quotient is negative.

$$\frac{+8}{+4} = +2 \qquad \frac{-8}{-4} = +2$$
$$\frac{+8}{-4} = -2 \qquad \frac{-8}{+4} = -2$$

Example

Divide.

a) $\dfrac{-42}{7}$ 　　　　　　　**b)** $\dfrac{-42}{-7}$

Solution

a) $\dfrac{-42}{7}$

The signs are different,
so the quotient is negative.

$\dfrac{-42}{7} = -6$

b) $\dfrac{-42}{-7}$

The signs are the same,
so the quotient is positive.

$\dfrac{-42}{-7} = 6$

You can check with a calculator.

For $\dfrac{-42}{7}$, press: (−) 42 ÷ 7 [ENTER =]

```
 -42/7

           -6
```

Exercises

1. Is each quotient positive or negative?

　a) $\dfrac{10}{2}$ 　　　　**b)** $\dfrac{-1}{-1}$ 　　　　**c)** $\dfrac{4}{-2}$ 　　　　**d)** $\dfrac{-6}{3}$

2. Divide.

　a) $\dfrac{24}{6}$ 　　　　**b)** $\dfrac{-24}{6}$ 　　　　**c)** $\dfrac{24}{-6}$ 　　　　**d)** $\dfrac{-24}{-6}$

3. Divide.

　a) $\dfrac{-14}{7}$ 　　　　**b)** $\dfrac{10}{5}$ 　　　　**c)** $\dfrac{-12}{-3}$ 　　　　**d)** $\dfrac{36}{-6}$

4. Divide.

　a) $\dfrac{15}{3}$ 　　　　**b)** $\dfrac{-56}{-8}$ 　　　　**c)** $\dfrac{-16}{4}$ 　　　　**d)** $\dfrac{20}{-5}$

5. Divide. Record only positive answers.

　a) $(-81) \div (9)$ 　　　　　　**b)** $(48) \div (6)$

　c) $(-72) \div (-8)$ 　　　　　　**d)** $(63) \div (-7)$

In a *proper fraction*, the numerator is less than the denominator.
To write a fraction in *simplest form*, reduce the fraction to *lowest terms*.

Example

Write $\dfrac{8}{12}$ in simplest form, or lowest terms.

Solution

Divide the numerator and denominator by the greatest common factor.

$$\frac{8}{12} = \frac{8 \div 4}{12 \div 4}$$

$$= \frac{2}{3}$$

The greatest common factor of 8 and 12 is 4.
So, divide 8 by 4, and divide 12 by 4.

$\dfrac{8}{12}$ and $\dfrac{2}{3}$ are *equivalent fractions*.

You can check with a calculator.

For $\dfrac{8}{12}$, press: 8 ⟨A%⟩ 12 ⟨ENTER ＝⟩

$\dfrac{8}{12}$ of the squares

$\dfrac{2}{3}$ of the rows

```
8 ⌐12

        2/3
```

Exercises

1. Write in simplest form.

a) $\dfrac{4}{8}$ b) $\dfrac{6}{10}$ c) $\dfrac{3}{9}$ d) $\dfrac{10}{100}$ e) $\dfrac{4}{6}$ f) $\dfrac{4}{12}$

2. Write in simplest form.

a) $\dfrac{2}{6}$ b) $\dfrac{10}{20}$ c) $\dfrac{8}{10}$ d) $\dfrac{4}{16}$ e) $\dfrac{4}{12}$ f) $\dfrac{90}{100}$

3. Simplify. Write only the fractions that are not equivalent to $\dfrac{3}{4}$.

a) $\dfrac{6}{8}$ b) $\dfrac{9}{12}$ c) $\dfrac{16}{24}$ d) $\dfrac{12}{16}$ e) $\dfrac{6}{9}$ f) $\dfrac{15}{20}$

4. Simplify.

a) $\dfrac{6}{24}$ b) $\dfrac{25}{100}$ c) $\dfrac{10}{12}$ d) $\dfrac{10}{15}$ e) $\dfrac{8}{16}$ f) $\dfrac{5}{20}$

Improper Fractions

In an *improper fraction*, the numerator is greater than the denominator.
An improper fraction can also be expressed as a *mixed number*.

Example

a) Write $\frac{6}{4}$ in simplest form.

b) Express $\frac{6}{4}$ as a mixed number in simplest form.

Solution

a) Divide the numerator and denominator by the greatest common factor.

$$\frac{6}{4} = \frac{6 \div 2}{4 \div 2}$$
$$= \frac{3}{2}$$

The greatest common factor of 6 and 4 is 2. So, divide 6 and 4 by 2.

b) Divide the numerator by the denominator.

$$\frac{6}{4} = 1\frac{2}{4}$$
$$= 1\frac{1}{2}$$

To write $\frac{2}{4}$ in simplest form, divide the numerator and denominator by the greatest common factor of 2 and 4. $\frac{2}{4} = \frac{1}{2}$

Discuss

In part b, could you have reduced to simplest form, and then changed to a mixed number?

Exercises

1. Write as a mixed number or a whole number.

a) $\frac{5}{5}$ b) $\frac{3}{2}$ c) $\frac{10}{8}$ d) $\frac{4}{3}$ e) $\frac{7}{4}$ f) $\frac{14}{6}$

2. Write in simplest form.

a) $\frac{15}{10}$ b) $\frac{10}{8}$ c) $\frac{2}{2}$ d) $\frac{8}{4}$ e) $\frac{14}{10}$ f) $\frac{24}{20}$

3. Write in simplest form.

a) $\frac{15}{12}$ b) $\frac{6}{6}$ c) $\frac{18}{16}$ d) $\frac{5}{4}$ e) $\frac{18}{12}$ f) $\frac{100}{10}$

Common Denominators

The fractions $\frac{2}{5}$ and $\frac{4}{5}$ have a *common denominator*.

The *lowest common denominator* is the least common multiple of the denominators.

Example

Write $\frac{5}{6}$ and $\frac{8}{9}$ with a common denominator.

Solution

$\frac{5}{6}$ and $\frac{8}{9}$

A common denominator is a common multiple of 6 and 9.
The lowest common denominator is the least common multiple of 6 and 9.

Multiples of 6 are: 6, 12, 18, 24, 30, …
Multiples of 9 are: 9, 18, 27, 36, 45, …

The least common multiple is 18.
Rewrite $\frac{5}{6}$ and $\frac{8}{9}$ with denominator 18.

$$\frac{5}{6} = \frac{5 \times 3}{6 \times 3} \qquad\qquad \frac{8}{9} = \frac{8 \times 2}{9 \times 2}$$
$$= \frac{15}{18} \qquad\qquad\qquad = \frac{16}{18}$$

Exercises

1. Write each equivalent fraction.

   a) $\frac{1}{4} = \frac{\square}{8}$ b) $\frac{5}{8} = \frac{\square}{24}$ c) $\frac{4}{5} = \frac{\square}{10}$ d) $\frac{3}{4} = \frac{\square}{16}$

2. Write an equivalent fraction with denominator 12.

   a) $\frac{1}{3}$ b) $\frac{3}{4}$ c) $\frac{5}{6}$ d) $\frac{1}{2}$ e) $\frac{1}{4}$ f) $\frac{2}{3}$

3. Write the least common multiple for each pair of numbers.

   a) 2, 4   b) 3, 4   c) 3, 2   d) 4, 6   e) 10, 5   f) 5, 4

4. Write each pair of fractions with a common denominator.

   a) $\frac{1}{2}, \frac{1}{4}$ b) $\frac{1}{3}, \frac{7}{4}$ c) $\frac{2}{3}, \frac{3}{2}$ d) $\frac{5}{4}, \frac{1}{6}$ e) $\frac{9}{10}, \frac{2}{5}$ f) $\frac{3}{5}, \frac{3}{4}$

5. Write each pair of fractions with the lowest common denominator.

   a) $\frac{2}{3}, \frac{4}{9}$ b) $\frac{7}{10}, \frac{3}{2}$ c) $\frac{5}{8}, \frac{5}{4}$ d) $\frac{3}{4}, \frac{5}{12}$ e) $\frac{7}{6}, \frac{1}{4}$ f) $\frac{11}{12}, \frac{2}{3}$

Adding Fractions

To add two fractions, their denominators must be equal. Only the numerators are added.

Example

Add.

a) $\dfrac{4}{5} + \dfrac{3}{5}$

b) $\dfrac{2}{9} + \dfrac{1}{3}$

Solution

a) $\dfrac{4}{5} + \dfrac{3}{5}$ The denominators are equal. Add the numerators.

$$\dfrac{4}{5} + \dfrac{3}{5} = \dfrac{4+3}{5}$$
$$= \dfrac{7}{5}$$

b) $\dfrac{2}{9} + \dfrac{1}{3}$ The denominators are different. Find a common denominator.

A common denominator is a number into which 9 and 3 divide.

The lowest common denominator is 9.

Write $\dfrac{1}{3}$ as an equivalent fraction with denominator 9.

$$\dfrac{2}{9} + \dfrac{1}{3} = \dfrac{2}{9} + \dfrac{1}{3} \times \dfrac{3}{3}$$
$$= \dfrac{2}{9} + \dfrac{3}{9}$$
$$= \dfrac{5}{9}$$

You can check with a calculator.

To add $\dfrac{2}{9} + \dfrac{1}{3}$, press: 2 [A⅘] 9 [+] 1 [A⅘] 3 [ENTER =]

```
2 ⌐9+1 ⌐3

          5 / 9
```

Exercises

1. Add.

a) $\dfrac{2}{5} + \dfrac{1}{5}$ b) $\dfrac{3}{7} + \dfrac{2}{7}$ c) $\dfrac{7}{9} + \dfrac{2}{9}$ d) $\dfrac{1}{3} + \dfrac{2}{3}$

2. Add.

a) $\dfrac{1}{2} + \dfrac{5}{8}$ b) $\dfrac{11}{12} + \dfrac{5}{3}$ c) $\dfrac{3}{2} + \dfrac{3}{10}$ d) $\dfrac{5}{6} + \dfrac{1}{3}$

3. Add.

a) $\dfrac{3}{4} + \dfrac{1}{3}$ b) $\dfrac{3}{4} + \dfrac{4}{5}$ c) $\dfrac{7}{6} + \dfrac{1}{4}$ d) $\dfrac{3}{8} + \dfrac{2}{3}$

Subtracting Fractions

To subtract two fractions, their denominators must be equal. Only the numerators are subtracted.

Example

Subtract.

a) $\dfrac{5}{3} - \dfrac{2}{3}$

b) $\dfrac{7}{10} - \dfrac{2}{3}$

Solution

a) $\dfrac{5}{3} - \dfrac{2}{3}$ The denominators are equal. Subtract the numerators.

$$\dfrac{5}{3} - \dfrac{2}{3} = \dfrac{5-2}{3}$$
$$= \dfrac{3}{3}$$
$$= 1$$

b) $\dfrac{7}{10} - \dfrac{2}{3}$ The denominators are different. The lowest common denominator is 30.

Write each fraction as an equivalent fraction with denominator 30.

$$\dfrac{7}{10} - \dfrac{2}{3} = \dfrac{7}{10} \times \dfrac{3}{3} - \dfrac{2}{3} \times \dfrac{10}{10}$$
$$= \dfrac{21}{30} - \dfrac{20}{30}$$
$$= \dfrac{1}{30}$$

You can check with a calculator.

To subtract $\dfrac{7}{10} - \dfrac{2}{3}$, press: 7 ⬚A⅗ 10 ⬚− 2 ⬚A⅗ 3 ⬚ENTER=

```
7⌐10−2⌐3
                1 / 30
```

Exercises

1. Subtract.

a) $\dfrac{5}{2} - \dfrac{3}{2}$ b) $\dfrac{7}{3} - \dfrac{1}{3}$ c) $\dfrac{8}{4} - \dfrac{5}{4}$ d) $\dfrac{6}{5} - \dfrac{1}{5}$

2. Subtract.

a) $\dfrac{3}{2} - \dfrac{1}{4}$ b) $\dfrac{5}{6} - \dfrac{1}{3}$ c) $\dfrac{3}{2} - \dfrac{3}{8}$ d) $\dfrac{4}{3} - \dfrac{5}{9}$

3. Subtract.

a) $\dfrac{1}{3} - \dfrac{1}{4}$ b) $\dfrac{3}{5} - \dfrac{2}{6}$ c) $\dfrac{5}{2} - \dfrac{3}{4}$ d) $5 - \dfrac{3}{8}$

4. How does stating $\dfrac{5}{6} - \dfrac{1}{6}$ as five-sixths subtract one-sixth explain why you subtract the numerators only?

Multiplying Fractions

To multiply fractions, multiply the numerators and multiply the denominators.

Example

Multiply.

$\frac{3}{4} \times \frac{2}{3}$

Solution

$\frac{3}{4} \times \frac{2}{3} = \frac{3 \times 2}{4 \times 3}$

$\qquad = \frac{6}{12}$ Reduce.

$\qquad = \frac{1}{2}$

Exercises

1. Copy and complete.

a) $\frac{1}{5} \times \frac{10}{8}$

$= \frac{\square}{40}$

$= \frac{\square}{4}$

b) $4 \times \frac{3}{5}$

$= \frac{4}{1} \times \frac{3}{\square}$

$= \frac{\square}{5}$

c) $\frac{2}{3} \times \frac{9}{2}$

$= \frac{18}{\square}$

$= \square$

d) $\frac{1}{4}$ of 15

$= \frac{1}{4} \times \frac{15}{1}$

$= \frac{\square}{\square}$

2. Multiply.

a) $\frac{1}{2} \times \frac{1}{4}$ b) $\frac{1}{3} \times \frac{3}{2}$ c) $\frac{3}{4} \times \frac{1}{5}$ d) $\frac{1}{2} \times \frac{1}{2}$ e) $\frac{3}{5} \times \frac{5}{2}$ f) $\frac{2}{3} \times \frac{3}{4}$

3. Multiply.

a) $\frac{1}{8} \times 2$ b) $\frac{7}{3} \times \frac{4}{7}$ c) $10 \times \frac{1}{5}$ d) $\frac{5}{9} \times \frac{2}{5}$ e) $\frac{9}{10} \times \frac{5}{9}$ f) $\frac{3}{8} \times \frac{4}{3}$

4. Multiply. What do you notice about the products? Why does this happen?

a) $\frac{3}{4} \times \frac{4}{3}$ b) $\frac{7}{10} \times \frac{10}{7}$ c) $\frac{1}{2} \times 2$ d) $\frac{5}{8} \times \frac{8}{5}$

5. Calculate.

a) $\frac{1}{2}$ of 10   b) $\frac{3}{4}$ of 28   c) $\frac{2}{3}$ of 15   d) $\frac{1}{8}$ of 20

Dividing Fractions

To divide fractions, multiply by the *reciprocal*. To write the reciprocal, invert the fraction.

Example

Divide.

$$\frac{2}{3} \div \frac{1}{6}$$

Solution

$$\frac{2}{3} \div \frac{1}{6} = \frac{2}{3} \times \frac{6}{1} \qquad \text{Invert the second fraction and multiply.}$$

$$= \frac{12}{3}$$

$$= 4$$

Exercises

1. Copy and complete.

a) $\frac{3}{8} \div 5$

$$= \frac{3}{\square} \times \frac{1}{\square}$$

$$= \frac{\square}{40}$$

b) $\frac{3}{4} \div \frac{9}{2}$

$$= \frac{\square}{\square} \times \frac{2}{\square}$$

$$= \frac{\square}{36}$$

$$= \frac{\square}{6}$$

c) $\frac{7}{10} \div \frac{1}{5}$

$$= \frac{7}{\square} \times \frac{\square}{1}$$

$$= \frac{\square}{10}$$

$$= \frac{7}{\square}$$

d) $6 \div \frac{2}{3}$

$$= \frac{\square}{1} \times \frac{\square}{\square}$$

$$= \frac{\square}{2}$$

$$= \square$$

2. Divide.

a) $\frac{1}{2} \div \frac{1}{4}$ b) $\frac{2}{5} \div 4$ c) $\frac{2}{3} \div \frac{2}{3}$ d) $\frac{2}{9} \div \frac{1}{3}$ e) $\frac{1}{3} \div \frac{3}{2}$ f) $\frac{5}{6} \div \frac{1}{2}$

3. Divide.

a) $5 \div \frac{1}{4}$ b) $\frac{3}{2} \div 2$ c) $\frac{3}{5} \div \frac{5}{2}$ d) $6 \div \frac{3}{4}$ e) $\frac{3}{10} \div \frac{3}{5}$ f) $\frac{3}{5} \div \frac{3}{4}$

4. Divide. What do you notice about the quotients? Why does this happen?

a) $\frac{1}{6} \div \frac{1}{6}$ b) $\frac{2}{5} \div \frac{2}{5}$ c) $\frac{3}{4} \div \frac{3}{4}$ d) $\frac{1}{2} \div \frac{1}{2}$ e) $\frac{7}{3} \div \frac{7}{3}$ f) $\frac{9}{10} \div \frac{9}{10}$

To write a fraction as a decimal, divide the numerator by the denominator.
Use a calculator if necessary.

Example

Write each fraction as a decimal.

a) $\dfrac{100}{6}$ **b)** $2\dfrac{1}{8}$

Solution

a) $\dfrac{100}{6}$

Press: 100 ÷ 6 (ENTER ═)

Draw a bar over the digit that repeats.

$\dfrac{100}{6} = 16.\overline{6}$

```
100/6
       16.66666667
```

b) $2\dfrac{1}{8}$

Consider only the fraction part.
Press: 1 ÷ 8 (ENTER ═)

Write the whole number, 2, then the decimal.

$2\dfrac{1}{8} = 2.125$

```
1/8
       0.125
```

The decimal in part a, $16.\overline{6}$, is a *repeating* decimal.
The decimal in part b, 2.125, is a *terminating* decimal.

Exercises

1. Write each fraction as a decimal.

  a) $\dfrac{1}{2}$ **b)** $\dfrac{3}{5}$ **c)** $\dfrac{3}{4}$ **d)** $\dfrac{1}{50}$ **e)** $\dfrac{9}{50}$ **f)** $\dfrac{2}{25}$

2. Write each fraction as a decimal. Use a bar for repeating
decimals.

  a) $\dfrac{5}{11}$ **b)** $1\dfrac{9}{20}$ **c)** $\dfrac{1}{4}$ **d)** $1\dfrac{2}{3}$

> A bar can be over more
> than one repeating digit.
> $\dfrac{1}{11} = 0.090909...$,
> so write $0.\overline{09}$.

3. Write each fraction as a decimal. Round to 2 decimal places
where necessary.

  a) $\dfrac{10}{9}$ **b)** $\dfrac{17}{10}$ **c)** $\dfrac{1}{8}$ **d)** $\dfrac{7}{29}$ **e)** $1\dfrac{9}{23}$

Decimals to Fractions

To convert a decimal to a fraction, use the place value of the right-most digit in the decimal.

Example

Write each decimal as a fraction in simplest form.

a) 4.5   **b)** 0.32

Solution

a) 4.5 means 45 tenths.

$$4.5 = \frac{45}{10}$$
$$= \frac{9}{2} \qquad \text{Reduce.}$$

b) 0.32 means 32 hundredths.

$$0.32 = \frac{32}{100}$$
$$= \frac{8}{25} \qquad \text{Reduce.}$$

Exercises

1. Write as a fraction in simplest form.

  a) 0.75   **b)** 1.75   **c)** 0.01   **d)** 1.01   **e)** 0.2   **f)** 1.2

2. Write as a fraction in simplest form.

  a) 0.25   **b)** 1.05   **c)** 2.2   **d)** 0.97   **e)** 0.33   **f)** 1.9

3. Write as a fraction in simplest form.

  a) 1.35   **b)** 0.09   **c)** 3.75   **d)** 1.8   **e)** 4.5   **f)** 0.6

4. Choose the fraction or mixed number, from the box, for each decimal.

  a) $0.\overline{4}$ **b)** $0.\overline{3}$ **c)** $0.\overline{36}$ **d)** $0.\overline{27}$

  e) $0.2\overline{7}$ **f)** $0.4\overline{4}$ **g)** $0.\overline{3}$ **h)** $0.3\overline{6}$

$$\frac{1}{3} \qquad \frac{4}{11} \qquad \frac{3}{11}$$
$$\frac{4}{9} \qquad \frac{1}{3}$$
$$\frac{4}{11} \qquad \frac{3}{11} \qquad \frac{4}{9}$$

Ratio

A *ratio* is a comparison of two or more quantities with the same units.

Example

In a band, 3 of the 9 members play the guitar. Write each ratio in simplest terms.

a) guitarists to all band members

b) all band members to guitarists

c) guitarists to other band members

Solution

a) The ratio of guitarists to all members is 3 to 9. This is written as 3 : 9.
To simplify a ratio, divide each term by the greatest common factor. 3 : 9 = 1 : 3

b) Ratio of all band members to guitarists: 9 to 3   In simplest form: 3 to 1
                                            9 : 3   3 : 1

c) Ratio of guitarists to other band members: 3 to 6 or 1 to 2
                                            3 : 6   1 : 2

Exercises

1. Why is the simplest form for all band members to guitarists 3 : 1, and not 3?

2. Write each ratio.

    a) rectangles to circles   **b)** circles to rectangles

    c) rectangles to geometric figures   **d)** circles to geometric figures

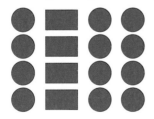

3. Write each ratio in simplest form.

    a) 5 : 10   **b)** 6 : 2   **c)** 8 : 12   **d)** 6 : 12   **e)** 8 : 4   **f)** 4 : 6

4. Write each ratio in lowest terms.

    a) 2 goals to 3 goals   **b)** 4 games to 10 games   **c)** $100 to $50

5. In the 2002 Olympic Winter Games, the Canadian women's hockey team
scored 3 goals while the American team scored 2 goals. What is the ratio
of all goals scored to those scored by Canada?

Rate

A *rate* is a comparison of two quantities with different units.

The speed 55 km/h is a rate. The distance in kilometres is compared to the time in hours.

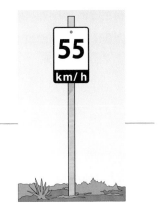

Example

Carole earns $58.50 in 9 h.

a) What is Carole's pay rate?

b) How much does Carole earn in 5 h?

Solution

a) Carole's hourly rate is $\dfrac{\text{earnings}}{\text{time}} = \dfrac{58.50}{9}$

$$= 6.5$$

Carole's pay rate is $6.50/h.

b) In 5 h, Carole earns $5 \times \$6.50 = \$32.50$.

Exercises

1. What is each hourly rate?

  a) $35 earned in 5 h   **b)** $170 earned in 20 h   **c)** $236.25 earned in 35 h

2. How much is earned?

  a) 7 h at $6.25/h   **b)** 10 h at $7.35/h

  c) 18 h at $8.15/h   **d)** 25 h at $6.65/h

3. Whose pay rate is the highest?

  Antonine earns $66 in 8 h.

  Leticia earns $72 in 9 h.

  Keon earns $51 in 5 h.

4. Find each speed.

  a) 300 km in 3 h   **b)** 150 km in 2 h

  c) 920 m in 10 h   **d)** 360 cm in 8 h

5. Which is faster?

  a) 320 km in 4 h or 320 km in 5 h   **b)** 12 km in 3 h or 2 km in 30 min

Percent

Percent means *per hundred* or out of 100. % means percent

Since 60 hundredths of the square are blue, 60% is blue.

Example

Write 60% as:

a) a fraction in simplest form   **b)** a decimal

Solution

a) 60% means 60 out of 100, or $\frac{60}{100}$.

$\frac{60}{100} = \frac{3}{5}$

So, 60% = $\frac{3}{5}$

b) 60% means 60 hundredths or 0.60.
So, 60% = 0.6

Exercises

1. Write the fraction, decimal, and percent that is blue.

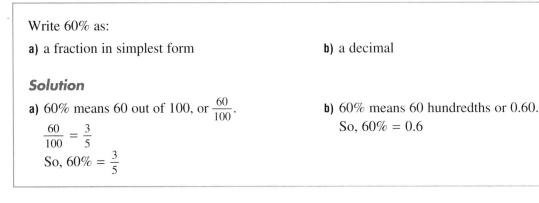

a)   **b)**   **c)**

2. Write each percent as a decimal and as a fraction in simplest form.

a) 71%   **b)** 9%   **c)** 20%   **d)** 25%   **e)** 50%   **f)** 5%

3. Write each percent as a fraction in simplest form and as a decimal.

a) Inhaled air is 21% oxygen, 75% nitrogen, and 4% carbon dioxide.

b) Exhaled air is 16% oxygen, 75% nitrogen, and 9% carbon dioxide.

4. Write each decimal as a percent.

a) 0.1   **b)** 0.2   **c)** 0.45   **d)** 0.7   **e)** 0.75   **f)** 0.95

5. Write each percent as a decimal or whole number.

a) 110%   **b)** 200%   **c)** 115%   **d)** 100%   **e)** 101%   **f)** 309%

Mental Math and Estimation with Fractions and Percent

To estimate fractions, or percents, you can predict whether the result will be close to a known value and whether it will be greater or less than a known value.

Example

a) Express $\frac{9}{20}$ as a percent.

b) Use the result from part a to estimate $\frac{9}{19}$ as a percent. Check the result.

Solution

a) $\frac{9}{20} = \frac{9}{20} \times 100\%$
$\qquad = 45\%$

b)

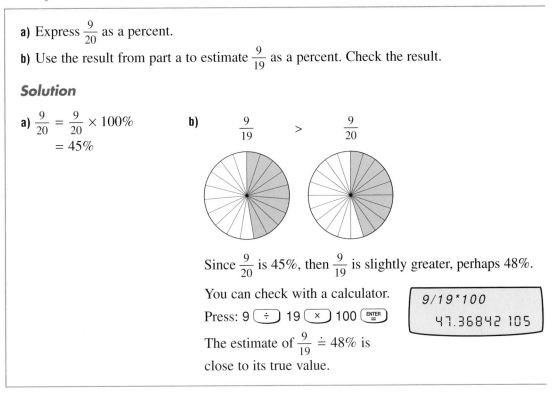

$\frac{9}{19} \qquad > \qquad \frac{9}{20}$

Since $\frac{9}{20}$ is 45%, then $\frac{9}{19}$ is slightly greater, perhaps 48%.

You can check with a calculator.

Press: 9 ÷ 19 × 100 ENTER

9/19*100
47.36842105

The estimate of $\frac{9}{19} \doteq 48\%$ is close to its true value.

In a fraction:

- When denominators are equal, the greater the *numerator*, the greater the fraction.
- When numerators are equal, the greater the *denominator*, the lesser the fraction.

Exercises

1. Order these fractions from least to greatest. Check by using a calculator.

a) $\frac{1}{102}, \frac{1}{100}, \frac{1}{98}, \frac{1}{99}, \frac{1}{101}$ 　**b)** $\frac{22}{23}, \frac{20}{23}, \frac{23}{23}, \frac{19}{23}, \frac{21}{23}$ 　**c)** $\frac{7}{11}, \frac{7}{13}, \frac{7}{10}, \frac{7}{12}, \frac{7}{9}$

2. Use a calculator to express $\frac{43}{67}$ as a percent. Use the result to estimate each as a percent.

a) $\frac{46}{67}$ 　　**b)** $\frac{40}{67}$ 　　**c)** $\frac{43}{70}$ 　　**d)** $\frac{43}{64}$ 　　**e)** $\frac{21}{67}$

3. In the 2002 Winter Olympics, Canada won 6 gold, 3 silver, and 8 bronze medals. What fraction of Canada's medals were gold?

One Number as a Percent of Another Number

To express one number as a percent of another number, use fractions.

Example

a) Write 3 as a percent of 9.

b) Write 3 as a percent of 2.

Solution

a) Write 3 as a fraction of 9. $\qquad \dfrac{3}{9}$

Then write $\dfrac{3}{9}$ as a percent. $\qquad \dfrac{3}{9} \times 100\% \doteq 33.3\%$

3 is approximately 33.3% of 9.

b) Write 3 as a fraction of 2. $\qquad \dfrac{3}{2}$

Then write $\dfrac{3}{2}$ as a percent. $\qquad \dfrac{3}{2} \times 100\% = 150\%$

3 is 150% of 2.

Exercises

1. Write each fraction as a percent. Round to the nearest percent, if necessary.

a) $\dfrac{9}{10}$ **b)** $\dfrac{1}{3}$ **c)** $\dfrac{1}{2}$

d) $\dfrac{8}{8}$ **e)** $\dfrac{7}{20}$ **f)** $\dfrac{3}{4}$

2. Write the first number as a percent of the second.

a) 37, 100 **b)** 9, 10 **c)** 2, 5

d) 11, 11 **e)** 0, 15 **f)** 1, 4

3. Write each fraction as a percent. Round to the nearest percent, if necessary.

a) $\dfrac{4}{5}$ **b)** $\dfrac{7}{7}$ **c)** $\dfrac{1}{6}$ **d)** $\dfrac{9}{15}$

4. a) Alberta, Saskatchewan, Manitoba, and Ontario are the only provinces that do not have any coastline. What percent of the 10 Canadian provinces do not have any coastline?

b) What percent of the provinces have a coastline?

c) Yukon Territory is the only one of the 3 territories that border the United States. What percent of the territories border the United States?

Percent of an Amount

Example

a) Calculate 24% of $356.

b) Calculate 115% of $356.

Solution

a) Write 24% as a decimal.

24% of $356 = 0.24 × $356
         = $85.44

24% of $356 is $85.44.

b) Write 115% as a decimal.

115% of $356 = 1.15 × $356
          = $409.40

115% of $356 is $409.40.

0.24

Use a calculator.

1.15

Use a calculator.

Exercises

1. Calculate. What happens when the amount is 100?

   a) 70% of 100   **b)** 135% of 100   **c)** 0.2% of 100   0.2% = 0.002

2. Calculate. What pattern do you notice?

   a) 100% of 400   **b)** 10% of 400   **c)** 1% of 400   **d)** 0.1% of 400

3. Calculate. Round to the nearest tenth if necessary.

   a) 20% of 160   **b)** 18% of 20   **c)** 0.5% of 720   **d)** 115% of 333

4. A pair of roller blades costs $159.98.

   a) Calculate the Ontario Provincial Sales Tax (PST) on the roller blades.

   b) Calculate the Goods and Services Tax (GST) on the roller blades.

   c) Calculate the total cost.

   d) Multiply the price of the roller blades by 1.15.
   What does the result represent?

Ontario PST is 8%. GST is 7%.

5. Calculate the total cost, including GST and PST, for each amount.

   a) $3.50   **b)** $99.99

   c) $249.99   **d)** $0.10

6. The list price of a DVD player is $479.99.
   What is the cost with taxes for each sale?

Mental Math and Estimation with Percent of an Amount

Example

Estimate the cost of this CD player with taxes.

Solution

Approximate price: $50
GST = 7%, PST = 8%
GST + PST: 15%

To calculate 15%, use 10%, and 5%.
10% of $50 = $5
Since 5% = $\frac{1}{2}$ of 10%, or $\frac{1}{2}$ of $5

Then, 5% of $50 = $\frac{1}{2} \times \$5$
$\qquad\qquad\qquad = \$2.50$

Price with taxes: $50 + $5 + $2.50 $\doteq$ $57.
The cost of this CD player is about $57.

Exercises

1. Is each amount greater than 75, less than 75, or neither?

  a) 102% of 75   **b)** 95% of 75   **c)** 100% of 75   **d)** 9.9% of 75

2. Calculate each percent. If possible, write the answer only.

  a) 1% of 60   **b)** 50% of 60   **c)** 100% of 60   **d)** 200% of 60

3. Refer to exercise 2. Estimate each percent.

  a) 2% of 60   **b)** 49% of 60   **c)** 53% of 60   **d)** 145% of 60

4. Calculate. If possible, write the answer only.

  a) 100% of 35.5   **b)** 50% of 40   **c)** 1% of 800   **d)** 200% of 30

5. What is the approximate cost of each item, including taxes?

  a) running shoes that cost $134.99   **b)** a CD that costs $17.99

6. The regular cost of a camera is $249.99. It is on sale for 15% off.
  Estimate the cost with taxes.

Rational Numbers

A *rational number* is a number that can be written as a fraction. This means that a rational number can also be written as a terminating decimal or a repeating decimal.

A rational number may be positive or negative.

These numbers are rational numbers: $3, -5, \frac{1}{4}, \frac{-3}{2}, 0.34, 0.\overline{2}$

Example

State the rational number for each letter on the number line.

C   B   A
−2   −1   0   1   2

Solution

A is halfway between 1 and 2. So, A is $1\frac{1}{2}$ or 1.5.

B is halfway between 0 and −1. So, B is $-\frac{1}{2}$ or −0.5.

C is halfway between −1 and −2. So, C is $-1\frac{1}{2}$ or −1.5.

Exercises

1. Write the rational number for each letter.

a)
A D   B   C
−2   −1   0   1   2

b)
C   D   B   A
−1   −0.5   0   0.5   1

2. Round each rational number, represented by the dot, to the nearest integer.

a)
−1   −0.5   0

b)
−2   −1.5   −1

3. Round each rational number to the nearest integer.

a) 4.3   b) −1.2   c) 6.7   d) 0.1   e) −3.9   f) −0.2

4. Write in simplest form.

a) $\frac{80}{100}$ b) $-\frac{5}{10}$ c) $-\frac{8}{12}$ d) $\frac{16}{20}$ e) $-\frac{4}{6}$ f) $-\frac{10}{15}$

5. Construct a number line. Mark a dot on the line to represent each rational number.

a) 0.5   b) $2\frac{1}{4}$ c) −3.75   d) $-4\frac{1}{2}$ e) 2.5   f) $-\frac{3}{2}$

Answers

Chapter 1 Relationships

Necessary Skills
Graphing Data
Exercises, page 4

1. a) 40 cm b) 150 cm c) 193 cm d) 70 cm e) 214 cm

2. a) 1.2 m b) 0.86 m c) 0.54 m d) 0.02 m e) 1.97 m

3. a)

Time (h)	0	2	4	6	8
Distance (km)	0	80	160	240	320

Time (h)	10	12	14	16	18
Distance (km)	400	480	560	640	720

Time (h)	20	22	24
Distance (km)	800	880	960

b)

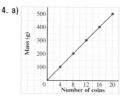

Distances Travelled at 40 km/h

4. a) 240 km b) 440 km c) 820 km
   d) 680 km e) 1040 km f) 1100 km

Reading a Graph
Exercises, page 6

1. a) 3 L b) 11 L c) 26 L d) 27.5 L

2. 185 km

3. a) 1996
   b) 24 000 000; 47 000 000
   c) It was assumed that the graph continues as a straight line.

1.1 Interpreting and Creating Graphs
Exercises, page 10

1. Graphs A, C, and D

2. Graphs A and D

3. a) Graph 2 b) Graph 1 c) Graph 3

5. a) The amount earned increases as the number of hours worked increases.
   b) As time passes, the number of bacteria increases slowly at first, and then more quickly.

c) The ticket cost increases as the number of tickets increases.

d) As time passes, the water remaining decreases slowly at first, and then more quickly.

8. a) 13.7 cm; 1 cm; 13.7 cm
   b) i) 0.3 s; 1.7 s; 2.4 s; 3.7 s; 4.3 s
      ii) 0.5 s; 1.4 s; 2.5 s; 3.4 s; 4.5 s
   c) 2 s

10. Graphs may vary.

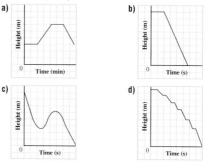

a)   b)

c)   d)

1.2 Investigating Relationships in Data
Exercises, page 19

1. a) Linear. The graph is a straight line.
   b) Non-linear. The graph is not a straight line.
   c) Linear. The graph is a straight line.
   d) Non-linear. The graph is not a straight line.

2. a) Linear. The differences are equal.
   b) Non-linear. The differences are not equal.
   c) Non-linear. The differences are not equal.
   d) Linear. The differences are equal.

3. a)

Difference
24
24
24
24

linear

b)

Difference
−14
−18
−20
−5

non-linear

c)

Difference
3
3
−1
−2

non-linear

4. a)

b) As the number of coins increases, the mass increases. For every 4 coins added, the mass increases by 100 g.
c) 25 g; 450 g

5. a)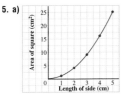

b) As the length of side increases, the area of the square increases. Area of square = (length)²

c) 12.25 cm²   **d)** 4.47 cm

e) No, the area is 4 times as great.

6. a)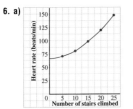

b) As the number of stairs climbed increases, the heart rate increases.

c) 112 beats/min; 90 beats/min

d) 12; 22

e) It would increase more rapidly at the beginning. It would increase less rapidly near the end as you reach your maximum heart rate.

7. a) graph for exercise 3a

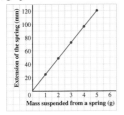

graph for exercise 3b

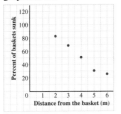

graph for exercise 3c

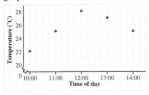

b) 3a: As the mass increases, the extension of the spring increases.

3b: As the distance from the basket increases, the percent of baskets sunk decreases.

3c: As the time increases to noon, the temperature increases. Past noon, the temperature decreases.

9. No.

11. a) This is the distance the car travels from the time the driver thinks of applying the brakes to the time when he/she actually applies the brakes.

b) This is the distance the car travels from the time the brakes are applied to the time the car stops.

c) Join the points with a smooth curve so the in-between values are included on the graph.

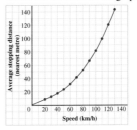

d) 35 m; 72 m

e) It increases the stopping distance.

f) i) The stopping distance would increase. The graph would be steeper.

ii) The stopping distance would decrease. The graph would be less steep.

iii) The stopping distance would increase. The graph would be steeper.

g) weather conditions; driver characteristics

12.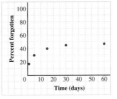

% forgotten = 100% − % remembered

Self-Check 1.1, 1.2

Exercises, page 23

2. Linear. As the Celsius temperature increases by 20°C, the Fahrenheit temperature increases by 36°F.

3. a)

Side length (cm)	1	2	3	4	5	6
Perimeter (cm)	3	6	9	12	15	18

b)

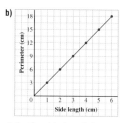

c) As the side length increases by 1 cm, the perimeter increases by 3 cm.

d) Linear. The differences in perimeter are constant. The graph is a straight line.

e) **i)** 10.5 cm **ii)** 12.75 cm **iii)** 1.5 cm **iv)** 2.25 cm

4. c

1.5 Relationships in Proportional Situations
Exercises, page 34

1. a) $3.87 **b)** $6.45 **c)** $25.80 **d)** $15.48

2. a) $1.44 **b)** $2.88 **c)** $4.32 **d)** $9.36

3. a) $1.60 **b)** $2.88 **c)** $0.01

4. a) $0.44 **b)** $0.09 **c)** $1.20

5. a) $4.80 **b)** $0.60 **c)** $1.20 **d)** $9.60

6. a) $0.29 **b)** $3.48

7. a) $1.89 **b)** $18.90; $75.60; $189.00

c)

Number of bottles	1	10	40	100
Cost ($)	1.89	18.90	75.60	189.00

d)

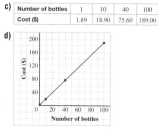

e) Yes. The graph is a straight line through the origin and goes up to the right.

8. a) $0.62/L **b)** $21.70 **c)** 16.1 L

9. a) $127 000; $382 500; $1 020 000

b)

Time (h)	1	3	8
Amount raised ($)	127 000	382 500	1 020 000

c)

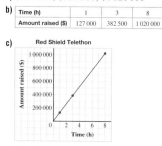

Red Shield Telethon

d) 7 h 51 min   **e)** The graph would be steeper.

f) Yes. The quantities are related by multiplication and division. The graph is a straight line through the origin and goes up to the right.

10. a) $8.20; $73.80; $98.40; $164.00 **b)** 35 h

c)

Time worked (h)	1	9	12	20	35
Amount earned ($)	8.20	73.80	98.40	164.00	287.00

d)

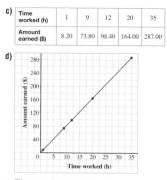

e) The graph would be steeper.

f) Yes. The graph is a straight line through the origin and goes up to the right.

11. a) 250

b) It is assumed that she will hit at a steady rate. This is not realistic.

12. The case of cola is a better value.

13. a) 150 kg

15. It would take approximately 31 s.

1.6 Mathematical Modelling:
Relating Animal and Human Lifetimes
Exercises, page 37

2. a)

Cat's age (years)	1	2	3	4	5
Person's age (years)	7	14	21	28	35

Cat's age (years)	6	7	8	9	10
Person's age (years)	42	49	56	63	70

b) It makes sense to join the points so that the in-between ages are included on the graph.

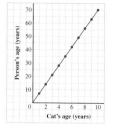

3. a)

Cat's age (years)	1	2	3	4	5
Person's age (years)	21	25	29	33	37

Cat's age (years)	6	7	8	9	10
Person's age (years)	41	45	49	53	57

b)

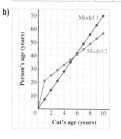

5. a)

Dog's age (years)	1	2	3	4	5
Person's age (years)	15	25	30	35	40

Dog's age (years)	6	7	8	9	10
Person's age (years)	45	50	55	60	65

b)

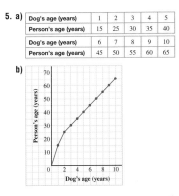

6. Model 1 is a proportional situation. The graph is a straight line through the origin.

Chapter 1 Review

Exercises, page 40

1. a) As time passes, the height of the ball increases, reaches a maximum, then decreases.

b) The amount collected increases as the number of tickets sold increases.

c) As time passes, the temperature rises quickly, then rises more slowly, then decreases.

2. a)

3. For every 2 min the tap is on, the depth of the pond increases by 1 cm.

7. a) $11.99   **b)** $10.97   **c)** $22.98   **d)** $14.99

8. a) $6.75   **b)** $81.00; $162.00   **c)** 32 h

d)

Time worked (h)	1	12	24	32
Amount earned ($)	6.75	81.00	162.00	216.00

e)

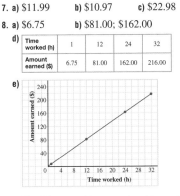

f) Yes. The quantities are related by multiplication and division and the graph is a straight line through the origin.

g) The graph would be less steep.

9. a) black: $1.41; orange: $1.28

b) 3 dozen orange pucks

Chapter 1 Self-Test

Exercises, page 42

2. a)

Width (cm)	1	2	3	4	6	8	12	24
Length (cm)	24	12	8	6	4	3	2	1

b)

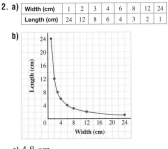

c) 4.8 cm

d) The length decreases as the width increases because the area remains constant.

e) Non-linear. The differences in length are not equal. The graph is not a straight line.

f) No. The quantities are not related by multiplication and division. The graph is not a straight line through the origin.

3. The graph would have a similar shape but would start at (1, 36) and end at (36, 1).

5. a) $1.29; $46.44; $64.50; $129.00

b)

Number of pens	1	36	50	100
Cost ($)	1.29	46.44	64.50	129.00

c)

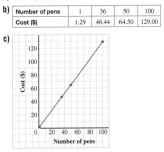

d) Yes. The graph is a straight line through the origin.

e) **i)** The graph would be less steep.
    ii) The graph would be steeper.

Preparation for Ontario Testing

Exercises, page 43

6. Sam: C; Dina: A; Nat: B

Chapter 2 Powers and Roots

Necessary Skills
Powers
Exercises, page 46

1. a) 100   **b)** 1000   **c)** 10 000   **d)** 100 000

2. The number of zeros equals the exponent.

3. a) 625   **b)** 343   **c)** 9   **d)** 100 000

4. a) 36   **b)** 125   **c)** 16   **d)** 1

5. A power with base 1 is always 1, no matter what the exponent.

6. a) 9261   **b)** 4 782 969   **c)** 285 610 000   **d)** 2 476 099

2.1 Powers with Integer and Rational-Number Bases

Exercises, page 50

1. a) −3125   b) 279 936   c) 6857.496
    d) 188.029   e) 0.016   f) 161.384

2. a) $(-2) = -2$ b) $(-2)(-2) = 4$
    c) $(-2)(-2)(-2) = -8$ d) $(-2)(-2)(-2)(-2) = 16$
    e) $(-2)(-2)(-2)(-2)(-2) = -32$
    f) $(-2)(-2)(-2)(-2)(-2)(-2) = 64$

3. a) $\left(-\frac{1}{2}\right) = -\frac{1}{2}$
    b) $\left(-\frac{1}{2}\right)\left(-\frac{1}{2}\right) = \frac{1}{4}$
    c) $\left(-\frac{1}{2}\right)\left(-\frac{1}{2}\right)\left(-\frac{1}{2}\right) = -\frac{1}{8}$
    d) $\left(-\frac{1}{2}\right)\left(-\frac{1}{2}\right)\left(-\frac{1}{2}\right)\left(-\frac{1}{2}\right) = \frac{1}{16}$
    e) $\left(-\frac{1}{2}\right)\left(-\frac{1}{2}\right)\left(-\frac{1}{2}\right)\left(-\frac{1}{2}\right)\left(-\frac{1}{2}\right) = -\frac{1}{32}$
    f) $\left(-\frac{1}{2}\right)\left(-\frac{1}{2}\right)\left(-\frac{1}{2}\right)\left(-\frac{1}{2}\right)\left(-\frac{1}{2}\right)\left(-\frac{1}{2}\right) = \frac{1}{64}$

4. a) 4   b) 7   c) 1   d) 10
    e) −4   f) −7   g) −1   h) −10

5. a) i) 100   ii) −1000   iii) 10 000
    iv) 100 000   v) 1 000 000
    b) The number of zeros equals the exponent.

6. a) i) −3   ii) 9   iii) −27
    iv) 81   v) −243
    b) If the exponent is even, the answer is positive. If the
    exponent is odd, the answer is negative.

7. a) 0.198   c) 0.017   e) −335.544

8. a) $\left(\frac{1}{3}\right)\left(\frac{1}{3}\right)\left(\frac{1}{3}\right)\left(\frac{1}{3}\right) = \frac{1}{81}$
    b) $\left(-\frac{3}{5}\right)\left(-\frac{3}{5}\right)\left(-\frac{3}{5}\right) = -\frac{27}{125}$
    c) $\left(-\frac{10}{3}\right)\left(-\frac{10}{3}\right)\left(-\frac{10}{3}\right)\left(-\frac{10}{3}\right) = \frac{10\,000}{81}$
    d) $\left(\frac{5}{8}\right)\left(\frac{5}{8}\right) = \frac{25}{64}$

9. a) 208.51   b) −24.76   c) 129.75   d) 0.01

10. a) 729   b) −1 953 125   c) 40.841
    d) 0.026   e) 8.352   f) −0.020

11. a) i) 16   ii) −16   iii) −16   iv) 16
    b) The negative sign inside the brackets is part of the base.

12. a) i) 0.015 625   ii) 0.015 625   iii) 0.4096
    iv) 0.4096   v) 0.25   vi) 0.25
    b) i and ii; iii and iv; v and vi; The fraction and the decimal
    are the same.

13. a) i) 65 610 000 years   ii) 31 087 100
    iii) 1 076 890.6 km^2

14. a) $(-2)^1 = -2$ $(-2)^5 = -32$
    $(-2)^2 = 4$ $(-2)^6 = 64$
    $(-2)^3 = -8$ $(-2)^7 = -128$
    $(-2)^4 = 16$ $(-2)^8 = 256$
    b) when n is even   c) when n is odd
    d) when n is odd   e) when n is even

2.2 Multiplying and Dividing Powers

Exercises, page 55

1. a) 2^9 b) 3^7 c) 10^{11} d) 12^{11} e) 7^6 f) 8^8

2. a) 2   b) 3^3 c) 10^7 d) 12^5 e) 7   f) 8^2

3. a) 3^{10} b) 7^{11} c) $(-5)^{25}$ d) 1.5^{12} e) $(-6)^6$ f) $(-2.3)^4$

4. a) 3^5 b) 2^9 c) $(-8)^{15}$ d) 2.1^{10} e) $(-8)^6$ f) $(-1.7)^7$

5. a) $3^8 = 6561$ b) $(-2.1)^7 = -180.109$
    c) $(-5)^5 = -3125$ d) $(-8.6)^2 = 73.96$
    e) $4.6^2 = 43\,581.766$ f) $(-1.25)^8 = 5.960$

6. a) $9^2 = 81$ b) $(-1)^3 = -1$
    c) $(-8.7)^3 = -658.503$ d) $(-0.2)^2 = 0.04$
    e) $6.84^4 = 2188.892$ f) $(-9)^4 = 6561$

7. a) $3^5 = 243$ b) $9^2 = 81$
    c) $(-8)^3 = -512$ d) $(-2.3)^4 = 27.9841$
    e) $2^6 = 64$ f) $7.1^2 = 50.41$

8. a) 9474.297   b) −4.913   c) 571.787
    d) −9493.188   e) 0.008   f) 0.001

9. a) $10^5 \text{ m} \times 10^3 \text{ m} = 10^8 \text{ m}^2$
    b) $\frac{10^9 \text{ m}^2}{10^4 \text{ m}} = 10^5 \text{ m}$

10. $\frac{10^4}{10^2} = 10^2 = 100$ times

11. a) i) 6^7 ii) 6^7 iii) 6^5 iv) 6^2
    v) $(-7)^3$ vi) $(-7)^5$ vii) $(-7)^8$ viii) $(-7)^8$

12. a) $2^1 = 2$ $2^5 = 32$
    $2^2 = 4$ $2^6 = 64$
    $2^3 = 8$ $2^7 = 128$
    $2^4 = 16$ $2^8 = 256$
    b) i) $2^4 \times 2^4 = 2^8 = 256$ ii) $2^5 \times 2^2 = 2^7 = 128$
    iii) $2^8 \div 2^3 = 2^5 = 32$ iv) $2^7 \div 2^5 = 2^2 = 4$

13. a) $\frac{10^{12}}{10^7} = 10^5 = 100\,000$ times   b) $10^{11} \times 10^{11} = 10^{22}$ stars

14. 16 min

15. a) $10^4 = 10\,000$ b) $2^6 = 64$ c) $3^5 = 243$
    d) $(-5)^6 = 15\,625$ e) $6^8 = 1\,679\,616$ f) $(-1)^4 = 1$

2.3 Power of a Power

Exercises, page 59

1. a) 2^2 b) 2^4 c) 2^6 d) 2^8
    e) 2^{10} f) 2^{12} g) 2^{14} h) 2^{16}

2. a) 2^2 b) 2^4 c) 2^6 d) 2^8
    e) 2^{10} f) 2^{12} g) 2^{14} h) 2^{16}

3. They are the same.

4. a) a^8 b) b^{15} c) c^{14} d) d^{12}

5. a) $10^6 = 1\,000\,000$ b) $3^4 = 81$
    c) $4^6 = 4096$ d) $10^8 = 100\,000\,000$

6. a) $5^4 = 625$ b) $4^8 = 65\,536$
    c) $2^{-6} = 0.015\,625$ d) $6^{-2} = 0.0278$

7. a) i) $9^4 = 6561$ ii) $3^8 = 6561$
    b) i) $64^2 = 4096$ ii) $(-2)^{12} = 4096$

8. a) 3^{14} b) 7^{22} c) 8^{-17} d) 29^0

9. a) 6^4 b) 15^2 c) 4^{-6} d) 101^{-3}

10. a) $2^7 \times 2^8 = 2^{15} = 32\,768$ **b)** $2^{12} \times 2^9 = 2^{21} = 2\,097\,152$

  c) $\frac{2^{16}}{2^{11}} = 2^5 = 32$ **d)** $\frac{2^{13}}{2^{10}} = 2^3 = 8$

  e) $(2^6)^3 = 2^{18} = 262\,144$ **f)** $(2^2)^7 = 2^{14} = 16\,384$

11. a) $2^{-3} \times 2^{-4} = 2^{-7} = 0.007\,812\,5$

  b) $2^{17} \times 2^{-7} = 2^{10} = 1024$

  c) $\frac{2^{14}}{2^{-5}} = 2^{19} = 524\,288$

  d) $\frac{2^{-6}}{2^{-5}} = 2^{-1} = 0.5$

  e) $(2^{-2})^3 = 2^{-6} = 0.015\,625$

  f) $(2^{-3})^{-2} = 2^6 = 64$

2.4 Zero and Negative Exponents

Exercises, page 63

1. a) $\frac{1}{2^7}$ **b)** $\frac{1}{3^2}$ **c)** $\frac{1}{4}$ **d)** $\frac{1}{5^8}$ **e)** $\frac{1}{2^9}$ **f)** $\frac{1}{10^3}$

2. a) 3^3 **b)** 4 **c)** 2^7 **d)** 10^6 **e)** 9^8 **f)** 5^5

3. a) $\frac{1}{3}$ **b)** $\frac{1}{2^2} = \frac{1}{4}$ **c)** $\frac{1}{7}$

  d) $\frac{1}{10^5} = \frac{1}{100\,000}$ **e)** $\frac{1}{3^3} = \frac{1}{27}$ **f)** $\frac{1}{6^2} = \frac{1}{36}$

4. a) $2^1 = 2$ **b)** $3^2 = 9$ **c)** $5^2 = 25$

  d) $2^3 = 8$ **e)** $-(4^2) = -16$ **f)** $-(10^4) = -10\,000$

5. a) 5 **b)** 16 **c)** 8 **d)** 1 **e)** 0.67 **f)** 0.694

6. a) i) 1 **ii)** 1 **iii)** 1 **iv)** 1 **v)** 1 **vi)** 1

  b) Anything to the exponent 0 equals 1.

7. a) $0.000\,977$ **b)** 0.0016 **c)** $0.000\,064$

  d) $-0.004\,630$ **e)** $0.161\,506$

8. a) 0.0041 **b)** 16 **c)** 23.3236

  d) 1 **e)** 0.0204 **f)** 1

9. a) 1000 **b)** 100 **c)** 10 **d)** 1

  e) 0.1 **f)** 0.01 **g)** 0.001 **h)** 0.0001

10. a) $64; \frac{1}{64}$ **b)** $64; -\frac{1}{64}$ **c)** $-64; -\frac{1}{64}$

12. $n = -2$ because $(-2)^{-2} = \frac{1}{(-2)^2} = \frac{1}{4}$

13. a) i) 1000 **ii)** 2000 **iii)** 4000 **iv)** 8000

  b) i) 8000 **ii)** $64\,000$ **iii)** $512\,000$ **iv)** $4\,096\,000$

  c) i) 500 **ii)** 250 **iii)** 125

  d) i) 125 **ii)** 63 **iii)** 16 **iv)** 4

14.

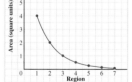

2.5 Scientific Notation

Exercises, page 68

1. a) 6 **b)** -4 **c)** 4 **d)** -8 **e)** 8 **f)** -5

2. a) 3.0×10^8 **b)** 3.0×10^7 **c)** 3.0×10^6 **d)** 3.0×10^5

  e) 3.0×10^4 **f)** 3.0×10^3 **g)** 3.0×10^2 **h)** 3.0×10

3. a) 4.0×10^{-1} **b)** 4.0×10^{-2} **c)** 4.0×10^{-3} **d)** 4.0×10^{-4}

  e) 4.0×10^{-5} **f)** 4.0×10^{-6} **g)** 4.0×10^{-7} **h)** 4.0×10^{-8}

4. a) $500\,000\,000$ **b)** $50\,000\,000$

  c) $5\,000\,000$ **d)** $500\,000$

  e) $50\,000$ **f)** 5000

  g) 500 **h)** 50

5. a) 0.63 **b)** 0.063

  c) 0.0063 **d)** $0.000\,63$

  e) $0.000\,063$ **f)** $0.000\,006\,3$

  g) $0.000\,000\,63$ **h)** $0.000\,000\,063$

6. a) 4.5×10^5 **b)** 2.01×10^2 **c)** 9.3×10^3 **d)** 3.7×10

  e) 5.8×10^4 **f)** 5.79×10^5 **g)** 6.0×10^4 **h)** 1.01×10^6

7. a) 2.9×10^{-3} **b)** 2.5×10^{-6} **c)** 1.8×10^{-5} **d)** 5.4×10^{-1}

  e) 4.8×10^{-6} **f)** 7.0×10^{-3} **g)** 5.1×10^{-4} **h)** 9.9×10^{-7}

9. a) $1.3 \times 10^6 \,°C$ **b)** 1.0×10^{-5} m

  c) $0.000\,000\,000\,000\,000\,000\,000\,000\,000\,92$ g

  d) 4.5×10^9 years   **e)** 5.0×10^{-9} cm

  f) $150\,000\,000$ km^2

10. a) i) 2.5×10^{12} **ii)** 6.25×10^{-10}

  b) i) 3.125×10^{-16} **ii)** 4.0×10^{24}

  c) i) $4.333\,33 \times 10^{22}$ **ii)** 5×10^{-40}

11. 15 is not between 1 and 10.

12. a) 1.2×10^3 **b)** 2.7×10^5 **c)** 4.0×10^2 **d)** 2.4×10^{-1}

  e) 7.0×10^{-4} **f)** 1.48×10^{-5} **g)** 1.36×10^4 **h)** 1.88×10^{-5}

  i) 1.8×10^3 **j)** 1.42×10^7 **k)** 1.6×10^{-1} **l)** 2.36×10^{-4}

13. a) $180\,000$ **b)** $29\,000$

  c) $33\,000\,000$ **d)** $4\,400\,000\,000$

  e) 0.16 **f)** 0.084

  g) $0.000\,224$ **h)** $0.000\,018\,8$

  i) $0.000\,000\,000\,241$ **j)** $1\,870\,000$

  k) $0.003\,02$ **l)** 0.216

14. a) 5.194×10^{24} **b)** 2.1358×10^{-16}

  c) 4.8×10^{-4} **d)** 3.9872×10^{-12}

15. a) 1.2×10^{16} **b)** 1.274×10^{16}

  c) 1.344×10^0 **d)** 1.328×10^{-34}

16. a) 5×10^3 **b)** 5×10^5 **c)** 5×10^6 **d)** 5×10^9

17. a) 2.773×10^{-2} **b)** 4.4125×10^{13}

  c) 1.56×10^{13} **d)** 2.0×10^{-10}

18. a) 2.53×10^2 **b)** 2.727×10^{-9}

  c) 1.06×10^{-3} **d)** 8.5×10^{-25}

19. a) 2.0×10^4; 8.0×10^9 **b)** 4.0×10^5 cm^2

  c) 4.0×10 m^2; The result is not reasonable.

20. a) $602\,200\,000\,000\,000\,000\,000\,000$

  b) 5.0×10^{-4} mm   **c)** 1.98×10^{30} kg

21. 9.4608×10^{12} km

22. 1.0×10^{-9} g; 2.0×10^{-3} mm

Self-Check 2.1–2.5

Exercises, page 71

1. a) $\left(\frac{7}{10}\right)\left(\frac{7}{10}\right) = \frac{49}{100}$

  b) $\left(-\frac{3}{8}\right)\left(-\frac{3}{8}\right)\left(-\frac{3}{8}\right)\left(-\frac{3}{8}\right) = \frac{81}{4096}$

  c) $\left(\frac{5}{6}\right)\left(\frac{5}{6}\right)\left(\frac{5}{6}\right)\left(\frac{5}{6}\right)\left(\frac{5}{6}\right) = \frac{3125}{7776}$

  d) $\left(-\frac{2}{11}\right)\left(-\frac{2}{11}\right)\left(-\frac{2}{11}\right) = -\frac{8}{1331}$

2. a) −100 000   **b)** 610.352   **c)** 531 441
   d) −0.059   **e)** 0.735

3. a) $4^4 = 256$ **b)** $(-7)^1 = -7$
   c) $5.1^8 = 457\,679.446$ **d)** $(-5.4)^2 = 29.16$

4. a) $2^6 = 64$ **b)** $7^4 = 2401$
   c) $1.6^8 = 42.950$ **d)** $(-2.1)^0 = 1$

5. a) $\frac{1}{7^5}$ **b)** 6^3 **c)** 2^9 **d)** $\frac{1}{8^6}$ **e)** 7^4

6. a) 0.000 064   **b)** 0.070 430   **c)** 0.16
   d) 1   **e)** 0.004 630

7. a) 1.3×10^5 **b)** 2.9×10^{-4} **c)** 4.5×10^6 **d)** 9.92×10^{-2}

8. a) 750 000   **b)** 0.008
   c) 1 020 000   **d)** 0.000 000 923

9. a) 1.4664×10^{12} **b)** 4.98×10^{-10}
   c) 8.33×10^2 **d)** 4.829×10^{-11}

10. b

2.6 Squares and Square Roots

Exercises, page 74

1. a) 16   **b)** 64   **c)** 1   **d)** 81   **e)** 196

2. a) 36 cm²   **b)** 0 cm²   **c)** 100 cm²   **d)** 49 cm²

3. a) 2 cm   **b)** 1 cm   **c)** 5 cm   **d)** 3 cm

4. a) 2, −2   **b)** 3, −3   **c)** 7, −7   **d)** 9, −9   **e)** 1, −1

5. a) 8, −8   **b)** 5, −5   **c)** 10, −10   **d)** 4, −4   **e)** 6, −6

6. a) 2.2, −2.2   **b)** 3.2, −3.2   **c)** 7.1, −7.1   **d)** 8.7, −8.7   **e)** 1.4, −1.4

7. a) 7.7, −7.7   **b)** 5.5, −5.5   **c)** 9.7, −9.7   **d)** 3.9, −3.9   **e)** 6.3, −6.3

8. a) 4   **b)** 2   **c)** 8   **d)** 6   **e)** 10

9. a) 3   **b)** 7   **c)** 9   **d)** 1   **e)** 5

10. The square roots of a number are both positive and negative. The radical sign means only the positive root.

11. a) 8.7   **b)** 9.3   **c)** 10.8   **d)** 11.8   **e)** 6.7   **f)** 10.2

12. a) 12   **b)** 120   **c)** 1200   **d)** 1.2   **e)** 0.12   **f)** 0.012

13. a) 10.24 cm²   **b)** 116.64 m²
   c) 0.01 cm²   **d)** 90 000 m²

14. a) 20 cm   **b)** 0.5 m   **c)** 9.5 cm
   d) 12.2 cm   **e)** 17.3 cm   **f)** 158.1 m

15. a) 1517 cm   **b)** 60.7 m

16. a) i) 229 m   **ii)** 90 km   **iii)** 101 m

18. a) i) 1732.05   **ii)** 173.205   **iii)** 17.3205
   iv) 1.732 05   **v)** 0.173 205   **vi)** 0.017 320 5
   b) The decimal shifts 1 place to the left each time.

19.

quadrant 1: (7, 0); (7, 7); (0, 7)

quadrant 2: (0, 7); (−7, 7); (−7, 0)
quadrant 3: (−7, 0); (−7, −7); (0, −7)
quadrant 4: (0, −7); (7, −7); (7, 0)

20. The calculator displays an error message because there is no square root of a negative number.

2.7 The Pythagorean Theorem

Exercises, page 79

1. a) b **b)** c **c)** c **d)** a

2. a) 5 cm   **b)** 13 cm   **c)** 20 cm

3. a) 8 cm   **b)** 24 cm   **c)** 20 cm

4. a) 9 cm   **b)** 30 cm   **c)** 15 cm

5. a) 6.4 cm   **b)** 17.9 cm   **c)** 5.7 cm
   d) 5.9 cm   **e)** 32.6 cm   **f)** 77.5 cm

6. a) 5 cm   **b)** 13 cm

7. a) 8.7 cm   **b)** 7.2 cm   **c)** 2.5 cm   **d)** 2.9 cm

8. a) 7.1 cm   **b)** 11.2 cm   **c)** 15.8 cm

9. a) 5.8 units   **b)** 7.3 units

10. AB: 3 units   CD: 5.7 units   EF: 6.7 units
   GH: 7.1 units   IJ: 5.8 units

11. a) 4.5 units   **b)** 2.8 units

   c) 6.4 units   **d)** 3.2 units

   e) 34.2 units   **f)** 3.6 units

12. b) JK: 5.1 units   KL: 4.5 units   JL: 7.6 units

13. a) length = 5.7 units; width = 2.8 units

   b) 15.96 square units   **c)** 6.3 units

14. a) 35 cm

15. a) i) 20 m   **ii)** 3879 cm   **iii)** 32 m   **iv)** 67 m

17. approx. 4.6 m

2.8 Mathematical Modelling: How Thick Is the Pile of Paper?

Exercises, page 83

2.

Number of folds	Number of layers
0	1
1	2
2	4
3	8
4	16
5	32
6	64

3. a) 8 **b)** $\frac{1}{8}$ mm

4. a) $2^{10} = 1024$ **b)** 128 mm

5. a) $2^{50} \doteq 1.126 \times 10^{15}$ **b)** about 1.408×10^{8} km
c) distance to the sun

6. a) 216 mm by 279 mm **b)** 60 264 mm^2

c)

Number of folds, f	Number of layers, l	Area of top layer, a (mm²)
0	1	60 264
1	2	30 132
2	4	15 066
3	8	7533
4	16	3766.5
5	32	1883.25
6	64	941.625

7. 58.85 mm^2

8. a) 5.35×10^{-11} mm^2 **b)** area of a pit in a CD track

9. It is assumed that the area of each layer is identical and that no area is "lost" in the folds.

10. a)

b) No, because there cannot be partial folds or layers.
c) Non-linear. The graph is not a straight line.
d) With each additional fold, the number of layers doubles.

11. a)

b) No, because there cannot be partial folds.
c) Non-linear. The graph is not a straight line.
d) With each additional fold, the area of the top layer is divided in half.

Chapter 2 Review

Exercises, page 87

1. a) $(1.4)(1.4)(1.4) = 2.744$
b) $(-8)(-8)(-8)(-8)(-8) = -32\,768$
c) $\left(-\frac{5}{8}\right)\left(-\frac{5}{8}\right) = 0.390\,625$
d) $(-2.6)(-2.6)(-2.6)(-2.6) = 45.6976$

2. a) -5.832 **b)** 16 **c)** 33.178
d) -0.729 **e)** 12.25 **f)** -0.8

3. a) 10 000 **b)** 1 000 000
c) 100 **d)** 1 000 000 000

4. a) 9 **b)** 4

6. a) -0.125 **b)** -0.125 **c)** -0.125 **d)** -0.125

7. a) 0.3164 **b)** 0.3164 **c)** 0.3164 **d)** 0.3164

8. a) 3^7 **b)** $(-2)^7$ **c)** 2^8 **d)** $(-15)^5$

9. a) 4^2 **b)** 3^2 **c)** 12 **d)** 16

10. a) $(-1)^4 = 1$ **b)** $3.2^8 = 10\,995.116$
c) $(-0.8)^2 = 0.64$ **d)** $6.25^5 = 9536.743$
e) $10^7 = 10\,000\,000$ **f)** $(-1.5)^3 = -3.375$

11. a) $8^4 = 4096$ **b)** $(-7)^1 = -7$
c) $(-1.6)^3 = -4.096$ **d)** $(-5.4)^2 = 29.16$
e) $(-0.9)^4 = 0.656$ **f)** $1.25^1 = 1.25$

12. a) 3^{10} **b)** 3^{20} **c)** 3^{-6} **d)** 3^0

13. a) m^{15} **b)** m^{12} **c)** m^5 **d)** m^{-6}

14. a) $2^6 = 64$ **b)** $(-4)^4 = 256$ **c)** $(-5)^0 = 1$ **d)** $3^6 = 729$

15. a) $\frac{1}{5^3}$ **b)** 4^2 **c)** $\frac{1}{6^4}$ **d)** 10^3 **e)** $\frac{1}{2^5}$ **f)** 3^6

16. a) 0.0010 **b)** -0.0046 **c)** 0.5556
d) 0.0865 **e)** 0.0016 **f)** -0.0723

17. a) 1 **b)** 1 **c)** 1 **d)** 1 **e)** 1 **f)** 1

18. a) 6.4×10^4 **b)** 4.5×10^{-3} **c)** 6.0×10^{-6}
d) 7.25×10^9 **e)** 4.0×10^5 **f)** 8.0×10^{-2}

19. a) 480 000 000 **b)** 0.000 731 **c)** 0.000 003
d) 107 **e)** 0.000 000 006 1 **f)** 0.000 080 2

20. If the zero placeholders come before the number, use a negative exponent. If the zero placeholders come after the number, use a positive exponent.

21. a) 3.2×10^{-2} **b)** 7.733×10^{11}
c) 2.7738×10^{-5} **d)** 2.698×10^{-3}

22. a) 8.875×10^{-11} **b)** 2.8736×10^3

23. 5.0×10^{-9} g

24. a) 0.000 000 000 000 000 000 000 000 000 911 g
b) 0.000 000 000 000 000 000 000 001 67 g

25. a) 8, -8 **b)** 2, -2 **c)** 6, -6 **d)** 12, -12 **e)** 1, -1

26. a) 3 **b)** 4 **c)** 10 **d)** 5 **e)** 11 **f)** 100

27. a) 8.9, -8.9 **b)** 5, -5 **c)** 9.9, -9.9
d) 12.2, -12.2 **e)** 9.1, -9.1 **f)** 14.5, -14.5

28. a) 4.5 **b)** 8.1 **c)** 13.4 **d)** 35.4 **e)** 30.8

29. a) 28 cm **b)** 49 cm

30. a) 8.9 cm **b)** 7.4 cm

31. a) 8.5 cm **b)** 13.4 cm

32. a) 5.8 units **b)** 6.7 units

c) 8.5 units

33. a) Yes. $h^2 = a^2 + b^2$

Chapter 2 Self-Test
Exercises, page 90

1. a) 2401   **b)** -0.4019 **c)** 1
   d) 0.0069   **e)** 0.0467   **f)** 1

2. a) $8^5 = 32\,768$ **b)** $(-1.4)^5 = -5.378$
   c) $5^4 = 625$ **d)** $(-10)^{11} = -100\,000\,000\,000$

3. a) 2.01×10^5 **b)** 9.0×10^{-4} **c)** 7.352×10^5 **d)** 7.8×10^{-6}

4. a) 0.000 009   **b)** 340 000 000
   c) 1 650 000 000   **d)** 0.000 822

5. If the exponent is positive, the number is large. If the exponent is negative, the number is small.

6. a) 7.6×10^{-1} **b)** 2.2075×10^4

7. a) 3.9, -3.9 **b)** 10, -10 **c)** 7.1, -7.1
   d) 1, -1 **e)** 9.1, -9.1

8. a) 8   **b)** 6.5   **c)** 11.0   **d)** 9   **e)** 2.4

9. a) 7.2 cm   **b)** 8.1 cm

10. a) The 6.0 m side, because it's the longest.
   b) Yes. $3.6^2 + 4.8^2 = 6.0^2$

11. The lengths of the diagonals double.

Preparation for Ontario Testing
Exercises, page 91

12. $A = lw$
$$= (2.8 \times 10^{-5} \text{ cm}) \times (1.6 \times 10^{-5} \text{ cm})$$
$$= 4.48 \times 10^{-10} \text{ cm}^2$$

Chapter 3 Algebra

Necessary Skills
Solving Equations by Inspection
Exercises, page 94

1. a) $x = 7$ **b)** $m = 5$ **c)** $a = 6$
   d) $n = 7$ **e)** $x = 17$ **f)** $m = 2$
   g) $a = 24$ **h)** $n = 2$

2. a) $a = 8$ **b)** $n = 8$ **c)** $x = 5$
   d) $m = 6$ **e)** $n = 6$ **f)** $x = 15$
   g) $m = 32$ **h)** $a = 9$

Writing Simple Equations
Exercises, page 95

1. a) $n + 2 = 9$ **b)** $n - 5 = 11$
   c) $12 - n = 6$ **d)** $n + 8 = 20$

2. a) $n = 7$ **b)** $n = 16$
   c) $n = 6$ **d)** $n = 12$

3. a) $5n = 20$ **b)** $\frac{n}{3} = 12$
   c) $4n = 28$ **d)** $\frac{n}{2} = 7$

4. a) $n = 4$ **b)** $n = 36$
   c) $n = 7$ **d)** $n = 14$

3.1 Representing Variables and Expressions
Exercises, page 99

1. $25(5 + 10)$; $(25 \times 5) + (25 \times 10)$

2. a) $15 + 21$ **b)** $114 - 54$
   c) $-20 + 30$ **d)** $12 + 42 + 6$
   e) $6 - 3 + 27$ **f)** $-20 - 25 + 10$

3. a) $-2x - 1$ **b)** $-2x + 1$
   c) $2x - 1$ **d)** $2x + 1$
   e) $-1 - 2x$ **f)** $-1 + 2x$

5. a) $4 - 3x$ **b)** $2 - 2x$
   c) $3x - 7$ **d)** $-2x - 3$

6. a) $-4 + 3x$ **b)** $-2 + 2x$
   c) $-3x + 7$ **d)** $2x + 3$

7. a) $15 + 24$ **b)** $30 - 20$
   c) $55 - 77$ **d)** $-48 + 24$
   e) $60 - 72$ **f)** $-28 + 36$
   g) $13 + 13h$ **h)** $88 - 8d$

8. a) $20 + 50 + 10$ **b)** $44 - 20 - 8$
   c) $36 + 45 - 72$ **d)** $-72 + 16 - 64$

9. a)

10. a)

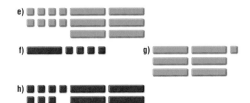

e)

f)

g)

h)

11. b; Expand using the distributive law.

12. a) i) $5k + 5$ **ii)** $6 - 4w$ **iii)** $8m + 4$
   iv) $-4 - 5y$ **v)** $-6 + 3p$ **vi)** $3 - 9b$
   vii) $-8t + 10$ **viii)** $-8s - 8$

   b) If you are multiplying 2 terms with the same sign, the answer will be positive. If the signs are different, the answer will be negative.

13. a) $3x + 2; 2 + 3x$ **b)** $-5g + 4; 4 - 5g$
   c) $7 - 2j; -2j + 7$ **d)** $-3 - 5b; -5b - 3$

14. b; Expand using the distributive law.

15. a) $3x + 6y - 21$ **b)** $-2a + 10b - 4$
   c) $-6m + 7n$ **d)** $36p + 4q - 36r$
   e) $5x + 30y - 20$ **f)** $21c - 27 + 3d$

16. a) $ab + 5b + 3a + 15; (a + 5)(b + 3); 5(b + 3) + a(b + 3);$
    $b(a + 5) + 3(a + 5)$

   b) When expanded using the distributive law, the last 3 expressions equal the first.

17. a) Always true   **b)** Always true
   c) Sometimes true

3.2 Combining Like Terms
Exercises, page 105

1. a, d, f, g

2. $2x, x; -3y, -y; 5w, 4w; 3, -1; 5z, -2z$

3. $2a, a, -2a$ **4.** $5, -9, 0, -1, 4$

5. $3, -8, 0, 10, -1$ **6.** $-s, 2y, 7m, -3a, 4x, n$

7. a) $2x + 5$ **b)** $-x + 4$ **c)** $3x - 3$

8. a) 0 **b)** 16 **c)** 0
   d) 0 **e)** 0 **f)** $-6b$

9. a) -7 **b)** 9 **c)** -9

10. a) $9s$ **b)** $2v$ **c)** b
   d) $9p$ **e)** $-9c$ **f)** $8t + 5$

11. a) $5 - 5a$ **b)** $-n + 6$ **c)** $9 - d$
   d) $5u - 3$ **e)** $2k$ **f)** $-7q - 7$

12. a) $4x$ **b)** $-2a$ **c)** $-8 + 2c$
   d) $2k - 1$ **e)** $13b + 5$ **f)** $-10u - 3$

13. a) 2 **b)** s **c)** 0
   d) $3a$ **e)** $-3 + y$ **f)** 2

15. a) $3x - 2; -2$ **b)** $5x - 3; -3$
   c) $1 + x; 1$ **d)** $5x + 3; 3$
   e) $3x + 1; 1$ **f)** $-9 - x; -9$

16. a) $-9x + 12; 3$ **b)** $-3x - 4; -7$
   c) $17x - 52; -35$ **d)** $21 - 5x; 16$
   e) $17x - 18; -1$ **f)** $10x + 12; 22$

17. a) $6x - 2; -20$ **b)** $-x - 2; 1$
   c) $4x - 9; -21$ **d)** $-5x + 21; 36$
   e) $14x - 6; -48$ **f)** $-31 + 10x; -61$

18. a) $11a - 3; 30$ **b)** $4m + 21; -7$
   c) $14s + 30; 30$ **d)** $14x - 3; 25$

19. a) $3x - 1$ **i)** 20 **ii)** -7
   b) $2x - 8$ **i)** 6 **ii)** -12
   c) $-5x + 6$ **i)** -29 **ii)** 16
   d) $2x + 12$ **i)** 26 **ii)** 8
   e) $-5x + 14$ **i)** -21 **ii)** 24
   f) $-13x + 11$ **i)** -80 **ii)** 37

20. Simplifying first makes the equation easier to solve.

21. a) $12a - 10$ **b)** $-15m - 5$
   c) $15s + 8$ **d)** $3x - 2$
   e) $2p - 11$ **f)** $-47g + 7$

22. a) $6m - 12$ **b)** $-3a + 10$
   c) $-4x - 2$ **d)** $s + 10$
   e) $-20d - 36$ **f)** $4q - 39$

23. a) i) $2 + 3x$ **ii)** $-6v + 3$
   iii) Not possible; There is only one term, so there is nothing to simplify.

24. a) $P = 2(x + 3)$ **b)** $P = 2(2x + x)$
      $= 2x + 6$ $= 6x$

3.3 Solving Equations Algebraically
Exercises, page 111

1. a) $a = 3$ **b)** $v = 5$ **c)** $c = 8$
   d) $b = -6$ **e)** $n = 8$ **f)** $s = 7$
   g) $j = -5$ **h)** $x = 4$

2. a) $t = 9$ **b)** $k = -5$
   c) $b = -2$ **d)** $s = -7$

3. a) $j = 3$ **b)** $p = -5$ **c)** $s = -3$
   d) $c = 3$ **e)** $p = 3$ **f)** $a = 2$
   g) $v = 5$ **h)** $t = 5$

4. a) not correct   **b)** correct   **c)** correct
   d) correct   **e)** not correct   **f)** correct
   g) not correct   **h)** not correct

5. a) $v = 3$ **b)** $j = 3$ **c)** $p = 4$
   d) $c = 7$ **e)** $q = 4$ **f)** $h = -9$
   g) $g = -\frac{3}{5}$ **h)** $c = 11$

6. a) $x = -7$ **b)** $a = 7$ **c)** $y = -5$
   d) $p = -2$ **e)** $z = 7$ **f)** $f = -\frac{7}{3}$

7. a) $x = -8$ **b)** $m = 4$ **c)** $e = \frac{1}{6}$
   d) $c = 3$ **e)** $b = \frac{4}{3}$ **f)** $b = 3$

8. a) $x = 4$ **b)** $a = \frac{20}{3}$ **c)** $z = \frac{3}{5}$
   d) $m = -\frac{9}{2}$ **e)** $x = -\frac{1}{2}$ **f)** $k = 3$

9. a) $x = \frac{36}{5}$ **b)** $a = \frac{4}{3}$ **c)** $x = \frac{1}{3}$
   d) $c = -\frac{6}{5}$ **e)** $a = \frac{5}{9}$ **f)** $n = 0$

10. a) $S = 101$ **b)** $n = 7$

11. a) i) 90 km   **ii)** 270 km   **iii)** 450 km   **iv)** 540 km
   b) i) 2 h   **ii)** $2\frac{1}{2}$ h   **iii)** 4 h   **iv)** $3\frac{1}{2}$ h

c) It was assumed that Callum continued to drive at 90 km/h, and that he made no stops.

12. a) 8000 is the fixed cost of production, in dollars. $9n$ is the variable cost, in dollars, that depends on the number of yearbooks printed.
b) $n = 222$ **c)** 1333

13. a) $10d$ is the temperature, in degrees Celsius, that varies with depth. 20 is the temperature, in degrees Celsius, of Earth's surface.
b) $d = 3$
c) i) 4 km **ii)** 7 km **iii)** 6 km **iv)** 5 km
d) 8 km
e) 3 km; 4 km; 5 km; 6 km; 7 km; 8 km

14. a) 90 m **b)** 145 m

16. a) "the same number" **b)** 3 cm
c) $P = 18\,\text{cm}; A = 18\,\text{cm}^2$

3.4 Simplifying Equations before Solving
Exercises, page 116

1. a) $b = -6$ **b)** $t = 10$ **c)** $q = -\frac{1}{5}$
d) $j = -2$ **e)** $k = -3$ **f)** $s = 9$

2. a) $x = -2$ **b)** $x = 7$
c) $x = -\frac{4}{3}$ **d)** $x = \frac{6}{5}$

3. a) $c = 4$ **b)** $y = -6$
c) $x = -4$ **d)** $n = 4$

4. a) $x = 1$ **b)** $x = 1$ **c)** $x = 1$
d) $x = 1$ **e)** $x = 1$ **f)** $x = 1$

5. a) $x = -3$ **b)** $x = -3$ **c)** $x = -3$
d) $x = -3$ **e)** $x = -3$ **f)** $x = -3$

6. a) $x = 3$ **b)** $x = 3$ **c)** $x = 3$
d) $x = 3$ **e)** $x = 3$ **f)** $x = 3$

7. a) $x = 9$ **b)** $x = 3$ **c)** $m = -\frac{5}{6}$
d) $n = -6$ **e)** $y = \frac{1}{2}$ **f)** $t = -3$

8. a) $x = \frac{1}{2}$ **b)** $x = -1$
c) $n = 5$ **d)** $d = 7$

9. a) $x = -\frac{5}{3}$ **b)** $y = \frac{1}{5}$ **c)** $x = 0$
d) $a = \frac{7}{2}$ **e)** $n = -\frac{1}{2}$ **f)** $p = 5$

11. a) 39 words/min **b)** 5 **c)** 180

12. a) $(7 + 3 + 6 + 5)h + 20 = 188$ **b)** $8/h

13. a) i) $42°F$ **ii)** $86°F$ **iii)** $30°F$ **iv)** $-10°F$
b) i) $-17.5°C$ **ii)** $25°C$ **iii)** $-30°C$ **iv)** $12°C$

Self-Check 3.1–3.4
Exercises, page 118

1. a) $12 + 8$ **b)** $10 - 5$
c) $6 + 4$ **d)** $10 - 15y$
e) $-6j - 2$ **f)** $21 + 28p$

2. a) $4a + 4$ **b)** $4k - 2$ **c)** $10 - 5b$

3. a) $-x - 6; -4$ **b)** $3x + 7; 1$
c) $-5 - 6x; 7$ **d)** $2x - 1; -5$

e) $28 - 4x; 36$ **f)** $-5x + 14; 24$

4. a) $x = -3$ **b)** $a = -9$ **c)** $b = 3$
d) $n = 6$ **e)** $z = -7$ **f)** $c = -\frac{1}{2}$

5. a) $m = -2$ **b)** $k = 9$ **c)** $y = -3$
d) $b = -1$ **e)** $j = 2$ **f)** $p = -2$

6. a) $x = 0$ **b)** $x = -16$ **c)** $x = \frac{11}{4}$
d) $x = -3$ **e)** $x = -4$ **f)** $x = 2$

7. a) $g = 4$ **b)** $x = 4$ **c)** $c = \frac{3}{8}$
d) $a = 5$

8. b

3.5 Solving Problems Using Algebraic Modelling
Exercises, page 120

1. a) $e + 5$ **b)** $3e$ **c)** $e - 3$
d) $2e + 10$ **e)** $5e - 5$

2. a) $a + 8$ **b)** $2a + 8$
c) Natasha: 17 years; Ravi: 25 years

3. a) $27 - y$ **b)** $2y$
c) Kirsten: 16 years; Victor: 11 years

4. a) $28 - m$ **b)** $3m$
c) Dog: 21 kg; Cat: 7 kg

5. a) $s - 7.5$ **b)** $2s - 7.5$
c) Lesley: 54.5 kg; Shelby: 62 kg

6. a) i) $n + 3$ **ii)** $n + 3 = 11; n = 8$
b) i) $2n$ **ii)** $2n = 24; n = 12$
c) i) $\frac{1}{3}n$ **ii)** $\frac{n}{3} = 9; n = 27$

7. Shaun: 16 bars; Livio: 32 bars

8. 136 and 137

9. Marisa: 3.5 km; Sandy: 5.5 km

10. Let x represent, in kilograms, the mass of fish caught by Jaquie. Then, $4x$ is the mass of fish caught by Michel.
$x + 4x = 25$
Jaquie: 20 kg; Michel: 5 kg

11. $142.50

12. a) $2p + 5 = 14$; $9.50
c) $10.50 **d)** $8.50

13. 228 cm

14. 50 cm and 68 cm

15. Car: 60 km/h; Airplane: 480 km/h

3.6 Mathematical Modelling: Estimating Heights
Exercises, page 123

5. d) The height increases.
e) The longer the lower arm is, the taller the person is.
f) Locate 24.5 cm on the horizontal axis. Move up to meet the graph. Move left to meet the vertical axis. Read the value. This is the height of the person.
g) Locate the person's height on the vertical axis. Move right to meet the graph. Move down to meet the horizontal axis. Read the value. This is the length of the lower arm.

6. a) 153.344 cm

No, the male's height would be 156.532 cm.

b) Female: 163.03 cm; Male: 166.015 cm

Chapter 3 Review
Exercises, page 125

1. a) $-(7x + 5); -7x - 5$ **b)** $-(4y - 1); -4y + 1$
c) $3b - 18; 3(b - 6)$ **d)** $-7(2s - 7); -14s + 49$

2. a) $5 + 30$ **b)** $-36 + 63$
c) $8 + 40$ **d)** $-15 + 27$
e) $-3 - 5 + 6$ **f)** $-8 + 64 - 32$

3. a) $4q + 16$ **b)** $3d - 15$
c) $4x + 18$ **d)** $-30 + 25a$
e) $24s + 48$ **f)** $-7 + 49r$

4. a) $10y$ **b)** $4a - 1$ **c)** $-s + 2$
d) $5x + 2$ **e)** $-4m - 10$ **f)** $2q + 6$

5. a) $-5y + 5$ **b)** $-13t - 6$ **c)** $-8m + 1$
d) $7x - 5$ **e)** $9x - 11$ **f)** $12x - 26$

6. a) $7x + 1; 29$ **b)** $12x + 6; 54$
c) $-4x - 4; -20$ **d)** $-x; -4$
e) $-7x - 6; -34$ **f)** $-10x - 17; -57$

7. a) $8 + x; 5$ **b)** $6x + 2; -16$
c) $-6 + 3x; -15$ **d)** $7x - 22; -43$
e) $2 - 6x; 20$ **f)** $-5x + 2; 17$

8. a) $c = -1$ **b)** $m = -2$ **c)** $y = 5$
d) $t = -3$ **e)** $p = 13$ **f)** $g = 9$
g) $u = 1$ **h)** $w = -8$ **i)** $h = -\frac{1}{5}$

9. a) $x = 2$ **b)** $x = 2$ **c)** $x = 3$
d) $x = -7$ **e)** $x = -3$ **f)** $x = 4$
g) $x = 4$ **h)** $x = 3$ **i)** $x = -3$

10. a) $x = 5$ **b)** $x = -6$ **c)** $x = -9$
d) $x = -5$ **e)** $x = \frac{1}{6}$ **f)** $x = 2$

11. a) $x = 1$ **b)** $x = 5$ **c)** $x = 1$
d) $x = 3$ **e)** $x = -2$ **f)** $x = 2$
g) $x = 2$ **h)** $x = -\frac{1}{2}$ **i)** $x = \frac{2}{3}$

12. a) $a = -\frac{4}{3}$ **b)** $g = -6$ **c)** $n = 4$
d) $k = -\frac{3}{2}$ **e)** $b = 4$ **f)** $j = \frac{7}{5}$
g) $y = -\frac{5}{4}$ **h)** $x = 1$ **i)** $r = 1$

13. a) $x = 8$ **b)** $x = \frac{5}{2}$ **c)** $x = -2$
d) $x = \frac{8}{5}$

14. a) $m + 5$ **b)** $2m$ **c)** 5 kg and 10 kg

15. 12 and 13

16. a) $w + 3$ **b)** $2w + 3$
c) $4w + 6$ **d)** $18 = 4w + 6$
e) 3 cm   **f)** 6 cm
g) $P = 3 + 6 + 3 + 6$
     $= 18$ cm

17. 11 cm by 16 cm

18. Delicious: 17; Macintosh: 136

Chapter 3 Self-Test
Exercises, page 128

1. a) $2j - 10$ **b)** $-4m - 1$
c) $-18 + 6g$ **d)** $15a - 15$
e) $8 - 28s$ **f)** $30r - 24$

2. a) $5b - 2$ **b)** $8 - 2d$
c) 5 **d)** $6f - 17$
e) $-9 + 4e$ **f)** $-t + 19$

3. a) $x = -6$ **b)** $k = -1$
c) $h = -10$ **d)** $f = 6$
e) $y = -14$ **f)** $j = -5$

4. a) $x = 6$ **b)** $x = -8$
c) $x = -1$ **d)** $x = 4$

5. a) $x = -4$ **b)** $x = 4$
c) $x = 1$ **d)** $x = -\frac{1}{2}$

8. $2x + 20 = 140$
     $x = 60$
Monday: $60; Tuesday: $80

9. $l - s = 6$ $P = 2(l + s)$
     $l = s + 6$ $40 = 2l + 2s$
                $40 = 2(s + 6) + 2s$
                  $s = 7$
The rectangle is 7 cm by 13 cm.

Preparation for Ontario Testing
Exercises, page 129

10. $s = 4d - 1$
     $91 = 4d - 1$
     $4d = 92$
      $d = 3$
Diagram 23 would have 91 squares.

11. $x + 2x + 3x = 180°$
           $6x = 180°$
             $x = 30°$
largest angle: $3x = 3(30°)$
                 $x = 90°$
other angle: $2x = 2(30°)$
               $x = 60°$
The angles of the triangle are 30°, 60°, and 90°.

Cumulative Review
Chapters 1–3
Exercises, page 130

1. a) ii; The graph is level when the car travels at a constant speed. The slope increases as the car speeds up. The slope is negative as the car slows down. The graph is level again when the car returns to the original speed.

3. a)

Circle radius (cm)	1	2	3
Circle area (cm²)	3.14	12.57	28.27
Circle radius (cm)	4	5	6
Circle area (cm²)	50.27	78.54	113.10

b)

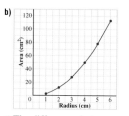

c) The differences between consecutive areas increase. The graph curves up. The area increases faster and faster as the radius increases.

d) Non-linear; Since the differences are not constant, the relation is not linear. Since the graph is not a straight line, the relation is not linear.

4. a) 20   **b)** 12.5 min

5. a) 4^6 **b)** $(-5)^5$ **c)** $(-3)^9$
d) 2^9 **e)** $(-1)^3$ **f)** 6^3
g) 4^5 **h)** 7^3

6. a) 1   **b)** 0.0041   **c)** –0.2
d) –0.0041   **e)** 1

7. a) 2.0×10^6 **b)** 5.0×10^{-3}
c) 5.27×10^5 **d)** 4.31×10^{-4}
e) 2.5×10^{-6} **f)** 7.0012×10^8
g) 1.9×10^4 **h)** 1.6×10^{-7}

8. a) 4   **b)** 2   **c)** 7
d) 8   **e)** 12

9. a) 5, –5   **b)** 16, –16   **c)** 13, –13
d) 9.5, –9.5   **e)** 2.2, –2.2

10. 7.7 m

11. The blue route is longer by about 0.7 km.

12. a) $6x + 21$ **b)** $-20 - 15n$
c) $48s - 60$ **d)** $-8b + 6$
e) $-6p - 10$ **f)** $18c + 30$

13. a) $6t - 1$; 5   **b)** $11a - 9$; 46   **c)** $-4x + 2$; 14

14. a) $x = -\frac{1}{4}$ **b)** $a = \frac{55}{4}$ **c)** $y = -14$
d) $m = -3$ **e)** $b = \frac{7}{3}$ **f)** $m = -1$

Chapter 4 Slope

Necessary Skills
Simplifying Fractions and Reciprocals
Exercises, page 134

1. a) –2   **b)** –3   **c)** 2   **d)** –2   **e)** 2   **f)** –3
2. a) $\frac{7}{4}$ **b)** –6   **c)** $\frac{3}{4}$ **d)** $-\frac{1}{4}$ **e)** 1   **f)** $-\frac{8}{5}$
3. a) $-\frac{1}{2}$ **b)** 5   **c)** –2   **d)** $\frac{3}{2}$
e) $\frac{1}{5}$ **f)** –4   **g)** 3   **h)** $-\frac{5}{4}$

Order of Operations
Exercises, page 135

1. a) –5   **b)** 11   **c)** –11   **d)** –5   **e)** –11   **f)** –11
2. a) 2   **b)** –16   **c)** 6   **d)** 10   **e)** –5   **f)** –25

4.1 Slope
Exercises, page 139

1. a) rise = 5; run = 9   **b)** rise = 1; run = 8
c) rise = 4; run = 1   **d)** rise = 7; run = 3
e) rise = 1; run = 1   **f)** rise = 2; run = 3

2. a)

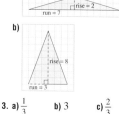

b)   **c)**

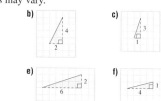

3. a) $\frac{1}{3}$ **b)** 3   **c)** $\frac{2}{3}$ **d)** $\frac{2}{3}$
4. a) $\frac{1}{4}$ **b)** 1   **c)** $\frac{2}{5}$ **d)** $\frac{4}{3}$ **e)** 0

5. Line segments may vary.

a)   b)   c)

d)   e)   f)

g)   h)

6. a) $\frac{1}{3}$ **b)** 3   **c)** $\frac{3}{2}$ **d)** $\frac{1}{3}$ **e)** $\frac{2}{3}$ **f)** 2
Slopes a and d are equal.

7. a) $\frac{2}{3}$ **b)** $\frac{1}{3}$

8. a) rise, run = 6; slope = 1   **b)** rise, run = 6; slope = 1

9. a) $\frac{3}{2}$ **b)** $\frac{1}{2}$ **c)** $\frac{1}{4}$

11. a) hill AB: 4 m; hill CD: 4 m
b) hill CD; It has a steeper slope.
c) The hills will have different widths.
d) A roller coaster will go faster down a steeper slope and slower up a steeper slope.

12. $\frac{5}{3}$

14. a) The slope decreases.   **b)** The slope decreases.
c) The slope stays the same.

4.2 The Coordinate Plane
Exercises, page 143

1. B(2, –4); C(–5, 3); D(2, 5); E(0, 3);
F(–4, –2); G(–3, 0); H(5, 0); J(0, –5)

2. a) 2   **b)** 3   **c)** 1   **d)** 4

3.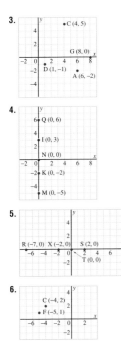

4.

5.

6.

7. a) G(−6, −7) and K(−7, −9)

b) Both the *x*- and *y*-coordinates are negative.

8. a)

b)

c)

10.

11. a)

b) (−10, 5); (−10, 6); (−12, 6); (−12, 7); (−14, 7)

12. (0, 0); the origin

13. a) All the *y*-coordinates are 0.

b) All the *x*-coordinates are 0.

c) Both the *x*- and *y*-coordinates are positive.

d) The *x*-coordinates are positive. The *y*-coordinates are negative.

15. a) i)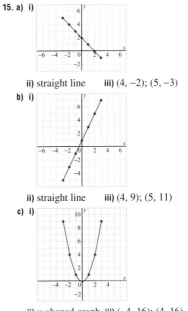

ii) straight line   **iii)** (4, −2); (5, −3)

b) i)

ii) straight line   **iii)** (4, 9); (5, 11)

c) i)

ii) u-shaped graph **iii)** (−4, 16); (4, 16)

16. (2, −2), (−2, −2) or (2, 6), (−2, 6)

4.3 Slope of a Line Segment

Exercises, page 149

1. a) $\frac{3}{2}$ **b)** $-\frac{1}{4}$ **c)** 0   **d)** −3

2. a) −4   **b)** $\frac{3}{5}$ **c)** $-\frac{2}{3}$ **d)** $-\frac{1}{4}$ **e)** $-\frac{4}{3}$ **f)** $\frac{1}{2}$

3. a) LM; RS; VW   **b)** They all fall to the right.

4. a) CD; IJ; KL   **b)** They are all vertical.

5. a) AB: $\frac{5}{8}$; AC: $\frac{3}{8}$; AD: $\frac{1}{8}$; AE: 0; AF: $-\frac{1}{4}$; AG: $-\frac{5}{8}$

b) PQ: $-\frac{7}{5}$; PR: $-\frac{7}{2}$; PS: undefined; PT: $\frac{7}{2}$; PU: $\frac{7}{4}$; PV: 1

6. a) $-\frac{1}{4}$ **b)** undefined   **c)** $\frac{4}{3}$

d) $-\frac{3}{4}$ **e)** $-\frac{3}{2}$ **f)** undefined

7. a) i)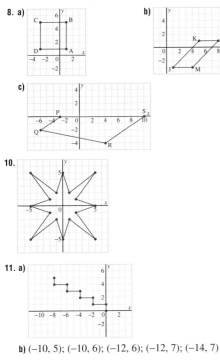

ii) falls to the right   **iii)** $-\frac{11}{8}$; negative

iv) A line segment falls to the right if the slope is negative.

b) i)

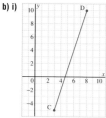

ii) rises to the right   **iii)** 3; positive

iv) A line segment rises to the right if the slope is positive.

c) i)

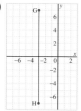

ii) vertical   **iii)** undefined; neither

iv) A line segment is vertical if the slope is undefined.

d) i)

ii) horizontal   **iii)** 0; neither

iv) A line segment is horizontal if the slope is zero.

8. a) AB: −1; BC: $\frac{9}{2}$; AC: $\frac{4}{7}$

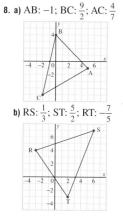

b) RS: $\frac{1}{3}$; ST: $\frac{5}{2}$; RT: $-\frac{7}{5}$

9. Line segments with positive slopes rise to the right. Line segments with negative slopes fall to the right.

10. a) The scale from 0 to 1600 is not included on the axis.

b) $\frac{1}{15}$; $-\frac{1}{50}$; $-\frac{1}{20}$; $-\frac{1}{40}$

11. A(17, 4); B(22, 10); C(25, 8); D(30, 6); E(31, 2); F(37, 1)

12. b) ii and vi

14. d) All 3 figures can be drawn.

4.4 Slopes of Parallel Line Segments

Exercises, page 156

1. a) $\frac{3}{2}$ **b)** −2   **c)** 0   **d)** $\frac{3}{12}$ **e)** $-\frac{1}{4}$ **f)** $-\frac{3}{4}$

2. b; c; f; g; Their slopes are not equal.

3. a; b; Their slopes are not equal.

4. a) i)

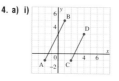

ii) AB: 2; CD: 2

iii) Yes. They have the same slope.

b) i)

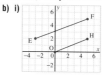

ii) EF: $\frac{3}{8}$; OH: $\frac{2}{5}$

iii) No. They do not have the same slope.

c) i)

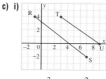

ii) RS: $-\frac{3}{4}$; TU: $-\frac{2}{3}$

iii) No. They do not have the same slope.

5. a)

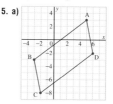

Yes. Both pairs of opposite sides have equal slopes and are therefore parallel.

b)

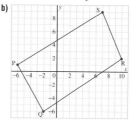

No. Both pairs of opposite sides do not have equal slopes and are therefore not parallel.

c)

Yes. Both pairs of opposite sides have equal slopes and are therefore parallel.

6. a)

b) AB: $\frac{3}{2}$; AC: $\frac{1}{3}$; BD: $\frac{1}{3}$; CD: $\frac{3}{2}$

c) Parallelogram. Both pairs of opposite sides have equal slopes and are therefore parallel.

7. a) 0

b) 0. It has the same slope as the *x*-axis.

8. a) undefined

b) Undefined. It has the same slope as the *y*-axis.

10. a)

b) D(0, 5.5)

11. a) The slope of all treads is 0. The slope of all risers is undefined.

b) The riser and tread form a 90° angle, so the stairs are level.

12. The slopes of the 2 line segments must be equal.

13. c) Both pairs of opposite sides have equal slopes.

4.5 Slopes of Perpendicular Line Segments
Exercises, page 161

1. a; d; The slopes are negative reciprocals.

2. a; c; The slopes are negative reciprocals.

3. a) $-\frac{3}{2}$ **b)** $-\frac{8}{5}$ **c)** $\frac{4}{3}$ **d)** 2   **e)** 3

4. a) i)

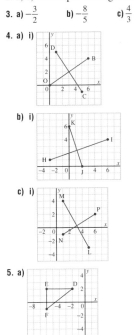

ii) OB: $\frac{2}{3}$; CD: $-\frac{3}{2}$

iii) Yes. The line segments have negative reciprocal slopes.

b) i)

ii) HI: $\frac{1}{3}$; JK: -3

iii) Yes. The line segments have negative reciprocal slopes.

c) i)

ii) LM: $-\frac{7}{4}$; NP: $\frac{3}{5}$

iii) No. The line segments do not have negative reciprocal slopes.

5. a)

Yes. Two sides of the triangle have negative reciprocal slopes and are therefore perpendicular.

b)

Yes. Two sides of the triangle have negative reciprocal slopes and are therefore perpendicular.

c)

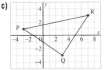

Yes. Two sides of the triangle have negative reciprocal slopes and are therefore perpendicular.

d)

No. Two sides of the triangle do not have negative reciprocal slopes and are therefore not perpendicular.

6. a)

b) AB: $\frac{3}{2}$; BC: $-\frac{2}{3}$; AC: $\frac{1}{5}$

c) Right triangle. The slopes of AB and BC are negative reciprocals and are therefore perpendicular.

7. a)

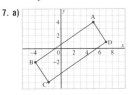

Yes. All adjacent sides are perpendicular, so there are 4 right angles.

b)

No. The adjacent sides are not perpendicular. There are not 4 right angles.

c)

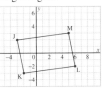

Yes. All adjacent sides are perpendicular, so there are 4 right angles.

8. a)

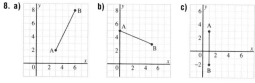

Coordinates of C may vary.

9. If the slopes of 2 line segments are negative reciprocals, the segments are perpendicular.

11. T(0, 0) or T(5, 0)

Self-Check 4.1–4.5

Exercises, page 163

1.

2. a) $-\dfrac{1}{2}$ **b)** 0 **c)** $\dfrac{1}{2}$

3. c) The line segment with a positive slope rises to the right. The line segment with a negative slope falls to the right.

4. a) parallel   **b)** neither   **c)** perpendicular

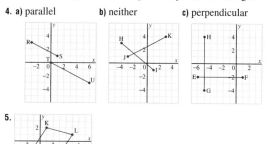

5.

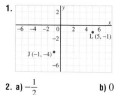

Yes. Both pairs of opposite sides have equal slopes.

6. c

4.6 Graphing Linear Relations

Exercises, page 170

1. a) Yes. The points lie on a straight line.
   b) Yes. The points lie on a straight line.

2. a) i) Yes. The values in the difference column are equal.
    ii) Yes. The values in the difference column are equal.
    iii) Yes. The values in the difference column are equal.
   b) i) 8   **ii)** -2 **iii)** 0

3. a) i)

x	y
0	3
1	5
2	7
3	9

ii)

x	y
0	5
2	−1
4	−7
6	−13

iii)

x	y
0	−12
1	−8
2	−4
3	0

b) i)

$y = 2x + 3$

ii) $y = 5 - 3x$ **iii)** $y = -12 + 4x$

c) i) 2   **ii)** -3 **iii)** 4

4. a) i)

x	y
−2	−9
−1	−5
0	−1
1	3
2	7

ii)

x	y
−4	14
−2	8
0	2
2	−4
4	−10

b) i)

$y = 4x - 1$

ii)

$y = -3x + 2$

c) i) 4   **ii)** -3

5. i) a)

x	y	Difference
−2	−8	
−1	−6	2
0	−4	2
1	−2	2
2	0	2
3	2	2
4	4	2

b)

x	y	Difference
−2	20	
−1	15	−5
0	10	−5
1	5	−5
2	0	−5
3	−5	−5
4	−10	−5

ii) a)

$y = 2x - 4$

b)

$y = -5x + 10$

iii) a) 2   **b)** -5
iv) a) Yes. The values in the difference column are equal.
   b) Yes. The values in the difference column are equal.

6. a)

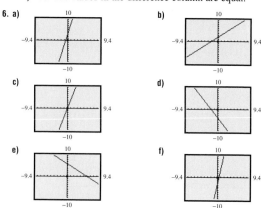

All the relations are linear. The graph of each relation is a straight line.

7. a)

t(h)	C($)
0	20
2	100
3	140
5	220

b)

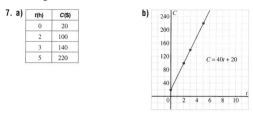

$C = 40t + 20$

c) Yes. The points lie on a straight line.
d) $180
e) 2 h

8. a)

x	y	Difference
0	3	
2	7	4
4	11	4
6	15	4
8	19	4
10	23	4

b)

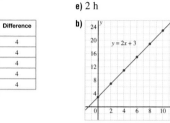

$y = 2x + 3$

c) Yes. The difference values are equal. The graph is a straight line.

9. a)

n	0	20	40	60	80	100
C(¢)	70	470	870	1270	1670	2070

b)

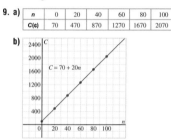

$C = 70 + 20n$

c) approximately $15.80   **d)** approximately 46
e) Yes. The graph is a straight line.

10. a)

n	0	2	4	6	8	10	12
C($)	300	340	380	420	460	500	540

b)

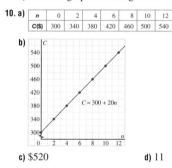

$C = 300 + 20n$

c) $520   **d)** 11

11. a) The graph would be steeper.
b) The cost would increase.

12. equation; table of values; graph

13. a)

F(°F)	100	150	200	250	300	350	400
C(°C)	38	66	93	121	149	177	204

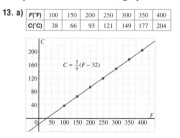

$C = \frac{5}{9}(F - 32)$

b) i) approximately 190°C   **ii)** approximately 162°C
   iii) approximately 136°C
c) i) approximately 190°C   **ii)** approximately 250°C
   iii) approximately 390°C
d) i) approximately −5°C   **ii)** approximately −19°C
   iii) approximately 219°C   **iv)** approximately −30°C
e) −40°C/°F

4.7 Graphing Non-Linear Relations
Exercises, page 177

1. a; b; The graphs are not straight lines.

2. a; c; The graphs are not straight lines.

3. a) Non-linear relation. The difference values are not equal.
   b) Linear relation. The difference values are equal.
   c) Non-linear relation. The difference values are not equal.

4. a) i)

x	y	Difference
−2	5	
−1	2	−3
0	−1	−3
1	−4	−3
2	−7	−3
3	−10	−3
4	−13	−3

The relation is linear.

ii)

x	y	Difference
−2	5	
−1	9	4
0	12	3
1	14	2
2	15	1
3	15	0
4	14	−1

The relation is non-linear.

iii)

x	y	Difference
−2	5	
−1	5	0
0	5	0
1	5	0
2	5	0
3	5	0
4	5	0

The relation is linear.

b) i) Straight line. The relation is linear.
   ii) Not a straight line. The relation is non-linear.
   iii) Straight line. The relation is linear.

5. a)

x	y	Difference
−2	5	
−1	2	−3
0	1	−1
1	2	1
2	5	3

The relation is non-linear because the difference values are not equal.

b)

x	y	Difference
0	2	
2	0	−2
4	−2	−2
6	−4	−2
8	−6	−2

The relation is linear because the difference values are equal.

c)

x	y	Difference
1	12	
2	6	−6
3	4	−2
4	3	−1

The relation is non-linear because the difference values are not equal.

d)

x	y	Difference
−1	−1	
0	3	4
1	7	4
2	11	4
3	15	4

The relation is linear because the difference values are equal.

6. a) linear   **b)** non-linear   **c)** linear   **d)** non-linear

7. a) $y = 2 - x; y = 3 + 4x; y = 1 - x; y = 2 + x$
   b) $y = x^2 + 1; y = \frac{12}{x}; y = 2 + x^2; y = 2 - x^2$

8. a)

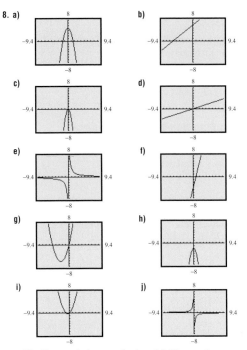

The linear relations are b, d, and f. The graphs are straight lines. The non-linear relations are a, c, e, g, h, i, and j. The graphs are not straight lines.

9. a) i)

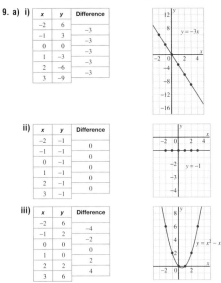

x	y	Difference
−2	6	
−1	3	−3
0	0	−3
1	−3	−3
2	−6	−3
3	−9	−3

$y = -3x$

ii)

x	y	Difference
−2	−1	
−1	−1	0
0	−1	0
1	−1	0
2	−1	0
3	−1	0

$y = -1$

iii)

x	y	Difference
−2	6	
−1	2	−4
0	0	−2
1	0	0
2	2	2
3	6	4

$y = x^2 - x$

b) i) Linear. The difference values are equal. The graph is a straight line.

ii) Linear. The difference values are equal. The graph is a straight line.

iii) Non-linear. The difference values are not equal. The graph is not a straight line.

11. ii; iii; v; vii

12. a) ii   **b)** iii   **c)** i

13. a)

t(s)	d(m)	Difference
0	0	
1	5	5
2	20	15
3	45	25
4	80	35

b) Non-linear. The difference values are not equal.

c)

$d = 5t^2$

d) The graph is not a straight line, so the relation is non-linear.

14. a)

s(SPF)	p(%)	Difference
2	50.0	
8	12.5	−37.5
15	6.7	−5.8
25	4.0	−2.7
35	2.9	−1.1

b) Non-linear. The difference values are not equal.

c)

$p = \dfrac{100}{s}$

d) The graph is not a straight line, so the relation is non-linear.

15. a) Non-linear. The difference values are not equal.

b) approximately 50 m

4.8 Mathematical Modelling: Designing a Staircase

Exercises, page 182

1. a) The number of risers equals the number of treads.

b) B   **c)** C   **d)** A

2. a) No. It depends on a person's size.

b) 50 mm

3. a) 220 mm; $\dfrac{10}{11}$ **b)** 185 mm; $\dfrac{37}{50}$ **c)** 15

Chapter 4 Review

Exercises, page 185

1. a) $\dfrac{4}{5}$ **b)** 0

2. a) $\dfrac{2}{5}$ **b)** 5   **c)** 1   **d)** $\dfrac{2}{3}$

3. A(−4, 3); B(2, −2); C(−2, −1); D(−5, 0); E(0, −3); F(3, 1); G(0, 5)

4.

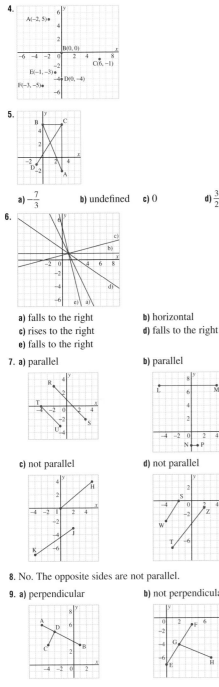

5.

a) $-\dfrac{7}{3}$ b) undefined c) 0 d) $\dfrac{3}{2}$

6.

a) falls to the right b) horizontal
c) rises to the right d) falls to the right
e) falls to the right

7. a) parallel **b)** parallel

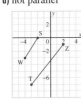

c) not parallel **d)** not parallel

8. No. The opposite sides are not parallel.

9. a) perpendicular **b)** not perpendicular

c) not perpendicular **d)** perpendicular

10. slope of PQ: $\dfrac{3}{5}$; slope of PR: $-\dfrac{5}{3}$

The slopes of 2 sides of the triangle are negative reciprocals. Therefore the sides are perpendicular and the triangle is a right triangle.

11. a) No. No sides are parallel.
b) No. No sides are perpendicular.

12. a)

x	y	Difference
−2	8	
−1	5	−3
0	2	−3
1	−1	−3
2	−4	−3

b)

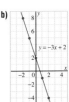

$y = -3x + 2$

c) −3 **d)** They are the same.
e) Yes. The differences in the table are the same and the graph is a straight line.

13. a) i)

x	y	Difference
−2	−2	
−1	1	3
0	4	3
1	7	3
2	10	3
3	13	3
4	16	3

The relation is linear. The difference values are equal.

ii)

x	y	Difference
−2	9	
−1	7	−2
0	5	−2
1	3	−2
2	1	−2
3	−1	−2
4	−3	−2

The relation is linear. The difference values are equal.

b) i) 3 **ii)** −2

14. a)

h(h)	C($)
0	5
1	15
2	25
4	45

b)

$C = 10h + 5$

c) Yes. The graph is a straight line.
d) $35 **e)** 4

15. a) i)

x	y	Difference
−2	−9	
−1	−7	2
0	−5	2
1	−3	2
2	−1	2

$y = 2x - 5$

ii)

x	y	Difference
−2	8	
−1	5	−3
0	4	−1
1	5	1
2	8	3

$y = x^2 + 4$

iii)

x	y	Difference
−2	−4	
−1	0	4
0	0	0
1	−4	−4
2	−12	−8

$y = -2x^2 - 2x$

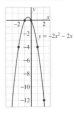

b) i) Linear. The difference values are equal.
The graph is a straight line.

ii) Non-linear. The difference values are not equal.
The graph is not a straight line.

iii) Non-linear. The difference values are not equal.
The graph is not a straight line.

16. a)

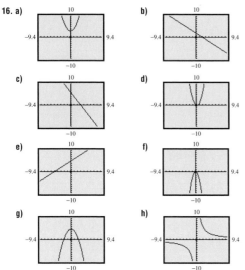

The linear relations are b, c, and e. The graphs are straight lines. The non-linear relations are a, d, f, g, and h. The graphs are not straight lines.

17. a) linear   **b)** non-linear   **c)** non-linear   **d)** non-linear

18. $\frac{2}{3}$

Chapter 4 Self-Test
Exercises, page 188

1. a) $\frac{4}{3}$ **b)** 1   **c)** 4

2.

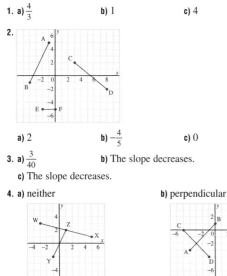

a) 2   **b)** $-\frac{4}{5}$ **c)** 0

3. a) $\frac{3}{40}$ **b)** The slope decreases.

c) The slope decreases.

4. a) neither   **b)** perpendicular

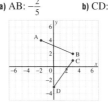

c) parallel

5. a) Non-linear. The graph is not a straight line.

b) Linear. The graph is a straight line.

c) Non-linear. The graph is not a straight line.

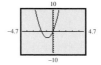

6. a) linear   **b)** non-linear   **c)** non-linear

7. Infinitely many parallelograms are possible.

Preparation for Ontario Testing
Exercises, page 189

8. He will need to increase the rise of the ramp by 8 m, from 4 m to 12 m.

9. The slopes of the segments are equal. They are equally steep.

Chapter 5 The Line

Necessary Skills
Slope of a Line Segment
Exercises, page 192

1. a) 0   **b)** $-\frac{2}{3}$ **c)** undefined

2. a) AB: $-\frac{2}{5}$ **b)** CD: $\frac{4}{3}$

c) EF: 0   **d)** GH: undefined

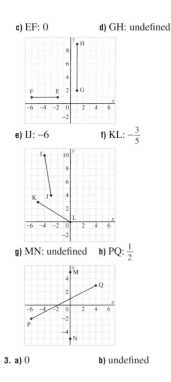

e) IJ: −6   **f)** KL: $-\dfrac{3}{5}$

g) MN: undefined   **h)** PQ: $\dfrac{1}{2}$

3. a) 0   **b)** undefined

Linear Relations
Exercises, page 193

1. a) i)

x	y	Difference
1	1	
2	5	4
3	9	4
4	13	4
5	17	4

ii)

x	y	Difference
1	−3	
2	−1	2
3	1	2
4	3	2
5	5	2

b) i)

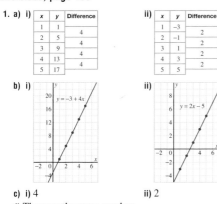

ii)

c) i) 4   **ii)** 2

d) They are the same number.

2. a) i) Yes.   **ii)** Yes.

b) If the values in the difference column are the same, the relation is linear.

c) Each segment of the graph has the same slope, so the relation is linear.

5.1 Slope of a Line
Exercises, page 196

1. a) 2   **b)** $-\dfrac{3}{2}$ **c)** $\dfrac{1}{2}$

2. a) undefined   **b)** $\dfrac{3}{2}$ **c)** 5

d) 0   **e)** −3   **f)** $-\dfrac{3}{5}$

3. a)

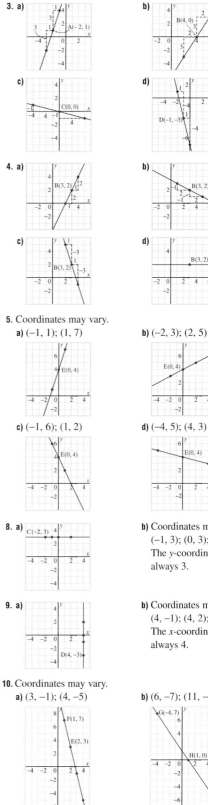

b)

c)

d)

4. a)   **b)**

c)   **d)**

5. Coordinates may vary.

a) (−1, 1); (1, 7)   **b)** (−2, 3); (2, 5)

c) (−1, 6); (1, 2)   **d)** (−4, 5); (4, 3)

8. a)   **b)** Coordinates may vary.
(−1, 3); (0, 3); (2, 3)
The y-coordinate is always 3.

9. a)   **b)** Coordinates may vary.
(4, −1); (4, 2); (4, 0)
The x-coordinate is always 4.

10. Coordinates may vary.

a) (3, −1); (4, −5)   **b)** (6, −7); (11, −14)

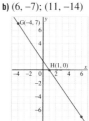

c) (16, 18); (−17, −12)

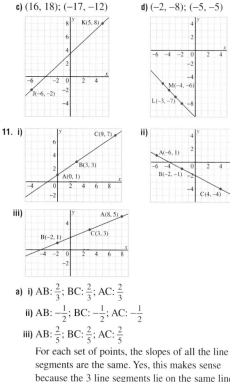

d) (−2, −8); (−5, −5)

11. i)

ii)

iii)

a) i) AB: $\frac{2}{3}$; BC: $\frac{2}{3}$; AC: $\frac{2}{3}$

ii) AB: $-\frac{1}{2}$; BC: $-\frac{1}{2}$; AC: $-\frac{1}{2}$

iii) AB: $\frac{2}{5}$; BC: $\frac{2}{5}$; AC: $\frac{2}{5}$

For each set of points, the slopes of all the line segments are the same. Yes, this makes sense because the 3 line segments lie on the same line.

b) i) AD: $\frac{2}{3}$ **ii)** AD: $-\frac{1}{2}$ **iii)** AD: $\frac{2}{5}$

Since segment AD lies on the same line, it has the same slope.

12. a) AB: 2; BC: $\frac{7}{4}$; AC: $\frac{13}{7}$ **b)** No.

13. −1

5.2 Graphing $y = mx$

Exercises, page 203

1. a) 2   **b)** $-\frac{1}{5}$ **c)** −1   **d)** $-\frac{4}{3}$

2. a) −2   **b)** $\frac{1}{4}$ **c)** 10

   d) $-\frac{4}{7}$ **e)** 0   **f)** undefined

3. a) $y = x$ **b)** $y = -x$ **c)** $y = -\frac{1}{4}x$

   d) $y = \frac{1}{3}x$ **e)** $y = 0$ **f)** $y = 10x$

4. a) $m = 4$; $y = 4x$ **b)** $m = -2$; $y = -2x$ **c)** $m = \frac{3}{5}$; $y = \frac{3}{5}x$

5. a) $y = -3x$ **b)** $y = \frac{3}{4}x$ **c)** $y = -\frac{1}{5}x$

6. a)

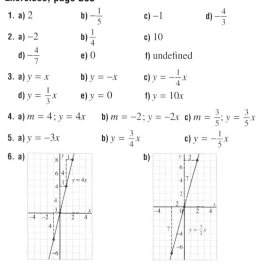

b)

c)

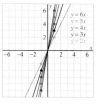

d)

e) $y = 0$

f) $x = 0$

7. a) i) $y = 5x$; $y = 6x$

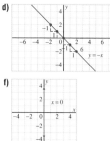

ii) $y = \frac{1}{8}x$; $y = \frac{1}{10}x$

iii) $y = -4x$; $y = -5x$

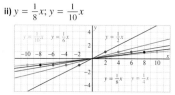

8. a) $x = 0$ **b)** $y = 0$

9. Its slope is undefined.

10. a)   **b)** 6

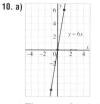

c) The cost of each ticket is $6.

11. Yes.

12.

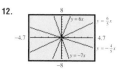

Coordinates may vary.

5.4 Graphing $y = mx + b$

Exercises, page 210

1. a) 3; 5   b) -2; 3   c) $\frac{2}{5}$; -4 d) $-\frac{1}{2}$; 6

2. a) -4; -7 b) $\frac{3}{8}$; -5 c) $\frac{4}{3}$; -2 d) $\frac{9}{5}$; 1

3. a) $y = 2x + 3$ b) $y = -x + 4$ c) $y = \frac{2}{3}x - 1$

   d) $y = -\frac{4}{5}x + 8$ e) $y = -3x + \frac{5}{2}$ f) $y = 3$

4. a) -2 b) 2   c) does not exist

5. a) i) $\frac{1}{2}$; 1   ii) $\frac{3}{2}$; -2 iii) -2; 1

   b) i) $y = \frac{1}{2}x + 1$ ii) $y = \frac{3}{2}x - 2$ iii) $y = -2x + 1$

6. a) $y = -x + 2$ b) $y = -\frac{3}{2}x - 3$ c) $y = \frac{2}{3}x$

7. a) b) c)

8. a) b) c)

9.

10. a)   b) $(6, 0)$

11. a)   b) $(1, 6)$

12. a)   b) $(1, -2)$; $(4, 4)$; $(-2, 7)$

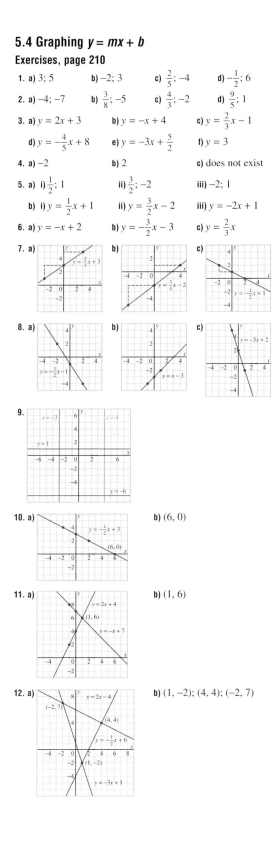

13. a) $x = 9$ b) $y = -8$

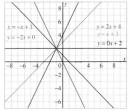

14. No. From the equation, the y-intercept is -2, but Maria graphed -2 as the x-intercept.

15. a) i) m decreases by 1; b increases by 1
    ii) For the first 3 equations: m is halved; b is halved
    For the last 3 equations: m is doubled; b is doubled
    b) i) All the lines intersect at $(-1, 2)$.

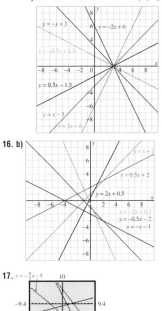

   ii) All the lines intersect at $(3, 0)$.

16. b)

17.

18. a) i) -5 ii) 7   iii) -11
    b) Substitute the x- and y-coordinates into the equation. Solve for b.

19. a) All equations have y-intercept 3.
    b) All equations have x-intercept and y-intercept 0. The graphs pass through the origin.
    c) All equations have x-intercept -3.

Self-Check 5.1–5.4

Exercises, page 213

1. a)
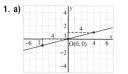

b)

2. Coordinates may vary.
a) $(-5, 7)$; $(1, -1)$

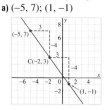

b) $(-1, -1)$; $(1, 3)$

3. Coordinates may vary.
a) $(-3, 0)$; $(1, 6)$

b) $(-2, 5)$; $(0, 1)$

c) $(-2, 2)$; $(0, 4)$

d) $(-6, 2)$; $(4, 4)$

e) $(-4, 5)$; $(2, 1)$

4. a) $y = 3x$ **b)** $y = -x$ **c)** $y = -\frac{1}{2}x$ **d)** $y = 0$

5. a)
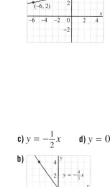

b)

c)

d)

6. a) $y = -3x - 1$ **b)** $y = \frac{1}{2}x + 2$ **c)** $y = -\frac{3}{5}x - 4$

7. a) $y = -2x + 1$ **b)** $y = \frac{1}{2}x - 3$ **c)** $y = -1$

8. a)
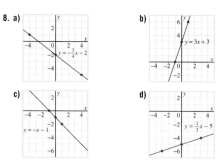

b)

c)

d)

9. d

5.5 The Equation of a Line

Exercises, page 216

1. a) $y = 4x + 3$ **b)** $y = -2x + \frac{1}{2}$

c) $y = -\frac{2}{3}x + \frac{3}{4}$ **d)** $y = \frac{7}{4}x - \frac{1}{4}$

2. a) $y = 5x - 3$ **b)** $y = -2x + 4$ **c)** $y = \frac{2}{3}x - 6$

3. a) i) A(3, −1) ii) A(2, 2) iii) A(−2, 3)

b) i) −1 ii) 2 iii) $-\frac{3}{2}$

c) i) 2 ii) −2 iii) 0

d) i) $y = -x + 2$ ii) $y = 2x - 2$ iii) $y = -\frac{3}{2}x$

4. a) i) A(−1, 3); B(1, −1) ii) A(0, −3); B(1, 0)

iii) A(−2, 2); B(2, −4)

b) i) −2 ii) 3 iii) $-\frac{3}{2}$

c) i) 1 ii) −3 iii) −1

d) i) $y = -2x + 1$ ii) $y = 3x - 3$ iii) $y = -\frac{3}{2}x - 1$

5. a) $y = \frac{5}{2}x + 3$ **b)** $y = -\frac{4}{3}x - 4$ **c)** $y = 4x + 2$

6. a) $y = -x + 3$ **b)** $y = 2x + 5$ **c)** $y = \frac{2}{3}x - 2$

7. a)
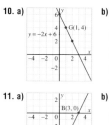

b)

c)

8. a, c, d, f

9. b, c

10. a)
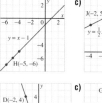

b)

c)

11. a)
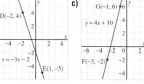

b)

c)

12. a)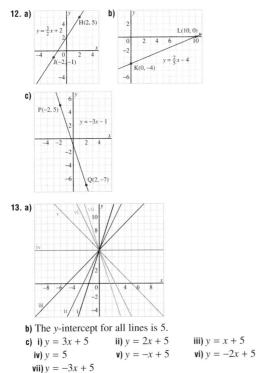

b)

c)

13. a)

b) The *y*-intercept for all lines is 5.

c) i) $y = 3x + 5$ **ii)** $y = 2x + 5$ **iii)** $y = x + 5$
   iv) $y = 5$ **v)** $y = -x + 5$ **vi)** $y = -2x + 5$
   vii) $y = -3x + 5$

d) The slope decreases by 1. The *y*-intercept is 5 for all equations.

14. • the slope and *y*-intercept
    • the slope and a point on the line
    • two points on the line

15. a)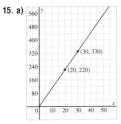

b) i) approx. \$280   **ii)** approx. \$185   **iii)** approx. \$530
c) $y = 11x$
d) i) \$275   **ii)** \$187   **iii)** \$528

16. a) i)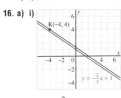

   ii) $y = -\frac{2}{3}x + 1$
   iii) No, but it passes close to the point.
   iv) The coordinates do not satisfy the equation. No. Yes.
   v) The true *y*-intercept lies somewhere between 1 and 2.

b) i) $y = \frac{3}{4}x + 2$

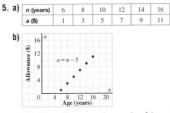

5.6 Applications of Linear Relationships: Part I
Exercises, page 222

1. a) 60   **b)** 1.15   **c)** 16

2. a) 19; 15   **b)** 9; 145   **c)** 25; 159

3. a) partial   **b)** direct   **c)** partial
   d) direct   **e)** direct   **f)** partial
   Direct variation: There is no *y*-intercept.
   Partial variation: There is a *y*-intercept.

4. a) partial   **b)** partial   **c)** direct
   Direct variation: The graph goes through the origin.
   Partial variation: The graph does not go through the origin.

5. a)

n (years)	6	8	10	12	14	16
a (\$)	1	3	5	7	9	11

b)

c) No. The allowance jumps by \$1 each year. There are no in-between values.
d) 1; It represents the increase in allowance per year.
e) \$13.00

6. a)

b) No. A partial photo cannot be processed. Only whole numbers are included on the graph.

c) $\frac{1}{4}$; It represents the cost to process one photo.

d) \$14.00

7. a)

k (kg)	3	4	5	6	7	8
t (h)	1.5	2	2.5	3	3.5	4

b)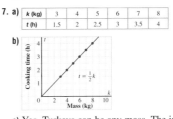

c) Yes. Turkeys can be any mass. The in-between values are included on the graph.

d) $\frac{1}{2}$; It represents the cooking time of $\frac{1}{2}$ hour per kilogram of turkey.

e) The slope of the graph would decrease.

f) The slope of the graph would increase.

8. < 400 copies: Blue Heron charges less.
400 copies: They charge the same.
> 400 copies: Miles Ahead charges less.

9. a)

t (h)	0	1	2	3	4	5
d (km)	400	320	240	160	80	0

b)
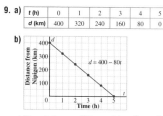

c) Yes. It is possible to drive for only part of an hour. The in-between values are included on the graph.

d) −80; It represents the average speed of the car in kilometres per hour.

e) The slope would be a larger negative number. The graph would be steeper.

f) The slope would be a smaller negative number. The graph would be less steep.

g) 400; This is the distance between the towns.

h) The d-intercept would be greater. The graph would shift up.

i) The d-intercept would be less. The graph would shift down.

11. a)

n	0	10	20	30	40	50
C ($)	1940	2740	3540	4340	5140	5940

b)
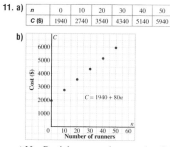

c) No. Partial runners do not exist. Only whole numbers are included on the graph.

d) 1940; It is the fixed cost of the bus.

e) 80; This is the cost per runner for meals and accommodation.

f) i) $3900   **ii)** $2900   **iii)** $5700

g) The slope would decrease to 32. The graph would be less steep. The equation would be $C = 1940 + 32n$.

h) The C-intercept would be 0. The graph would start at the origin. The equation would be $C = 80n$.

5.7 Applications of Linear Relationships: Part II
Exercises, page 227

1. a) C = Paul's commission; s = Paul's sales

b) T = the amount of GST; c = the cost of the goods and services

c) d = the distance travelled, in kilometres; t = the time spent travelling, in hours

d) n = the number of posters; t = the total time required, in minutes

2. a) $T = 31d$ **b)** $T = 134d$ **c)** $T = 239d$

d) $T = 90d$ **e)** $T = 160 + 305d$

3. $d = 65h$

4. a) $C = 86h$ **b)** $C = 164h$ **c)** $C = 110 + 95h$

5. a) direct   **b)** partial   **c)** direct
Direct variation: The graph goes through the origin.
Partial variation: The graph does not go through the origin.

6. a) $C = 3800 + 200d$

b)
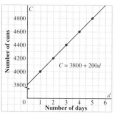

c) 5800

7. ≤ 66 people: The *Example 1* hall is cheaper.
> 66 people: The *Example 2* hall is cheaper.

8. a) $t = 5n + 20$

b)
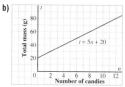

c) 5; 20

d) It represents the mass of the empty box.

e) It represents the mass of one candy. The units are grams per candy.

f) i) The slope would be 7. The graph would be steeper.
ii) The t-intercept would be 30. The graph would shift up.

g) i) $t = 7n + 20$ **ii)** $t = 5n + 30$

9. a) $T = 180b + 14\,000$

b)
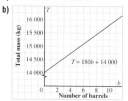

c) 180; 14 000

d) It represents the mass of the empty truck.

e) It represents the mass of 1 barrel of oil. The units are kilograms per barrel.

f) The T-intercept would be greater. The graph would shift up.

10. a) $T = 20 + 10d$

b)
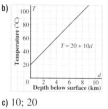

c) 10; 20

d) It represents Earth's surface temperature.

e) It represents the increase in temperature for each kilometre below the surface. The units are °C/km.

f) i) The T-intercept would be 5.

ii) The T-intercept would be 40.

g) i) $T = 5 + 10d$ **ii)** $T = 40 + 10d$

11. a) 480   **b)** It is the t-intercept.

12. a) $T = 100 - 3.4h$

b)

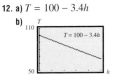

c) -3.4; 100

d) It represents the boiling point of water at sea level.

e) It represents the decrease in the boiling point of water per kilometre above sea level. The units are °C/km.

f) approx. 70°C

13. a)

Number of people	0	6	12	18	24
Batter mix (cups)	0	4	8	12	16

b)

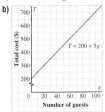

c) 20   **d)** 18

e) The slope would be steeper.

14. a) $T = 200 + 5g$

b)

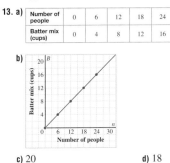

c) 5; 200

d) It represents the cost per guest.

e) It represents the fixed cost of the community centre.

f) i) $425   **ii)** $460   **iii)** $605

g) i) $435   **ii)** $450   **iii)** $595

h) The slope would be 7. The graph would be steeper. The equation would be $T = 200 + 7g$.

5.8 Mathematical Modelling: Setting Up for a Banquet

Exercises, page 231

Room	Area (sq. ft.)	Number of people		
		Theatre	Oblong	Round
Classroom	-	-	-	-
Cafeteria	-	-	-	-
Canadian Room	13 277	2212	1659	1327
Imperial Room	6048	1008	756	604
Manitoba Room	1210	201	151	121

4. a) $y = \frac{1}{6}x$

b)

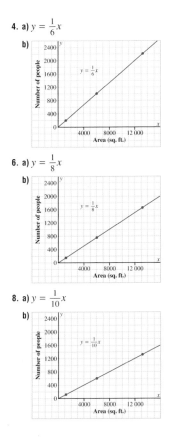

6. a) $y = \frac{1}{8}x$

b)

8. a) $y = \frac{1}{10}x$

b)

Chapter 5 Review

Exercises, page 234

1. a)   **b)**   **c)**

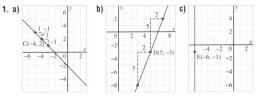

2. Coordinates may vary.

a) $(-3, 1)$; $(5, -5)$ **b)** $(-1, 3)$; $(7, -3)$

c) $(-4, 3)$; $(4, -3)$ **d)** $(-7, 2)$; $(1, -4)$

3. Coordinates may vary.

a) (−2, 4); (6, 6)　　　**b)** (−5, −2); (1, −6)

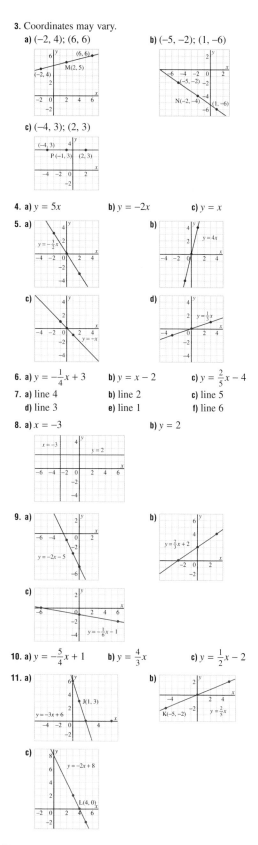

c) (−4, 3); (2, 3)

4. a) $y = 5x$　　　**b)** $y = -2x$　　　**c)** $y = x$

5. a)　　　**b)**

c)　　　**d)**

6. a) $y = -\frac{1}{4}x + 3$　　**b)** $y = x - 2$　　**c)** $y = \frac{2}{5}x - 4$

7. a) line 4　　　**b)** line 2　　　**c)** line 5
d) line 3　　　**e)** line 1　　　**f)** line 6

8. a) $x = -3$　　　　　**b)** $y = 2$

9. a)　　　**b)**

c)

10. a) $y = -\frac{5}{4}x + 1$　　**b)** $y = \frac{4}{3}x$　　**c)** $y = \frac{1}{2}x - 2$

11. a)　　　**b)**

c)

12. a) $y = x + 2$　　**b)** $y = -2x - 3$　**c)** $y = \frac{1}{2}x$　　**d)** $y = -\frac{5}{6}x + 5$

13. a)

t (h)	0	1	2	3	4	5
d (km)	0	65	130	195	260	325

b)

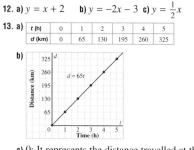

c) 0; It represents the distance travelled at the start of the trip.
d) 65; It represents the average speed of the car in kilometres per hour.
e) The slope of the graph would be steeper.

14. a) $T = 75 + 15p$
b) No. It is impossible to sell numbers of products that are not whole numbers.

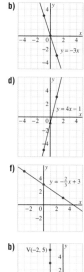

c) 75; It represents Olaf's fixed daily pay.
d) Partial variation. The equation is in the form $y = mx + b$. The graph does not go through the origin.
e) $165　　　　　　　**f)** $T = 95 + 10p$

Chapter 5 Self-Test
Exercises, page 236

1. a)　　　**b)**

c)　　　**d)**

e)　　　**f)**

2. a)　　　**b)**

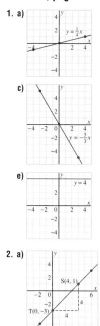

c)

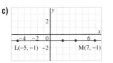

i) a) 1   **b)** undefined   **c)** 0

ii) Coordinates may vary.

  a) $(-2, -5)$; $(6, 3)$ **b)** $(-2, 3)$; $(-2, -1)$ **c)** $(2, -1)$; $(4, -1)$

iii) a) $y = x - 3$ **b)** $x = -2$ **c)** $y = -1$

3. a) $d = 450 + 70h$ **b)** 660 km

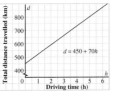

c) 450; It represents the distance travelled by air.

d) The slope would be greater than 70. The graph would be steeper.

e) The d-intercept would be less than 450. The graph would shift down.

4. a)   **b)**

c)

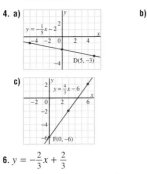

6. $y = -\dfrac{2}{3}x + \dfrac{2}{3}$

Preparation for Ontario Testing

Exercises, page 237

7. The slope of the line is the reduction in the number of hectares of forest each year. Each year, the forest is 2000 hectares smaller in area.

The vertical intercept is the size of the forest at the beginning. The forest was 16 000 hectares before logging began.

The horizontal intercept is the year when the forest disappeared. After 8 years, there were 0 hectares of forest.

8.

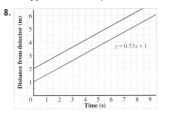

Chapter 6   Polynomials

Necessary Skills

Exponent Laws for Multiplying and Dividing Powers

Exercises, page 240

1. a) $2^5 = 32$ **b)** $4^4 = 256$

  c) $3^7 = 2187$ **d)** $10^7 = 10\,000\,000$

  e) $6^2 = 36$ **f)** $10^4 = 10\,000$

  g) $7^5 = 16\,807$ **h)** $4^3 = 64$

2. a) $3^2 = 9$ **b)** $10^3 = 1000$

  c) $4^3 = 64$ **d)** $5^2 = 25$

  e) $6^1 = 6$ **f)** $2^8 = 256$

  g) $10^4 = 10\,000$ **h)** $1^4 = 1$

Exponent Law for a Power of a Product

Exercises, page 241

1. a) $4a^2$ **b)** $8a^3$ **c)** $16a^4$ **d)** $-32a^5$

2. a) $9x^2$ **b)** $-125a^3$ **c)** $16x^4$ **d)** $-32a^5$

3. a) $256b^4$ **b)** $36z^2$ **c)** $-243c^5$ **d)** $625m^4$

  e) $64t^6$ **f)** $-343x^3$ **g)** $-16\,384z^7$ **h)** $6561q^8$

The Distributive Law

Exercises, page 242

1. a) $6 + 3a$ **b)** $6 - 3a$

  c) $8x + 4$ **d)** $8x - 4$

2. a) $60(170 + 80)$; $60(140 + 110)$

3. a) $24x + 54$ **b)** $-15c - 9$

  c) $33 - 88z$ **d)** $20 - 70y$

  e) $30z + 10$ **f)** $-3y + 6$

6.1 What Is a Polynomial?

Exercises, page 247

1. $37 Can; $37 U.S.

2. $x + y = 74$

3. a) binomial; 2 terms   **b)** monomial; 1 term

  c) binomial; 2 terms   **d)** monomial; 1 term

  e) trinomial; 3 terms   **f)** monomial; 1 term

  g) trinomial; 3 terms   **h)** binomial; 2 terms

4. a) $3x^2 + 4x + 3$ **b)** $4x^2 + 6x - 3$

  c) $x^2 - 5x + 4$ **d)** $-2x^2 - 5x - 6$

5. a)   **b)**

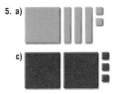

c)

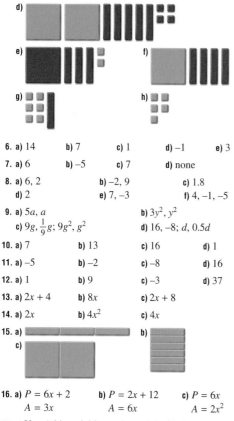

d)

e)

f)

g)

h)

6. a) 14   **b)** 7   **c)** 1   **d)** −1   **e)** 3

7. a) 6   **b)** −5   **c)** 7   **d)** none

8. a) 6, 2   **b)** −2, 9   **c)** 1.8
   d) 2   **e)** 7, −3   **f)** 4, −1, −5

9. a) $5a$, a **b)** $3y^2$, y^2
   c) $9g$, $\frac{1}{9}g$; $9g^2$, g^2 **d)** 16, −8; d, $0.5d$

10. a) 7   **b)** 13   **c)** 16   **d)** 1

11. a) −5   **b)** −2   **c)** −8   **d)** 16

12. a) 1   **b)** 9   **c)** −3   **d)** 37

13. a) $2x + 4$ **b)** $8x$ **c)** $2x + 8$

14. a) $2x$ **b)** $4x^2$ **c)** $4x$

15. a)   **b)**
   c)

16. a) $P = 6x + 2$ **b)** $P = 2x + 12$ **c)** $P = 6x$
     $A = 3x$ $A = 6x$ $A = 2x^2$

17. a) Yes. A binomial is a polynomial with 2 terms.
   b) No. A monomial has only 1 term.

18. a) $4x + 6$ **b)** $6x + 10$ **c)** $8x + 10$

19. a) $P = 22\,\text{cm}$; $P = 14\,\text{m}$
   b) $P = 34\,\text{cm}$; $P = 22\,\text{m}$
   c) $P = 42\,\text{cm}$; $P = 26\,\text{m}$

20. a) x^2
   b) i) $4x^2$ **ii)** x^2 **iii)** $3x^2$
   c) i) $36\,\text{cm}^2$ **ii)** $9\,\text{cm}^2$ **iii)** $27\,\text{cm}^2$

21. 47.5 m; 170 m

6.2 Adding Polynomials

Exercises, page 252

1. a) $3x^2 + 5x + 2$ **b)** $4x^2 - 3x + 1$
   c) $-4x^2 - 8x - 5$ **d)** 0

2. a) $(-2x^2 + 5x - 3) + (x^2 + x + 7)$
   b) $-x^2 + 6x + 4$

3. a) $-3x + 5$ **b)** $-x^2 - 5x + 2$
   c) $x^2 - 4$ **d)** $2x^2 + x + 3$

4. a) $2a + 2$ **b)** $3a + 3$
   c) $4a + 4$ **d)** $5a + 5$
   e) $6a + 6$ **f)** $7a + 7$

5. a) $3k + 2$ **b)** $4k + 1$
   c) $5k$ **d)** $6k - 1$

6. a) $5h^2 + 6$ **b)** $5h^2 - 6$
   c) $5h^2 + 4h$ **d)** $5h^2 - 4h$
   e) $5h^2 + 4h + 6$ **f)** $5h^2 - 4h - 6$

7. a) $9x + 6$ **b)** $7a + 4$
   c) $5 - 6m$ **d)** $6x + 2$

8. a) $6n^2 - 8n - 4$ **b)** $-2x^2 + 5x - 4$
   c) $7 - 7c - 3c^2$ **d)** $5 - 3n + 3n^2$
   e) $3b^3 - b - 11$ **f)** $-5m^4 - 2m^2 + 6m + 5$

9. a) $4x^2 + 2x + 7$ **b)** $4x^2 - 2x - 7$
   c) $3m^2 + 5m + 6$ **d)** $-m^2 + 5m - 6$

10. a) $8c^4 + c^3 - 6$
   b) $-4q^5 - q^4 - 6q^3 + 3q^2 - 3q - 7$
   c) $6t^3 + 2t^2 + t - 7$
   d) $5t^4 - 5t^3 - 4$

11. a) $2x^5 + 3x^4 + 2x^3 + 8x^2 - 7$
   b) There are no tiles to represent powers of x greater than x^2.

12. $-5x^2 + x - 6$; -10

13. $-5x^2 + x - 4$; -26

14. a) $4y^2 + 3$; 39   **b)** $y^4 - 2y^3 - y^2 + y - 6$; 117
   c) $-y^4 + 4y^3 + 2y^2 - 4y + 4$; -155

15. a) x^2, $2x$; $x^2 + 2x$ **b)** x^2, $4x$, 16; $2x^2 + 12x + 16$
   c) x^2, $3x$; $4x^2 + 6x$

16. a) $-4x^2 - 2x + 10$ **b)** $x^2 - 4x + 15$
   c) $x^3 - 10x^2 + 2x + 8$ **d)** $8x - 7$

18. a) i) $x - 7$ **ii)** $x + 7$
   iii) $3x - 3$; $3x$; $3x + 3$ **iv)** $9x$
   b) Divide the sum by 9.

19. a) $P = 2x^3 + 6x^2 - 9x + 1$ **b)** 23 units

6.3 Subtracting Polynomials

Exercises, page 256

1. a)

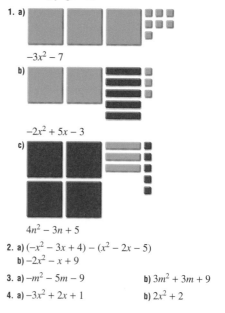

$-3x^2 - 7$

b)

$-2x^2 + 5x - 3$

c)

$4n^2 - 3n + 5$

2. a) $(-x^2 - 3x + 4) - (x^2 - 2x - 5)$
   b) $-2x^2 - x + 9$

3. a) $-m^2 - 5m - 9$ **b)** $3m^2 + 3m + 9$

4. a) $-3x^2 + 2x + 1$ **b)** $2x^2 + 2$

5. a) $-5x - 2$
   b) $-2 + 3a$
   c) $-7x^2 + 5x - 4$
   d) $-5 + 2m + 4m^2$
   e) $-6n^2 + 3n - 1$
   f) $2x^3 + 5$

6. a) $(3x^2 + 5) + (-2x^2 - 1)$
   b) $(x^2 + 2x) + (x + 1)$
   c) $(x^2 + 3x - 2) + (x^2 + x - 1)$

7. a) The first terms have the same sign.
   b) The first terms have different exponents.
   c) The last terms have the same sign.
   d) The last terms are not the same.

8. a) $7s + 7$
   b) $7s^2 + 7s + 7$
   c) $9s + 9$
   d) $9s^2 + 9s + 9$

9. a) $-5x + 1$
   b) $n + 2$
   c) $14a^2 - 2a - 10$
   d) $-10x^2 + 7x - 4$

10. a) $-2n^2 + 4n - 4$
   b) $9x^2 - 5$
   c) $-5t^2 + 2$
   d) 0

11. a) 0; The opposite terms cancel each other out.
   b) No.

12. a) $2x - 1$
   b) $-4a + 4$
   c) $4x^2 - 5x$
   d) $2t - 3$
   e) $2x^2 - 6x + 3$
   f) $-4n + 6$

13. a) $2x^2 + 3x + 7$
   b) $4m^2 - 6m + 11$
   c) $3a^2 - a^3 + 6$
   d) $-9x^2 + 5x - 12$

14. $5x^2 - 15x + 3$; 3

15. $2x^3 + x^2 - 7x - 5$; -3

16. a) i) $4m^2 - 9m + 1$
         ii) $2m^2 - 2m - 1$
   b) i) 1, 35
        ii) -1, 11

17. a) i) $y^2 - 5$
         ii) $10y$
   b) i) 11, -14
        ii) 40, 10

18. a) $-7x^2 - 10x + 25$
   b) -23

6.4 Multiplying Monomials
Exercises, page 260

1. a) $10x^6$
   b) $10x^6$
   c) $-10x^6$
   d) $-10x^6$
   e) $-36x^8$
   f) $42z^7$

2. a) $12x^5$
   b) $-2x^8$
   c) a^6
   d) $-30a^3$

3. a) $36x^5$
   b) $27z^8$
   c) $-16a^{12}$
   d) $16n^8$

4. a) $12b$
   b) $-14k$
   c) $20t$
   d) $-16p$
   e) $5a^2$
   f) $-3p^2$
   g) $4n^2$
   h) $-2x^2$

5. a) $6a^2$
   b) $-10c^2$
   c) $10a^2$
   d) $21x^2$
   e) $-56y^2$
   f) $5x^2$

6. a) $144x^2$
   b) $-27y^3$
   c) $-25b^2$
   d) $-81m^{10}$
   e) $-125b^6$
   f) $-9n^8$

7. a) $-x^5$
   b) $6p^5$
   c) $-12y^4$
   d) $6b^3$

8. a) $21m^9$
   b) $8x^5$
   c) $56a^{14}$
   d) $-10b^7$
   e) $-18x^8$
   f) $48p^6$

9. a) $(3x)(3x)$
   b) $9x^2$

11. No, there are many possible answers.

6.5 Dividing Monomials
Exercises, page 262

1. a) $2x$
   b) $3x^2$
   c) $4x^3$
   d) $4x^4$
   e) x^2
   f) x^3

2. a) $2x$
   b) $2x$
   c) $2x$
   d) $2x$

3. a) $-3x$
   b) $-3x$
   c) $-3x$
   d) $-3x$

4. a) $81x^2$
   b) $-64d$
   c) $200a^2$
   d) $48t$

5. a) $\frac{5}{2}m^2$
   b) $-\frac{5}{2}x^3$
   c) $-5x^4$

6. a) $4x^3$
   b) $2y^4$
   c) $-3m^2$
   d) $9y^2$
   e) $\frac{3}{5}n^2$
   f) -5

7. a) $5x^2$
   b) $-3y$
   c) $-5a$
   d) $3b$
   e) $5m^3$
   f) 3

8. a) $-7a^5$
   b) $-4s^2$
   c) $4c^6$
   d) $5x^6$
   e) $6y^2$
   f) $3b$

9. a) $7m^8$
   b) $4k$
   c) 5
   d) $7z^3$
   e) $7a$
   f) 4

10. a) $40\,000v^2$
   b) $1024p^4$

11. No. He divided the exponents instead of subtracting them.

12. a) $10m^5$
   b) $-3x^5$
   c) $\frac{2}{3}x^2$
   d) $-\frac{3}{4}m^3$
   e) $6b^7$
   f) $-3x^2$

13. a) $10d^7$
   b) $5m$
   c) $-5x^3$
   d) $30a^4$
   e) $6x^2$
   f) $-\frac{5}{3}a^5$

15. No. There are many possible answers.

16. a) 32
   b) -72
   c) 16

Self-Check 6.1–6.5
Exercises, page 264

1. a) binomial; 2 terms
   b) trinomial; 3 terms
   c) monomial; 1 term
   d) binomial; 2 terms

2. $-3x^2 + 2x + 4$

3. a) $9x + 2$
   b) $3x^2 - 5x$
   c) $2n - n^2 - 12$
   d) $8 - 5a - 6a^2$

4. a) $-7x - 8$
   b) $2x^2 + 6x - 10$
   c) $-3g^2 + 3$
   d) $-b^3 - 3b^2 - 3b - 5$

5. a) $x^2 + 3x - 4$; 0
   b) $x^4 + 2x^3 - 4x - 5$; 139

6. a) $-12f^2$
   b) $15r$
   c) $-36t^2$
   d) $7p^8$
   e) $16w^7$
   f) $-48x^2$

7. a) $64x^3$
   b) $-3125y^{15}$
   c) $4t^{10}$
   d) $1296f^{20}$
   e) w^{18}
   f) $81g^{24}$

8. a) $4x$
   b) $-4h^2$
   c) $6y^2$
   d) $-3b^3$
   e) $6s^4$
   f) $-5c^3$

9. a

6.6 Multiplying a Polynomial by a Monomial

Exercises, page 267

1. a) $x(x)$ **b)** $(x + 2)x$ **c)** $x(2x + 1)$
   d) $x(x + 2)$ **e)** $(x + 2)2x$ **f)** $3x(2x)$

2. a) $x^2 + x$ **b)** $3x^2 + 2x$ **c)** $2x^2 + 2x + 6$
   d) $2x^2 + 4x$

3. a) $2x + 6$ **b)** $-2x - 6$ **c)** $3x - 6$
   d) $-3x + 6$ **e)** $8x + 4$ **f)** $-8x - 4$
   g) $20 - 5x^2$ **h)** $-20 + 5x^2$

4. a) $x^2 + 3x$ **b)** $-x^2 - 3x$ **c)** $x^2 - 2x$
   d) $-x^2 + 2x$ **e)** $2x^2$ **f)** $-2x^2 - x$
   g) $4x - x^3$ **h)** $-4x + x^3$

5. a) $5x - 15$ **b)** $7a + 7$ **c)** $-6 - 3n$
   d) $4x + 8$ **e)** $18x - 12$ **f)** $5x^2 - 30x + 15$

6. a) ii   **b)** vi   **c)** v
   d) iii   **e)** i   **f)** iv

7. a) $3x^2 + 2x$ **b)** $5a^2 - a$ **c)** $3n - 7n^2$
   d) $-x^2 + 2x$ **e)** $5y - y^2$ **f)** $-7x + 2x^2 - x^3$

8. a) $x^2 + 3x$ **b)** $-5a + 15$
   c) $2b^3 - 3b^2 + b$ **d)** $4p - 3p^2 - p^3$
   e) $36t^2 - 24t$ **f)** $-k^3 + 5k^2 - k$

9. a) $5x^3 - 6x$ **b)** $2x + 6x^2$
   c) $-3b^4 + 3b^3$ **d)** $6a^2 + 2a$
   e) $-4m^3 + 4m^2$ **f)** $x^2 - x^5$

10. a) $10x^2 + 15x$ **b)** $6a^2 - 8a$
   c) $15c - 6c^2$ **d)** $-8n^2 + 4n$
   e) $-2q^3 - 3q^2 + q$ **f)** $18k - 6k^2 + 12k^3$

11. a) 1652   **b)** $14x^2 + 21x + 42 = 1652$
   c) The answers are equal.

12. a) i) $3x^2$ **ii)** $5x - 1$
   iii) $15x^3 - 3x^2$ **iv)** $3x^2$
   v) $15x^2 - 3x$ **vi)** $5x^2 - x$
   vii) $46x^2 - 8x$
   b) $4998\,\text{cm}^3$; $2198\,\text{cm}^2$

13. a) $\frac{3}{4}x$ **b)** $\frac{3}{4}(x + 4) = \frac{3}{4}x + 3$
   c) $x(\frac{3}{4}x) = \frac{3}{4}x^2$

6.7 Mathematical Modelling: Could a Giant Survive?

Exercises, page 270

1.

Edge length, x (cm)	Volume, V (cm³)	Surface area, A (cm²)	$\dfrac{\text{Volume}, V}{\text{Surface area}, A}$
1	1	6	$\frac{1}{6}$
2	8	24	$\frac{1}{3}$
3	27	54	$\frac{1}{2}$
4	64	96	$\frac{2}{3}$
5	125	150	$\frac{5}{6}$
6	216	216	1
7	343	294	$\frac{7}{6}$
8	512	384	$\frac{4}{3}$
9	729	486	$\frac{3}{2}$
10	1000	600	$\frac{5}{3}$

2. a) Volume   **b)** It increases.

3. a) i)

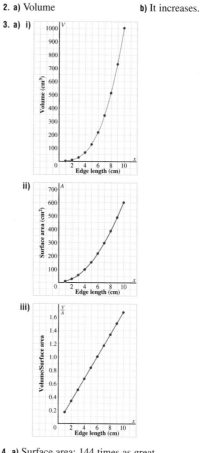

   ii)

   iii)

4. a) Surface area: 144 times as great
     Volume: 1728 times as great
   b) It would be 12 times as great.

5. a) Surface area: 1024 times as great
     Volume: 32 768 times as great
   b) It would be 32 times as great.

Chapter 6 Review

Exercises, page 273

1. a)

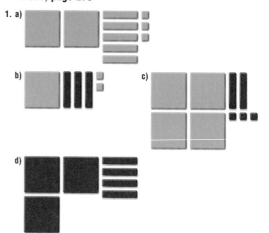

   b)   **c)**

   d)

2. a) $4x + 8$; $x^2 + 4x$ **b)** $6x + 8$; $2x^2 + 5x + 3$
c) $6x + 12$; $2x^2 + 11x + 5$

3. All of them are polynomials.

4. a) binomial; 2 terms **b)** monomial; 1 term
c) binomial; 2 terms **d)** trinomial; 3 terms

5. a) 5 **b)** −2 **c)** 1 **d)** 3

6. a) 4 **b)** 3 **c)** −1 **d)** −1

7. a) $5x − 3$ **b)** $5s + 1$
c) $3a^2$ **d)** $2d^2 − d − 1$

8. a) $4x + 3$; −5 **b)** $x^2 + 3x$; −2
c) $8 − 4x$; 16 **d)** $2x^2 − 5$; 3

9. a) $6u^2 − 7u + 1$ **b)** $2r^3 − 4r + 4$
c) $j^4 − 3j^2 + 8$ **d)** $−3k^4 + 6k^2 + k − 1$
e) $2t^3 − 5t^2 + 7t + 1$ **f)** $2p − 5$

10. a) $−q − 6$ **b)** $−2r + 4$
c) $−4x^2 − 6x + 7$ **d)** $6 + 2h^2 − 4h$
e) $6t^4 + 2t^3 − 5t + 4$ **f)** $2d^2 + 1 − d^4 + 5d^3$

11. a) $4y − 7y^2$ **b)** $12x − 1$
c) $15a^2 − 2a − 10$ **d)** $2z^2 − 2z − 1 − 2z^4$
e) $3x^2 − 5x$ **f)** $c^2 + 9c − 2$

12. a) $2 − x$; 0.5 **b)** $3x^2 − 2x + 12$; 20, 45

13. a) $8y^7$ **b)** $−64a^7$ **c)** $−3m^{19}$ **d)** $4c^{10}$

14. a) $−9r$ **b)** $−6y$ **c)** $10k$ **d)** $28q$
e) $16x^2$ **f)** $−35b^2$ **g)** $24a^2$ **h)** $−9c^2$

15. a) $343m^3$ **b)** $16d^4$ **c)** $−16q^2$
d) $−125p^3$ **e)** $−g^{10}$ **f)** $−64y^6$
g) $81w^{20}$ **h)** $−4t^6$

16. a) $−18n^4$ **b)** $16c^5$ **c)** $35x^5$
d) $−40n^4$ **e)** $−6j^6$ **f)** $6t^9$

17. a) $4a^7$ **b)** $−144q^6$ **c)** $128x^{13}$

18. a) $12a^2$ **b)** $−2b^2$ **c)** $−7h^5$
d) $−6x^3$ **e)** $−6y$ **f)** $4z^3$

19. a) $9y^4$ **b)** $9n^4$ **c)** $−5x^4$
d) $−4a^2$ **e)** $6m$ **f)** $9b^3$

20. a) $108k^4$ **b)** $1024s^2$ **c)** $2025d^2$

21. a) $x^2 + 5x$ **b)** $2x^2 + x$ **c)** $4x^2 + 8x$

22. a) $4y − 8$ **b)** $8a − 24$ **c)** $−4x − 8$
d) $15x − 3x^2$ **e)** $2y^2 − 12y$ **f)** $−15x + 5x^2$

23. a) $−12d^2 − 8d$ **b)** $35h − 10h^2$
c) $18t^3 + 6t^2 + 3t$ **d)** $−p^3 + 5p^2 − 3p$
e) $4w − 2w^2 + 12w^3$ **f)** $12x^4 − 18x^3 − 24x^2$

Chapter 6 Self-Test

Exercises, page 276

1. a) $7x − 1$; −8 **b)** $4x^2 + 7x + 7$; 4
c) $3x + 3$; 0 **d)** $5x^4 − 5x^2 − 5$; −5

2. a) $−30j$ **b)** $−8a^2$ **c)** $−28y^2$
d) $16g^2$ **e)** $24f^5$ **f)** $5e^{13}$
g) $−18k^9$ **h)** $−80p^{10}$

3. a) $25r^{12}$ **b)** $−27d^9$ **c)** $16s^{16}$
d) $64a^6$

4. a) $−16t^2$ **b)** $2w^3$ **c)** $−7b$
d) $6m^9$ **e)** $−6k^2$ **f)** $7n^2$

5. a) i) $4m^4$ **ii)** $−3x^2$
iii) $5s$ **iv)** $−27h^3$
b) i) $(2m)(4m^4) = 8m^5$ **ii)** $(−3x^2)(5x^2) = −15x^4$
iii) $(5s)(−4s^7) = −20s^8$ **iv)** $(−27h^3)(−h^3) = 27h^6$

6. a) $3x$ **b)** Yes, it is.
c) $−3x$; Yes, it is.

7. a) $9x$

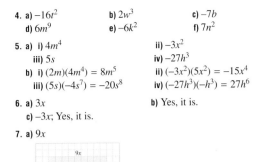

b) There are 3 possibilities: $12x$ by $3x$, $6x$ by $6x$, x by $36x$

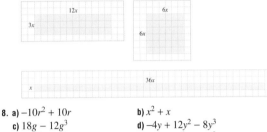

8. a) $−10r^2 + 10r$ **b)** $x^2 + x$
c) $18g − 12g^3$ **d)** $−4y + 12y^2 − 8y^3$
e) $10h^3 − 6h^2$ **f)** $4q^4 + 8q^3 − 12q^2$

Preparation for Ontario Testing

Exercises, page 277

9. $2ab + 4ab = 6ab$

10.

Cumulative Review

Chapters 1–6

Exercises, page 278

1.

3. a) 3^6 **b)** $(−6)^3$ **c)** $(−8)^{−5}$ **d)** 5^7

4. a) 1.43×10^{18} km³ **b)** 2.24×10^{10} km³

5. a) $x = 12$ **b)** $a = 2$ **c)** $a = 2$ **d)** $y = 5$

6. a) $12y − 24$ **b)** $−5m + 35$ **c)** $4d^2 + 8d$ **d)** $−12x^2 + 18x$

7. a) $25x^2$ **b)** $2y^2$ **c)** $27m^5$ **d)** $−2w^4$

8. a) $m = \dfrac{12}{7}$ **b)** $m = -1$

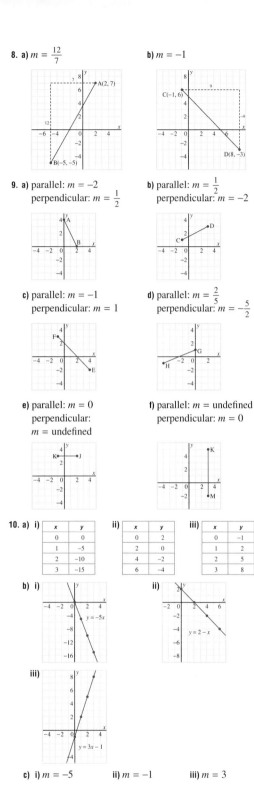

9. a) parallel: $m = -2$
perpendicular: $m = \dfrac{1}{2}$

b) parallel: $m = \dfrac{1}{2}$
perpendicular: $m = -2$

c) parallel: $m = -1$
perpendicular: $m = 1$

d) parallel: $m = \dfrac{2}{5}$
perpendicular: $m = -\dfrac{5}{2}$

e) parallel: $m = 0$
perpendicular:
$m =$ undefined

f) parallel: $m =$ undefined
perpendicular: $m = 0$

10. a) i)

x	y
0	0
1	−5
2	−10
3	−15

ii)

x	y
0	2
2	0
4	−2
6	−4

iii)

x	y
0	−1
1	2
2	5
3	8

b) i) $y = -5x$

ii) $y = 2 - x$

iii) $y = 3x - 1$

c) i) $m = -5$ **ii)** $m = -1$ **iii)** $m = 3$

11. a) linear   **b)** non-linear

c) linear   **d)** non-linear

e) non-linear   **f)** linear

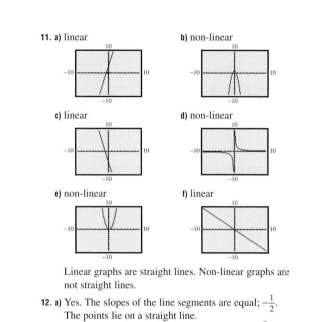

Linear graphs are straight lines. Non-linear graphs are not straight lines.

12. a) Yes. The slopes of the line segments are equal; $-\dfrac{1}{2}$. The points lie on a straight line.

b) Yes. The slopes of the line segments are equal; $\dfrac{9}{2}$. The points lie on a straight line.

13. a) $m = -1$; $b = 1$ **b)** $m = \dfrac{2}{3}$; $b = -8$
c) $m = 0$; $b = -1$

14. a) i) $y = 2x - 1$ **ii)** $y = -\dfrac{1}{2}x + 3$

iii) $y = x + 4$ **iv)** $y = -3$

b) First, plot the y-intercept. Then use the slope to plot 2 more points. For example, if the slope is 2, move up 2 and right 1 from the y-intercept. Repeat for a second point. Join the 3 points with a straight line.

15. a) $y = -x - 5$ **b)** $y = 1.5x - 5.5$

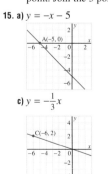

c) $y = -\dfrac{1}{3}x$

16. a) $y = \frac{1}{2}x + 2$ **b)** $y = -\frac{4}{3}x - 4$

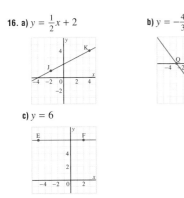

c) $y = 6$

Chapter 7 Line of Best Fit

Necessary Skills
Mean, Median, and Mode
Exercises, page 282

1. a) 4.8; 6; 6

b) 3.86; 2; 2 and 7

c) 13.63; 13; 13 and 16

d) 24.1; 23; 20, 21, and 29

7.1 Sampling
Exercises, page 285

1. a) Only the first 200 people in the mall who are wearing athletic shoes will be sampled. The sample is not random or representative of the population.

b) Your friends are not representative of the entire school population, and your sample was not chosen randomly.

c) Only people in Alberta will be sampled and they will be biased towards their own NHL team. The sample is not representative of all Canadians, and is not chosen randomly.

2. a) All people who wear athletic shoes

b) All students at your school

c) All Canadians

3. a) The sample is taken only from one grade. It does not represent the entire school population. The sample is not random.

b) The sample only includes seniors. It does not represent all Canadians. The sample is not random.

c) Your friends probably like the same movies as you do, and so your sample may be biased. The sample does not represent all teenagers and is not random.

4. No. The sample of viewers is not chosen at random. Only those viewers willing to pay the charge and call in will be included in the sample.

5. Method d gives a representative sample. All the students have an equal chance of being selected. The sample is chosen randomly and will represent the entire student population.

6. Method b gives a representative sample. Every carton has an equal chance of being selected, and each chip has an equal chance of being selected. The sample is chosen randomly and represents the entire chip population.

7. a) All flash bulbs

b) All Canadians

c) All ski equipment

d) All North Americans

8. a) There are too many people getting their licences. It is impractical and difficult to survey the whole population.

b) The testing destroys the light bulbs, so only a sample can be tested.

c) The population is too large to measure the volume of every bag. It is impractical and time-consuming to collect data on the whole population.

9. Yes. The wine in the bottle will be the same as all the other bottles of that particular wine because it comes from the same large batch. One bottle should represent the whole population.

10. No. Bakers usually test the centre of cakes to check if they are done, since the centre takes the longest to cook.

7.2 Collecting and Analysing Data
Exercises, page 289

1. b) 3.7; 4; 4

c) 10.5; 10; 10

Self-Check 7.1, 7.2
Exercises, page 290

1. a) All students at the school

b) All cars in that city

c) All customers of the coffee shop

2. a) Some of the students chosen to be surveyed may not use the cafeteria.

b) Only one intersection is studied. Different kinds of cars may be driven in different regions of the city.

c) Only customers who go to the coffee shop between 9 AM and 11 AM are surveyed. This excludes people who are at work during the day.

3. The sample is not random because only those customers who want the free tickets will fill out the survey. The sample does not represent all the customers.

5. d

7.4 The Line of Best Fit
Exercises, page 295

1. Graph b. The line fits the data points more closely than in the other graphs.

2. a) approximately 250

b) approximately 150

c) Yes. More people will be hot and thirsty and will buy pop when the temperature outside is higher.

3. a) The value of the new car is at least $15 000 because the value at one year is $15 000.

b) approximately $5000

5. a) Yes. The data points almost lie on a straight line.

b) No. A line of best fit does not have to pass through the origin. In this case, it crosses the y-axis at about 10.

c) No. All points must be considered. Joining the first and last points will not usually give the line of best fit.

6. Answers may vary.
a) $y = 0.3038x − 536.44$
b) 75 m

7. No. The data points do not approximate a straight line. They appear to form a curve.

9. a)

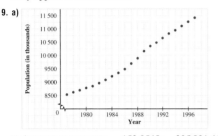

b) Answers may vary; $y = 153.8545x − 295\,891.41$
c) Answers may vary; approx. 13 356 000
d) It was assumed that the population continued to grow at the same rate.

7.5 Using Technology to Draw Lines of Best Fit
Exercises, page 300

1. a) 2   **b)** 2   **c)** 1

2. a) Linear
d) As the growing time increases, the height of the seedlings increases. The relationship is linear.
e) Answers may vary; $y = 4.5128x + 0.41$

g) The slope represents how much the seedlings grow in one day. Each day, the seedlings grow about 4.5 mm.

5. a) Linear
b)

c) i) As the age of the tree increases, the DBH increases.
ii) Linear
d) Answers may vary; $y = 0.7400x − 0.10$
e) The growth of a tree depends on environmental conditions like temperature, rainfall, and soil. Red pines in different regions will have different growth rates.

7.6 Mathematical Modelling: Good News for Migraine Sufferers
Exercises, page 304

5. The equation would be $y = x$. If it had no effect, the number of migraines would be the same before and after taking the placebo.

6. If the medication had no effect, the slope would be 1. The slope is less than 1 (0.83), and so the medication was effective.

Chapter 7 Review
Exercises, page 305

1. a) All Canadian teenagers   **b)** All Ontarians
c) All cars manufactured by the company

2. a) Only teenagers with Internet access can respond to the survey.
b) The only Ontarians being surveyed are college and university students.
c) Cars are sampled from only one of the company's factories.

3. No. Only the listeners of that particular radio station are sampled. This excludes all other types of music not played by this station. It also excludes all regions of Canada not within the station's range.

5. a)

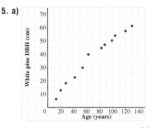

b) Answers may vary; approx. 55 cm
c) Answers may vary; approx. 40 years

6. a)

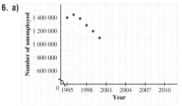

b) approximately 450 000

7. Answers may vary.
a) Men: $y = −0.0827x + 267.98$; 100.60 s
Women: $y = −0.1915x + 496.89$; 109.29 s
b) approximately 2104

8. Answers may vary.
a) $y = −0.0094x + 0.0943$

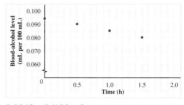

b) 0.0943 mL/100 mL

9. a) $y = 0.5x + 0.3$ **b)** $y = 1.5x + 0.5$

10. b) $y = 11.0833x − 6.75$
c)

d) It represents the number of centimetres the tree grows in one year.

Chapter 7 Self-Test
Exercises, page 308

1. Only the students who go to the gym would see the list, and their favourite sport may not be on the checklist.

2.

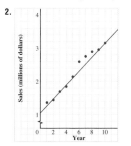

3. At least 2 points are needed, but the more the better.

4. $y = 0.8631x + 1.48$

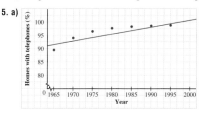

d) It represents the number of points scored per minute.

5. a)

c) $y = 0.2779x - 454.06$

d) Approximately 1994; This is not reasonable because in 1995 only 98.7% of homes have a telephone. The data points do not fit a straight line very well. This is not a good model for this data.

Preparation for Ontario Testing
Exercises, page 309

6. $y = 6.67x + 10$

7. Randomly select a number of students from each grade. The number from each grade should be proportional to the total number of students in that grade.

Chapter 8 Measurement

Necessary Skills
Perimeters of Figures
Exercises, page 313

1. a) 13 cm   b) 12 cm   c) 10.68 cm

2. a) 15.4 cm   b) 14.8 cm   c) 11.31 cm   d) 5.65 cm

Areas of Figures
Exercises, page 315

1. a) 948.64 cm^2 b) 875.5 cm^2 c) 824.48 cm^2
   d) 346.5 cm^2 e) 484.5 cm^2 f) 496 cm^2

2. a) 42.51 cm^2 b) 146.41 cm^2 c) 28.91 cm^2 d) 319.8 cm^2
   e) 60.82 cm^2 f) 15.21 cm^2 g) 69.44 cm^2

3. a) 9 cm^2 b) 9 cm^2 c) 9.08 cm^2

4. 11.76 cm^2; 13.69 cm^2

5. 10.18 cm^2; 2.54 cm^2

The Pythagorean Theorem
Exercises, page 316

1. a) 6.40 cm   b) 11.19 cm   c) 6.20 cm

2. a) 11.06 cm   b) 10.48 cm   c) 11.86 cm

8.1 Perimeters and Areas of Composite Figures
Exercises, page 320

1. a) 22.4 cm^2 b) 13.5 cm^2

2. a) 20 cm^2 b) 15.82 cm^2

3. a) 20.4 cm   b) 16.24 cm

4. a) 13 cm^2 b) 14.28 cm^2 c) 16.07 cm^2 d) 208.25 m^2

5. a) i) 5.66 cm   ii) 5 cm
   b) i) 25.16 cm^2 ii) 19.63 cm^2
   c) i) 16 cm^2 ii) 6 cm^2
   d) i) 9.16 cm^2 ii) 13.63 cm^2

6. a) 30 cm^2 b) 21.46 cm^2 c) 60 km^2 d) 62.83 cm^2

7. a) 414.25 cm
   b) No. It does not account for the overlap in the corners of the frame.

8. a) 416 cm^2 b) 100 cm
   c) The answer does not change.

9. a) the area between two concentric circles, one with radius 5.2 and the other with radius 4.8
   b) the area of a rectangle with length 4 and width 3, with a semicircle of radius 1.5 at one end

10. a) 63.6 m   b) 9540 m^2 d) 120   e) $1516.80

11. a) i) $A_{\text{shaded rectangle}} + A_{\text{triangle}}$
    $A_{\text{outside rectangle}} - 2(A_{\text{white rectangle}}) - 2(A_{\text{white triangle}})$
    ii) $A_{\text{large shaded triangle}} + 2(A_{\text{small shaded triangle}})$
    $A_{\text{outside rectangle}} - 2(A_{\text{parallelogram}})$
    b) i) 528 m^2 ii) 320 mm^2

12. a) 7   b) 14

Triangle	Area (cm^2)	Rectangle	Area (cm^2)	Rectangle	Area (cm^2)
AKJ	10	INMH	2	CDLN	9
ABJ	10	PQLN	6	NIGF	8
CBJ	5	CDQP	3	CNFE	12
CIJ	5	DEFL	3	AKIC	30
MHG	3	MHGF	6	CIGE	20
MFG	3	ABJK	20	AKGE	50
ACJ	15	BCIJ	10	JGEB	30

13. a) 76.5 m^2 b) 6

8.3 Optimal Values of Measurement: Part I

Exercises, page 328

1. a) 1 cm^2 **b)** 4 cm^2 **c)** 9 cm^2 **d)** 16 cm^2 **e)** 25 cm^2

2. a) 81 cm^2 **b)** 64 cm^2 **c)** 49 cm^2
d) 100 cm^2 **e)** 2500 cm^2

3. a) 6 m^2 **b)** 25 m^2 **c)** 100 m^2 **d)** 272 m^2 **e)** 600 m^2

4. a) 21 m by 24 m **b)** No

5. a) 0.6 m by 21.6 m **b)** 3.6 m by 3.6 m

6. a) 1.8 m by 7.2 m; 3.6 m by 3.6 m
b) 12.96 m^2; 19.44 m^2

7. $\frac{20}{4} = 5$; Each side is 5 m long.

8. a) Yes **b)** 50 m; $15\,000 \text{ m}^2$
c) i) 75 m; $18\,750 \text{ m}^2$ **ii)** 100 m; $20\,000 \text{ m}^2$
iii) 125 m; $18\,750 \text{ m}^2$ **iv)** 150 m; $15\,000 \text{ m}^2$

d)

Length of side parallel to beach (m)	Length of side perpendicular to beach (m)	Total length of rope (m)	Area enclosed (m²)
300	50	400	15 000
250	75	400	18 750
200	100	400	20 000
150	125	400	18 750
100	150	400	15 000

e) 200 m by 100 m; The length of the side parallel to the beach is two times the length of the side perpendicular to the beach.

9. a) 1.5 m by 1.5 m **b)** 1.5 m by 3 m **c)** 3 m by 3 m

10. a) 18 m by 42 m or 21 m by 36 m
b) 39 m by 39 m

11. a) 216 m^2

b)

Number of stands along each of the 3 sides	Number of stands along each of the other 2 sides	Overall width (m)	Overall length (m)	Combined area (m²)
6	4	18	12	216
2	10	6	30	180
4	7	12	21	252

c) 4 stands along each of the 3 sides and 7 stands along each of the other 2 sides; 12 m by 21 m

12. The rectangle closest to a square will have the least perimeter.

13. a) a circle **c)** a circle with $d \doteq 13.5 \text{ cm}$

8.4 Surface Area and Volume of a Prism

Exercises, page 335

1. a) 60 m^3 **b)** 1.66 mm^3 **c)** 187 cm^3

2. a) 114 m^2 **b)** 11.56 mm^2 **c)** 298 cm^2

3. a) 96 cm^2 **b)** 161.5 cm^2 **c)** 59.5 cm^2 **d)** 73.5 cm^2

4. a) 64 cm^3 **b)** 105 cm^3 **c)** 27.5 cm^3 **d)** 42.88 cm^3

5. a) 50.81 cm^2 **b)** 33.47 cm^2 **c)** 92.06 cm^2 **d)** 184 cm^2

6. a) 20 cm^3 **b)** 9 cm^3 **c)** 30 cm^3 **d)** 120 cm^3

7. a) i) 4.0 cm **ii)** 264 cm^2 **iii)** 180 cm^3
b) i) 6.93 cm **ii)** 343.44 cm^2 **iii)** 332.64 cm^3

8. The soil was piled higher than the sides of the truck.

9. 228 cm^2

10. a) 3 cm **b)** 10 cm **c)** 16 cm

11. b) 20 cm by 10 cm by 10 cm

12. The true capacity is 49.6 L. The manufacturer probably rounded up to 50 L.

13. a) $1\,000\,000$ **b)** 25%

15. a) The volume is doubled.
b) The volume is 4 times greater.
c) The volume is 8 times greater.

16. a) The surface area is $1.\overline{6}$ times greater.
b) The surface area is $2.\overline{6}$ times greater.
c) The surface area is 4 times greater.

8.6 Optimal Values of Measurement: Part II

Exercises, page 341

1. a) 2 cm by 2 cm by 2 cm **b)** 3 cm by 3 cm by 3 cm
c) 4 cm by 4 cm by 4 cm

2. a) 24 cm^2 **b)** 54 cm^2 **c)** 96 cm^2

3. a) 2 cm by 2 cm by 5 cm **b)** 4 cm by 4 cm by 3 cm
c) 2 cm by 2 cm by 13 cm

4. a) 48 cm^2 **b)** 80 cm^2 **c)** 112 cm^2

5. a) 32 cm^2 **b)** 94 cm^2 **c)** 46 cm^2

6. a)

Length (cm)	Width (cm)	Height (cm)
1	1	24
2	1	12
2	2	6
2	3	4
3	1	8
4	1	6

b) 2 cm by 3 cm by 4 cm

7. a)

Length (cm)	Width (cm)	Height (cm)
1	1	32
2	1	16
2	2	8
4	1	8
4	2	4

b) 4 cm by 2 cm by 4 cm

8. a)

Length (cm)	Width (cm)	Height (cm)
1	1	100
1	10	10
2	1	50
2	2	25
2	5	10
4	1	25
5	1	20
5	5	4

b) 5 cm by 5 cm by 4 cm

9. a) Yes, they do.
b) 1260 m^2; 990 m^2; The two-floor design is cheaper because it has less surface area.

10. The rectangular prism with the least surface area will be closest to a cube.

11. a) 40 cm; 1700 cm^2
b) i) 27.78 cm; 1477.44 cm^2 **ii)** 20.41 cm; 1338.96 cm^2

c)

Length (cm)	Width (cm)	Height (cm)	Volume (cm³)	Surface area (m²)
10	10	40	4000	1700
12	12	27.78	4000	1477.44
14	14	20.41	4000	1338.96

d) 20 cm by 20 cm by 10 cm

12. No

14. a) 216 square units

c) 6 units by 6 units by 4 units

15. a) 384 cm^2; 768 cm^2; 1536 cm^2

b) 3072 cm^2

c) The total surface area doubles each step.

16. a) 40   **b)** 320

17. a) 921.6 cm^3

c)

Length of the cutout square (cm)	Length of the box (cm)	Width of the box (cm)	Height of the box (cm)	Volume of the box (cm³)
1	26	19.6	1	509.6
2	24	17.6	2	844.8
3	22	15.6	3	1029.6
4	20	13.6	4	1088.0
5	18	11.6	5	1044.0
6	16	9.6	6	921.6
7	14	7.6	7	744.8
8	12	5.6	8	537.6
9	10	3.6	9	324.0

c) i) The volume of the box increases until the length of the cutout square is 4 cm, then the volume decreases.

ii) The volume of the box would decrease.

d)

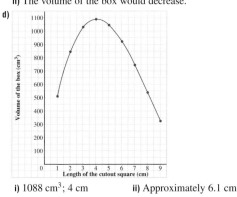

i) 1088 cm^3; 4 cm   **ii)** Approximately 6.1 cm

Self-Check 8.1–8.6
Exercises, page 345

1. a) 37 m   **b)** 75.40 m

2. 150.80 m^2

3. a square 10 units by 10 units

4. 2.07 m^3

5. 27 000 cm^3

6. 4924.92 cm^2

7.

Length (cm)	Width (cm)	Height (cm)
1	1	36
1	2	18
1	3	12
1	4	9
1	6	6
2	2	9
2	3	6
3	3	4

b) 3 cm by 3 cm by 4 cm

8.

Length (ft.)	Width (ft.)	Height (ft.)
1	1	24
1	2	12
1	3	8
1	4	6
2	2	6
2	3	4

b) 2 ft. by 3 ft. by 4 ft.

9. d

8.7 Surface Area and Volume of a Cylinder
Exercises, page 349

1. a) 314.2 cm^2 **b)** 50.3 cm^2 **c)** 141.0 cm^2

2. a) 12.6 cm^2 **b)** 1256.6 cm^2 **c)** 75.4 cm^2 **d)** 171.4 cm^2

3. a) 18.8 cm^2 **b)** 1885.0 cm^2 **c)** 175.9 cm^2 **d)** 201.8 cm^2

4. a) 6.3 cm^3 **b)** 6283.2 cm^3 **c)** 150.8 cm^3 **d)** 188.5 cm^3

5. a) 84.8 cm^2 **b)** 160.2 cm^2 **c)** 68.7 cm^2

6. a) 53.0 cm^3 **b)** 148.9 cm^3 **c)** 43.3 cm^3

7. a) 3141.6 cm^2 **b)** 12 566.4 cm^3

8. No

9. a) 1097.8 cm^2 **b)** 559.9 cm^2

10. 16.3 cm

11. a) 240.5 cm^2 **b)** 34.2 cm^2 **c)** 308.9 cm^2

12. a) 14 261.6 m^3 **b)** 510

13. 618.5 cm^2

14. 60 243.2 cm^2

15. $SA = 2(SA_{end}) + SA_{curved\ region}$
$= 2\pi r^2 + 2\pi rh$

16. a) 325 117 cm^3; 325.117 L   **b)** 28 149 cm^2

17. 790.8 cm

18. a) 3.18 cm   **b)** 463.1 cm^2

19. a) The total surface area is 1.5 times greater.

b) The total surface area is 3 times greater.

c) The total surface area is 4 times greater.

8.9 Volume of a Cone
Exercises, page 357

1. a) 235.62 m^3 **b)** 187.82 cm^3 **c)** 1.77 cm^3 **d)** 1.80 cm^3

2. a) 1256.6 cm^3 **b)** 115.8 m^3 **c)** 20 944.0 cm^3

d) 22.9 m^3 **e)** 12 959.1 cm^3 **f)** 219 861.2 cm^3

3. a) 9.38 cm^3 **b)** 0.23 m^3

c) 1809.56 cm^3 **d)** 105 293.62 cm^3

4. 32 cm^3

5. 162 cm^3

6. 146.3 cm^3

7. a) 785.40 cm^3 **b)** 261.80 cm^3

8. 1466.87 m^3

9. Cone A

10. The height of the cone is 3 times the height of the cylinder.

11. 10.0 m

12. 21.2 m

8.10 Volume of a Sphere
Exercises, page 361

1. a) 4189 cm^3 **b)** 524 cm^3 **c)** 14 710 cm^3

2. a) 212.17 cm^3 **b)** 41.63 cm^3
c) 26.52 cm^3 **d)** 4780.11 cm^3

3. a) 6.91 × 10^{13} km^3 **b)** 1.69 × 10^{10} km^3

4. a) 1.08 × 10^{12} km^3; 1.09 × 10^{12} km^3
b) The polar radius

5. 27 times

6. a) 11.94 cm **b)** 7130.20 cm^3

7. 523.60 cm^3

8. The new volume is 8 times greater.

9. The sphere

10. 2.22 m

11. a)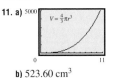

b) 523.60 cm^3 **c)** 2.88 cm

8.11 Mathematical Modelling: Designing a Cooler
Exercises, page 363

2. a) 8125.44 cm^2; 7502.17 cm^2
b) The cylinder model **c)** 623.27 cm^2

3. a) 22.85 cm **b)** 6563.43 cm^2

4. The sphere model

5. It would roll.

6. a) $V = \frac{10}{3}\pi r^3$; $V = \frac{8}{3}\pi r^3$
b) $50\,000 = \frac{10}{3}\pi r^3$; $50\,000 = \frac{8}{3}\pi r^3$
c) 16.84 cm; 18.14 cm

7. a) $A = 8\pi r^2$; $A = 7\pi r^2$
b) 7126.35 cm^2; 7235.73 cm^2
c) The surface area of the combination model is greater than that of the sphere model but less than that of the cylinder model.

Chapter 8 Review
Exercises, page 366

1. a) 38.4 mm **b)** 38.00 m **c)** 34.21 cm

2. a) 60.48 km^2 **b)** 121.5 m^2 **c)** 42.5 m^2

3. a) 11.94 m **b)** 29.08 m^2

4. a) 256 m^2 **b)** 156.25 m^2

5. 4.5 m by 4.5 m

6. Yes; 4 m by 5 m

7. a) 599.04 cm^2 **b)** 224.34 m^2

8. a) 6125 cm^3 **b)** 2205 cm^2

9. 5 mm

10. 110 cm^2

11. 2 ft. by 3 ft. by 3 ft.; 1 ft. by 3 ft. by 6 ft.; 1 ft. by 2 ft. by 9 ft.

12. a) 402.12 m^3 **b)** 190.85 mm^3

13. a) 301.59 m^2 **b)** 212.06 mm^2

14. a) 13 916.27 L **b)** 32.69 m^2

15. No, the height of the can does not equal the diameter of the base.

16. 108 mL

17. a) 821.00 cm^3 **b)** 9.62 m^3

18. 121.87 mL

19. a) 9202.77 cm^3 **b)** 113.10 m^3 **c)** 1538.82 mm^3

20. 3053.63 cm^3

Chapter 8 Self-Test
Exercises, page 368

1. a) 37.6 cm; 67.2 cm^2 **b)** 22.88 m; 6.50 m^2

2. a) 358.14 cm^3 **b)** 904.78 cm^3

3. The first cylinder has the minimum surface area because the height of the cylinder is virtually equal to its diameter.

4. 14.475 m^3

5. 33 m^2

Preparation for Ontario Testing
Exercises, page 369

6. 60 000 BTUs

7. The pipe is open-ended. Anita should not include $2\pi r^2$ in her calculation.

Chapter 9 Geometry

Necessary Skills
Identifying Figures and Angles
Exercises, page 372

1. a) iii **b)** i **c)** v **d)** ix
e) iv **f)** vi **g)** xi **h)** vii
i) ii **j)** x **k)** viii

9.3 Medians of Triangles
Exercises, page 383

1. 36 cm^2

2.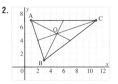
a) (2, 4); (7, 4); (6, 7)
b) (5, 5)

3. a) It should balance because the areas on each side of the median are equal.

4. a) No
  b) Yes. The median divides the area in half.
  d) No

9.5 Altitudes of Triangles
Exercises, page 391

1. a) 25 cm^2 **b)** 32 cm^2 **c)** 96 cm^2

2. 6 cm

3. a) $A_{triangle} = 14$ m^2; $A_{trapezoid} = 22.95$ m^2
  b) 73.9 m^2

4. a) 7.39 m^2 **b)** 81.29 m^2

5. a) 7.4 m^2 **b)** 81.3 m^2

6. 28

9.7 Angle Bisectors of Triangles
Exercises, page 396

1. a) 3 cm **b)** 62°

2. a) 30° **b)** 20.5° **c)** 32°
  d) 46° **e)** 36° **f)** $x = 32$°; $y = 58$°

3. 115°

4. 90°

Self-Check 9.1–9.7
Exercises, page 397

1. 12.5 mm^2

2. a) The triangles are congruent with sides 2.89 cm, 5.00 cm, 5.77 cm and angle measures 30°, 60°, 90°.
  b) The medians of equilateral triangles intersect to form 6 congruent right triangles.

3. a) 30 m^2 **b)** 13 m **c)** 2.3 m

4.
  a) (5, 1)
  b) $x = 5$ (for y-values 1 to 7)

5. $\angle APC = 90$°; $\angle PAC = 30$°

6. d

9.9 Interior and Exterior Angles
Exercises, page 405

1. a) 99° **b)** 40° **c)** 45° **d)** 105°

2. a) 135° **b)** 35° **c)** 125° **d)** 127°

3. a) $x = 36$°; $3x = 108$°
  b) $x = 29$°; $x + 6 = 35$°; $5x = 145$°

4. a) 280° **b)** $x = y = 108$°

9.11 Angles and Parallel Lines
Exercises, page 412

1. $\angle LPN = 135$° $\angle LQW = 135$° $\angle LRM = 130$°
  $\angle NPV = 45$° $\angle LQU = 45$° $\angle LRT = 50$°
  $\angle SPR = 135$° $\angle WQV = 45$° $\angle MRV = 50$°
  $\angle UQV = 135$°

2. a) $\angle ABE$, $\angle BEF$
  b) $\angle GBA$, $\angle GED$ or $\angle FEH$, $\angle CBE$
  c) $\angle ABE$, $\angle BED$ or $\angle CBE$, $\angle BEF$

3. l_1 and l_3

4. a) 50° **b)** 70°
  c) $x = 98$°; $y = 118$° **d)** $a = b = 78$°

5. a) $a = 55$°; $b = 50$°; $c = 55$°
  b) $u = 35$°; $w = x = 40$°; $y = 105$°

6. No

9.13 Sides and Diagonals of Quadrilaterals
Exercises, page 422

1. a) rhombus **b)** trapezoid **c)** square

2. a) 13 cm **b)** 5 cm

3. a) Yes. A square's opposite sides are parallel and its diagonals bisect each other.
  b) Yes. A square's diagonals bisect each other and are perpendicular.

4. a)

All sides equal	square, rhombus
2 pairs of opposite sides equal	perallelogram, rectangle, square, rhombus
1 pair of opposite sides parallel	trapezoid
2 pairs of opposite sides parallel	square, rectangle, perallelogram, rhombus
Equal diagonals	square, rectangle
Diagonals bisect each other	square, rectangle, perallelogram, rhombus
Perpendicular sides	square, rectangle
Perpendicular diagonals	square, rhombus, kite

b) **c)** **d)** **e)** **f)** **g)** **h)**

Chapter 9 Review
Exercises, page 428

1. A median is a line from one vertex to the midpoint of the opposite side.

2. 18 mm^2

3. 8 cm

4. a) acute triangle **b)** obtuse triangle

5. $x = 16$°; $y = 45$°; $z = 29$°

6. $x = y = 30$°

7. a) 124° **b)** $x = 30$°; $2x = 60$°; $3x = 90$°

8. a) 120° **b)** $x = 60$° **c)** $x = 52$°; $y = 30$°

9.

10. a) $x = y = 48.5$° **b)** $b = 49$°; $c = 90$°

11. a) 90° **b)** $a = 135$°; $b = c = 45$° **c)** 72°

12. AB = DC; BC = AD; AE = CE; BE = DE

13. QR = QP; RS = PS; RT = PT
  $\angle RTQ = \angle PTQ = \angle RTS = \angle PTS$

Chapter 9 Self-Test

Exercises, page 430

1. 21 cm²

2. a) i) $a = 157°; b = 113°; a + b = 270°$
ii) $a = 140°; b = 130°; a + b = 270°$
b) The sum of the exterior angles of a right triangle formed by extending the legs is 270°.

3. $x = 85°; y = 45°$

4. right triangle

5. a) rhombus   **b)** square   **c)** kite   **d)** trapezoid

6. A rectangle must have 2 pair of opposite sides that are parallel, equal in length, and meet at 90°. A square has these properties.

Preparation for Ontario Testing

Exercises, page 431

7. The diagonals should be equal in length.

8. ∠EBC and ∠BCD are alternate angles; alternate angles are equal.
∠BCD and ∠ADC are interior angles; interior angles add to 180°.

Cumulative Review

Chapters 1–9

Exercises, page 424

1. a)

Regular Hexagons						
Side length (m)	1	2	3	4	5	6
Perimeter (m)	6	12	18	24	30	36

b)

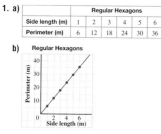

The points should be joined because the side length does not have to be a whole number. It is possible for it to be a decimal.

c) For every metre increase in side length, the perimeter increases by 6 m. The difference in consecutive perimeter values is constant at 6 m. This is seen in the slope of the graph, which is 6.

d) Linear. From the table, the difference in consecutive perimeter values is constant. From the graph, the relation is a straight line.

2. a) i)

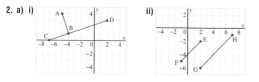

ii)

iii)

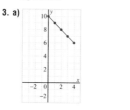

iv)

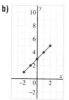

b) i) AB: –3; CD: $\frac{1}{3}$ **ii)** EF: 1; GH: 1
iii) WX: 0; YZ: undefined   **iv)** PQ: $-\frac{3}{4}$; RS: –1

c) i) perpendicular; slopes are negative reciprocals
ii) parallel; slopes are equal
iii) perpendicular; lines intersect at 90°
iv) neither

3. a)

b)

4. a) $0.96   **b)** approximately 276 g

5. a) $y = 2x - 1$ **b)** $y = \frac{4}{3}x + 3$ **c)** $y = -\frac{1}{2}x - 5$

6. a)   **b)**   **c)**

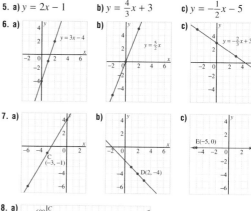

7. a)   **b)**   **c)**

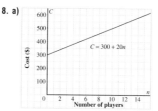

8. a)

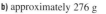

b) 20; It represents the additional cost per player.
c) 300; It represents the fixed cost to play in the tournament.

9. a) 25   **b)** $\frac{1}{6}$ **c)** 1   **d)** $\frac{1}{16}$

10. a) 4, –4   **b)** 5, –5   **c)** 8, –8   **d)** 9, –9   **e)** 12, –12

11. a) 8.6 m   **b)** 20.1 cm

12. a) $2x + 9$ **b)** $2x^2 + 2x - 3$
c) $2x - 4$ **d)** $2x^2 - x - 8$

13. a)   **b)**

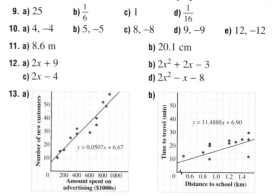

14. a) 268.1 cm³   **b)** 942.5 m³   **c)** 358.1 cm³

15. a) Different birds require different entrance sizes because different bird species are different sizes.

b), c)

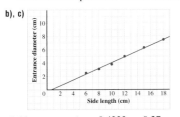

d) 11 cm   **e)** $y = 0.4322x - 0.27$ **f)** 10.8 cm

g) They are close. The equation gives a more exact answer.

16. a) $x = 220°$; $y = 80°$ **b)** $x = 113°$; $y = 120°$; $z = 67°$

17. a) $x = 51°$ **b)** $x = 36°$

Numeracy Skills Appendix

Factors
Exercises, page A2

1. a) 1, 2, 5, 10   **b)** 1, 2, 4, 8, 16   **c)** 1, 2, 3, 6
d) 1, 7   **e)** 1, 2   **f)** 1, 3, 5, 15

2. a) 1, 2, 3, 4, 6, 8, 12, 24   **b)** 1, 2, 4, 5, 10, 20, 25, 50, 100
c) 1, 5, 25   **d)** 1, 2, 4, 8

3. a) 4: <u>1</u>, <u>2</u>,④; 12: <u>1</u>, <u>2</u>, 3,④, 6, 12
b) 16: <u>1</u>, <u>2</u>,④, 8, 16; 20: <u>1</u>, <u>2</u>,④, 5, 10, 20
c) 8: <u>1</u>, <u>2</u>,④, 8; 12: <u>1</u>, <u>2</u>, 3,④, 6, 12
d) 3: <u>1</u>,③; 9: <u>1</u>,③, 9

4. a) 2   **b)** 12   **c)** 20   **d)** 6

Multiples
Exercises, page A3

1. 6, 12, 18, 24, 30

2. a) 20, 25, 30, 35, 40   **b)** 16, 20, 24, 28, 32
c) 28, 35, 42, 49, 56   **d)** 40, 50, 60, 70, 80
e) 400, 500, 600, 700, 800   **f)** 100, 125, 150, 175, 200
g) 48, 60, 72, 84, 96   **h)** 36, 45, 54, 63, 72

3. a) 6: <u>6</u>, 12, 18, 24, 30; 2: 2, 4, <u>6</u>, 8, 10
b) 3: 3, 6, 9, <u>12</u>, 15; 4: 4, 8, <u>12</u>, 16, 20
c) 2: 2, 4, 6, 8, <u>10</u>; 10: <u>10</u>, 20, 30, 40, 50
d) 4: 4, 8, <u>12</u>, 16, 20; 6: 6, <u>12</u>, 18, 24, 30

4. a) 4   **b)** 20   **c)** 8   **d)** 12
e) 24   **f)** 100   **g)** 18   **h)** 8

5. a) 6   **b)** 12   **c)** 18   **d)** 24

6. 3 packages of buns; 2 packages of veggie burgers

Place Value and Rounding
Exercises, page A4

1. a) 1   **b)** 3   **c)** 9   **d)** 1

2. a) 2   **b)** 1   **c)** 5

3. a) 19   **b)** 128   **c)** 14 299   **d)** 10   **e)** 153
4. a) 7   **b)** 6   **c)** 5   **d)** 9
5. a) 9   **b)** 0   **c)** 6

Estimating Sums and Differences
Exercises, page A5

Estimations may vary. Actual answers are given in brackets.

1. a) 21 000 (21 191) **b)** 8500 (8551)   **c)** 2500 (2543)
d) 41 (40.59)   **e)** 105 (104.19)

2. a) $88 000 ($88 144)   **b)** 45 (44.36)
c) 1.2 (1.192)   **d)** $3 ($2.65)
e) 9900 (9935)

3. a) $15 ($15.67)   **b)** $12 ($11.50)

Mental Math for Sums and Differences
Exercises, page A6

1. a) 20   **b)** 20   **c)** 10   **d)** 1010   **e)** 200   **f)** 1000
2. a) 100   **b)** 104   **c)** 200   **d)** 198   **e)** 97   **f)** 703
3. a) 711   **b)** 3   **c)** 5611   **d)** 1461   **e)** 60 453 **f)** 23 190

Estimating Products and Quotients
Exercises, page A7

Estimations may vary. Actual answers are given in brackets.

1. a) 4000 (3825)   **b)** 4800 (4659.2)
c) 240 (257.04)   **d)** 28 000 (26 790)

2. a) 20 (19.125)   **b)** 7 (7.807)
c) 1000 (1089.8)   **d)** 2 (1.997)

3. a) 5400 (5525)   **b)** 42 000 (43 092)
c) 180 (183.35)   **d)** 32 (31.82)

4. 1800 km (1788 km)

Mental Math for Products and Quotients
Exercises, page A8

1. a) 10, 1000, 100 000, 10 000 000
b) 42, 4200, 420 000, 42 000 000
c) 270, 27, 2.7, 0.27

2. a) 10, 100, 1000, 10 000   **b)** 7, 70, 700, 7000

3. a) 0   **b)** 1   **c)** 0   **d)** 0   **e)** 0

4. a) 28 512   **b)** 792   **c)** 285 120 **d)** 7920   **e)** 360

5. a) 47.1   **b)** 4.71   **c)** 0.471   **d)** 0.0054 **e)** 0.54

6. a) 100   **b)** 1   **c)** 200   **d)** 4   **e)** 0.06

7. bamboo: 280 cm; giant bamboo: 630 cm

Integers
Exercises, page A9

1. a) 8°C   **b)** −6°C   **c)** 35°C
2. a) −16°C   **b)** +1°C   **c)** +7°C
d) −9°C   **e)** +$25   **f)** −$109

3. a) −8   b) +2   c) +1
d) −24   e) −9   f) +15

4. a) −5   b) +2   c) −1

5. 0

Adding Integers
Exercises, page A10

1. a) 8   b) −8   c) −4   d) 4
e) 0   f) 0   g) 0   h) 0

2. a) 7   b) 5   c) 7   d) −2
e) −9   f) 0   g) −14   h) −4

3. a) positive   b) negative   c) positive
d) negative   e) negative   f) positive

Subtracting Integers
Exercises, page A11

1. a) −1   b) 7   c) 1   d) −7

2. a) 6   b) −8   c) 8   d) −6

3. a) −9   b) 2   c) −2   d) 10

4. a) 8   b) −4   c) −1   d) 0

5. 74°C

Adding and Subtracting Integers
Exercises, page A12

1. a) 3   b) −1   c) −3   d) 1
e) 4   f) −4   g) −2   h) 2

2. a) −1   b) 9   c) 1   d) −9
e) 1   f) −1   g) −9   h) 9

3. a) 2   b) 3   c) −7
d) −10   e) 6   f) 5

Multiplying Integers
Exercises, page A13

1. a) negative   b) positive   c) negative   d) positive

2. a) 2   b) −2   c) 2   d) −2
e) −30   f) 6   g) 1   h) 0

3. a) $(-7)(-2) = 14$ b) $(4)(1) = 4$
   $(-7)(-1) = 7$ $(3)(1) = 3$
   $(-7)(0) = 0$ $(2)(1) = 2$
   $(-7)(1) = -7$ $(1)(1) = 1$
   $(-7)(2) = -14$ $(0)(1) = 0$
   $(-7)(3) = -21$ $(-1)(1) = -1$
c) $(-9)(3) = -27$ d) $(4)(-4) = -16$
   $(-9)(2) = -18$ $(3)(-3) = -9$
   $(-9)(1) = -9$ $(2)(-2) = -4$
   $(-9)(0) = 0$ $(1)(-1) = -1$
   $(-9)(-1) = 9$ $(0)(0) = 0$
   $(-9)(-2) = 18$ $(-1)(1) = -1$

4. a) −512   c) −3534

5. a) 70   b) 0   c) −27   d) −54

Dividing Integers
Exercises, page A14

1. a) positive   b) positive   c) negative   d) negative

2. a) 4   b) −4   c) −4   d) 4

3. a) −2   b) 2   c) 4   d) −6

4. a) 5   b) 7   c) −4   d) −4

5. b) 8   c) 9

Proper Fractions
Exercises, page A15

1. a) $\frac{1}{2}$ b) $\frac{3}{5}$ c) $\frac{1}{3}$ d) $\frac{1}{10}$ e) $\frac{2}{3}$ f) $\frac{1}{3}$

2. a) $\frac{1}{3}$ b) $\frac{1}{2}$ c) $\frac{4}{5}$ d) $\frac{1}{4}$ e) $\frac{1}{3}$ f) $\frac{9}{10}$

3. c) $\frac{2}{3}$ e) $\frac{2}{3}$

4. a) $\frac{1}{4}$ b) $\frac{1}{4}$ c) $\frac{5}{6}$ d) $\frac{2}{3}$ e) $\frac{1}{2}$ f) $\frac{1}{4}$

Improper Fractions
Exercises, page A16

1. a) 1 b) $1\frac{1}{2}$ c) $1\frac{1}{4}$ d) $1\frac{1}{3}$ e) $1\frac{3}{4}$ f) $2\frac{1}{3}$

2. a) $\frac{3}{2}$ b) $\frac{5}{4}$ c) 1 d) 2 e) $\frac{7}{5}$ f) $\frac{6}{5}$

3. a) $\frac{5}{4}$ b) 1 c) $\frac{9}{8}$ d) $\frac{5}{4}$ e) $\frac{3}{2}$ f) 10

Common Denominators
Exercises, page A17

1. a) $\frac{2}{8}$ b) $\frac{15}{24}$ c) $\frac{8}{10}$ d) $\frac{12}{16}$

2. a) $\frac{4}{12}$ b) $\frac{9}{12}$ c) $\frac{10}{12}$ d) $\frac{6}{12}$ e) $\frac{3}{12}$ f) $\frac{8}{12}$

3. a) 4 b) 12 c) 6 d) 12 e) 10 f) 20

4. a) $\frac{2}{4}, \frac{1}{4}$ b) $\frac{4}{12}, \frac{21}{12}$ c) $\frac{4}{6}, \frac{9}{6}$ d) $\frac{15}{12}, \frac{2}{12}$ e) $\frac{9}{10}, \frac{4}{10}$ f) $\frac{12}{20}, \frac{15}{20}$

5. a) $\frac{6}{9}, \frac{4}{9}$ b) $\frac{7}{10}, \frac{15}{10}$ c) $\frac{5}{8}, \frac{10}{8}$ d) $\frac{9}{12}, \frac{5}{12}$ e) $\frac{14}{12}, \frac{3}{12}$ f) $\frac{11}{12}, \frac{8}{12}$

Adding Fractions
Exercises, page A18

1. a) $\frac{3}{5}$ b) $\frac{5}{7}$ c) 1 d) 1

2. a) $\frac{9}{8}$ b) $\frac{31}{12}$ c) $\frac{18}{10} = \frac{9}{5}$ d) $\frac{7}{6}$

3. a) $\frac{13}{12}$ b) $\frac{31}{20}$ c) $\frac{17}{12}$ d) $\frac{25}{24}$

Subtracting Fractions
Exercises, page A19

1. a) 1 b) 2 c) $\frac{3}{4}$ d) 1

2. a) $\frac{5}{4}$ b) $\frac{3}{6} = \frac{1}{2}$ c) $\frac{9}{8}$ d) $\frac{7}{9}$

3. a) $\frac{1}{12}$ b) $\frac{8}{30} = \frac{4}{15}$ c) $\frac{7}{4}$ d) $\frac{37}{8}$

Multiplying Fractions
Exercises, page A20

1. a) $= \frac{10}{40}$ **b)** $= \frac{4}{1} \times \frac{3}{5}$ **c)** $= \frac{18}{6}$ **d)** $= \frac{15}{4}$

$= \frac{1}{4}$ $= \frac{12}{5}$ $= 3$

2. a) $\frac{1}{8}$ **b)** $\frac{3}{6} = \frac{1}{2}$ **c)** $\frac{3}{20}$

d) $\frac{1}{4}$ **e)** $\frac{15}{10} = \frac{3}{2}$ **f)** $\frac{6}{12} = \frac{1}{2}$

3. a) $\frac{2}{8} = \frac{1}{4}$ **b)** $\frac{28}{21} = \frac{4}{3}$ **c)** 2

d) $\frac{10}{45} = \frac{2}{9}$ **e)** $\frac{45}{90} = \frac{1}{2}$ **f)** $\frac{12}{24} = \frac{1}{2}$

4. a) 1 **b)** 1 **c)** 1 **d)** 1
They all equal 1 because the fractions are reciprocals.

5. a) 5 **b)** 21 **c)** 10 **d)** $\frac{20}{8} = \frac{5}{2}$

Dividing Fractions
Exercises, page A21

1. a) $= \frac{3}{8} \times \frac{1}{5}$ **b)** $= \frac{3}{4} \times \frac{2}{9}$ **c)** $= \frac{7}{10} \times \frac{5}{1}$ **d)** $= \frac{6}{1} \times \frac{3}{2}$

$= \frac{3}{40}$ $= \frac{6}{36}$ $= \frac{35}{10}$ $= \frac{18}{2}$

$= \frac{1}{6}$ $= \frac{7}{2}$ $= 9$

2. a) 2 **b)** $\frac{1}{10}$ **c)** 1 **d)** $\frac{2}{3}$ **e)** $\frac{2}{9}$ **f)** $\frac{5}{3}$

3. a) 20 **b)** $\frac{3}{4}$ **c)** $\frac{6}{25}$ **d)** 8 **e)** $\frac{1}{2}$ **f)** $\frac{4}{5}$

4. a) 1 **b)** 1 **c)** 1 **d)** 1 **e)** 1 **f)** 1
They all equal 1 because you multiply by the reciprocal.

Fractions to Decimals
Exercises, page A22

1. a) 0.5 **b)** 0.6 **c)** 0.75
d) 0.02 **e)** 0.18 **f)** 0.08

2. a) $0.\overline{45}$ **b)** 1.45 **c)** 0.25 **d)** $1.\overline{6}$

3. a) 1.11 **b)** 1.7 **c)** 0.12 **d)** 0.24 **e)** 1.39

Decimals to Fractions
Exercises, page A23

1. a) $\frac{3}{4}$ **b)** $\frac{7}{4}$ **c)** $\frac{1}{100}$ **d)** $\frac{101}{100}$ **e)** $\frac{1}{5}$ **f)** $\frac{6}{5}$

2. a) $\frac{1}{4}$ **b)** $\frac{21}{20}$ **c)** $\frac{11}{5}$ **d)** $\frac{97}{100}$ **e)** $\frac{1}{3}$ **f)** $\frac{19}{10}$

3. a) $\frac{27}{20}$ **b)** $\frac{9}{100}$ **c)** $\frac{15}{4}$ **d)** $\frac{9}{5}$ **e)** $\frac{9}{2}$ **f)** $\frac{3}{5}$

4. a) $\frac{4}{9}$ **b)** $\frac{1}{3}$ **c)** $\frac{4}{11}$ **d)** $\frac{3}{11}$

e) $\frac{3}{11}$ **f)** $\frac{4}{9}$ **g)** $\frac{1}{3}$ **h)** $\frac{4}{11}$

Ratio
Exercises, page A24

1. It is not just 3 because a ratio is a comparison of 2 or more quantities.

2. a) 4 : 12 **b)** 12 : 4 **c)** 4 : 16 **d)** 12 : 16

3. a) 1 : 2 **b)** 3 : 1 **c)** 2 : 3
d) 1 : 2 **e)** 2 : 1 **f)** 2 : 3

4. a) 2 : 3 **b)** 2 : 5 **c)** 2 : 1

5. 5 : 3

Rate
Exercises, page A25

1. a) $7/h **b)** $8.50/h **c)** $6.75/h

2. a) $43.75 **b)** $73.50 **c)** $146.70 **d)** $166.25

3. Keon's

4. a) 100 km/h **b)** 75 km/h **c)** 92 m/h **d)** 40 cm/h

5. a) 320 km in 4 h **b)** They are the same.

Percent
Exercises, page A26

1. a) $\frac{27}{100}$; 0.27; 27% **b)** $\frac{9}{100}$; 0.09; 9% **c)** $\frac{81}{100}$; 0.81; 81%

2. a) 0.71; $\frac{71}{100}$ **b)** 0.09; $\frac{9}{100}$ **c)** 0.2; $\frac{1}{5}$

d) 0.25; $\frac{1}{4}$ **e)** 0.5; $\frac{1}{2}$ **f)** 0.05; $\frac{1}{20}$

3. a) $\frac{21}{100}$, 0.21; $\frac{3}{4}$, 0.75; $\frac{1}{25}$, 0.04

b) $\frac{4}{25}$, 0.16; $\frac{3}{4}$, 0.75; $\frac{9}{100}$, 0.09

4. a) 10% **b)** 20% **c)** 45%
d) 70% **e)** 75% **f)** 95%

5. a) 1.1 **b)** 2 **c)** 1.15
d) 1 **e)** 1.01 **f)** 3.09

Mental Math and Estimation with Fractions and Percent
Exercises, page A27

1. a) $\frac{1}{102}, \frac{1}{101}, \frac{1}{100}, \frac{1}{99}, \frac{1}{98}$

b) $\frac{19}{23}, \frac{20}{23}, \frac{21}{23}, \frac{22}{23}, \frac{23}{23}$

c) $\frac{7}{13}, \frac{7}{12}, \frac{7}{11}, \frac{7}{10}, \frac{7}{9}$

2. Estimations may vary. Actual answers are given in brackets.
$\frac{43}{67}$ is approximately 64%.

a) 68% (68.66%) **b)** 60% (59.70%) **c)** 60% (61.43%)
d) 68% (67.19%) **e)** 31% (31.34%)

3. $\frac{6}{17}$

One Number as a Percent of Another Number
Exercises, page A28

1. a) 90% **b)** 33% **c)** 50% **d)** 100% **e)** 35% **f)** 75%

2. a) 37% **b)** 90% **c)** 40% **d)** 100% **e)** 0% **f)** 25%

3. a) 80% **b)** 100% **c)** 17% **d)** 60%

4. a) 40% **b)** 60% **c)** $33.\overline{3}$%

Percent of an Amount

Exercises, page A29

1. a) 70　　　　　**b)** 135　　　　　**c)** 0.2
The answer is the same as the percent, but without the percent sign.

2. a) 400　　　**b)** 40　　　**c)** 4　　　**d)** 0.4
Each answer is the previous one divided by 10.

3. a) 32　　　**b)** 3.6　　　**c)** 3.6　　　**d)** 383

4. a) $12.80　　**b)** $11.20　　**c)** $183.98　　**d)** the total cost

5. a) $4.03　　**b)** $114.99　　**c)** $287.49　　**d)** $0.12

6. a) $496.79　　**b)** $138.00　　**c)** $275.99　　**d)** $386.39

Mental Math and Estimation with Percent of an Amount

Exercises, page A30

1. a) >75　　　**b)** <75　　　**c)** neither　　　**d)** <75

2. a) 0.6　　　**b)** 30　　　**c)** 60　　　**d)** 120

3. a) 1.2　　　**b)** 29.4　　　**c)** 31.8　　　**d)** 87

4. a) 35.5　　　**b)** 20　　　**c)** 8　　　**d)** 60

Estimations may vary. Actual answers are given in brackets.

5. a) $155.25 ($155.24)　　　**b)** $20.70 ($20.69)

6. $244.38 ($244.37)

Rational Numbers

Exercises, page A31

1. a) $A = -1.75; B = -0.25; C = 0.5; D = -1.25$
b) $A = 0.9; B = 0.3; C = -0.6; D = -0.1$

2. a) 0　　　**b)** −2

3. a) 4　　**b)** −1　　**c)** 7　　**d)** 0　　**e)** −4　　**f)** 0

4. a) $\frac{4}{5}$　　**b)** $-\frac{1}{2}$　　**c)** $-\frac{2}{3}$　　**d)** $\frac{4}{5}$　　**e)** $-\frac{2}{3}$　　**f)** $-\frac{2}{3}$

5. a) 　　**b)**

c) 　　**d)**

e) 　　**f)**

Glossary

acute angle: an angle measuring less than 90°

acute triangle: a triangle with three acute angles

additive inverses: a number and its opposite; the sum of additive inverses is 0; for example, +3 + (−3) = 0

algebraic expression: a mathematical expression containing a variable: for example, $6x - 4$ is an algebraic expression

alternate angles: angles that are between two lines and are on opposite sides of a transversal that cuts the two lines

Angles 1 and 3 are alternate angles.
Angles 2 and 4 are alternate angles.

altitude: the perpendicular distance from the base of a figure to the opposite side or vertex

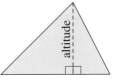

angle: the figure formed by two rays from the same endpoint

angle bisector: the line that divides an angle into two equal angles

approximation: a number close to the exact value of an expression; the symbol $\doteq$ means "is approximately equal to"

area: the number of square units needed to cover a region

average: a single number that represents a set of numbers; see *mean*, *median*, and *mode*

balance: the result when money is added to or subtracted from an original amount

bar notation: the use of a horizontal bar over a decimal digit to indicate that it repeats; for example, $1.\overline{3}$ means 1.333 333 …

base: the side of a polygon or the face of a solid from which the height is measured; the factor repeated in a power

bias: an emphasis on characteristics that are not typical of the entire population

binomial: a polynomial with two terms; for example, $3x - 8$

bisector: a line that divides a line segment into two equal parts

The broken line is a bisector of AB.

Calculator-Based-Ranger™ unit: a sonic motion detector that collects data and displays them on the calculator screen

capacity: the amount a container can hold

Cartesian plane: the *x*- and *y*-axes used to plot a point identified by a pair of numbers; see *coordinate axes*

CBR™: see *Calculator-Based-Ranger™ unit*

cell reference: the name of a cell in a spreadsheet, given by indicating the column and row to which it belongs; for example, cell B3 is the cell in column B and row 3 of a spreadsheet document

centroid: the point where the three medians of a triangle intersect

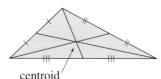

centroid

circle: the set of points in a plane that are a given distance from a fixed point (the centre)

O

circumcentre: the point where the perpendicular bisectors of the sides of a triangle intersect

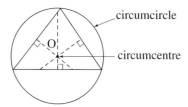

circumcircle

O

circumcentre

circumcircle: a circle drawn through each of the vertices of a triangle, and with its centre at the circumcentre of the triangle

circumference: the distance around a circle

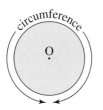

O

coefficient: the numerical factor of a term; for example, in the terms $3x$ and $3x^2$, the coefficient is 3

collecting like terms: putting together terms with exactly the same variable expressions, then simplifying by addition or subtraction

collinear points: points that lie on the same line

4 collinear points   4 non-collinear points

commission: a fee or payment given to a sales-person, usually a specified percent of the person's sales

common denominator: a number that is a multiple of each of the given denominators; for example, 12 is a common denominator for the fractions $\frac{1}{3}$, $\frac{5}{4}$, and $\frac{7}{12}$

common factor: a number that is a factor of each of the given numbers; for example, 3 is a common factor of 15, 9, and 21

commutative property: the property stating that two numbers can be added or multiplied in any order; for example, $6 + 8 = 8 + 6$ and $4 \times 7 = 7 \times 4$

complementary angles: two angles whose sum is 90°

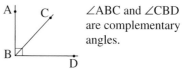

∠ABC and ∠CBD are complementary angles.

composite number: a number with three or more factors; for example, 8 is a composite number because its factors are 1, 2, 4, and 8

cone: a solid formed by a region (the base) with all line segments joining points on the boundary of the region to a point not in the region

congruent: figures that have the same size and shape, but not necessarily the same orientation

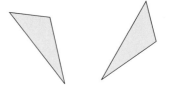

consecutive numbers: integers that come one after the other without any integers missing; for example, 34, 35, 36 are consecutive numbers, so are −2, −1, 0, and 1

constant term: a number

coordinate axes: the horizontal and vertical number lines on a grid that represents a plane

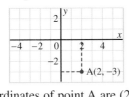

coordinate plane: a two-dimensional surface on which a coordinate system has been set up

coordinates: also called Cartesian coordinates; the numbers in an ordered pair that locate a point in the coordinate plane

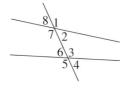

The coordinates of point A are (2, −3).

corresponding angles: angles that are on the same side of a transversal that cuts two lines and on the same side of each line

Angles 1 and 3 are corresponding angles.
Angles 2 and 4 are corresponding angles.
Angles 5 and 7 are corresponding angles.
Angles 6 and 8 are corresponding angles.

cube: a rectangular solid whose length, width, and height are all equal

cubic units: units that measure volume

cylinder: a solid with two parallel, congruent, circular bases

data: facts or information

database: an organized collection of facts or information, often stored on a computer

denominator: the term below the line in a fraction

density: the mass of a unit volume of a substance

dependent variable: the output of a relation, often denoted y; also called the responding variable

diagonal: a line segment that joins two vertices of a figure, but is not a side

diameter: the distance across a circle, measured through the centre; a line segment through the centre of the circle with its endpoints on the circle

digit: any of the symbols used to write numerals; for example, in the base-ten system the digits are 0, 1, 2, 3, 4, 5, 6, 7, 8, and 9

dilatation: a transformation in which the image is the same shape as the object, but is enlarged or reduced in size

direct variation: a relation that has the form $y = mx$

distributive law: the property stating that a product can be written as a sum or difference of two products; for example, for all real numbers a, b, and c: $a(b + c) = ab + ac$ and $a(b − c) = ab − ac$

equation: a mathematical statement indicating that two expressions are equal; for example, $2x + 5y = −4$

equation of a line: an equation that gives the relationship between the coordinates of every point on the line; the slope-intercept form is $y = mx + b$, where m is the slope of the line and b is the y-intercept of the line

equidistant: the same distance apart

equilateral triangle: a triangle with three equal sides

evaluate: to substitute a value for each variable in an expression

even number: an integer that has 2 as a factor; for example, 2, 4, −6

event: any set of outcomes of an experiment

expanding: multiplying a polynomial by a polynomial

exponent: a number, shown in a smaller size and raised, that tells how many times the number before it is used as a factor; for example, 2 is the exponent in 6^2

expression: a mathematical phrase made up of numbers and/or variables connected by operations

extrapolate: estimate a value beyond the known values

Using the graph to estimate the distance travelled after 10 h requires extrapolation; the last known value occurs when the time is 8 h.

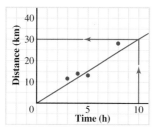

extremes: the highest and lowest values in a set of numbers

factor: to factor means to write as a product; to factor a given integer means to write it as a product of integers, the integers in the product are the factors of the given integer; to factor a polynomial with integer coefficients means to write it as a product of polynomials with integer coefficients

fixed cost: a cost, such as rent, that remains constant over a time period

formula: an equation that is used to describe the relationship between two or more quantities; for example, the formula that describes how the volume, V, of a sphere is related to its radius, r, is

$$V = \frac{4}{3}\pi r^3$$

fraction: an indicated quotient of two quantities

frequency: the number of times a particular number occurs in a set of data

graph: a drawing that shows the relationship between certain sets of quantities by means of lines, points, or bars

grouping property of addition (and multiplication): when three or more terms are added (or multiplied), the operations can be performed in any order

hectare: a unit of area that is equal to 10 000 m²

hendecagon: a polygon with 11 sides

hexagon: a six-sided polygon

horizontal intercept: the horizontal coordinate of the point where the graph of a line or a relation intersects the horizontal axis

hypotenuse: the side that is opposite the right angle in a right triangle

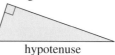
hypotenuse

identity for addition: a number that can be added to any number without changing the number; 0 is the identity for addition of real numbers

identity for multiplication: a number that can be multiplied by any number without changing the number; 1 is the identity for multiplication of real numbers

image: the figure that results from a transformation

incentre: the point at which the three angle bisectors of a triangle intersect

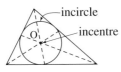

incircle: a circle drawn inside a triangle, with its centre at the incentre and with the radius the shortest distance from the incentre to one of the sides of the triangle

independent variable: the input variable in a relation, often called *x*; also called the manipulated variable

inequality: a statement that one quantity is greater than (or less than) another quantity

integers: the set of numbers that contains all positive and negative whole numbers, together with zero

… −3, −2, −1, 0, 1, 2, 3 … is the set of integers.

intercepts: the horizontal and vertical coordinates of the points at which a graph crosses the horizontal and vertical axes

interest: money that is paid for the use of money, usually according to a predetermined percent

interpolate: to estimate a value between two known values

intersecting lines: lines that meet or cross; lines that have one point in common

interval: a regular distance or space between values

inverse: see *additive inverses* and *multiplicative inverses*

irrational number: a number that cannot be written in the form $\frac{m}{n}$ where *m* and *n* are integers ($n \neq 0$); for example, π and $\sqrt{2}$ are irrational numbers

isosceles acute triangle: a triangle with two equal sides and all angles less than 90°

isosceles obtuse triangle: a triangle with two equal sides and one angle greater than 90°

isosceles right triangle: a triangle with two equal sides and a 90° angle

isosceles triangle: a triangle with two equal sides

kite: a quadrilateral with two pairs of equal adjacent sides

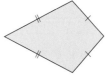

legs: the sides of a right triangle that form the right angle

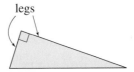

light-year: a unit for measuring astronomical distances; one light-year is the distance light travels in one year

like terms: terms that have the same variables; for example, $4x$ and $-3x$ are like terms

line of best fit: a line that passes as close as possible to a set of plotted points; it can be estimated by eye

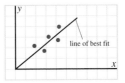

line segment: the part of a line between two points on the line, including the two points

line symmetry: a figure that maps onto itself when it is reflected in a line is said to have line symmetry; for example, line *l* is the line of symmetry for figure ABCD

linear relation: a relation that can be represented by a straight-line graph

mass: the amount of matter in an object

mean: the sum of a set of numbers divided by the number of numbers in the set

median: the middle number of a set of numbers arranged in numerical order; if there are two middle numbers, their average is the median of the data set

> For the data 2, 4, 8, 9, and 11 the median is 8. For the data 2, 4, 6, 8, 9, and 11 the median is 7, since $\frac{6+8}{2} = 7$.

median of a triangle: a line from one vertex to the midpoint of the opposite side

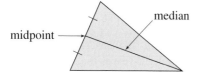

midpoint: the point that divides a line segment into two equal parts

mode: the number that occurs most often in a set of numbers

monomial: a polynomial with one term; for example, 14 and $5x^2$ are each monomials

multiple: the product of a given number and a natural number; for example, some multiples of 8 are 8, 16, 24,...

multiplicative inverses: a number and its reciprocal; the product of multiplicative inverses is 1; for example, $3 \times \frac{1}{3} = 1$

natural numbers: the set of numbers 1, 2, 3, 4, 5,...

negative number: a number less than 0

net: a diagram of the faces of a hollow three-dimensional object arranged so that the faces could be folded to form the three-dimensional object

non-linear relation: a relation that cannot be represented by a straight-line graph

numeracy: the ability to read, understand, and use numbers

numerator: the term above the line in a fraction

obtuse angle: an angle greater than 90° and less than 180°

obtuse triangle: a triangle with one angle greater than 90°

octagon: an eight-sided polygon

odd number: an integer that does not have 2 as a factor; for example, 1, 3, –7

operation: a mathematical process or action such as addition, subtraction, multiplication, or division

opposite angles: the equal angles that are formed by two intersecting lines

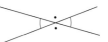

opposite number: a number whose sum with a given number is 0; for example, 3 and –3 are opposites

opposites: two numbers whose sum is zero; each number is the opposite of the other

optimization: making a system or object as efficient as possible

order of operations: the rules that are followed when simplifying or evaluating an expression:

> Complete all operations within brackets following the order of operations.
>
> Evaluate all exponents.
>
> Complete all multiplication and division in the order they appear from left to right.
>
> Complete all addition and subtraction in the order they appear from left to right.

order property of addition (and multiplication): two terms that are added (or multiplied) can be added (or multiplied) in any order

ordered pair: a pair of numbers, written as (x, y), that represents a point on the coordinate plane; see *coordinates*

orthocentre: the point at which the altitudes of a triangle intersect

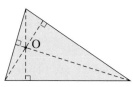

outcome: a possible result of an experiment or a possible answer to a survey question

parallel lines: lines in the same plane that do not intersect

parallelogram: a quadrilateral with opposite sides parallel

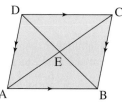

A parallelogram has the following properties:

The opposite sides have equal lengths. AB = CD and AD = BC

The opposite angles have equal measures (congruent). ∠A = ∠C and ∠B = ∠D

The diagonals bisect each other (cut each other into equal lengths). AE = EC and DE = EB

partial variation: a relation that has the form $y = mx + b$

pentagon: a five-sided polygon

per capita: for each person

percent: the number of parts per 100; the numerator of a fraction with denominator 100

perfect square: a number that is the square of a whole number; a polynomial that is the square of another polynomial

perimeter: the distance around a closed figure

perpendicular: intersecting at right angles

Two lines are perpendicular if their slopes are negative reciprocals of one another.

perpendicular bisector: the line that is perpendicular to a line segment and divides it in two equal parts

The broken line is the perpendicular bisector of AB.

pi (π): the ratio of the circumference of a circle to its diameter; $\pi \doteq 3.1416$

plane geometry: the study of two-dimensional figures; that is, figures drawn or visualized on a plane

point of balance: see *centroid*

point of intersection: the point that is common to two or more figures

polygon: a closed figure that consists of line segments; for example, triangles and quadrilaterals are polygons

polynomial: a mathematical expression with one or more terms, in which the exponents are whole numbers and the coefficients are real numbers

population: the set of all things or people being considered

population density: the average number of people for each square unit of land

positive number: a number greater than 0

power: an expression of the form a^n, where a is called the base and n is called the exponent; it represents a product of equal factors; for example, $4 \times 4 \times 4$ can be expressed as 4^3

prime number: a whole number with exactly two factors, itself and 1; for example, 3, 5, 7, 11, 29, 31, and 43

prism: a solid that has two congruent and parallel faces (the *bases*), and other faces that are parallelograms

proportion: a statement that two ratios are equal

pyramid: a solid that has one face that is a polygon (the *base*), and other faces that are triangles with a common vertex

Pythagorean Theorem: for any right triangle, the area of the square on the hypotenuse is equal to the sum of the areas of the squares on the other two sides

In right triangle ABC: $a^2 + b^2 = c^2$

quadrant: one of the four regions into which the coordinate axes divide the plane, usually numbered as shown in the diagram

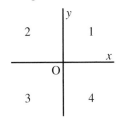

quadrilateral: a four-sided polygon

radius (plural, **radii**): the distance from the centre of a circle to any point on the circumference, or a line segment joining the centre of a circle to any point on the circumference

radius bone: one of the two bones of the forearm that is shorter and thicker and is on the thumb side

random numbers: a list of numbers in a given range such that each number has an equal chance of occurring

random sample: a sampling in which all members of the population have an equal chance of being selected

rate: a certain quantity or amount of one thing considered in relation to a unit of another thing

ratio: a comparison of two or more quantities with the same unit

rational number: a number that can be written in the form $\frac{m}{n}$ where m and n are integers ($n \neq 0$)

real numbers: the set of rational numbers and the set of irrational numbers; that is, all numbers that can be expressed as decimals

reciprocals: two numbers whose product is 1; for example, $\frac{3}{4}$ and $\frac{4}{3}$ are reciprocals, 2 and $\frac{1}{2}$ are reciprocals

rectangle: a quadrilateral that has four right angles

rectangular prism: a prism that has rectangular faces

rectangular pyramid: a pyramid with a rectangular base

reflection: a transformation that maps every point P onto an image point P′ such that P and P′ are equidistant from line l, and line PP′ is perpendicular to line l

reflex angle: an angle between 180° and 360°

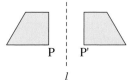

regular hexagon: a polygon that has six equal sides and six equal angles

regular octagon: a polygon that has eight equal sides and eight equal angles

regular polygon: a polygon that has all sides equal and all angles equal

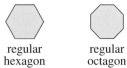

regular   regular
hexagon   octagon

relation: a connection between a pair of quantities, often expressed in words, as a table of values, a graph, or an equation

relationship: see *relation*

rhombus: a parallelogram with four equal sides

right angle: a 90° angle

right triangle: a triangle that has one right angle

rise: the vertical distance between two points; see *slope*

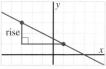

rotation: a transformation in which the points of a figure are turned about a fixed point

rotational symmetry: a figure that maps onto itself in less than one full turn is said to have rotational symmetry; for example, a square has rotational symmetry about its centre O

run: the horizontal distance between two points; see *slope*

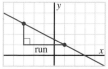

sample/sampling: a representative portion of a population

scale: the ratio of the distance between two points on a map, model, or diagram to the distance between the actual locations; the numbers on the axes of a graph

scale break: a small zig-zag mark on a graph's axis to indicate a break in the scale

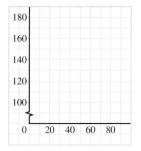

scale factor: the ratio of corresponding lengths on two similar figures

scalene triangle: a triangle with no two sides equal

scatter plot: a graph of data that are a series of points

Height (cm)	154	162	172	178
Mass (kg)	56.3	60.1	72.2	64.3

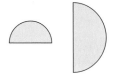

scientific notation: a way of expressing a number as the product of a number greater than -10 and less than -1, or greater than 1 and less than 10, and a power of 10; used to express very large and very small numbers

$$47\ 000 = 4.7 \times 10^4, \text{ and } -26 = -2.6 \times 10^1$$

semicircle: half a circle

similar figures: figures with the same shape, but not necessarily the same size

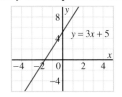

slope: describes the steepness of a line or line segment; the ratio of the rise of a line or line segment to its run

slope y-intercept form: the equation of a line in the form $y = mx + b$, where m is the slope of the line and b is the y-intercept of the line

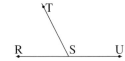

The equation $y = 3x + 5$ is that of a line with slope 3 and y-intercept 5.

sphere: the set of points in space that are a given distance (radius) from a fixed point (centre)

spreadsheet: a computer-generated arrangement of data in rows and columns, where a change in one value results in appropriate calculated changes in the other values

square: a rectangle with four equal sides

square of a number: the product of a number multiplied by itself; for example, 25 is the square of 5

square root: a number which, when multiplied by itself, results in a given number; for example, 5 and -5 are the square roots of 25

statistics: the branch of mathematics that deals with the collection, organization, and interpretation of data

straight angle: an angle measuring 180°

supplementary angles: two angles whose sum is 180°

$\angle$RST and $\angle$TSU are supplementary angles.

surface area: a measure of the area on the surface of a three-dimensional object

symmetrical: possessing symmetry; see *line symmetry* and *rotational symmetry*

term: when an expression is written as the sum of several quantities, each quantity is called a term of the expression

tetrahedron: a solid with four triangular faces

three-dimensional: having length, width, and depth or height

transformation: a mapping of the points of a figure that results in a change in position, shape, size, or appearance of the figure; for example, translations, rotations, reflections, and dilatations are transformations

translation: a transformation that moves a point or a figure in a straight line to another position in the same plane

transversal: a line crossing two or more lines

trapezoid: a quadrilateral that has only one pair of parallel sides

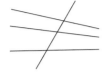

triangle: a three-sided polygon

trinomial: a polynomial with three terms; for example, $3x^2 + 6x + 9$

two-dimensional: having length and width, but no thickness, height, or depth

unit fraction: a fraction that has a numerator of 1

unit price: the price of one item, or the price for a particular mass or volume of an item

unit rate: the quantity associated with a single unit of another quantity; for example, 6 m in 1 s is a unit rate

unlike terms: terms that have different variables, or the same variable but different exponents; for example, $3x$, $-4y$ and $3x^2$, $-3x$

variable: a letter or symbol representing a quantity that can vary

vertex: the corner of a figure or solid

vertex

vertical intercept: the vertical coordinate of the point where the graph of a line or a relation intersects the vertical axis

volume: the amount of space occupied by an object

whole numbers: the set of numbers 0, 1, 2, 3,…

x-axis: the horizontal number line on a coordinate grid

x-intercept: the x-coordinate where the graph of a line or a relation intersects the x-axis

y-axis: the vertical number line on a coordinate grid

y-intercept: the y-coordinate where the graph of a line or a relation intersects the y-axis

Zero Principle: the sum of opposites is zero

Index

A

Algebra tiles, 96–99, 102–104, 243–246, 250, 255, 265–266

Altitude of a triangle
definition, 384, 425
properties, 389, 425

Angle bisector
definition, 392
properties, 395, 425–426

Angles
alternate, 411, 426–427
corresponding, 411, 426–427
interior, 411, 426–427
supplementary, 411, 426–427

Area
of a circle, 313–314, 365
of a parallelogram, 313–314, 365
of a rectangle, 313–314, 365
of a square, 313–314, 365
of a trapezoid, 313–314, 365
of a triangle, 17, 313–314, 365

Atoms, 65, 71

B

Binomial, 245, 272

C

Calculator
graphing, 24–31, 164–166, 174–175, 198–199, 205, 225–227, 288, 298–300, 304
scientific, 47–49, 55, 67, 73, 115, 167, 312, 314, 348, 356, 361, A10, A11, A13–A15, A18, A19, A22, A27

Calculator-Based Ranger™ (CBR), 29–31

Centroid, 380–382, 425

Chòu-peï, 76

Circle, 312–313

Circumference, 312, 365

Coefficient, 104

Cone, 355–356

Coordinate plane, 142–143

Cylinder, 346–349, 352–354

D

Decimals
as a fraction, percent, A22–A23, A26
bar notation, A22
estimating sums, differences, products, quotients, A5, A7
place value, A4
repeating, 47, A22
terminating, 47, A22

Diatoms, 70

Digit, A4

Direct variation, 200, 225–226, 233

Discuss, 10, 16–17, 33–34, 54, 62, 66–67, 77–78, 98, 104–105, 109–110, 114–115, 120, 138, 146, 155, 160–161, 168–169, 177, 195, 208, 220–221, 226–227, 250–251, 256, 266–267, 293, 295, 314, 335, 347–348, 361, 396, 412, A16

Distributive law, 96–99, 125, 242, 265–267, 272

E

Eiffel Tower, 75

Equation(s)
direct variation, 200, 225–226, 233

linear relations, 164, 167, 184–185
non-linear relations, 176, 185
of a line, 198–202, 205–210, 214–215, 233
of horizontal lines, 209–210, 233
of the axes, 202
of the line of best fit, 294–295, 298–300, 305
of vertical lines, 209–210, 233
partial variation, 206–207, 226–227, 233
slope y-intercept form, 207, 233
solving, 94–95, 108–110, 114–115, 119–120, 125

Equidistant, 395, 425

Expanding, 97–99, 125, 266

Exponent, 46
law for a power of a power, 58, 86
law for a power of a product, 241, 272
law for dividing powers, 54, 86, 240
law for multiplying powers, 54, 86, 240
negative integer, 61–62, 86
zero, 61–62, 86

Exterior angles
properties, 398, 400–405, 426

F

Factors, 259, 261, A2
common factors, A2
greatest common factor, A2

Fractions
adding subtracting, multiplying, dividing, A18–A21

PHOTO CREDITS AND ACKNOWLEDGMENTS

The publisher wishes to thank the following sources for photographs, illustrations, articles, and other materials used in this book. Care has been taken to determine and locate ownership of copyright material used in the text. We will gladly receive information enabling us to rectify any errors or omissions in credits.

PHOTOS

p. x (top left), Dave Starrett Photography; **p. x** (top centre), Dave Starrett Photography; **p. x** (top right), Ian Crysler; **p. ix** (bottom right), Grant V. Faint/Image Bank/Getty Images; **p. xi** (centre right), Randy Faris/Firstlight.ca; **p. xiv** (top centre), Ian Crysler; **p. xiv** (top right), Dave Starrett Photography; **p. xv** (bottom right), Rick Fischer/Masterfile; **p. ix** (bottom right) Grant V. Faint/Image Bank/Getty Images; **p. 7** (centre), Photo Courtesy Kevin Reid www.PCWjunkies.com; **p. 8** (centre left), Photo Courtesy Paramount Canada's Wonderland; **p. 12** (centre right), Michael Rosenfeld/Stone/Getty Images; **p. 14** (centre right), Dave Starrett Photography; **p. 14** (bottom left), Dave Starrett Photography; **p. 15** (top right), Dave Starrett Photography; **p. 24** (top right), Ian Crysler; **p. 25** (centre right), Dave Starrett Photography; **p. 29** (top right), Dave Starrett Photography; **p. 30** (top right), Ian Crysler; **p. 33** (centre right), Artbase Inc.; **p. 36** (centre right), David Michael Allen; **p. 36** (bottom right), Vic Cox/Peter Arnold Inc.; **p. 38** (centre), L.J. Lozano; **p. 38** (bottom left), L.J. Lozano; **p. 57** (centre), Artbase Inc.; **p. 57** (top left), Artbase Inc.; **p. 57** (top right), Artbase Inc.; **p. 57** (left), Artbase Inc.; **p. 57** (left), Artbase Inc.; **p. 57** (right), Artbase Inc.; **p. 57** (right), Artbase Inc.; **p. 57** (bottom left), Artbase Inc.; **p. 57** (bottom left), Artbase Inc.; **p. 57** (bottom left), Artbase Inc.; **p. 57** (bottom centre), Artbase Inc.; **p. 57** (bottom centre), Artbase Inc.; **p. 57** (bottom right), Artbase Inc.; **p. 57** (bottom right), Artbase Inc.; **p. 57** (bottom right), Artbase Inc.; **p. 70** (centre right), M. Kage/Peter Arnold Inc.; **p. 71** (bottom right), Andy Caulfield/Image Bank/Getty Images; **p. 75** (centre left), Stephen Studd/Stone/Getty Images; **p. 75** (centre right), Artbase Inc.; **p. 76** (centre right), David Michael Allen; **p. 82** (top right), Dave Starrett Photography; **p. 83** (right), Ron Tanaka; **p. 91** (right), Taxi/Getty Images; **p. 93** (right), Artbase Inc.; **p. 97** (centre), Dave Starrett Photography; **p. 112** (bottom), Gloria H. Chomica/Masterfile; **p. 113** (top right), Artbase Inc.; **p. 117** (right), Pronk&Associates; **p. 120** (right), Bill Ivy/Ivy Images; **p. 121** (bottom right), Dave Starrett Photography; **p. 122** (right), Artbase Inc.; **p. 123** (right), Artbase Inc.; **p. 127** (bottom), Daryl Benson/Masterfile; **p. 136** (centre), L.J. Lozano; **p. 138** (bottom right), Alex Williams/TCL/Masterfile; **p. 141** (centre right), Lloyd Sutton/Masterfile; **p. 142** (right), Pronk&Associates; **p. 143** (right), Dave Starrett Photography; **p. 145** (right), Dave Starrett Photography; **p. 148** (right), Ken Straiton/Firstlight.ca; **p. 150** (bottom right), Manfred Mehlig/Stone/Getty Images; **p. 152** (top right), Artbase Inc.; **p. 152** (bottom right), Dave Starrett Photography; **p. 158** (top right), Boden Ledingham/Masterfile; **p. 158** (bottom right), Dave Starrett Photography; **p. 181** (top right), Courtesy of NASA/Finley Holiday; **p. 185** (centre right), Ray Lum Photography; **p. 189** (bottom centre), Rick Fischer/Masterfile; **p. 219** (bottom right), Dave Starrett Photography; **p. 220** (centre), Dave Starrett Photography; **p. 220** (inset bottom right), Dave Starrett Photography; **p. 226** (centre right), Ken Straiton/Firstlight.ca; **p. 231** (top right), Buenos Dias Bildagentur/Liaison International/Getty Images; **p. 238** (top left), Can Press Picture Archives; **p. 242** (bottom left), Peter Eriksson/Image Bank/Getty Images; **p. 243** (right), Bruce Coleman Inc.; **p. 244** (top right), Dave Starrett Photography; **p. 254** (centre), David E. Meyers/Stone/Getty Images; **p. 269** (top right), Dave Starrett Photography; **p. 271** (bottom centre), Artbase Inc.; **p. 271** (top), The Everett Collection Inc.; **p. 278** (bottom left), Artbase Inc.; **p. 289** (centre), Artbase Inc.; **p. 290** (bottom right), Bisson Bernard/CORBIS Sygma/MAGMA; **p. 291** (top right), Dave Starrett Photography; **p. 292** (centre right), Can Press Picture Archives (Associated Press); **p. 297** (top right), Dave Starrett Photography; **p. 298** (centre), Dave Starrett Photography; **p. 301** (top right), Dave Starrett Photography; **p. 301** (bottom right), Dave Starrett Photography; **p. 302** (right), Grant V. Faint/Image Bank/Getty Images; **p. 304** (left), Artbase Inc.; **p. 317** (left), Ken Straiton/Firstlight.ca; **p. 317** (centre), Artbase Inc.; **p. 330** (bottom right), Pronk&Associates; **p. 331** (centre), Artbase Inc.; **p. 331** (top right), Artbase Inc.; **p. 331** (top left), Isaac Hernandez/Mercury Press 2002 all rights reserved; **p. 331** (right), Artbase Inc.; **p. 333** (bottom right), Brian Milne/Firstlight.ca; **p. 334** (top left), Dave Starrett Photography; **p. 339** (centre right), Dave Starrett Photography; **p. 341** (top right), Dave Starrett Photography; **p. 346** (top right), Artbase Inc.; **p. 346** (top left), Artbase Inc.; **p. 346** (top centre), Artbase Inc.; **p. 346** (centre left), Pronk&Associates; **p. 347** (bottom), Pronk&Associates; **p. 348** (top right), David Michael Allen; **p. 349** (top right), picked up from Addison-Wesley Mathematics 9 Ontario Edition; **p. 350** (centre left), Pronk&Associates; **p. 350** (centre right), David Michael Allen; **p. 350** (bottom right), Pronk&Associates; **p. 351** (top right), Pronk&Associates; **p. 352** (centre right), Dave Starrett Photography; **p. 355** (top centre), Bodo A. Schieren/Maxx Images Inc.; **p. 355** (top right), David Michael Allen; **p. 356** (centre right), David Michael Allen; **p. 359** (top right), Artbase Inc.; **p. 359** (centre left), Pronk&Associates; **p. 359** (centre right), Pronk&Associates; **360** (top left), Pronk&Associates; **360** (top right), Pronk&Associates; **p. 370** (top left), British Museum; **p. 370** (top centre), Collection of Stadelsches Kunstinstitut; **p. 370** (centre), The National Gallery of London; **p. 378** (top), Masterfile; **p. 383** (bottom left), Dave Starrett Photography; **p. 383** (centre right), David Michael Allen; **p. 384** (top), Frank Hudec/Firstlight.ca; **p. 384** (inset right), CORBIS/Jim Sugar Photography/MAGMA; **p. 391** (centre right), Dave Starrett Photography; **p. 407** (centre), Dave Starrett Photography; **p. 414** (top right), John de Visser/Masterfile; **p. 423** (top), Brian Sytnyk/Masterfile; **pp. 44–45** (spread), Ron Tanaka; **pp. 92–93** (spread), Luca I. Tettoni/CORBIS/MAGMA; **pp. 132–133** (spread), Randy Faris/Firstlight.ca; **pp. 190–191** (spread), Buenos Dias Bildagentur/Liaison International/Getty Images; **pp. 238–239** (background), Hulton Archive/Getty Images; **pp. 238–239** (inset foreground centre), Bettmann/CORBIS/MAGMA; **pp. 310–311** (background), Dave Starrett Photography; **pp. 310–311** (foreground), Dave Starrett Photography; **pp. 370–371** (background), Artbase Inc.

ILLUSTRATIONS

pp. 2–3 (background) Greg Stevenson; **p. 24** (bottom left) Margo Davies Leclair/Visual Sense; **p. 32** (bottom right) Jun Park; **p. 53** (centre right) Michael Herman; **p. 70** (bottom right) Steve Attoe; **p. 82** (bottom left) Jun Park; **p. 85** (top right) Steve Attoe; **p. 96** (top right) Michael Herman; **p. 99** (bottom left) Michael Herman; **p. 115** (top right) Michael Herman; **p. 119** (top) Pronk&Associates; **p. 123** (centre left) Pronk&Associates; **p. 131** (right) Pronk&Associates; **p. 144** (right) Pronk&Associates; **p. 151** (centre) Jun Park; **p. 157** (centre) Jun Park; **p. 164** (top) Michael Herman; **p. 166** (centre left) Michael Herman; **p. 172** (centre) Michael Herman; **p. 180** (bottom centre) Jun Park; **p. 181** (top left) Michael Herman; **p. 182** (top left) Jun Park; **p. 188** (centre right) Pronk&Associates; **p. 189** (top) Pronk&Associates; **p. 232** (bottom right) Michael Herman; **p. 232** (top right) Michael Herman; **p. 232** (centre right) Michael Herman; **p. 232** (bottom right) Michael Herman; **p. 247** (top right) Steve Attoe; **p. 261** (centre right) Michael Herman; **pp. 280–281** (top centre) Artbase Inc.; **pp. 280–281** (top left) Artbase Inc.; **pp. 280–281** (bottom centre) Artbase Inc.; **pp. 280–281** (background) Artbase Inc.; **pp. 280–281** (bottom) Artbase Inc.; **pp. 280–281** (top centre); Artbase Inc.; **pp. 280–281** (background) Greg Stevenson; **p. 325** (bottom) Michael Herman; **p. 326** (top left) Michael Herman; **p. 326** (top right) Michael Herman; **p. 329** (centre right) Rose Zgodzinski; **p. 343** (top left) Pronk&Associates; **p. 345** (top right) Pronk&Associates; **p. 356** (top right) Jun Park; **p. 366** (centre right) Pronk&Associates; **p. 416** (bottom) Michael Herman; **p. 431** (centre) Pronk&Associates